High Voltage Integrated Circuits

OTHER IEEE PRESS BOOKS

High Voltage Integrated Circuits

Edited by
B. Jayant Baliga

Coolidge Fellow and Manager of
High Voltage Device Programs
General Electric Research Center

A volume in the IEEE PRESS Selected Reprint Series,
prepared under the sponsorship of the
IEEE Electron Devices Society.

IEEE
PRESS

The Institute of Electrical and Electronics Engineers, Inc., New York

IEEE Order Number: PC0232-9

Library of Congress Cataloging-in-Publication Data

High voltage integrated circuits/edited by B. Jayant Baliga.

p.   cm. — (IEEE Press selected reprint series)
''Prepared under the sponsorship of the IEEE Electron Devices Society.''
Includes bibliographies and indexes.
ISBN 0-87942-242-4
1. Power electronics.   2. Power semiconductors.   I. Baliga, B. Jayant, 1948-.
II. IEEE Electron Devices Society.
TK7881.15.H54   1988   87-36144
621.31'7—dc19   CIP

Contents

Introduction

A majority of the activity in the development of integrated circuits has been focussed upon signal processing applications. Within this realm, the technology has diversified into many different types of circuits which can be broadly classified into either the digital or analog categories. Numerous books devoted to the design and fabrication of these circuits are available. These circuits share one feature. All the circuit elements are designed to be operated at low voltage and current levels. In fact, the push to increase transistor density in very-large-scale-integrated (VLSI) circuits is creating the need to reduce the power supply voltage from the standard 5 volts that is commonly used today. Further, the devices are designed with small sizes to maximize the number of transistors per chip in order to increase circuit functionality. This restricts the current handling capability of the devices to less than a milliampere.

During the 1980s, it has become increasingly apparent that the application of solid state technology to systems is being curtailed by the lack of low cost, highly reliable power electronics. With the vast cost reductions achieved in information processing using high density signal level integrated circuits, the cost of the power section has become dominant. The high cost of the power electronics can be directly traced to the use of complex multicomponent power circuits that were developed using the power bipolar transistor in the 1970s. High voltage power bipolar transistors must be fabricated with relatively thick base regions in order to support the high operating voltages and to avoid current crowding effects during current conduction, as well as during turn-off. This limits their current gain to less than 10 even when a cascaded (Darlington) topology is utilized. Consequently, the power bipolar transistor is a current controlled device which requires substantial input current to maintain it in its on state, and to switch it rapidly from the on state to the off state. For example, in the case of a motor-drive circuit, where the device must deliver 50 amperes of current at 500 volts, an input base drive current of 5 amperes must be supplied. Such high control currents cannot be delivered efficiently from an integrated circuit. The bipolar transistor-based power circuits are, therefore, composed of numerous stages of discrete devices resulting in a high system weight, size, and cost.

To address the problems experienced with the power bipolar transistor, a new power device technology evolved in the 1980s based upon the MOS technology developed for CMOS integrated circuits. Two of the devices that have become well established in this technology are the power MOSFET for low voltage (less than 100 volts) applications, and the power MOS-IGT for high voltage (greater than 100 volts) applications. These devices offer the important feature of exhibiting a high input impedance to the control circuit. This greatly decreases the current levels that must be delivered from the gate drive circuits resulting in reducing their size and complexity. This creates the opportunity to integrate the complete control circuit on a single silicon chip. However, in most of the applications, such as motor drives, it is still necessary to perform level shifting of the control signal between the power output devices that are working at large potential differences. The control circuit must, therefore, be capable of operating at high voltage levels even if the current levels are small. This has created the need to develop techniques that allow the integration of high voltage device structures with low voltage circuitry on a single silicon chip. This new technology can be broadly classified as high voltage integrated circuits (HVICs). The development of the power MOS-controlled output devices and the HVIC has resulted in a tremendous simplification of power circuits, with up to a tenfold reduction in the size, weight, and cost of the power electronics. This has created the opportunity for a rapid penetration of power electronics in aerospace, industrial, and consumer products.

The applications for power semiconductor technology stretch over a very large range of power levels. To appreciate the requirements for this technology, the current and voltage handling needs for various applications are provided in Fig. 1. It can be seen that at one extreme the technology must serve the ability to control 1000 amperes and up to one million volts in an HVDC transmission network. This function can be performed by using a series string of light triggered thyristors capable of blocking 3000 to 10,000 volts and being gated via a fiber optic cable. At slightly lower power levels, traction drives are being served by gate turn-off (GTO) thyristors. The high voltage integrated circuit technology has not found an application in this arena as yet. However, with the expected development of MOS controlled power devices capable of handling these higher power levels in the future, the integration of the control circuit may become viable.

The rest of the applications indicated in the figure are already being impacted by high voltage integrated circuit technology. Among these applications, those requiring a higher power handling capability, such as motor control and factory automation systems, are being served by power modules containing a combination of discrete devices and high voltage integrated circuits. In these cases, the high currents are handled by the discrete devices, and the integrated circuit is used to provide the gate drive and protection features.

The other applications require either high voltage operation at low current levels or high current operation at low voltages. These needs can be served by single chip monolithic integrated circuits. The applications, such as telecommunications and display drives, require high voltage transistors that can deliver currents in the range of 100 milliamperes. This has become feasible with the advent of the development of high voltage integrated circuits containing analog and digital control circuitry. The applications, such as automotive electronics for lamp and motor control, requiring the handling of tens of

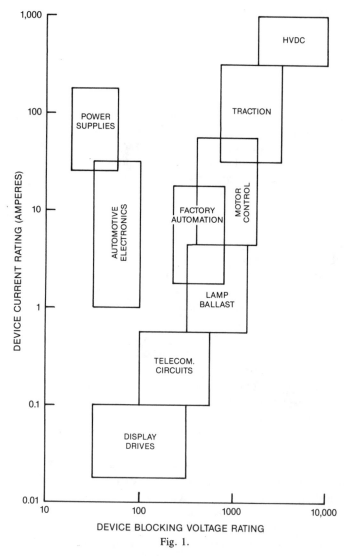

Fig. 1.

• Part III—process technology
• Part IV—smart power integrated circuits
• Part V—display drives
• Part VI—power amplifiers
• Part VII—telecommunication circuits
• Part VIII—dielectric isolation technology.

Since Parts II and III on high voltage lateral transistors and process technology are of general interest, it is recommended that these parts be studied by all readers. The remaining parts address the specific needs for particular applications. These can be selectively studied by those readers that are interested in that application.

In addition to the papers chosen for reprinting in this book, an extensive bibliography is provided at the end of the book. Although these papers were not reproduced in the book in the interest of conserving space and to avoid redundant material, many of them contain very useful information regarding specific issues that might be of interest to the reader.

This book has been prepared with the intention of highlighting a new and rapidly growing area of application-specific integrated circuits (ASICs). It will not only serve as a self-study guide for practicing engineers in the electronics industry, but will be of value in teaching a course on the subject at universities.

REFERENCES

For those readers that are unfamiliar with the physics of the operation of high voltage power devices, it is recommended that they read the following books:

[1] S. K. Ghandi, *Semiconductor Power Devices*. New York, NY: John Wiley, 1977.
[2] B. J. Baliga, *Modern Power Devices*. New York, NY: John Wiley, 1987.
[3] B. J. Baliga and D. Y. Chen, *Power Transistors*. New York, NY: IEEE PRESS, 1984.
[4] A. Blitcher, *Field Effect and Bipolar Transistor Physics*. New York, NY: Academic Press, 1981.
[5] E. S. Oxner, *Power FETs and Their Applications*. Englewood Cliffs, NJ: Prentice-Hall, 1982.
[6] P. Antognetti, *Power Integrated Circuits*. New York, NY: Mc-Graw-Hill, 1986.

The first two of these books are written in a tutorial vein as graduate level textbooks. They provide a thorough discussion of the physics of operation of bipolar and MOS-based power devices. The last reference provides a good review of design options for power integrated circuits, and deals with practical issues such as thermal dissipation and reliability.

amperes of current at low voltages are being addressed by the smart power chips which contain a combination of a vertical power transistor with control circuitry.

This book consists of eight parts. In Part I, a set of review papers is provided. These papers should be initially read in order to obtain a broad perspective of power semiconductor technology, and the evolution of the high voltage integrated circuits being discussed in this book. Parts II to VIII contain reprints of papers that deal with specific issues. These parts consist of:

• Part II—lateral high voltage transistor design

2

THIS section provides an overview of high voltage integrated circuit technology. In general, a high voltage integrated circuit can be defined as a monolithic chip containing either multiple high voltage devices or a monolithic chip containing both low and high voltage devices. Within this definition, many unique approaches have evolved to address the needs of specific applications.

The earliest technology to be developed was aimed at display drives. In this case, multiple high voltage output devices have been integrated with logic circuitry on a single silicon chip. This was achieved with small modifications of the existing CMOS technology because the output devices operate at relatively low voltages (in the range of 100 volts), and a common source device configuration can be used with all the high voltage drains bonded off the chip. The problems associated with performing high voltage interconnection on the chip are therefore avoided. The high voltage device structure utilized was either an extended drain NMOS transistor or, preferably, a lateral DMOS transistor.

As the benefits of the development of more versatile high voltage integrated circuit technology became recognized, unique processing approaches were created in order to incorporate a wider range of circuit elements. At present, high voltage integrated circuits containing both analog and logic circuits, together with the high voltage devices, are available. In order to obtain the most efficient design, these circuits utilize bipolar devices (usually vertical NPN transistors and lateral PNP transistors) for accomplishing the analog functions, and CMOS technology for performing the logic functions. The high voltage devices are formed by using either a vertical device architecture or by using a lateral architecture. In the case of the vertical architecture, the device design becomes similar to that used for discrete power devices. These devices can be either DMOSFETs or bipolar transistors. Their voltage rating is limited to below several hundred volts by the maximum allowable epitaxial layer thickness because of the difficulty in forming the required isolation diffusions. In the case of the lateral architecture, an optimally chosen epitaxial layer charge leads to the ability to support high voltages laterally, and to spread the field into the substrate. Since only a thin epitaxial layer similar to that used in signal integrated circuits is utilized, this approach is expected to dominate because it allows the optimization of the high voltage devices without degradation in the operation of the low voltage devices.

Another category of high voltage integrated circuits that is worthy of special attention is the ''smart power'' technology. In general, the smart power IC can be defined as an integrated circuit containing at least one high current vertical power device similar to a discrete power transistor, together with low voltage analog and/or logic circuitry integrated on the same chip. The simplest example of this type of high voltage integrated circuit is a power device with its drive transistor integrated on the same chip. In the case of bipolar transistors, this is the well-known monolithic Darlington transistor. However, the recent thrust has been directed towards using a high voltage power DMOSFET or power MOS-IGT as the discrete device, and incorporating analog and logic circuitry on the chip to achieve over-current, over-voltage, and over-temperature protection. In addition, this technology is being directed towards automotive electronics which utilize multiplexed wiring schemes. Here, the smart power device must be capable of decoding incoming logic signals and actuating loads, such as motors and lamps, while also being capable of sending messages on the status of the load to a central microprocessor.

In this review part, four papers are provided which give the reader an overview of the high voltage integrated circuit technology. The first paper by Adler, Owyang, Baliga, and Kokosa was published in the centennial issue of the IEEE TRANSACTIONS ON ELECTRON DEVICES. It describes the evolution of power semiconductor technology starting with bipolar devices, such as the thyristor and transistor, until the development of MOS-based power devices, such as the DMOSFET and IGT in the 1980s. The advent of the high voltage integrated circuit is also briefly discussed. Trends in the development of devices with higher power handling capability, and the prospects for further enhancements in high voltage integrated circuits are included.

The next two papers in this review section are authored by Rumennik in IEEE SPECTRUM and by Baliga in the special issue on power and high voltage integrated circuits in the IEEE TRANSACTIONS ON ELECTRON DEVICES. These papers provide a description of the status of high voltage integrated circuit technology. As described in these papers, power integrated circuits have been developed with current handling capability ranging from 0.5 to 30 amperes and voltage handling capability ranging from 50 to 500 volts. Typical applications for these circuits are in telecommunications, linear and switching regulators, electronic ballasts for lamps, ac motor controls, and automotive electronics. As highlighted in these papers, the key problem with the development of the ICs has been the ability to isolate devices operating at large potential differences. Three technological approaches that have been developed are self-isolation, junction-isolation, and dielectric-isolation. Although dielectric-isolation provides the greatest freedom in circuit design, its relatively high cost has limited its application to telecommunications. Most of the high voltage integrated circuits are fabricated today using either self-isolation or junction-isolation. Some recent work, described in a later part on new approaches to forming the dielectric-isolation, promises to result in significant cost reduction for this technology. If this occurs, it is likely that all high voltage integrated circuits, apart from the smart power devices, will be made using the dielectric-isolation technology.

The last paper in the review section, by Murari, was published in 1978 in the IEEE JOURNAL OF SOLID-STATE-CIRCUITS. This paper emphasizes circuit design aspects in high voltage and power integrated circuits. Design issues dealing with short-circuit and over-voltage protection are discussed. Although the paper focusses on bipolar technology, the problems and solutions described are generally applicable.

It is recommended that the papers in this review section be read before those from the rest of the book are perused. They provide a guide to understanding the basic concepts that are treated in greater depth in the other articles. In fact, those readers who are only interested in one specific application will find that it is sufficient to read this part and the parts dealing with process technology and lateral high voltage devices in addition, of course, to the part regarding the specific application of interest to the reader.

REPRINT PAPERS

[1] M. S. Adler, K. W. Owyang, B. J. Baliga, and R. A. Kokosa, "The Evolution of Power Device Technology," *IEEE Trans. Electron Devices,* vol. ED-31, pp. 1570–1591, 1984.

[2] V. Rumennik, "Power Devices Are in the Chips," *IEEE Spectrum,* vol. 22, pp. 42–48, 1985.

[3] B. J. Baliga, "Power Integrated Circuits—A Brief Overview," *IEEE Trans. Electron Devices,* vol. ED-33, pp. 1936–1939, 1986.

[4] B. Murari, "Power Integrated Circuits: Problems, Tradeoffs, and Solutions," *IEEE J. Solid-State Circuits,* vol. SC-13, pp. 307–319, 1978.

The Evolution of Power Device Technology

MICHAEL S. ADLER, SENIOR MEMBER, IEEE, KING W. OWYANG, MEMBER, IEEE, B. JAYANT BALIGA,
FELLOW, IEEE, AND RICHARD A. KOKOSA, SENIOR MEMBER, IEEE

Abstract—Power semiconductor devices and their associated technology have come a long way from their beginnings with the invention of the bipolar transistor in the late 1940's. Presently, the spectrum of what are referred to as "power devices" span a very wide range of devices and technology from the massive 4 in, 3000-A thyristor to the high-voltage integrated circuit and the power MOSFET, a device of VLSI complexity containing up to 150 000 separate transistors.

In this paper, the past, present, and future of power devices will be reviewed. The first section will be a historical perspective indicating the key events and developments of the past that brought the power devices of today to their present state. The second section of the paper will review the technology and characteristics of bipolar power devices with separate subsections on thyristors, the gate turn-off thyristor (GTO), and the bipolar transistor. Within the thyristor subsection there will be discussions of the phase control thyristor, the inverter thyristor, the asymmetric thyristor (ASCR) the reverse conducting thyristor (RCT), the gate-assisted turn-off thyristor (GATT), and finally the light-triggered thyristor (LTT).

The third section of the paper is devoted to the new field of integrated power devices and will review the evolution to the present power MOS devices including the power MOSFET, the insulated gate transistor (IGT), and the high voltage IC (HVIC).

The last section of the paper reviews the future of power devices with projections as to future ratings of power devices for both the traditional bipolar devices, such as the thyristor, GTO, and bipolar transistor, as well as the integrated devices such as the MOSFET and the IGT. In case of the former, in particular the thyristor, the maximum device ratings will be tied to the availability of large area float zone material, currently difficult to obtain in the high resistivities needed for power devices. In the case of integrated devices, the maximum ratings will be limited by the maximum die area for which acceptable device yields can be obtained. This is identical to the situation for conventional IC's since much of the unit processing is the same.

Manuscript received July 1, 1984; revised July 15, 1984.
The authors are with General Electric Company, Corporate Research and Development Center, Schenectady, NY 12301.

I. HISTORICAL PERSPECTIVE AND INTRODUCTION
Process Technology

TODAY it is difficult to imagine a world of power conversion and control without silicon power devices. Forty years ago, the introduction of selenium rectifiers was heralded as a major advance over the thyratrons, ignitrons, and even copper-oxide devices of that time. However, the selenium era proved to be short-lived. In the late 1940's a number of important successive developments initiated the dawn of today's semiconductor era. Although point contact diodes were in use in the 1940s, most important was the discovery of the point contact transistor in 1947 [1], [2] and the invention of the junction transistor in 1949 [3] at Bell Labs. Supported by countless process innovations, device concepts, and developments in physical understanding, the junction transistor formed the foundation for today's integrated circuits and power electronics businesses.

In 1952, Hall [4] demonstrated the first significant power devices based upon semiconductor technology. The devices were fabricated using germanium mesa alloy junctions and resulted in a rectifier with impressive electrical characteristics for that time, i.e., a continuous forward current capability of 35 A and a reverse blocking voltage of 200 V. Hall also used the recently developed theories of carrier recombination, generation [5], [6], and current flow [7] to successfully model the electrical characteristics of power rectifiers and transistors.

In the mid 1950's power device characteristics capitalized on the development of single-crystal silicon technology. The larger band gap of silicon rectifiers resulted in higher reverse voltage capability and higher operating temperatures. By the late 1950's, 500-V rectifiers were available in alloy junctions.

Reprinted from *IEEE Trans. Electron Devices*, vol. ED-31, pp. 1570–1591, Nov. 1984.

The introduction of diffused junctions combined with mesa technology in the late 1950's proved to be the step necessary to realize reverse blocking capability of several kilovolts in later years. By the mid 1960's, theoretical avalanche breakdown voltages of up to 9000 V [8] had been achieved by optimized contouring of mesa junctions [9]. Increased current handling capability became a possibility by optimizing device packaging for minimum thermal and mechanical stress on the chip. Today, 77-mm diam silicon rectifiers are available with continuous current ratings of 5000 A and reverse voltages of 3000 V.

To put this development in perspective, while the first commercially available silicon transistors were announced by TI in 1954 [10], it was almost a decade later that their practical application to high-power conversion and control began. Emitter current crowding [11], reliability, and materials processing challenges precluded economic justification. The introduction of the planar process by Fairchild [12] plus the application of photolithography techniques to wafer processing resulted in the birth of the power transistor business in the 1960's. A decade of effort in the industry related to second breakdown [13], power/speed performance and unique processes such as epitaxy deposition [14] paid off. By the late 1970's 200-A 500-V bipolar Darlington transistors with a gain of 50 were available together with 100-V 10-A transistors which could operate at frequencies up to 1 MHz. Since then, however, the application of MOS technology to power transistors has been a major focus of the industry due to the promise of high-speed and high-input impedance in many low-voltage applications.

Device Technologies

Beyond the important developments in material and process technology described above, there have been many significant device developments. One of the first of these was the publication of the P-N-P-N transistor switch concept in 1956 by Moll *et al.* [15]. Although probably envisioned to be used for Bell's signal applications, engineers at General Electric quickly recognized its significance to power conversion and control and within nine months announced the first commercial silicon controlled rectifier in 1957. This three-terminal power switch was fabricated using a 5-mm square alloy-diffused mesa silicon chip and had a continuous current rating of 25 A and a blocking voltage capability of 300 V. The shorted emitter concept [16] plus the planar process resulted in planar diffused SCR's in 1962. These processes resulted in high-voltage blocking capability at junction temperatures of 125°C and made practical power control and conversion possible.

Since the early 1960's, thyristor producers have capitalized upon the process innovations of the signal industry while introducing new devices or structural improvements to existing devices. In 1961 a gate turnoff thyristor (GTO) was disclosed [17] which combined the switching properties of a transistor with the low conduction losses of an SCR. In 1964 a bidirectional ac switch (TRIAC) was introduced by General Electric [18] principally for 60-cycle consumer lighting and motor speed control. In 1965, light-triggered thyristors were developed [19] which later found significant application in opto-electronic couplers. In the late 1960's a number of advances were made in the design of thyristor cathode gate structures. Incorporation of interdigitated gates made possible high-power 20-kHz inverters. Similarly, the inclusion of pilot gating techniques [20] decreased the gating requirements as well as improved high-frequency and pulse-duty operation. The reverse conducting thyristor (RCT) and asymmetrical SCR were developed in 1970 [21] to provide higher speed capability in those inverter applications where reverse blocking voltage was not required. In the mid 1970's, thyristor designers were intrigued with electric field (or voltage) controlled thyristors [22] which held promise for higher speed performance. The later, however, never came to fruition and the application of MOS concepts has proven to offer similar benefits, but with greater ease of manufacture.

The most recent trend in power devices has been to utilize VLSI technology to create a whole new generation of integrated power devices. This started with the power MOS transistor in the late 1970's [23] and has evolved toward totally new devices such as the MOS-gated thyristor [24], [25] and, most recently, the insulated gate transistor (IGT) [26] also known as the COMFET [27]. This latter device combines the best features of the MOSFET and the bipolar transistor in a device that conducts more current in a unit area than either. In addition to the new discrete devices, monolithic high-voltage integrated circuits (HVIC) that combine power and signal circuitry on a chip have come on the scene. These devices are a dramatic extension of the trend towards mixed technologies in the IC industry and for the first time allow the cost efficiencies of integrated circuitry to be applied in the power area. The initial application areas have been in telecommunications [28], power supplies [29], high-voltage displays [30], and most recently power circuits [31], [32]. However, this is just the beginning and these new devices and HVIC's represent a genuine revolution in the power electronics area. The net result could well be a vast extension of electronics into many new application areas in the home and industry that have been precluded because of the limited capabilities and high cost of power electronics.

Foreword

In this paper, the current status of power device technology will be reviewed in several sections. The first and largest section of the paper will be in the traditional area of high-power devices and will include reviews of thyristors, gate turn-off thyristors (GTO), and bipolar transistors. The second section will deal with the new field of integrated power electronic devices. This will include a review of the evolution of power MOS technology together with a presentation of the characteristics of some of the recent new power devices such as the IGT. Also included in this section will be a review of the important area of HVIC's. The final section of the paper will be projections of device ratings for thyristors, GTO's and bipolar transistors, IGT's, and MOSFET's over the next 10 years. This will include both ratings of terminal currents and voltages as well as a comparison of these devices for power switching applications that will aid the power circuit designer in selecting the optimum device. The comparison will be based on switching efficiency and will be done as a function of frequency in 5 distinct voltage ratings.

II. BIPOLAR POWER DEVICES

Thyristors

Ever since its introduction, circuit design engineers have been subjecting the thyristor to increasing levels of operating stress and demanding that these devices perform satisfactorily there. The different stress demands that the thyristor must be able to meet are:

1) Higher blocking voltages
2) More current carrying capability
3) Higher di/dt's
4) Higher dv/dt's
5) Shorter turn-off times
6) Lower gate drive
7) Higher operating frequencies.

There are many different thyristors available today which can meet one or more of these requirements but, as always, an improvement in one characteristic is usually only gained at the expense of another. As a result, different thyristors have been optimized for different applications. Today's thyristors can be classified into six general types, namely:

a) Phase Control Thyristor
b) Inverter Thyristor
c) Asymmetrical Thyristor
d) Reverse Conducting Thyristor (RCT)
e) Gate-Assisted Turn-Off Thyristor
f) Light-Triggered Thyristor.

The voltage and current capabilities of various thyristor types are summarized in Fig. 1. The salient design features, structures, and applications of these different SCRs are discussed in the following subsections:

a) *Phase control thyristors:* "Phase Control" or "Converter" thyristors generally operate at line frequency. They are turned off by natural commutation and do not have special fast-switching characteristics. Current ratings of phase-control thyristors cover the range from a few amperes to about 3000 A, and the voltage ratings from 50 to around 4000 V.

For a 77-mm diam phase-control thyristor, conduction voltages vary from 1.5 for 600 V rated devices, to 2.3 for 3000 V rated devices, and to 2.6 for 4000 V rated devices. For a given size device with a given voltage design, the widths of the bases and the junction profiles are fixed by punchthrough and current-gain considerations. Because of this, the forward drop becomes mainly dependent upon the diffusion length L (or lifetime, τ) in the wide n-base region and the ohmic contact losses at the end regions of the device and careful consideration of the diffusion profiles and diffusion technique must be taken to insure low forward drop.

Other key considerations of present day phase control thyristors are enhancement of the dynamic dv/dt capability and improvement of the gate sensitivity. In case of the former, the rate of rise of the voltage reapplied at the end of the turn-

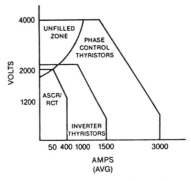

Fig. 1. Summary of present day thyristor rating capabilities.

off interval (dv/dt effect) in conjunction with the device capacitance produces a displacement current which can turn on the device if sufficiently large. The use of emitter shorting structures which provide a shunting path for the displacement current has greatly improved dynamic dv/dt capabilities with typical dv/dt ratings of greater than 100 V/μs routinely achieved. The high-temperature performance has been improved significantly by emitter shorting, since the shorts will also bypass thermally generated currents around the emitter.

In order to simplify the gate-drive requirement and increase sensitivity, the use of amplifying gate, which was originally developed for fast switching "inverter" thyristors, is widely adopted in phase control SCR. As a result, gate drive can usually be limited to 1 to 2 A for a 50-mm device.

b) *Inverter thyristors:* The most common feature of an inverter thyristor which distinguishes it from a standard phase control type is that it has fast turnoff time, generally in the range of 5 to 50 μs, depending upon voltage rating. Maximum average current ratings of 1500 and 1200 A have been achieved with 1200 and 2500 V rated inverter thyristors, respectively.

Inverter thyristors are generally used in circuits that operate from dc supplies, where current in the thyristor is turned off either through the use of auxiliary commutating circuitry, by circuit resonance, or by "load" commutation. Whatever the circuit turn-off mechanism, fast turn-off is important because it minimizes sizes and weight of commutating and/or reactive circuit components.

For inverter/thyristors, the turn-off time is dependent upon the stored charge at the time of current reversal, the amount of charge removed during the recovery phase, the rate or recombination during the recombination phase, and the amount of charge injected during reapplication of the forward voltage. The general practice for achieving short turn-off times reduction is to "kill" the lifetime by introducing recombination centers in the device structure using gold or platinum doping and electron irradiation. However, one of the problems in doing this is the adverse effect it has on the forward conduction drop [33], the turn-on time, and the plasma spreading properties of the device [34]. As a result, a trade-off has to be made in selecting the appropriate lifetime. Incorporating cathode shorting will aid in this trade-off by reducing the initial stored charge and the amount of charge injected during the reapplication of the forward voltage. While it will not

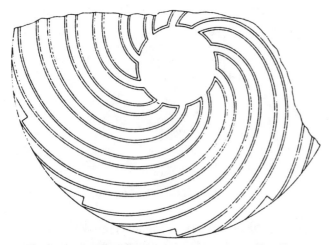

Fig. 2. The involute gate structure used in inverter thyristors.

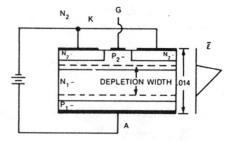

Cross-Sectional View of Conventional Center Gate SCR and Electric Field During Off-State.

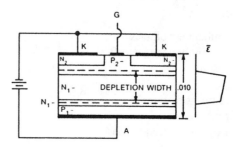

Asymmetric SCR Cross-Sectional View.

Fig. 3. Symmetrical and asymmetrical thyristor structures.

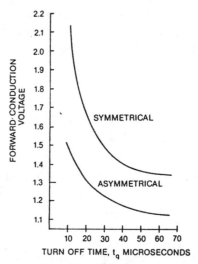

Fig. 4. Typical forward conduction voltage versus turn-off time, t_q for 1200 V rated symmetrical and asymmetrical thyristors.

speed up the recovery and the recombination process, the advantage of emitter shorting over lifetime reduction is that it has a much less adverse effect on forward drop.

In addition to fast turn off, fast turn-on time and *di/dt* capability are usually important for inverter thyristors. Achieving this requires proper design of the gate structure with the objective being to design the device so that no part of the cathode has a potential greater than that of the gate electrode. This mandates the use of a gate electrode with a large perimeter ensuring that the adjacent cathode area is as large as possible. A number of interdigitated designs have been developed to achieve this goal. Perhaps the most effective design in achieving good utilization of the device area is a structure in which both the gate and the cathode have an involute pattern [35]. Fig. 2 presents the geometric aspects of one arm (gate or cathode) of such a structure. Typically, a center gate is used to maintain maximum symmetry. The use of involute gate structures has resulted in an improvement in the *di/dt* capability of inverter thyristors by a factor of as much as 25. Modern devices of this type can be designed to have *di/dt* ratings in excess of 100 A/μs. Involute gate structures are widely used in inverter thyristors with 40-mm diam and below. Other distributed gate structures, such as the "snow flakes" pattern, are being used for inverter thyristors with larger diameter.

c) Asymmetrical thyristors (ASCR): One of the main salient characteristics of asymmetrical thyristors (ASCR) is that they do not block significant reverse voltage. They are typically designed to have a reverse blocking capability in the range of 400 to 2000 V. The ASCR finds applications in many voltage-fed inverter circuits that require antiparallel feedback rectifiers that keep the reverse voltage to less than 20 V.

The fact that ASCR needs only to block voltage in the forward direction provides an extra degree of freedom in optimizing turn-off time, turn-on time, and forward voltage drop. Fig. 3 compares the basic structure of an ASCR with that of a conventional thyristor. The main difference is the insertion of a N buffer layer between the N base and the P+ anode. The buffer N-layer serves as a "field stopper" and allows the N

base region to be reduced to half the width of a conventional thyristor. Because the forward voltage across the thyristor depends on $(d^2/D\tau)$ where d is the N base width, D is the diffusion coefficient and τ is the minority-carrier lifetime, halving d allows the lifetime to be reduced by 4 times, while maintaining the same forward drop. This translates to 50 percent or more improvement in turn-off time as shown in Fig. 4, which compares the typical forward voltage drop versus turn-off time τ_q for a 1200-V symmetrical and asymmetrical thyristor. The thinner N base width also improves the *di/dt* capability during turn-on because the spreading velocity is inversely proportional to the N base width. As a result, the ASCR can be made to have faster turn-on without compromising significantly the *di/dt* capability and turn-off time.

The spectrum of voltages and current ratings presently covered by ASCR's is shown in Fig. 1. The ASCR market is still

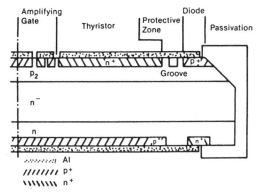

Fig. 5. Cross section of the RCT.

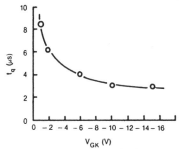

Fig. 6. Turn-off time versus reverse gate bias for GATT ($TJ = 125^{\circ}$C).

in its infancy stage, but is gathering momentum. As the market develops, other ASCR types will certainly appear and extend the present rating boundaries.

d) Reverse conducting thyristor (RCT): The reverse conducting thyristor (RCT) represents the monolithic integration of an asymmetrical thyristor with an antiparallel rectifier. Beyond obvious advantages of the parts count reduction, the RCT eliminates the inductively induced voltage within the thyristor-diode loop (virtually unavoidable to some extent with separate discrete components) and essentially limits the reverse voltage seen by the thyristor to only the conduction voltage of the diode.

Features such as the asymmetrical structure, lifetime control, high-density cathode shorts, and amplifying gates that are used in ASCR can be effectively implemented in RCT. However, the monolithic incorporation of the antiparallel diode presents a special problem. A cross section of the RCT is shown in Fig. 5. When the voltage across the device is reversed, the monolithic antiparallel diode (p_2 n^- n^+) becomes forward biased, thereby flooding the n-base region with minority carriers. The device will fail to achieve forward blocking unless a long interval of time is provided during which no anode-to-cathode voltage is present. To meet a high commutating dv/dt requirement, the monolithic diode is integrated into the structure at a distance from the main thyristor (a few diffusion lengths) causing it to divert the flow of injected carriers during the supply reversal phase. To further provide isolation, a groove is etched in the p_2 region. These methods have proved to be largely effective and are able to provide a dynamic dv/dt larger than 1000 V/μs [36].

The spectrum of voltage and current ratings of the RCT is similar to ASCR and is shown in Fig. 1. The one drawback of the RCT is that the ratio between the thyristor and diode current carrying capabilities is fixed for a given design. The RCT is, therefore, likely to serve specific "dedicated" applications, while the ASCR should find more general industry-wide usage.

e) Gate-assisted turn-off thyristor (GATT): Gate-assisted turn-off is the name given to the method for turning off a thyristor with the usual commutation of the anode current, but with the addition of a negative pulse applied to the gate during the time when forward anode voltage is being reapplied. Fig. 6 gives typical data that show how the turn-off time is decreased by the negative gate drive. By using gate assisted turn-off, the normal trade-off between turn-off loss and con-

duction loss can be relaxed. Typically, a 50-percent reduction in turn-off time can be achieved for the same on-state voltage. It was generally believed [37] that the effect of the gate-assist pulse was to sweep out excess carriers. Works by Schlegel [38] prove that this is not the case. In actuality, the gate assist reverse bias works to reduce the injection efficiency of the cathode junction to assist in breaking the regenerative thyristor action during turn-off.

GATT's are designed with interdigitated cathodes in order to achieve both fast, low-loss turn-on and effective gate-assisted turn-off. Cathode shorts were not generally used in GATT design because it was thought that their inclusion would only add parasitic gate current. It is found that [38], [39] cathode shorts not only improve dv/dt capability as in standard thyristor design, but actually direct the current paths in such a manner that the effect of the gate-assist bias becomes more reliable and requires lower drive voltage.

Overall, the GATT has extended the operating frequency of the thyristor into the 20-kHz range. Turn-off time of less than 4 μs has been reported for a 1200-V 400-A GATT [40].

f) Light-triggered thyristors: Most recent developments in thyristors have been in the area of light-triggered thyristors. Direct irradiation of silicon with light creates electron–hole pairs which, under the influence of an electric field, produce a current that triggers the thyristors.

The turn-on of a thyristor by optical means is an especially attractive approach for devices that are to be used in extremely high-voltage circuits. A typical application area is in switches for dc transmission lines operating in the hundreds of kilovolts range, which use series connections of many devices, each of which must be triggered on command. Optical firing in this application is ideal for providing the electrical isolation between trigger circuits and the thyristor which floats at a potential as high as hundreds of kilovolts above ground.

The main requirement for an optically-triggered thyristor is high sensitivity while maintaining high dv/dt and di/dt capabilities. Because of the small and limited quantity of photo energy available for triggering the thyristor from practical light sources, very high gate sensitivity of the order of 100 times that of the electrically triggered device is needed. However, high gate sensitivity always leads to higher sensitivity to noise or low dv/dt capability. This design problem has reportedly been solved [41], [42], [43] by going to small light active regions and physically small initial turn-on regions. Typical gate regions have areas about 10 to 100 times smaller than the gate or pilot thyristor of the corresponding electrically fired device. The main problem dealing with the dv/dt

sensitivity trade-off in this manner is the reduction of the *di/dt* capability of the thyristor. The general approach to this has been to use multiamplifying gates [44], [45], each providing increased current to gate the following stage. Computer models [44] have been developed to assist in the design of amplifying stage devices, which otherwise become difficult as the number of stages increases.

Prototype light-triggered thyristors rated 4 kV and 1500 A, requiring light-triggering power as low as a few tens of milliwatts and having *dv/dt* ratings of 1500 to 2000 V/μs, and *di/dt* ratings of 250 A/μs have been developed. Significant progress has been made not only in higher device ratings, but also in new device features [46], [47] such as "controlled turn-on" which protect thyristors from destructive *di/dt* failure during turn-on and "voltage breakover" (VBO) protection, which prevents destructive failure due to triggering by avalanche current.

Gate Turn-off Thyristors

The gate turn-off thyristor (GTO) is a thyristor-like latching device that can be turned off by application of a negative pulse of current to its gate. This gate turn-off capability is advantageous because it provides increased flexibility in circuit application, where it now becomes possible to control power in dc circuits without the use of elaborate commutation circuitry.

a) *Performance considerations:* Prime design objectives for GTO devices are to achieve fast turn-off time and high current turn-off capability and to enhance the safe operating area during turn-off. Significant progress has been made in both areas during the last few years, largely due to a better understanding of the turn-off mechanisms.

The GTO's turn-off occurs by removal of excess holes in the cathode-base region by reversing the current through the gate terminal. Similar to the transistor, the electron–hole plasma is squeezed toward the center [48] during the turn-off process, thereby creating a high current density filament which not only slows down the turn-off process, but can lead to device failures [48]–[51].

An expression for the controllable current I_{ATO} which can be turned off and which takes into account the two-dimensional nature of the problem can be written

$$I_{ATO} = \frac{4G\,V_{GK}}{R_B}$$

where V_{GK} is the breakdown voltage of the cathode gate junction, and R_B the lateral resistance of the p-base layer below the cathode, and G is the turn-off gain of the device. In order to obtain high I_{ATO}, R_B is required as low as possible and therefore, it is necessary that the p-base impurity concentration in GTO's be higher than that in conventional thyristors. However, the high p-base impurity concentration results in lowering the breakdown voltage for the emitter junction and increases the on-state voltage and gate trigger current (I_{GT}). As a result, a balance must be made in choosing the optimum p-base doping profile. It is reported [52] that the p-base impurity concentration at the cathode junction should

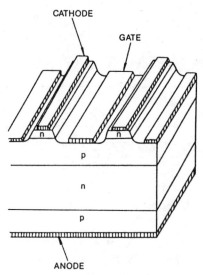

Fig. 7. MESA emitter structure for GTO's.

be kept in the 0.5×10^{18} to 1.5×10^{18} cm^{-3} range to provide a satisfactory compromise for the different conflicting requirements.

b) *Cathode structures and designs:* New cathode-gate structures and advanced cathode designs are being investigated to further improve turn-off performance of GTO's. For high current GTO, a mesa structure as shown in Fig. 7 is used at the cathode junction for the purpose of obtaining higher breakdown voltage and also to facilitate contact of the cathode region in a conventional press pak package. A modified planar structure [52] as shown in Fig. 7 has been proposed to alleviate problems such as a complicated passivation process and variation in etching depth encountered in the standard mesa structure. Improvements in I_{GT} and I_{ATO} have been demonstrated with the modified planar gate structure which is being used by many commercial GTO devices.

In order to further increase the gate-cathode reverse breakdown voltage, a buried-gate structure [53] has been proposed and developed. It has been demonstrated that with this structure the reverse breakdown voltage of gate-cathode junction can be extended to 60 and to 100 V. This improvement, in turn, translates to higher controllable current that can be turned off.

Cathode patterns used in GTO's are highly interdigitated as compared to conventional thyristors. In order to reduce the lateral resistance of the p-base layer. Experimentally it has been demonstrated [54] that the maximum gate turn-off current I_{ATO} increases with decreasing cathode finger width. However, because of the variations in the etching process to form the cathode junction, a larger finger width has to be maintained than is ideal. Typical finger widths used in today's GTO designs range from 10 to 12 mils. Some advanced cathode pattern designs have been reported and demonstrated to make significant improvements in the device. One of these [55] uses a two interdigitating level (TIL) pattern which is formed of alternating shallow and deep diffused n± cathode layers. The purpose is to minimize current crowding at the center of the cathode finger during turnoff. This is similar to two-step emitter designs for bipolar transistors [56] which

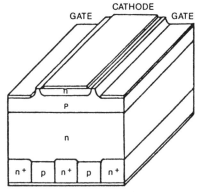

Fig. 8. Modified planar structure for GTO's.

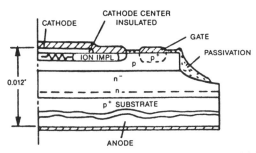

Fig. 9. Schematic of epi-GTO featuring a resistive cathode with isolated center to achieve dynamic ballasting (defocusing).

is described below. A 20-percent improvement in I_{ATO} and a turn-off gain G of greater than 10 are reported with the TIL cathode pattern. In addition, a very high dynamic dv/dt capability is found (> 1 kV/μs) and, unlike the cathode shorts in conventional thyristors, the TIL design does not degrade the turn-on sensitivity.

Another cathode design that is aimed at minimizing current pinching at the center of the cathode finger during turn-off has been proposed by Becke [57]. In this approach, the standard high concentration phosphorous cathode is replaced with a resistive ion-implemented layer. In addition, the center of the cathode is insulated so that only the edge is contacted with the metal electrode. This is shown in Fig. 9. The resistively ballasted cathodes are reported to widen the operational range and improve safe turn-off for GTO's by counteracting the formation of high-current density filaments.

c) *Lifetime control and anode design:* In addition to the cathode design, the turn-off time of GTO's also depends on the anode design and lifetime control in the wide n-base region. To achieve a better trade-off between turn-on and turn-off characteristics, work [57] has been performed to vary lifetimes vertically across the n-base region. A nonsymmetric gold distribution profile which is high in the vicinity of the p-base, n-base junction and low in the vicinity of the anode junction is used to improve the trade-offs.

In many applications, reverse blocking capability is not needed since the GTO is normally provided with an antiparallel diode for inverter operation. In such cases anode shorting can be used to improve the switching characteristics. With the use of anode shorting, the carrier lifetime in the n-base need not be reduced as much to achieve a given switching time since many carriers in the wide base can be swept out and need not be recombined. GTO's without reverse block-

TABLE I

Phase SCR	Inverter SCR	ASCR/RCT	Assisted Turn-off SCR (GATT)	GTO
Rev. Blocking	Rev. Blocking	Nonreverse	Rev. Blocking	Rev. Blocking*
Amplifying Gate	Amplifying Gate	Amplifying Gate	Amp. Gate with By-pass Diode	No Amp. Gate
Noninterdigitated	Interdigitated and Noninterdigitated	Interdigitated and Noninterdigitated	Medium Interdigitated	Fine Interdigitated
$50 < \tau_q < 300 \mu s$	$15 < \tau_q < 75 \mu s$	$5 < \tau_q < 75 \mu s$	$4 < \tau_q < 30 \mu s$	$2 < \tau_{fall} < 15 \mu s$
				$5 < \tau_{storage} < 30 \mu s$

*In practice, most devices are made without reverse blocking capability to optimize for speed.

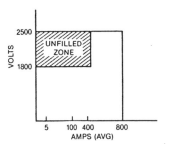

Fig. 10. Ratings covered by available GTO's.

ing capability can also be made with an additional n$^+$ layer in the n-base adjacent to the anode emitter junction, which is similar to the asymmetric thyristor (ASCR). This provides favorable trade-offs between on-state voltage and turn-off performance and is generally preferred for high-voltage (>2000 V) applications. Overall, the anode shorted and asymmetric GTO offer the best tradeoff between forward drop and switching time. However, the gold diffused device is technically simpler to fabricate and is currently more widely available in high-power versions. The asymmetric GTO probably represents the optimum design approach, but is also technically more difficult and, therefore, more costly to produce.

d) *Device characteristics:* It is apparent from the above discussions that GTO device technology represents a marriage between that of transistor and thyristor. The design and structure of the cathode-emitter are similar to those of transistors, but the vertical structures resemble those of thyristors. It is instructive to compare some of the salient features and operating characteristics with that of the other members of the thyristor family. This is shown in Table I.

With improved cathode emitter geometries and better optimized vertical structures, today's GTO's have made significant progress in turn-off performance—the prime weakness of earlier day GTO's. Fig. 10 shows the available GTO ratings and, as can be seen, they cover quite a wide spectrum. However, the main applications lie in the higher voltage end (>1200 V) where bipolar transistors and power MOSFET's are unable to compete effectively. The GTO with the highest voltage–current ratings reported to date is a 2500 V rated device with a 1000-A turn-off capability [58]. The di/dt and dv/dt ratings are reported to be 2500 A/μs and 200 V/μs, respectively.

Power Transistors

During the last few years, attention has been focused on high power transistors as switching devices in the use of high-speed inverter applications. New devices with faster

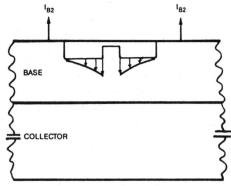

Fig. 11. New transistor design during turn-off.

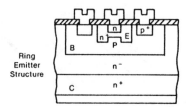

Fig. 12. Ring emitter structure for bipolar transistors.

switching speeds and lower switching losses are being developed that offer performance beyond that of thyristors. With their faster speed, they can be used in an inverter circuit operating at frequencies over 100 kHz. In addition, these devices can be readily turned off with a low-cost reverse base drive without the costly commutation circuits required by thyristors. Most of these improvements have resulted from significant progress made in the last few years in understanding the switching dynamics of high-voltage transistors [59], [60] and implementing improvements based on this understanding.

The prime design objectives for high-voltage power transistors designed for power switching applications are similar to those mentioned for GTO's. These are to achieve high switching efficiency in a high-voltage transistor structure and to achieve a large reverse bias safe operating area (RBSOA) without sacrificing forward drop current gain. In this subsection, the key design and performance considerations will be reviewed.

a) *Emitter structure:* The emitter design has a great impact on the turn-off performance of power transistors. An innovative "two step" emitter structure, as shown in Fig. 11, has been developed [56] and used in many high-performance power transistors commercially available today. In this emitter structure, the center portions of the emitter fingers consist of shallow diffused n^+ regions with doping concentrations just slightly higher than that of the base region. As a result, the injection efficiency at the centers of the emitter fingers is negligible compared to that near the edges. This structure reduces conduction at the center of the fingers during the turnoff and confines conduction to the deeper emitter region where stored charge is more easily removed. This feature minimizes voltage "tailing" and results in reduced turnoff times. In addition, because of the more uniform current density across the emitter fingers, the device will be more rugged in reverse second breakdown. It also should be noted that little performance is sacrificed in the on-state due to this emitter design because conduction occurs mostly near the emitter periphery.

The "two step" emitter has been shown [56] to reduce switching loss by 3 times, fall time by 4 times and improve RBSOA performance by 15 percent. It can be implemented with very little change in the standard transistor processing and can be used in conjunction with any of the existing transistor emitter patterns such as the "comb-" or "spine-like" emitter geometry.

A natural evolution of the "two step" emitter concept is the dot emitters approach where many small individual emitter islands are connected in parallel. When emitter islands are so connected, it is necessary to provide a means of distributing the current uniformly between the emitter islands in order to operate at a safe current density. A practical implementation of the dot emitters approach has been achieved by the Ring Emitter Transistor (RET) [61]. The RET typically consists of several hundred small, ring-shaped emitters connected by a common emitter electrode through diffused resistors. These resistors act to ballast the current and insure uniform distribution of current, thus preventing thermal runaway. A cross section is shown in Fig. 12. Each ring emitter island is basically a "two step" emitter structure, but with an addition of a diffused ballast resistor at the center. It has been demonstrated that the RET transistor is far superior compared to conventional power transistors for applications where high RBSOA and fast switching speed are required. In high switching regulators, a 400-V 15-A RET transistor [61] is reported to achieve 80 percent efficiency at a switching frequency of 0.5 MHz.

b) *Collector structure:* The collector structure plays an important role in determining switching loss and RBSOA performance. Switching loss is found to increase with collector thickness. This is to be expected since transistors with larger collector thickness will have a larger quasi-saturation region, which results in more voltage tailing during turn-off. On the other hand, RBSOA performance improves with increasing collector thickness due to lower induced field caused by the space charge limited current in the collector [59], [60].

The trade-off between switching loss and RBSOA performance can be greatly relaxed if a multiple epitaxial collector structure [56] is used. It consists of a n-epitaxial layer collector first grown on the n^+ substrate which is slowly graded to a high resistivity n- epitaxial layer. With a properly graded epitaxial layer structure in a 400-V transistor, a dramatic 60-percent improvement in RBSOA can be obtained while maintaining low switching loss and good high current gain hold up. This occurs because the graded buffer layer lowers the current induced field at the n-n^+ collector, substrate junction when the transistor is turning off in an inductive switching circuit. Similar results can be achieved with single crystal silicon using a carefully-controlled triple-diffusion process. However, this process cannot be extended to 5-in silicon due to the increased wafer thickness and thus the epitaxial process will be more cost effective in the long term.

c) *Darlington design:* For a given collector current and current gain requirement, the current density (J_E) of a transistor declines rapidly as the sustaining voltage [V_{CEO} (SUS)] increases. This is due to the current-induced base widening effect [62]. For a Darlington where a monolithic driver tran-

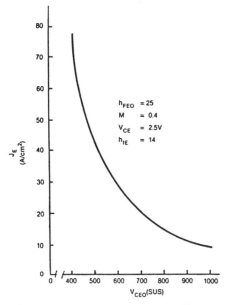

Fig. 13. Current density as a function of V_{CEO}(SUS).

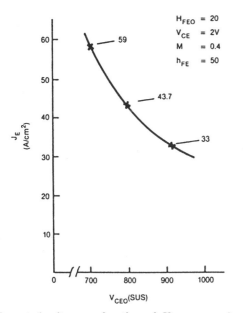

Fig. 14. Current density as a function of V_{CEO}(SUS) for a power Darlington transistor.

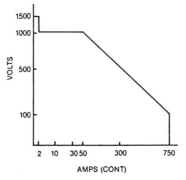

Fig. 15. Summary of present-day power transistor rating capabilities.

For example, for a 400-V Darlington, the optimum design occurs when the output stage area is approximately twice that of the driver [63]. This is arrived at based strictly on static parameter considerations. If switching speed is taken into account, the area of output stage is usually 3 to 4 times that of the driver transistor. The reason is that during turn off of a Darlington, switching loss to first order is determined by the output stage and a lower current density in the output transistor will give lower turn-off loss.

d) *Device characteristics and ratings:* The spectrum of voltage and current ratings presently covered by power transistors/Darlingtons is shown in Fig. 15. The majority of the devices fall into three voltage ranges: V_{CEO}(SUS) $\leqslant 120$ V, V_{CEO} (SUS) $\leqslant 450$–500 V, and V_{CEO} (SUS) $\leqslant 1200$ V. For the 120-V type, peak currents are being offered up to 1200 A. Most of the high current products are fabricated with a simple single-diffusion process and may be offered with multiple chips in one package. Switching peformances are characterized by very slow speed, but very rugged performance. These are used in battery-operated inverter/chopper circuits that switch at 500 Hz or below.

In the 450- to 500-V range, devices are fabricated with the triple diffusion process or with the epitaxial collector approach. Devices above 50 A are usually monolithic Darlington rather than discrete transistors. These devices are mainly targeted for 230-V line applications either in motor control or in switching power supplies.

In the 1000- to 1200-V range, devices are predominantly fabricated with a single-crystal substrate using a triple diffusion process. The epitaxial approach is not widely used because of higher defect density associated with the thicker epitaxial layer required by the 1000 to 1200 V. In addition, good lifetime is required with the thicker collector in order to maintain good current gain holdup and the epitaxial collector usually has lower lifetime than single crystal. Except at the very low current range ($\leqslant 5$ A), practically all devices in this voltage range are Darlingtons or triple Darlingtons with many of these multiple chips either in parallel or in a multiple stage Darlington configuration. These devices are mainly used for 480-V line applications.

sistor is driving the base of the main transistor, the current density is much improved as compared to that of the transistor. This is shown in Figs. 13 and 14. In Fig. 13, the current density of the transistor is calculated as a function of V_{CEO} (SUS) for a current gain H_{FE} of 14. From Fig. 14 it can be see that the current density is significantly higher than that of a transistor, even though the current gain for the Darlington is 50. In applications requiring higher V_{CEO} (SUS) voltage, the use of a power Darlington will result in a smaller, less expensive device for a given collector current and current gain. Another view on this is that for a given chip size and current level, the power Darlington is much higher in current gain and, thereby, minimizes base-drive requirements and system costs.

In Darlington design, the area ratio between the driver-stage and output-stage can be varied to obtain the smallest total chip area for a given collector current and gain requirement.

III. INTEGRATED POWER ELECTRONIC DEVICES

Evolution of Power MOS Technology

The power MOS Field-Effect Transistor (MOSFET) is a device that evolved from MOS integrated circuit technology.

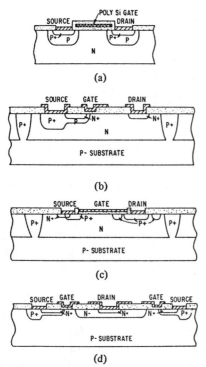

Fig. 16. Lateral DMOS structure for high-voltage drivers in integrated circuits.

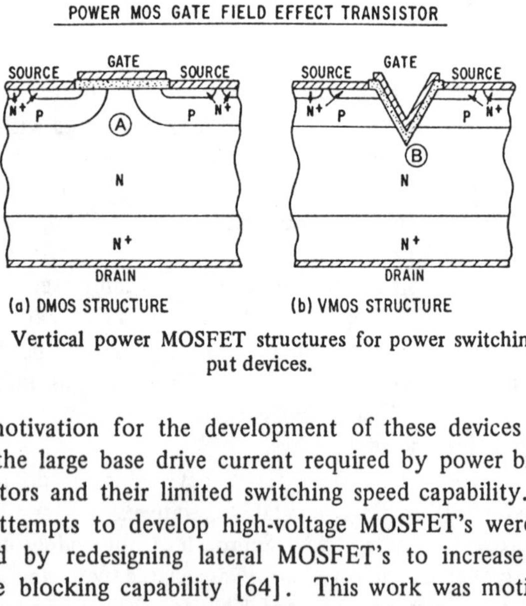

POWER MOS GATE FIELD EFFECT TRANSISTOR

(a) DMOS STRUCTURE   (b) VMOS STRUCTURE

Fig. 17. Vertical power MOSFET structures for power switching output devices.

The motivation for the development of these devices arose from the large base drive current required by power bipolar transistors and their limited switching speed capability. The first attempts to develop high-voltage MOSFET's were performed by redesigning lateral MOSFET's to increase their voltage blocking capability [64]. This work was motivated by the interest in developing high-speed switches for driving piezoelectric devices in medical electronics. The technology developed for these devices was lateral, double-diffused MOS (DMOS), as illustrated in Fig. 16. Parallel with this effort, several groups were working on the development of vertical power MOSFET's. This effort was motivated by the improved breakdown voltages and higher current ratings that could be obtained by moving the drain from the top to the bottom of the wafer, as shown in Fig. 17(a) and (b). Although the vertical DMOS structure has been adapted by virtually all manufacturers of power MOSFET's today, the initial work in the early 1970's began with the use of the V-groove process. One of the first high-voltage (600 V) V-MOS power FET's was developed at the General Electric Research Laboratory in

1978 [65] with lower voltage devices (200 V) having been developed and marketed by Siliconix. The initial focus on the VMOS process was based upon the belief that the JFET pinchoff action caused by current flowing between the p-base regions of adjacent cells in region A (see Fig. 17(a)) would result in a significantly higher resistance for the DMOS devices compared with the VMOS devices. However, detailed modeling studies of breakdown voltage of these devices pointed out the existence of very high electric fields at the bottom *B* of the V-grooves (see Fig. 17(b)). This high field resulted in a significant reduction in the breakdown voltage compared to the DMOS geometry for the same drift layer doping and thickness. Since the on-resistance of the power MOSFET increased as the 2.5 power of the breakdown voltage rating, the VMOS structure was found to have a higher on-resistance than the DMOS structure for the same breakdown voltage [65], [66]. Further, the V-groove process exposed the gate oxide to ionic contamination resulting in unstable device threshold voltages which compromised production yield and device reliability.

The introduction of DMOS power FET's was originally regarded as a major threat to the power bipolar transistor. Initial claims of infinite current gain for the power MOSFET's were diluted by the need to design the gate drive circuit to account for the pulse currents required to charge and discharge the high input capacitance of these devices. This was especially true in high-frequency applications where the power MOSFET was particularly valuable due to its inherently high switching speed. The high-speed capability was the result of current transport occurring solely via majority carriers. This eliminated the large storage and fall times observed in bipolar transistors due to minority-carrier transport. The power MOSFET's were also found to exhibit superior safe-operating-area and output characteristics for paralleling when compared with the bipolar transistor. However, these merits of the power MOSFET were offset by a higher on-resistance per unit area and a much larger processing cost when compared to the bipolar transistor. In order to derive good characteristics, high-resolution lithography with good registration between masking levels was crucial to power MOSFET fabrication, and the yield was much lower than for bipolar transistors of the same size. Consequently, the high cost of power MOSFET's restricted their application to high-frequency circuits (such as those used in switch-mode power supplies) and to low-voltage (<100 V) circuits where their on-resistance reached acceptable values.

With improvements made in process technology to obtain better yields and performance, the ratings of power MOSFET's continued to grow over the last 10 years. At present, devices are available with breakdown voltages of up to 1000 V at current levels of about 1 A and current handling capability of over 20 A at breakdown voltages below 100 V. The maximum pellet size that is in production today is about 250 mils × 250 mils in size although larger devices (300 mils × 300 mils) have been reported in the literature [67]. These large area, low-voltage devices are being developed for use as synchronous rectifiers which are very low forward drop diodes that are aimed at replacing the Schottky output rectifiers in low voltage (<5 V) switching power supplies.

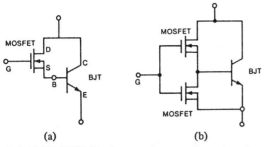

Fig. 18. Hybrid MOSFET bipolar transistor configurations for achieving a high input impedance and low on-resistance.

MOS-Bipolar Hybrid Devices

With the discovery that power MOSFET's are not in a strong position to displace the power bipolar transistor, many researchers began to look at the possibility of combining these technologies to achieve a hybrid device which has a high input impedance and a low on-resistance. The most obvious step in this direction was to simply drive the bipolar transistors with a power MOSFET in the Darlington configuration shown in Fig. 18(a). This circuit element could now be gated on like a power MOSFET and yet have a lower on-resistance because most of the output current was handled by the bipolar transistor. One application for this configuration was the development of motor drives and processes to integrate these devices together on a monolithic chip [68]. The drawback to this approach was again the poor performance of the power bipolar transistor. The low current gain (typically 10) of high-voltage bipolar transistors made it essential to use a high-voltage MOSFET of equal size as a driver. In addition, the usual reverse base drive current applied to the bipolar transistor during turn-off could not be used without the addition of another expensive power MOSFET as illustrated in Fig. 18(b). It is also worth pointing out that this hybrid approach could only result in an average current density which was in between that obtainable for the power MOSFET and bipolar transistors, while requiring process technology that must optimize the performance of both devices simultaneously.

An interesting alternative hybrid approach to obtaining an MOS high-input impedance device configuration with a high forward conduction current density was also developed in the late 1970's. In this approach, the power field controlled thyristor was used as the main current carrying high-voltage device as illustrated in Fig. 19 and a power MOSFET was used to control the output current [69]. The field controlled thyristor (FTC) is a device which operates like a p-i-n diode in its forward conduction mode. This results in very high current densities in this device compared with the bipolar transistor even at high breakdown voltages. Before the development of this gating scheme shown in Fig. 19, it had been necessary to apply a negative voltage to the gate of the FCT to hold it in the offstate and to provide large gate current pulses to achieve high-speed turn-off [70]. These problems were eliminated by the circuit shown in Fig. 19 with the use of a low-voltage power MOSFET connected in series with the FCT. These MOSFET's were considerably smaller than those required for the Darlington configuration in Fig. 17(b). Yet it was highly desirable to integrate the MOSFET with the FCT to obtain a single monolithic device.

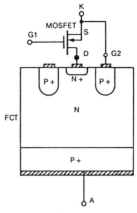

Fig. 19. Hybrid MOS/bipolar configuration for achieving high input impedance and high forward conduction current density by using a power MOSFET and field-controlled thyristor.

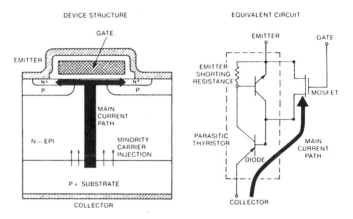

Fig. 20. The insulated gate transistor structure and its equivalent circuit.

MOS-Bipolar Functional Integration

The process of integration of the series MOSFET with the field-controlled thyristor led to the invention of the insulated gate transistor (IGT) shown in Fig. 20 [26]. This device structure is deceptively similar to that of the DMOSFET shown in Fig. 17. At first glance, it appears like the DMOSFET with its N+ substrate (drain region) was replaced with a P+ substrate (collector region). However, this simple substitution creates a four-layer (p^+-n-p-n^+) thyristor structure as illustrated in the equivalent circuit for the IGT in Fig. 20. This MOS gated thyristor structure had been conceptualized in the early 1970's and experimentally demonstrated for the first time in 1978 [71]. These devices had also been built in the triac form [72], [24] and later introduced by Motorola as a commercial product [25]. Their application was limited by the loss of gate control after turn-on which made them unacceptable as replacements for bipolar transistors.

It took a conceptual breakthrough in the early 1980's to realize that the parasitic thyristor inherent in the IGT could be defeated by adequate emitter shorting as illustrated in Fig. 20. This was achieved at the General Electric Research Laboratory by a combination of strengths in two-dimensional device modeling capability [73] and extensive experience with process development for DMOSFET's and other novel

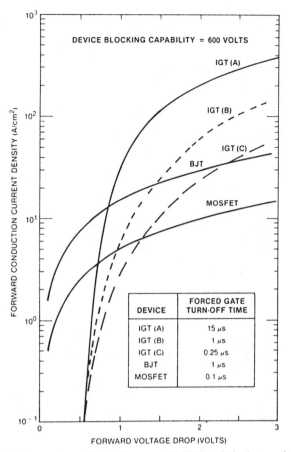

DEVICE BLOCKING CAPABILITY = 600 VOLTS

DEVICE	FORCED GATE TURN-OFF TIME
IGT (A)	15 μs
IGT (B)	1 μs
IGT (C)	0.25 μs
BJT	1 μs
MOSFET	0.1 μs

Fig. 21. Comparison of IGT with power MOSFET and bipolar transistor.

device structures. (The device was also disclosed independently by the RCA Research Laboratory [27].) The modeling indicated that it was necessary to include a highly doped P$^+$ region in the center of each DMOS cell to reduce the lateral resistance in the p-base in order to suppress latchup of the parasitic thyristor. The ability to incorporate this P$^+$ region into a power MOSFET production process with a minimum of process modification allowed device development and transition into production to occur within 6 months. The very first devices [IGT (A) in Fig. 21] exhibited excellent characteristics with forward conduction current densities 20 times higher than for MOSFET's and 5 times greater than for a bipolar transistor operating at a current gain of 10. These results demonstrated the value of functionally integrating the physics of an MOS structure for controlling current and bipolar physics for conducting the current. However, the introduction of minority carriers for current transport resulted in a slower switching speed. The first IGT's had forced gate turn-off times of 10 to 20 μs. This relatively slow switching speed would have restricted the application of these devices to circuits operating at low frequencies such as directly off the ac power line. In order to use the device for a wider range of applications, including motor drives, it became necessary to develop a lifetime control process by which the turn-off speed could be controlled without degrading the MOS gate structure. This was achieved by using an electron irradiation process [74] originally developed for controlling the speed of p-i-n rectifiers [75]. This process created the ability to control the switching speed of

the IGT in the range of turn-off times from 0.2 to 20 μs. This made the IGT a unique and versatile device which could be optimized to achieve the lowest combination of conduction and switching power losses for each application depending upon the operating frequency [76].

With the advent of these devices, the bipolar transistor is seriously threatened with replacement. The high operating current density of the IGT more than offsets the higher cost of MOS fabrication. Its advantages of a much lower gate-drive power which can be derived from low cost, integrated electronics, its unique reverse blocking capability, superior safe-operating area, and high temperature performance make it an ideal choice for high-voltage (>100 V), lower-frequency (<50 kHz) applications. Since the power MOSFET offers significantly superior performance compared to the bipolar transistor at breakdown voltages of less than 100 V and at frequencies above 50 kHz, it can be predicted that the power bipolar transistor is likely to be replaced with power MOS devices in the near future.

High-Voltage Integrated Circuits

One of the more exciting trends in power electronics has been the advent of the high-voltage integrated circuit (HVIC). The first HVIC's were primarily used for telecommunications [28] and display applications [30] with the former being built in dielectrically isolated material and the latter using junction isolation. There is also another class of devices that do not combine multiple high-voltage devices on a chip but rather have a single vertical power device together with on-chip logic devices. Power supply applications dominate the applications for these devices [29]. Figs. 22, 23, and 24 show examples of cross sections for these three types of HVIC's, with the first two having multiple 400-V devices and the latter having a single 80-V device.

These early HVIC's all were somewhat limited in their capabilities to handle a wide variety of applications because they either lacked the necessary voltage rating for the high-voltage devices or the flexibility to handle the many different device types and circuits often found in power circuits. Recently, several new HVIC processes have been disclosed which offer both extended device voltage ratings and capabilities [31], [32]. Figs. 25 and 26 show a new junction isolated HVIC and process which has over a 500-V rating for the high-voltage devices together with flexibility to have both 20-V complementary MOS and bipolar devices. In addition, the process makes it possible to make resistors and capacitors giving it a full range of digital and analog current capabilities. This flexibility has largely been possible because of the use of a thin epitaxial layer and the lateral charge control technique [77], [78] for making lateral high-voltage devices. By doing this instead of using the thick epitaxial layers needed to make vertically oriented high-voltage devices, it is possible to make high quality 20-V bipolar transistors using buried layers.

One of the key early questions about this procedure was the issue of the yield of the high-voltage elements, particularly in view of the need to control the doping thickness product of an epitaxial layer. The problem was solved by use of a charge control implant by which 90 percent of the charge is put in using the precise control inherent in ion implantation.

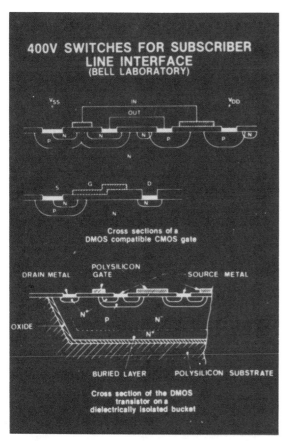

Fig. 22. Cross section of 400-V devices used in dielectrically isolated IC used for telecommunications (after Mattheus).

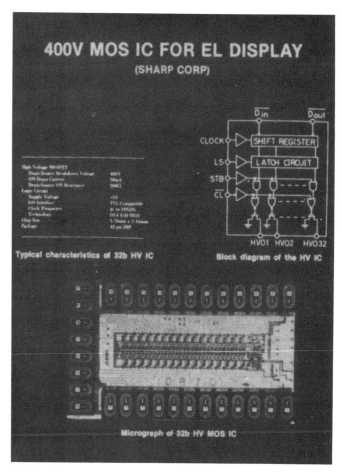

Fig. 23. Description of micrograph of power supply chip (after Ruggles).

This made control of the epitaxial charge less critical [78]. This can be seen on Fig. 27 which shows the voltage variation across a 3-in wafer as a function of the drift layer length for HVIC's made with both ion implanted charge control and charge control done using only control of the epitaxial process.

Another of the unique features of the above HVIC process has been achieving 500-V devices that are largely free of unwanted parasitics while using low-cost junction isolation technology. One example of how this is done is shown in the bottom device cross section in Fig. 25. This device is a 500-V bipolar transistor which does not inject charge into the substrate when saturated. This happens because the emitter and base regions are surrounded by a heavily doped N^+ region which breaks the gain of the parasitic substrate p-n-p. This same N^+ region would otherwise preclude high-voltage operation, but this problem is solved because the N^+ region forms the source of a self-biasing lateral JFET as shown. When the device is in a blocking state, the N^+ region floats up in potential until the channel under the junction gate (which is tied to the substrate) is pinched off. When the device is turned-on, electric charge injected from the emitter reduces the potential of the N^+ region allowing current to flow through the lateral JFET.

The commonly accepted practice for achieving parasitic free 500-V devices required the use of the much more expensive dielectric isolation (DI) technology. In the long run, how-

ever, DI will be required to achieve even higher levels of parasitic free operation, circuit flexibility, and performance. This is particularly true at high temperature and in circuits requiring high-voltage complementary devices or devices that must be referenced in both polarities relative to the substrate. Achieving these goals in a cost-effective DI technology will require a significant breakthrough in the present cumbersome method to make DI and/or progress in the silicon on insulator (SOI) technologies. Examples of promising SOI approaches include recrystalization of polysilicon or massive implantation of oxygen (nitrogen) to form a buried insulating layer [79]. In both cases it will be necessary to have advances both in the material and production equipment technologies.

An additional key issue is that of high-voltage interconnection. An effective means for doing this must be solved since without it a true HVIC is not possible. Presently most HVIC's sidestep the issue by bonding directly out from the high-voltage devices. Methods such as the use of field shields or thick insulators must be devised to make high-voltage interconnects a reality. Fig. 28 shows several approaches to this problem.

IV. PROJECTIONS OF DEVICE RATINGS

As one charts the future of power semiconductor devices, there are several facets involved. The first is the evolution of

17

Fig. 24. Description and micrograph of 400-V electroluminescent driver chip (after Fujii).

existing devices such as the thyristor, the bipolar transistor, and the power MOS transistor. The second is the emergence of new devices such as the insulated gate transistor (IGT) and the high voltage integrated circuit (HVIC). In this section both of these subjects will be reviewed starting first with a projection on ratings for existing devices.

Thyristors and Rectifiers

The history and evolution of thyristors and rectifiers has been closely associated with the availability of ever increasing sizes of silicon wafers. Fig. 29 shows the availability of float zone wafers and the time lag between their introduction and thyristors using that size of silicon. Some of the questions confronting the high power semiconductor industry is whether ever increasing sizes of float zone material will continue to become available or whether the industry will have to adapt

to the Czochralski grown material being grown in larger wafer sizes as directed by the IC industry. The major issue here is the high oxygen content of the Czochralski material and the resultant low carrier lifetime. This problem is magnified because the thyristors most likely to use larger diameter wafers are those at the highest voltage, since the larger wafer is used to offset the increased forward drop for these devices. These high-voltage devices are, in turn, the ones requiring the highest lifetime because of the increased width of the N-base. As a result, it is the projection here that thyristors larger than 100 mm will not be available unless larger, high resistivity float zone material becomes available. Since the IC industry is driving the materials developments, this is not likely.

Figs. 30 and 31 give a projection of the maximum thyristor average current rating and peak reverse voltage rating, respectively, with the year of the projection shown as a parameter.

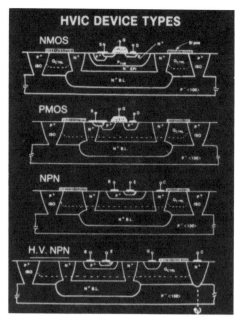

Fig. 25. Cross section of devices implemented in 500-V junction isolated HVIC.

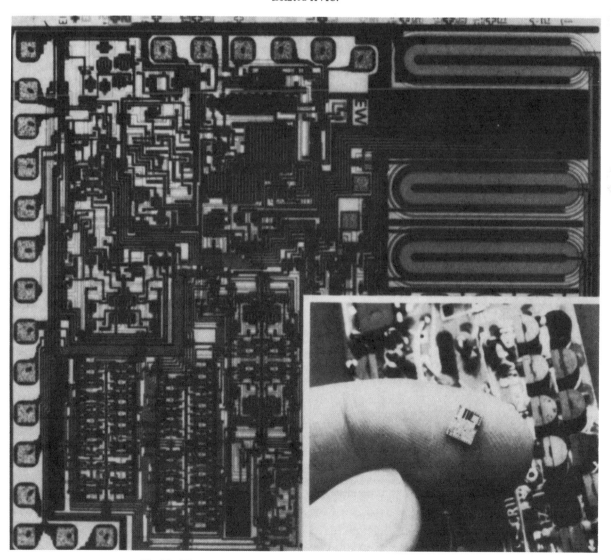

Fig. 26. Micrograph of 500-V junction isolated HVIC used for power conditioning applications.

19

SCATTER IN BREAKDOWN VOLTAGE ON SAME WAFER

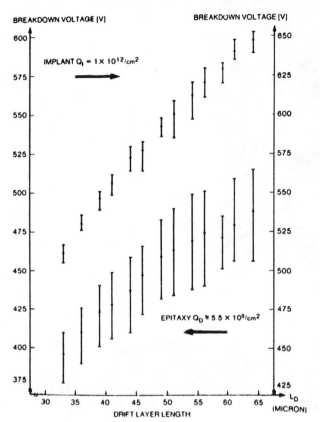

Fig. 27. Breakdown voltage for HVIC's as a function of drift region length for implanted drift region and drift region implemented using epitaxial layer.

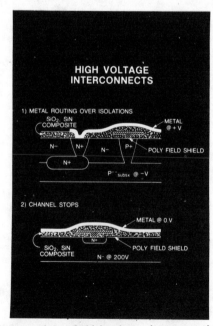

Fig. 28. Cross section of high-voltage interconnection approaches using field shields to present premature breakdown when metal runs cross heavily doped regions in HVIC's.

In Fig. 30, it can be seen that the projections for average current have historically been low due to increases in the available sizes of wafers. However, a change in this pattern has now occurred in the last 5 years because silicon larger than

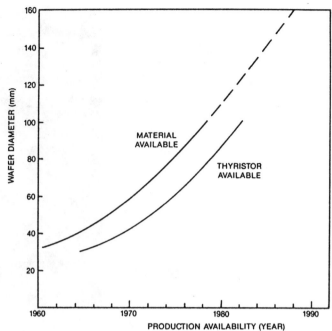

Fig. 29. Prediction of wafer size and availability of thyristor using wafer size as a function of year.

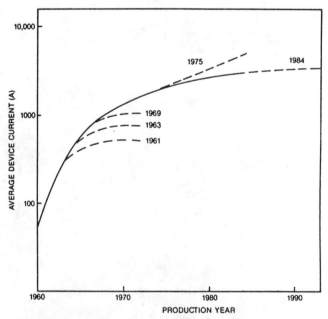

Fig. 30. Maximum average current rating for thyristor as a function of year with year of production as a parameter.

100 mm has not occurred as explained above. As a result, the peak current ratings can be expected to saturate at 3000 A unless larger silicon becomes available. It can also be expected that even if this occurs, there may be little increase because the larger silicon will most likely be used for higher voltage devices and most of the benefit in the increased area will be lost due to the resultant lower current densities.

The curves in Figs. 29–31 are updates of curves previously done [80]. The biggest change from the previous set of projections made in 1975 is the likelihood of 10 000-V thyristors emerging in the next several years. These devices are being developed for HVDC applications where, because of

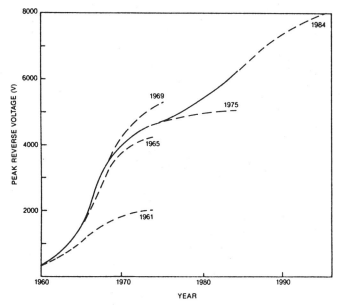

Fig. 31. Maximum voltage rating of thyristors with year of prediction as a parameter.

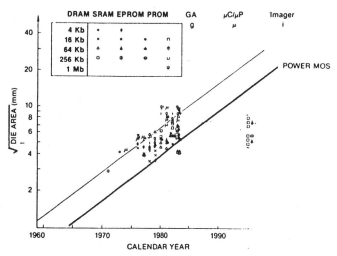

Fig. 32. Die size as a function of year for integrated circuits with curve shown for integrated power MOS devices (after Meindl).

the extremely high voltages being switched (>100 kV), economies can be realized by going from 5000 to 10 000 V due to the halfing the number of devices. However, due to the fact that at rated temperatures (125°C) the background doping of the substrate is approaching the intrinsic carrier concentrations, these devices are likely to be asymmetrical, having only forward blocking capability. While higher blocking voltages are possible for asymmetrical devices, this is not considered likely because of the poor tradeoff against forward conduction [8]. The problem is that carrier lifetimes greater than several hundred microseconds are difficult to achieve and it makes better economic sense to partition the device voltage ratings at a voltage where the base width is no larger than several diffusion lengths.

Transistors, GTO's, IGT's, and MOSFET's

The maximum ratings for the class of devices that can be turned off, unlike thyristors, is not set by the size of silicon wafers that are available. These ratings are set by a combination of factors ranging from cost performance competition among devices and demand based on what applications are being served, to technological issues such as the rapid yield fall off for MOS-gated devices for chips larger than 6 mm on a side.

Dealing with this latter issue first, the maximum die size will track the rapid progress in device fabrication skills and in new processing equipment much as is the case for IC's. A projection as to the latter can be seen in Fig. 32 where die size is projected up until the year 2000. Similar behavior can be expected for integrated MOS-gated devices, such as the MOSFET and the IGT, since these devices have similar unit process steps as are found in IC's and progress in IC fabrication will rapidly be translated into progress for power MOS devices. Taking the 6-mm die size as a starting point, Fig. 32 shows a projection of die size for power MOS devices. On this basis, the die size can be expected to triple over the next ten years from 6 to 18 mm.

110 VAC (≥ 250 VDC)

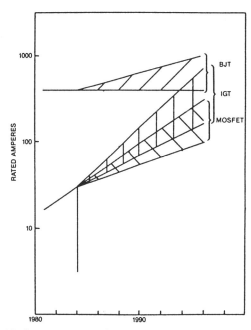

Fig. 33. Maximum current ratings for devices rated at 250 V over the next ten years.

Turning now to the actual device ratings, this is most conveniently done separately for three distinct device voltage ratings corresponding to power switching applications from the 110-V ac, 220-V ac, and 440-V ac lines. These in turn correspond to dc device blocking voltage ratings of 250, 450, and 1000 V, respectively. Taking the 250-V rating first, Fig. 33 shows the projection for device current ratings from the present up through 1994. Only the bipolar transistor (BJT), the insulated-gate transistor (IGT), and MOSFET are considered, since at this low voltage the GTO is not available. The ratings shown for each device span a range starting at the maximum rating for devices available today. The upper projection is the maximum technological rating (MTR) set by issues such as maximum die size. The lower rating is the maximum likely rating (MLR) set by applications demand and

220 VAC (≥ 450 VDC)

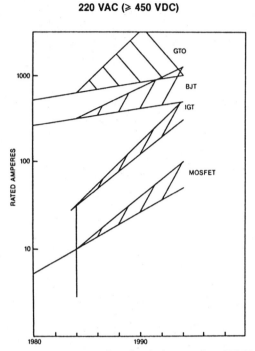

Fig. 34. Maximum current ratings for devices rated at 450 V over the next ten years.

460 VAC (≥ 1000 VDC)

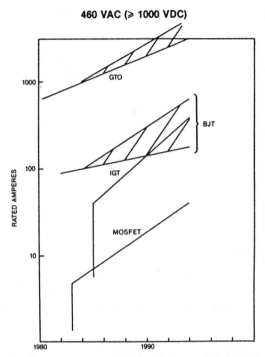

Fig. 35. Maximum current ratings for devices rated at 1200 V over the next 10 years.

competition with other devices. In the case of the BJT and the GTO, the MTR is set by an expectation that the maximum device die area will be under 75 mm for the next 10 years. The MTR for MOS-gated devices is set by the maximum die size that is believed to be consistent with acceptable device yield as shown in Fig. 32.

As can be seen from Fig. 33, the current rating for BJT's at the 250-V rating are not expected to increase beyond the 400-A rating of today because of a lack of probable demand for such a high current device serving applications requiring 250-V blocking. This particular device corresponds to a 35-mm Toshiba Grant Transistor. In the case of the MOSFET, the MLR is set by a belief that most of the applications requiring high currents will best be served by the IGT since these applications are not likely to need switching speeds above 50 kHz (where the MOSFET is the best choice). The MLR for the IGT is largely set by a projection of where most of the volume of applications for this voltage rating will occur.

Fig. 34 shows the projections for devices rated at 450 V and it can be seen that there is less spread between the MLR and the MTR since applications for devices at this voltage demand higher currents. For example, at the 110-V ac line, motor drives above 1 to 2 hp (requiring devices with rating 20 to 40 A at 250 V ac) are uncommon while, at a 220-V ac line, motor drives up to 10 hp are found (requiring devices with 100-A 450-V ratings). This trend continues, of course, with motor drives above 10 hp usually being built for the 460-V ac line. This is the main reason why the MLR for IGT's is only 300 A in 1994. The story for GTO's at this voltage rating is quite different. This is the lowest voltage rating at which GTO's are used and there is a large difference between the MTR and the ratings that are required by applications at this voltage.

The last of this set of figures is shown in Fig. 35 for the

devices rated at 1000 V. Except for the BJT, most of the devices' ratings are set close to their MTR's since applications at this high voltage require high currents and most of the limiting issues are technological. In the case of the BJT, however, the MLR is set by a belief that most of the applications requiring devices above 100 A will be best served by the GTO in the near term and possibly by the IGT in the years after 1990 (up to 400 A). The problem for the BJT at this voltage is that the device areas required for current gains greater than 10 make the device economically noncompetitive with the GTO (or the IGT when available).

Devices Above 2000 V and Under 100 V

The regime or power switching devices at the extremes of voltage, either high or very low, is somewhat specialized since the choice narrows to only one device in each case. Above 2000 V the GTO is the only turn-off device that is or will be available. Presently GTO devices of 3000 V and 1000 A are being reported [58] based on 40-mm wafer sizes. By going to 75-mm wafers, it can be expected that the ratings will increase to over 3000 A. It should also be noted that at these and higher voltages, competition between the GTO and the SCR is intense with the cost of gate drives and snubbers being traded off against forced commutation circuits, respectively. The actual choice in a given application will depend on the specific details.

In the case of devices rated under 100 V, the MOSFET is the device of choice because of a combination of the ease of the MOS-gating relative to the BJT and the low forward drop of MOSFET's at this voltage relative to the IGT. In the case of the latter, the penalty of the built-in series diode drop proves to be too significant at these low voltages and the MOSFET is the device of choice. The only exception to this would be applications where the built-in parasitic

Fig. 36. Large area power MOSFET chip containing 150 000 separate cells in a 330 mil × 330 mil die.

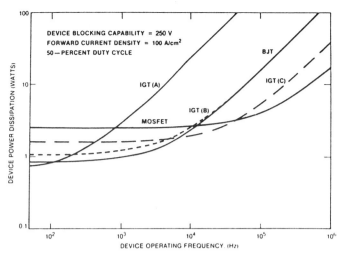

Fig. 37. Comparison of power dissipation of power switches rated at 250 V as a function of switching frequency.

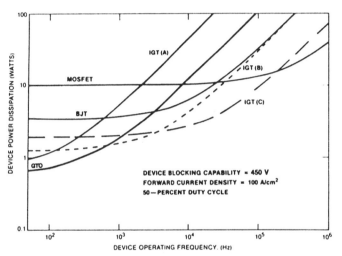

Fig. 38. Comparison of power dissipation of power switches rated at 450 V as a function of switching frequency.

diode in the MOSFET is a problem and it becomes necessary to put a diode in series to prevent current flow from source to drain when the drain voltage goes negative. In this case, the IGT would be preferable since this blocking diode is inherent in the device and thus one gets the diode plus the overall benefits of a much lower forward drop than the MOSFET/series diode combination. Presently MOSFET devices with on-resistance values as low as 12 mΩ have been reported [67] in a 300 mil × 300 mil chip. This gives a specific on-resistance of 7×10^{-3} $\Omega \cdot cm^2$. Over the next 10 years this specific on-resistance will drop to under 2×10^{-3} $\Omega \cdot cm^2$ because of improvements in design and processing. When combined with larger die areas of over 3 cm^2, this will produce devices of 6×10^{-4} Ω resistance. For applications such as a synchronous rectifier, in switching power supplies, this could be used as a 300-A rectifier with a 0.2-V drop. Such devices would also be very attractive in other applications, such as in automotive electronics, for switching virtually all the loads in an automobile. A micrograph of a device which represents the first step in this direction can be seen on Fig. 36, which shows a developmental 330 mil × 330 mil chip that is expected to have less than 0.003-Ω resistance and contains over 150 000 cells. This chip was fabricated at the GE Research and Development Center as a MOSFET synchronous rectifier under contract to the Naval Research Laboratory.

Comparison Between Devices

The previous sections discussed the probable evolution of device ratings over the next 10 years. In this section the question of how to select the optimum device type for a given application will be discussed. Of course, the issue is only a relevant one where multiple devices of a particular current and voltage rating are available. Consequently, much of the following analysis will be largely academic for applications requiring devices of very high currents where only GTO's or SCR's are available.

Figs. 37, 38, and 39 show comparisons based on power dissipation for devices rated at 250, 450, and 1000 V, respectively. This discussion will purposely leave out any comparison with SCR's since in applications that do not require a turn-off type device, the SCR is the logical choice and in most applications requiring turn off, the SCR is largely precluded. The discussion here will largely be centered on the issue of power dissipation since for most power switching applications the device size is largely determined by a requirement that the chip temperature is kept under a maximum junction temperature such as 150°C. As such, the relative chip areas for two devices (and to first order, cost), are approximately related to the square root of the ratio of power dissipation levels (the square root relation is exact for resistive devices). Additional issues, such as savings due to loss of gate drive and to different fabrication costs for devices of different technologies, can then be factored in to the degree required. In each of the figures, the power dissipation is plotted as a function of switching frequency for inductive switching with a duty cycle of 50 percent. All of the devices have equal chip areas of 0.01 A/cm^2 and carry 1 A or current (translating to a current density of 100 A/cm^2). At low frequency, the power loss is dominated by conduction loss and at high frequency by switching loss,

23

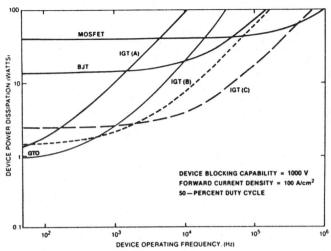

Fig. 39. Comparison of power dissipation of power switches rated at 1000 V as a function of switching frequency.

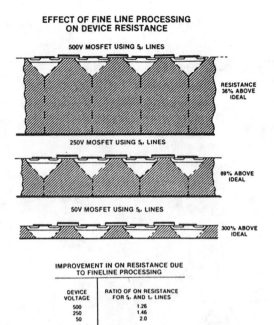

EFFECT OF FINE LINE PROCESSING ON DEVICE RESISTANCE

DEVICE VOLTAGE	RATIO OF ON RESISTANCE FOR 5μ AND 1μ LINES
500	1.26
250	1.46
50	2.0

IMPROVEMENT IN ON RESISTANCE DUE TO FINELINE PROCESSING

Fig. 40. Effect of design rule on the specific on-resistance of power MOSFET's.

which is proportional to frequency and becomes the dominant factor. Additional discussion on this means of making device comparisons can be found elsewhere [83]. It should also be noted that for each figure 3 IGT curves are presented. These correspond to the three different IGT's discussed in the context of Fig. 21, where increased switching speed has been traded off against increased conduction losses. This can easily be done by electron irradiating the devices after the fabrication sequence has been otherwise completed. This ability to customize the IGT for a given application is one of the significant advantages that the IGT possesses.

Looking first to low-frequency performance, it can be seen that the MOSFET has the highest power dissipation of all of the devices for all three voltages for frequencies below 10 kHz. At the lowest frequencies (<100 Hz), the GTO has the lowest loss with the IGT being a close second. At this same low-frequency regime, the losses for the BJT lie above that for the IGT but below that of the MOSFET. This pattern of relative performance is most pronounced for the 1000-V comparisons and the smallest for the 250-V devices. As noted earlier, below 100-V the MOSFET becomes the device of choice, and in the context of the present discussion this occurs because the MOSFET is the lowest loss device at this voltage.

The situation in the medium frequency regime (500 Hz < f < 10 kHz) is much more complicated. However, the IGT is a good choice at these frequencies because device B (see Figs. 37–39) is close to being the lowest loss device in all cases and, when this is combined with the circuit savings inherent with MOS gate drives, the IGT is a very attractive device (assuming it is available in the required ratings).

At frequencies above 100 kHz the MOSFET is the obvious choice for all these voltages, but IGT device C makes a good choice for applications with frequencies under 50 kHz. Additional factors alluded to earlier, such as the desirability or lack of having the parasitic diode inherent in the MOSFET, will also contribute to the decision as to optimum device type.

Future Directions in Power Devices

When viewed together, it is clear that for the last several years a revolution has been occurring in power electronics with the introduction of the class of integrated power devices such as the MOSFET, the IGT, and the HVIC. These new devices have been made possible by the increasing sophistication of integrated circuit processing technology, since much of the technology inherent in these devices is borrowed from advances in IC fabrication. The MOSFET described earlier in Fig. 36, which contains 150 000 cells, is the best example to date of VLSI technology implemented in power electronics. This trend will continue as IC technology advances further with increasing levels of integration being applied to both increase the size and improve the performance of MOS power devices.

There is an example of the latter in Fig. 40 that illustrates the effect that finer line width has on the specific on-resistance of low-voltage MOSFET's. As can be seen, a reduction of a factor of three is possible by reducing the minimum feature size from the present 5-μ design rule to a 1-μ design rule. This occurs due to the fact that the resistance from current spreading from the top surface of the device into the bulk is the dominant component of resistance in low-voltage MOSFET's. This effect is magnified in low-voltage MOSFET's where the vertical epitaxial thickness is small compared to the pitch of the unit cell. This makes most of the area of the device inactive in conducting current (cross-batched area in Fig. 40). Thus as one can see, dramatic improvements in the low-voltage MOSFET can be expected over the next 10 years as power device manufacturers continue to take advantage of improvements coming from IC technology.

The trend to combining MOS and bipolar in monolithic structures, begun with the IGT, will also continue. In particular, the IGT which combines the best features of MOSFET's and bipolar devices in a totally new device that is distinct from the simple constituent devices can be referred to as an example of vertical integration. This is distinct from horizontal integration found in IC's which combine multiple devices as a single chip. The IGT is an early example of devices and other devices with mixed technologies can be expected. As a general comment, the trend to mix technologies with logic and driver devices added to discrete power devices will continue.

HVIC's can also be expected to increase in capability and complexity. This will include the integration of higher gate count logic and analog circuitry together with smart sensors and high-voltage devices with higher levels of output power capabilities. One should expect that, as the chip areas increase as shown in Fig. 32, single-chip power circuits with over a 10-A capability at the 110-V ac line will emerge.

Second Electronic Revolution

The effect of the recent revolution in integrated power electronics with the introduction of both new discrete devices, such as the IGT and power MOSFET, and the HVIC, has been to achieve up to a factor of twenty cost reduction in power electronics in the low to medium power area. These cost reductions rival the effect that the IC has had on signal level electronics over the past 10 years. This in turn is opening up new applications for electronics, in general, where the major impediment in many cases had become the cost of power electronics after the signal IC had reduced the cost of the control function. Examples of this are the many consumer products such as appliances, air conditioners, and lighting which is all electrical but has been devoid of electronics due to the high cost. Examples in the industrial area include programmable controls, machine tool controls, and robotics. This new generation of integrated power electronic devices will open up a second electronic revolution that could surpass the size and scope of the IC-based revolution in its impact on the entire scope of consumer and industrial electronics.

REFERENCES

[1] J. Bardeen and W. H. Brattain, "The transistor, a semiconductor triode," *Phys. Rev.*, vol. 74, pp. 230–231, 1948.
[2] ——, "Physical principles involved in transistor action," *Phys. Rev.*, vol. 75, pp. 1208–1225, 1949.
[3] W. Shockley, "The theory of p-n junctions in semiconductors and p-n junction transistors," *Bell Syst. Tech. J.*, vol. 28, pp. 435–489, 1949.
[4] R. N. Hall, "Power Rectifiers and transistors," *Proc. IRE*, vol. 40, no. 11, pp. 1512–1518, 1952.
[5] R. H. Hall, "Electron-hole recombination in germanium," *Phys. Rev.*, vol. 87, pp. 387–392, 1952.
[6] W. Shockley and W. T. Read, Jr., "Statistics of recombination of holes and electrons," *Phys. Rev.*, vol. 87, pp. 835–842, 1952.
[7] ——, *Electronic and Holes in Semiconductors*. Princeton, NJ: Van Nostrand, 1950.
[8] R. A. Kokosa and R. L. Davies, "Avalanche breakdown of diffused silicon p-n junctions," *IEEE Trans. Electron Devices*, vol. ED-13, pp. 874–881, 1966.
[9] R. L. Davies and F. E. Gentry, "Control of electric fields at the surface of p-n junctions," *IEEE Trans. Electron Devices*, vol. ED-11, pp. 313–323, 1964.
[10] G. K. Teal, "Some recent developments in silicon and germanium materials and devices," presented at National IRE Conf., (Dayton, OH), 1954.
[11] N. H. Fletcher, "Some aspects of the design of power transistors," *Proc. IRE*, vol. 43, no. 5, pp. 551–559, 1955.
[12] J. A. Hoerni, "Planar silicon transistors and diodes," presented at IRE Electron Devices Meet., (Washington, DC), 1969.
[13] H. A. Schafft, "Second breakdown—A comprehensive review," *Proc. IEEE*, vol. 55, no. 8, pp. 1272–1287, 1967.
[14] E. S. Wajda, B. W. Keppenhan, and W. H. White, "Expitaxial growth of silicon," *IBM J. Res. Develop.*, vol. 4, pp. 288–296, 1960.
[15] J. L. Moll, M. Tanenbaum, J. M. Goldey, and N. Holonyak, Jr., "p-n-p-n transistor switches," *Proc. IRE*, vol. 44, p. 1174, 1956.
[16] R. W. Aldrich and N. Holonyak, Jr., "Multi-terminal p-n-p-n switches," *Proc. IRE*, vol. 46, pp. 1236–1239, 1958.
[17] J. M. Goldey, I. M. Makintosh, and I. M. Ross, "Turn-off gain in p-n-p-n triodes," *Solid-State Electron.*, vol. 3, p. 119, 1961.
[18] F. E. Gentry, R. T. Scace, and J. K. Flowers, "Bidirectional triode p-n-p-n switches," *Proc. IEEE*, vol. 53, pp. 355–369, 19.
[19] E. K. Howell, "The light actuated SCR," Appl. Note 200.34, General Electric Co., Schenectady, NY, 1965.
[20] F. E. Gentry and J. Moyson, "The amplifying gate thyristor," presented at IEEE Int. Electroc Device Meet., Washington, DC, 1968.
[21] R. A. Kokosa and B. R. Tuft, "A high-voltage, high temperature reverse conducting thyristor," *IEEE Trans. Electron Devices*, vol. ED-17, no. 9, pp. 667–672, 1970.
[22] D. E. Houston, S. Krishna, D. Piccone, R. J. Finke, and Y. S. Sun, "Field-controlled thyristor (FCT)—A new electronic component," presented at IEEE Int. Electron Device Meet., Washington, DC, 1975.
[23] V.A.K. Temple and R. P. Love, "A 600 V MOSFET with near ideal on-resistance " in *IEDM Tech. Dig.*, pp. 664–666, 1978.
[24] J. D. Plummer and B. W. Scharf, "Insulated gate planar thyristors," *IEEE Trans. Electron Devices*, vol. ED-27, pp. 380–394, 1980.
[25] A. Pshaenich, "The MOS-SCR, A new thyristor technology," Motorola Engineering Bull. ED-103, 1982.
[26] B. J. Baliga, M. S. Adler, P. V. Gray, R. P. Love, and N. Zommer, "The insulated gate rectifier (IGR): A new power switching device," in *IEDM Tech. Dig.*, pp. 264–267, 1982.
[27] J. P. Russell, A. M. Goodman, L. A. Goodman, and J. M. Neilson, "The COMFET—A new high conductance MOS-gates device," *IEEE Electron Device Lett.*, vol. EDL-4, pp. 63–65, 1983.
[28] P. W. Shackle, A. R. Hartmen, T. J. Riley, J. C. North, and J. E. Berthold, "A 500 V monolithic bidirectional 2 × 2 crosspoint array," *ISSCC Dig. Tech. Papers*, pp. 170–171, 1980.
[29] T. E. Ruggles and G. V. Fay, "Mixed process puts high power under fine control," *Electron. Design*, pp. 69–73, 1982.
[30] K. Fujii, Y. Torimaru, K. Nakagawa, T. Fujimoto, and Y. Aoko, "400 MOS-IC for EL display," in *ISSCC Dig. Tech. Papers*, pp. 46–47, 1981.
[31] P. W. Shackle and R. S. Pospisil, "Using the HV-100 induction motor energy saver," Harris Semiconductor Application Note no. 542, Jan. 1983.
[32] E. J. Wildi and T. P. Chow, "A 500 V junction isolated BIMOS high voltage IC," in *Proc. Electro 1984*, Session 25, paper no. 4, 1984.
[33] M. Otsuka, "The forward characteristics of thyristors," *Proc. IEEE*, vol. 55, no. 8, Aug. 1967.
[34] T. Matsuzawa, "Spreading velocity of the on-state in high speed thyristors," *Trans. IEEE Japan*, 1973.
[35] H. F. Storm and J. G. St. Clair, "An involute gate-emitter configuration for thyristors," *IEEE Trans. Electron Devices*, vol. ED-21, no. 8, pp. 520–522, 1974.
[36] A. A. Jaecklin, "Structure of an efficient high power reverse conducting thyristor," presented at IEEE Power Division Colloquium, London, England, Dec. 1, 1978.
[37] P. S. Raderecht, "The development of a gate-assisted turn-off thyristor for use in high frequency applications," *Int. J. Electron.*, vol. 36, pp. 399–416, 1974.
[38] E. S. Schlegel, "Gate-assisted turn-off thyristor," *IEEE Trans. Electron Devices*, vol. ED-23, pp. 888–892, 1976.
[39] J. Shimiza et al. "High-voltage high-power gate-assisted turn-off thyristor for high-frequency use," *IEEE Trans. Electron Devices*, vol. ED-23, no. 8, pp. 883–887, 1976.
[40] A. Tada, T. Nakagawa, H. Iwamoto, and K. Ueda, "1200 V, 400 Amperes, 4 μs gate-assisted turn-off thyristor for high frequency inverter use," in *Proc. Industry Application Society IEEE IAS Ann.* Meet., pp. 731–734, 1981.
[41] V.A.K. Temple and A. P. Ferro, "High power dual gate light-triggered thyristors," *IEEE Trans. Electron Devices*, vol. ED-23, p. 893, 1976.
[42] P. DeBruyne and R. Sittig, "Light sensitive structure for high voltage thyristors," in *Tech. Dig. IEEE Power Electronics Specialists Conf.*, p. 262, 1976.
[43] E. Schlegal and D. Page, "A high power light activated thyristor," in *IEDM Tech. Dig.*, p. 483, 1976.

[57] H. W. Becke and R. P. Misra, "Investigation of gate turn-off structures," in *IEDM Tech. Dig.* pp. 649-653, 1980.

[58] T. Nagano, T. Yatsuo, and M. Okamura, "Characteristics of a 3000 V, 1000 A gate turn-off thyristor," in *Proc. IEEE Industry Application Society Conf.*, pp. 750-753, 1981.

[59] P. L. Hower and V. G. Reddi, "Avalanche injection and second breakdown in transistors," *IEEE Trans. Electron Devices*, vol. ED-17, pp. 320-335, April 1970.

[60] S. Krishna and P. L. Hower, "Second breakdown of transistors during inductive turn-off," *Proc. IEEE*, vol. 61, no. 3, pp. 393-395, Mar. 1973.

[61] Y. Nakatani, H. Nakazawa, Y. Nawata, K. Ono, M. Kobayashi, and M. Kohno, "A new ultra-high speed high voltage switching transistor," in *Proc. Power Conf.* 7, 1980.

[62] L. E. Clark, "High current density beta diminution," *IEEE Trans. Electron Devices*, vol. ED-17, pp. 661-666, Sept. 1970.

[63] P. L. Hower, "Optimum design of power transistor switches," *IEEE Trans. Electron Devices*, vol. ED-20, pp. 426-435, Apr. 1973.

[64] M. J. Declereq and J. D. Plummer, "Avalanche breakdown in high voltage D-MOS devices," *IEEE Trans. Electron Devices*, vol. ED-23, pp. 1-6, 1976.

[65] V.A.K. Temple and P. V. Gray, "Theoretical comparison of DMOS and VMOS structures for voltage and on-resistance," in *IEDM Tech. Dig.*, pp. 88-93, 1979.

[66] S. C. Sun and J. D. Plummer, "Modeling of the on-resistance of LDMOS, VDMOS, and VMOS power transistors," *IEEE Trans. Electron Devices*, vol. ED-27, pp. 356-367, 1980.

[67] R. P. Love, P. V. Gray, and M. S. Adler, "A large area power MOSFET designed for low conduction losses," *IEEE Trans. Electron Devices*, vol. ED-31, pp. 817-820, 1984.

[68] N. Zommer, "The monolithic HV BIPMOS," in *IEDM Tech. Dig.*, pp. 263-266, 1981.

[69] B. J. Baliga, "High gain power switching using field controlled thyristors," *Solid-State Electron.*, vol. 25, pp. 345-353, 1982.

[70] ——, "The asymmetrical field-controlled thyristor," *IEEE Trans. Electron Devices*, vol. ED-27, pp. 1262-1268, 1980.

[71] ——, "Enhancement and depletion mode vertical channel MOS gated thyristors," *Electron. Lett.*, vol. 15, pp. 645-647, 1979.

[72] L. Leipold, W. Baumgartner, W. Ladenhauf, and J. P. Stengl, "A FET-controlled thyristor in SIPMOS Technology," in *IEDM Tech. Dig.*, pp. 79-82, 1980.

[73] M. S. Adler and V.A.K. Temple, "The dynamics of the thyristor turn-on process," *IEEE Trans. Electron Devices*, vol. ED-27, pp. 483-494, 1980.

[74] B. J. Baliga, "Fast switching insulated gate transistors," *IEEE Electron Device Lett.*, vol. EDL-4, pp. 42-454, 1983.

[75] B. J. Baliga and E. Sun, "Comparison of gold, platinum, and electron irradiation for controlling lifetime in power rectifiers," *IEEE Trans. Electron Devices*, vol. ED-24, pp. 685-688, 1977.

[76] B. J. Baliga, "The new generation of MOS power devices," in *Proc. Drive/Motors/ Controls Conf.*, pp. 139-141, 1983.

[77] J. A. Appels and H.M.J. Vaes, "High voltage thin layer devices (resurf devices)," in *IEDM Tech. Dig.*, pp. 238-241, 1979.

[78] E. J. Wildi, P. V. Gray, T. P. Chow, and H. R. Chang, "Modeling and process implementation of implanted resurf devices," in *IEDM Tech. Dig.*, pp. 268-271, 1982.

[79] H. W. Lam, "Silicon on insulating substrates—Recent advances," in *IEDM Tech. Dig.*, pp. 348-351, 1983.

[80] J. D. Harnden, "1977 solid-state power technology," General Electric TIS Rep. no. 77CRD114.

[81] V.A.K. Temple, "Development of a 10 kV light triggered thyristor with built-in self-protection," General Electric Technical Proposal Prepared for Electric Power Research Institute, Nov. 1982, no. CRD5110.001E.

[82] J. D. Meindl, "Theoretical, practical, and analogical limits in ULSI," in *IEDM Tech. Dig.*, pp. 8-13, 1983.

[83] M. S. Adler and S. R. Westbrook, "Power semiconductor switching devices—A comparison based on inductive switching," *IEEE Trans. Electron Devices*, vol. ED-29, pp. 947-952, 1982.

Power devices are in the chips

New power integrated circuits, called PICs, put both power-handling semiconductors and logic on the same IC chip; soon they may be part of every household appliance

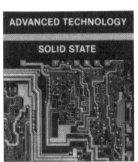

ADVANCED TECHNOLOGY

SOLID STATE

Today's automobile is burdened with some 100 pounds of wiring. It could be cut to 50. Commercial airliners carry some 8000 lb of electric wiring. It could be cut to a few hundred pounds. Standard power integrated circuits could help do the job, if only they were available. Power integrated circuits would help utilities and their rate-payers as well; ac motors consume more than 50 percent of all the electricity used in the United States, much of which is wasted because the motors run at constant speed. Variable-speed motors in washing machines, air conditioners, and machine tools—under the control of power ICs—would eliminate this vast waste.

Power integrated circuits, long a sleeper in the electronics industry, are stirring to life after a decade of incubation in the laboratory. Almost overnight, power ICs—or PICs, as researchers refer to them—have grabbed a significant share of attention at electronics technical conferences and within the research and development organizations of potentially big users of the chips. A look at the many types of PICs indicates that commercial applications will soon follow.

PICs are being investigated for power conversion and control of high voltages and high currents in automobiles, television and audio equipment, home appliances, robotics, aircraft, motors, switching devices, flat-panel electroluminescent displays, and electrostatic printing [Fig. 1]. And no wonder. The power delivered by the PIC into a load can be tens, hundreds, or even thousands of watts. PICs can deliver either high-output current at low supply voltage, low-output current at high supply voltage, or medium-output current at medium supply voltage.

When a power device is integrated with a control circuit on a single chip, there are substantial improvements in performance, at lower costs than when logic devices and power ICs are packaged separately and then connected. The savings come from eliminating the many packages to house individual chips, abolishing the interface circuits between power ICs and control ICs, and shrinking the overall system size [Fig. 2].

Furthermore, the integration of power devices and control ICs brings about a range of functions—temperature control, overvoltage and undercurrent protection, and others—that have been unavailable with discrete power devices.

Many advances, but obstacles remain

Improved fabrication processes and better device design have spurred the recent development of PICs. Many new power devices, such as vertical MOS and bipolar transistors, are now fabricated with the same processing techniques used for logic ICs and with similar minimum device sizes. CMOS, because of its relatively low power dissipation, has become the technology of choice for PICs, as it has for many conventional ICs.

But even with the tremendous improvements in power ICs,

technical hurdles remain. Among the major accomplishments needed before these chips become a dominant force in the semiconductor field:
- Developing adequate isolation between high-voltage devices and low-voltage circuits.
- Designing devices and fabrication processes that yield both high voltage and high current at an economical level.
- Designing high-voltage, high-current devices that can operate as a current source.

If these goals can be achieved, the semiconductor industry expects to produce low-cost PICs able to handle tens of amperes at operating voltages of 500 V and above, with operating frequencies over 100 kilohertz. These PICs would carry many control circuits on a chip, allowing direct interfacing with microprocessors. Such chips would dissipate large amounts of power and would therefore be designed for housing in an appropriate package with a heat sink.

It is important to distinguish PICs from high-voltage integrated circuits (HVICs), which are designed to deliver relatively low

---

Defining terms

Bias: a nonequilibrium state of a p-n junction that exists when a voltage is placed between the two junction regions.

Breakdown: a state of a circuit device in which the electric field exceeds a maximum allowed value. A sharp current increase results, which may destroy the device.

Buried layer: an underlying layer of a silicon IC formed by introducing impurities into the silicon, then covering it with additionally grown silicon.

Doped region: a layer of an IC in which impurities have been introduced.

Epitaxial layer: a layer of silicon grown atop single-crystal silicon that reproduces the same crystallographic orientation as the single-crystal material.

Isolation: a method for implementing electrical independence of devices integrated on the same IC.

Latchup: a parasitic effect in ICs that occurs when both p- and n-regions inject charge carriers; a low resistance path forms between otherwise unrelated devices, and unwanted charge flows between them.

Reverse-biased: a state of the p-n junction in which a positive voltage is applied to the n-region of the junction.

Supply voltage: a voltage that powers an IC—usually the maximum voltage the device can handle.

Tub: an island of single-crystal silicon isolated from the surrounding polycrystal substrate by a silicon dioxide film.

Vertical transistor: a configuration in which the current flows vertically down from an electrode at the top of the transistor to an electrode at the bottom.

Well: a region of silicon formed by introducing impurities of opposite polarity, usually in the substrate, which is used to separate MOS transistors there.

Vladimir Rumennik   Philips Laboratories

Reprinted from *IEEE Spectrum*, vol. 22, pp. 42–48, July 1985.

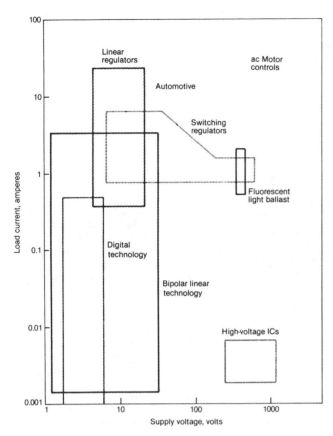

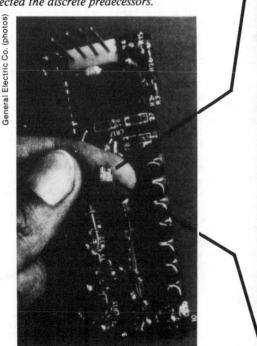

[2] *General Electric's PIC, measuring 1/10 in. on a side (below), replaces a 1½-by-3½-in. circuit board full of discrete power and logic devices. The junction-isolated chip, fabricated with a bipolar-MOS process, mixes 1000 gates of CMOS logic (lower right of magnified version), 20-V analog and digital circuitry (lower left and upper right), and high-voltage (up to 500 V) transistors (upper left)—all on one monolithic chip. The integration of logic, analog, and high-voltage devices results in new power control circuits that eliminate costly and space-hungry packages, interface circuits, and the wires that interconnected the discrete predecessors.*

General Electric Co. (photos)

[1] *Power integrated circuits that can handle between 0.5 and 30 A and operate between 50 and 500 V are finding applications in linear and switching regulators, ac motor controls, automotive control circuits, and electronic ballasts for fluorescent lights. To operate off line voltage that is typical of homes in both the United States and abroad, the PICs must be able to handle over 400 V to insure appliance protection from surges. Off-line operation could reduce the cost of the overall power system by making voltage transformers unnecessary. So-called high-voltage ICs comprise a group of circuits similar to PICs that can handle voltages up to 1000 V, but only relatively low output currents—up to 100 mA. These HVICs find applications in electrostatic and ink-jet printers and plasma displays.*

output current at high supply voltage. The on-chip power dissipation of an HVIC may be low enough to permit the placement of silicon chips in standard packages. In any case, the same fabrication process may yield ICs with low and high output current, making them HVICs or PICs depending on the application.

Tackling the isolation problem

Before PICs stepped into the limelight, the stage had been set by advances in high-voltage, high-current MOS and bipolar transistors suitable for integration. First priority was given to establishing electrical isolation of high-voltage and low-voltage transistors. At present the techniques being used are p-n junction isolation, self-isolation, and dielectric isolation; each technique has some advantages and certain limitations.

In p-n junction isolation, a very high resistance of the reverse-biased junction is used for electrical isolation between transistors [Fig. 3A]. The process of forming p-n junction-isolated wells (zones in the IC substrate that have been doped with chemical impurities) begins with a lightly doped p-type substrate. The wafers are patterned, and the buried layer is introduced at desirable sites, usually by implanting n-type impurities, such as antimony

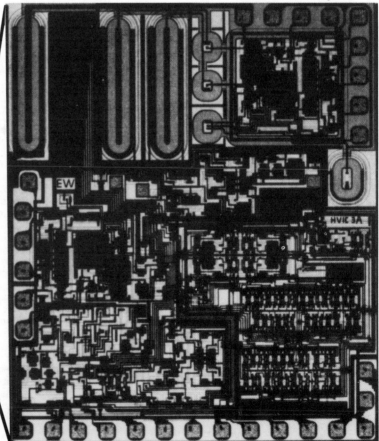

28

or arsenic. Then a lightly doped n-type epitaxial layer of an appropriate thickness is grown. This is followed by wafer patterning again and boron and phosphorous diffusions. The p^+ regions isolate the n-type islands from each other in the p-substrate. The n^+ diffused regions provide access to the buried n^+ regions. (The plus sign refers to a heavy concentration of diffusion impurities; a minus sign indicates a low concentration of impurities.)

As a result of these arrangements, isolated n-type wells are created in a p-type substrate. When reverse voltage is applied between well and substrate, the resistance of this p-n junction is quite high, isolating the devices fabricated in these wells from each other. The buried layer is multipurpose. For example, in conjunction with vertical n^+ access-regions, it provides for low series-resistance of the devices. Its presence also may serve as a barrier for the holes emitted toward the substrate. The p-n junction-isolated technologies, more than 15 years old, are used extensively in bipolar ICs.

In self-isolation, used mostly in MOS technologies, the source and drain p-n junctions isolate themselves from each other when they are reverse-biased [Fig. 3B]. The self-isolation techniques have seen widespread use in large-scale integrated circuits.

In this process, the silicon p-type wafer is initially oxidized, followed by deposition of a silicon nitride film (Si_3N_4). The sili-

con nitride film is patterned and etched, and the p^+ regions are implanted. Then the wafers are oxidized, during which a thick layer of silicon dioxide is thermally grown in the areas unprotected by Si_3N_4 films. After the Si_3N_4 film is removed, the polysilicon gate is formed, and the n-type impurities are implanted in the drain and source areas. The impurities form source and drain p-n junctions, isolating themselves.

The third technique, dielectric isolation, enables designers to fabricate ICs that are free of latchup and have substantially reduced crosstalk between elements. At elevated temperatures, when p-n junctions leak more current, dielectric isolation remains a good protection from parasitic-device interactions. Although more costly to produce, devices based on this technique demonstrate superior isolation, for excellent performance.

In fabricating the dielectrically isolated wafer, initial oxidizing takes place after n^+ or p^+ layers are locally diffused in a single crystal wafer [Fig. 3C]. The grooves are patterned, anisotropically etched, and oxidized. A thick polysilicon layer is deposited, followed by wafer lapping and polishing from the single crystal side to expose islands in which devices can then be built. Foundry services are available for dielectrically isolated wafers.

One approach: PICs with p-n junction isolation

Early transistors used in bipolar ICs had collector breakdown voltages of up to 50 V and required a relatively thick epitaxial layer. In one of the first attempts to increase the breakdown voltage of bipolar transistors, the thickness of the epitaxial layer was expanded, allowing for a wider depletion region for the collector junction while also achieving high junction breakdown. It seemed to be a straightforward proposition at first glance; however, deep p^+ isolation and n^+ access diffusions take many hours, and it is impractical and costly to diffuse through epitaxial layer thicknesses exceeding 20 micrometers. Further improvements in process and design are leading to additional device modifications.

One example is the isolation-diffusion of boron from the top and bottom side of the epitaxial layer, which makes much deeper isolation possible. At the same time, series-collector resistance of the devices has been reduced by introduction of a highly doped n^+ access path to the buried n^+ layer, which is also diffused from the top and bottom sides of the epitaxial layer.

Using the junction-isolation approach and vertical power devices, the SGS Semiconductor Corp. of Agrate Brianza, Italy, last year began using a PIC technology capable of incorporating low-voltage, bipolar, CMOS, and vertical double-diffused MOS and bipolar power transistors [Fig. 4A]. The company says that in high-frequency switching applications, the circuits will deliver output power as high as 200 W at a current level of 10 A. The double-diffused vertical MOS transistor has an on-resistance of 0.15 ohms, which can be controlled by changing its size so that designers can trade off power dissipation and silicon area.

The first generation of PICs from this company (called MD²MOS) has been released for applications in 60-V power supplies, and the company expects to announce new products with voltage capabilities of 250 V this year and 400 V at a later date. Applications for the MD²MOS circuits include dc-to-dc converters, audio amplifiers, and dc motor control. [See "Solid state," *Spectrum*, January 1985, p. 49.]

A somewhat different approach in PIC design, which also uses p-n junction isolation, has been taken by the Motorola Corp. of Phoenix, Ariz. Its technology, which it calls Smart Power, combines vertical power transistors having a high-current electrode on the back of the die with complementary MOS and bipolar transistors built in the epitaxial layer.

In the device [Fig. 4B], the charge carriers flow downward and are collected by the back electrode. This approach offers much higher current capabilities since the bottom series-resistance is quite small. The breakdown voltage in this design depends on the thickness of the p-epitaxial layer. This approach limits the designers to one power device per chip because there is no isolation between high-voltage devices.

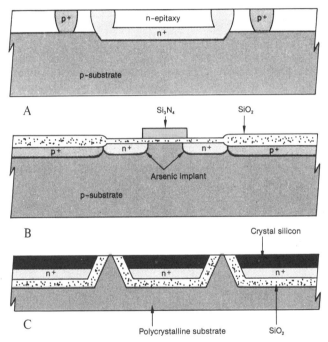

[3] The key to making PICs is isolating the high-voltage and low-voltage transistors on the monolithic chip, which can be done in three ways. The p-n junction isolation (A) is achieved when the epitaxial layer is surrounded with p-type silicon. The depth of the epitaxial well is limited by the ability to diffuse impurities downward and to merge the p^+ region with the p^- substrate. Self-isolation (B) is achieved by forming a p-n junction between implanted impurities and the substrate. When the junction is reverse-biased, its resistance becomes very high, and the interaction between p-n junctions is limited. In this sense, neighboring junctions become isolated. This method utilizes only the top portion of the silicon wafers, and it does not require deep diffusions. Dielectric isolation (C) is achieved by forming islands of single-crystal silicon in the polycrystal substrate, separated from each other by a layer of silicon dioxide. This film is virtually free from leakage current; the only coupling between elements is a capacitance. The higher cost of dielectrically isolated products stems from the initial sequence of operations required to fabricate dielectrically isolated islands of silicon, separated from polysilicon substrate.

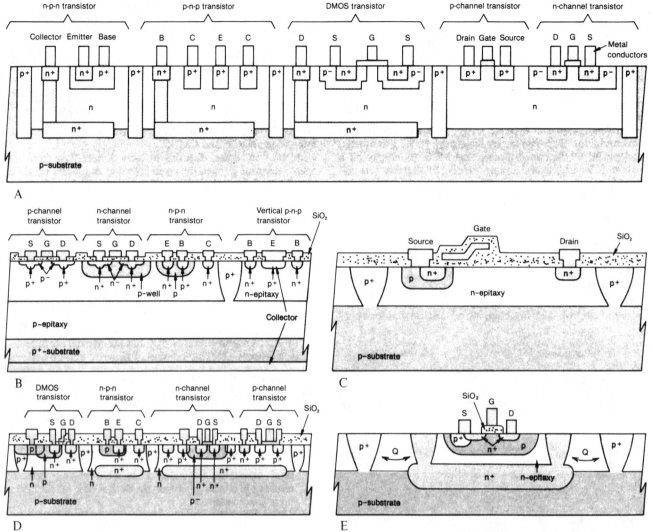

[4] There are various fabrication processes for integrating high- and low-voltage logic and power circuit devices. SGS Semiconductor, for example, uses a process called MD²MOS (A) to combine bipolar analog, DMOS power, and CMOS logic capabilities. In the Smart Power technology developed by Motorola (B), a vertical power transistor rated at up to 20 A is integrated with low-voltage MOS and bipolar devices. A lateral double-diffused MOS transistor designed at Philips Laboratories (C) with the Resurf concept has an epitaxial layer thickness of only 5 to 10 micrometers, while vertical discrete devices would require three to five times that thickness when operating at 500 V. Another process developed by Siliconix Inc. (D) allows maximum use of both MOS and bipolar transistors, which are placed in separate p-n junction–isolated wells. General Electric's complementary bipolar/MOS process (E) utilizes both high-voltage lateral MOS and bipolar transistors. These transistors can operate at greater than 500 V, but the current must remain relatively low—around 100 mA.

In addition to the bipolar power p-n-p transistor, other power devices can be fabricated with this design, such as vertical MOS power transistors and silicon controlled rectifiers (SCRs). The Smart Power series was designed and is commercially available for applications in high-current regulators, voltage supplies, and dc motor controls. The PICs can handle currents up to 20 A and operating voltages up to 110 V.

The art of designing high-voltage lateral transistors was considerably advanced in 1979 by J.A. Appels and H.M.J. Vaes of Philips Gloeilampen Fabriken, in Eindhoven, the Netherlands. They introduced a new concept—Resurf (reduced surface field). The technique utilizes a two-dimensional electric-field control near the surface of the devices by selecting appropriate impurity concentrations and epitaxial layer thicknesses. This concept has been further developed in lateral double-diffused MOS transistors [Fig. 4C]. The electrons in these transistors flow from the source through a short inversion channel under the gate, through the epitaxial drift region, then into the drain.

The epitaxial layer in the devices is relatively thin—5 to 10 micrometers—and isolation diffusion does not present any difficulties. With this technology, device ratings are scaled with ease. For a given substrate and epitaxial layer, increasing the distance between the source and the drain leads to an increase in the breakdown voltage. In fact, a variety of breakdown voltages can be obtained for devices on the same IC, but only through geometrical changes. This approach is attractive for manufacturing, since a single production process can yield the whole gamut of device ratings. Since only a thin epitaxial layer is required for high-voltage lateral double-diffused MOS devices, both high-voltage devices and low-voltage bipolar and MOS devices can be fabricated with the same process.

Siliconix Inc. of Santa Clara, Calif., has devised a process in which the lateral double-diffused MOS devices, capable of switching a few amperes and operating at high voltages, are integrated with the CMOS and n-p-n transistors [Fig. 4D]. The power devices commercially built with this process can handle a few hundred volts, but the company plans to increase the breakdown voltage to 500 V. The maximum current rating of this IC can be as high as 20 A for 80-V operation, and the device can be switched at a rate exceeding 200 kHz. The high switching speed of lateral double-diffused MOS transistors results from the low input capacitance. Applications of this technology range from low-cost remote telephone-line power converters to integrated power-supply controllers and electroluminescent flat-panel display drivers.

Last year, General Electric Corp.'s Power Electronics Semiconductor Department in Syracuse, N.Y., announced development of the mixed bipolar and MOS technology on a single chip. It yields lateral double-diffused MOS transistors and lateral high-voltage bipolar transistors, both operating at 500 V [Fig. 4E]. This technology also incorporates low-voltage CMOS devices, as well as n-p-n and p-n-p transistors. Lateral high-voltage n-p-n transistors use the basic lateral double-diffused structure with a separate base in the channel area.

This mixed technology addresses the aspects of circuit design most often needed in power systems, while providing maximum flexibility. The potential applications include high-voltage, low-current, multioutput drivers for electrostatic printing and plasma displays, switching-mode power regulators, electronic ballast, and motor control. GE's first chip, introduced last year for a proprietary application, incorporates several high-voltage outputs with relatively low current capability—100 mA.

Self-isolated PICs developed

In the MOS area, the low-doped offset channel near the drain has been used to fabricate self-isolated lateral high-voltage transistors. This widespread technique is also used with MOS transistors that have very small geometries, to offset the high electric field near the gate oxide and drain region. The fabrication process used to make these high-voltage transistors is well-suited for low-voltage NMOS and CMOS.

In the "on" state, electrons in these devices flow from the source electrode through the gated inversion and n-offset regions into the drain. In the "off" state, the drain voltage is supported in the lateral direction by the depleted n-region. The n-drift region in this type of device is a major contributor to on-resistance. No deep diffusions are required, and the process is less complex than the p-n junction or the dielectric isolation processes.

Many companies, including Hitachi Ltd. of Tokyo, the Sharp Corp. of Nara, Japan, and Xerox of El Segundo, Calif., have demonstrated experimentally the feasibility of the devices, with breakdown voltage in excess of 500 V. NMOS transistors with an offset channel and breakdown voltage exceeding 1000 V have also been demonstrated by Tektronix Inc. of Beaverton, Ore.

Xerox manufactures NMOS ICs for internal use in printing systems. One chip consists of 16 active pull-up devices, 16 corresponding pull-down drivers, and a 16-bit register with latch for serial-to-parallel conversion and gating logic. The chip operates from a 600-V supply.

Dielectric isolation offers best separation

Both the p-n junction and self-isolation techniques suffer from an increase of leakage current at high temperatures. Although this increase is acceptable in most power applications, it reduces the isolation between on-chip devices, resulting in crosstalk between the devices and voltage latch-up in some instances.

The dielectric isolation technique is practically free from leakage current. The only coupling between elements is a capacitance of the isolation oxide, because the leakage current through the dielectric is very small even at high temperatures. Devices based on dielectric isolation, although more costly to produce, have superior isolating properties.

Since this technique was introduced in the 1960s, various devices have been fabricated within single crystal wells. Some electrical characteristics are unique—obtainable only in the devices built in the dielectrically isolated wells. The quality of the silicon in the wells is similar to that of the single-crystal material. Thus device behavior can be predicted in the same way as for the devices with p-n junction isolation.

Except for dielectric isolation outside the n-tub, the bipolar transistor is similar to one built with p-n junction isolation, resulting in almost identical electrical device characteristics. For both vertical n-p-n and MOS transistors [Fig. 5A], the electrons flow downward through the high-resistivity tub into the n+ collector and then into the electrode at the top of the wafer. Again, as in the case of p-n junction isolation, the breakdown voltage of the devices increases along with the tub depth.

However, since the tub depth is defined by the etching rather than by diffusion, it is somewhat easy to form a deeper well and to achieve higher breakdown voltage. On the negative side, the thermal conductivity of the polysilicon substrate and of the isolation oxide film are substantially lower than the thermal conductivity of a single silicon crystal, resulting in lower on-chip power dissipation. This limitation restricts dielectric isolation in high-power applications.

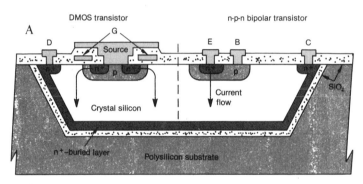

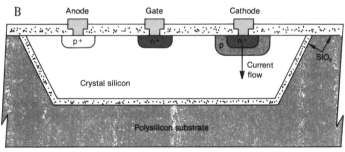

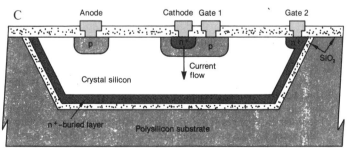

[5] In vertical double-diffused MOS and bipolar transistors fabricated with dielectric isolation (A), the current first flows downward, then through the n+ buried layer, and finally returns to the surface. A high-voltage gated diode from AT&T Bell Laboratories (B) employs dielectric isolation. The high-resistivity silicon is modulated by minority carriers injected from the anode and cathode. In another experimental approach using a lateral SCR from Nippon Telegraph & Telephone (C), the conduction state can be initiated either by gate 1 or gate 2.

Only a few companies are experienced in making ICs on which a handful to hundreds of transistors are directly isolated from one another. These companies have used this approach to build radiation-hardened and high-speed bipolar ICs.

AT&T Bell Laboratories in Murray Hill, N.J., and others—in work directed initially at subscriber-loop interface circuits—have advanced dielectric isolation to the point where commercial products are feasible. One of the first ICs introduced for the company's internal use was a high-voltage (500 V) and low-current (under 100 mA) crosspoint array fabricated by Western Electric [Fig. 5B]. It has a center gate between the anode and cathode contacts of a diode (the p⁺/silicon/p⁺ path in Fig. 5B). The cathode is surrounded by a punch-through shield region, which allows for relatively close spacing of the cathode and gate. The switch can be gated through the diffused n⁺ gate.

Another experimental approach to building efficient high-voltage switches for use in communications employs a similar structure [Fig. 5C]. However, in this method, used by Nippon Telegraph & Telephone of Japan, the gating can be provided by either the base contact or through the buried n⁺ region. The presence of the minority carriers allows for relatively low on-state resistance at the expense of switching speed, which is in the range of a few microseconds.

Further research on dielectric isolation has led to one of the first monolithic ICs that can operate directly from ac line voltage—the HV-1000 energy-saving IC from the Harris Corp. in Melbourne, Fla. Commercially introduced last year, the IC achieves high-level integration at a vast reduction in both the cost and the size of motor-control circuits. The entire circuit can be stored within the motor frame.

The high-voltage transistors used in this application operate at 400 V and can sustain surges up to 1000 V. Although these high-voltage technologies are designed to handle relatively low current, the same approaches can be used for high-current applications in power control.

In yet another development, Siliconix has reported an experimental process that yields dielectrically isolated vertical transistors operating at 400 V and CMOS control circuits.

As for bipolar devices fabricated on dielectrically isolated wafers, Harris introduced a chip last year for high-voltage, high-current telecommunications circuits. The process integrates a 200-V complementary pair of vertical bipolar transistors with I²L logic. It is likely that a 500-V dielectrically isolated chip with a current rating approaching 500 mA will emerge this year.

CMOS adds advantages

Low-voltage CMOS has proved to be as cost-effective as the rival NMOS and bipolar technologies, with lower power consumption and greater flexibility in circuit design. Compared with other PIC technologies, CMOS offers reduced power consumption, high linearity, and high slew rate of analog circuits.

At present, most power IC circuits use only power n-channel MOS transistors or bipolar transistors. The major disadvantage of p-channel power transistors is their low hole mobility—one-fifth of the electron mobility. This is directly translated into higher on-resistance of the p-channel devices per unit area, larger chip size, and higher cost. Of course, the technology chosen involves a tradeoff between product cost and circuit performance. In some IC applications, the use of complementary technology is essential, since CMOS devices offer better linearity, which is important in the design of some linear amplifiers.

Several experimental high-voltage CMOS technologies for switching applications were developed by scientists at Stanford University in California in 1974 and the University of Dortmund, West Germany, in 1982 [Fig. 6A]. These CMOS technologies can operate at voltages up to 200 V using lateral double-diffused

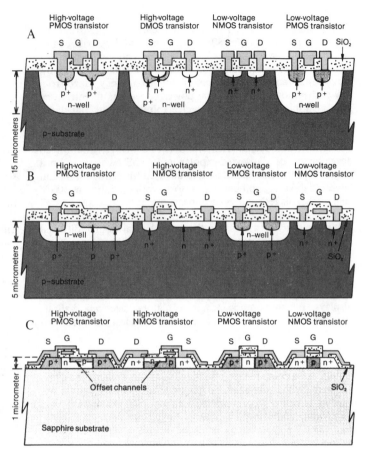

[6] Three different approaches to fabricating high- and low-voltage CMOS transistors on the same chip are being attempted. The University of Dortmund scheme (A) employs a well 15 micrometers deep to fabricate high-voltage CMOS transistors. One-dimensional electric field scaling is used. A CMOS process developed by Xerox Corp. (B) requires only a 5-micrometer-deep well to fabricate PMOS transistors with high breakdown voltage and an offset channel using a charge-controlled technique. With an SOS process developed by NEC Corp. (C), a design in which the current flows within a few tenths of a micron beneath the surface, only 1 micrometer of silicon is needed to build transistors with breakdown voltages of more than 1000 V.

MOS devices and p-channel MOS transistors with offset gate. For isolation, the transistors are placed in deep diffused or epitaxially formed n-wells. To achieve high breakdown voltage, the well junction has to be relatively deep, and forming the well itself requires long diffusion time.

To circumvent the problem of the deep well formation, scientists at Xerox devised a laboratory process with an n-well 4 to 5 micrometers deep. Although the well is quite shallow, the breakdown voltage of the n- and p-channel transistors exceeds 250 V and can be made even higher.

This development is significant. The fabrication process for CMOS devices in a shallow well is quite similar to that of standard low-voltage CMOS technology, thus allowing the integrated high-voltage and low-voltage devices to be fabricated by the same standard CMOS process. The high-voltage p-channel transistor is built inside the n-type well [Fig. 6B], and the p-type offset channel is used to separate the drain area from the gate. Because the fabrication process for low- and high-voltage devices is the same, the other electrical parameters of low- and high-voltage devices are also equal, thus enhancing on-chip design flexibility.

The on-state operation of these devices is similar in principle to that of the n-channel transistor with an offset channel. However, in the off mode, the offset p-channel is depleted, and it simultaneously depletes the well underneath; thus high drain voltage can be accommodated within the shallow well. This approach can be used to design fast, medium-power switches and amplifiers with high-frequency response.

Designers at the Nippon Electric Corp. have come up with an experimental silicon-on-sapphire (SOS) process that yields low-voltage CMOS devices and power p-channel and n-channel transistors with breakdown voltages in excess of 1000 V [Fig. 6C]. Compared with devices built in bulk silicon, transistors on SOS need a very thin layer of silicon—1 to 2 micrometers. NEC has used this approach to make prototype PICs for use in gas-discharge electroluminescent displays and in high-voltage pulse generators. Although the performance of SOS devices is quite spectacular, this technology is limited in the marketplace because the manufacturing costs are several times higher than those for PICs built in a single crystal. There is no indication so far that other companies are attempting to fabricate PICs in SOS.

Dissipating heat is vital

In the operation of any PIC, the internal heat generated is critical to both device performance and the chip's operating temperature. A device's usefulness is an exponential function of junction temperature; the lifespan decreases by about a factor of two for every 10 °C increase in temperature. Adequate chip cooling or heat sinks must be employed to prevent a device's junction temperature from failing. In PICs, the temperature of the chip can be easily monitored by using readily available sensitive elements, such as resistors and p-n junctions.

With these components, control circuits can monitor the chip temperature and regulate it by reducing the operating current or shutting it down to prevent overheating. For example, if the temperature in Motorola's Smart Power chips becomes higher than 125 °C, a short circuit is placed directly across the line. A vertical output device is used as a crowbar element. Thermal management of the chip remains an important factor in determining the PIC's overall product cost.

What lies ahead for PICs? As large-scale integration (LSI) fabrication processes mature and reach micrometer and submicrometer dimensions, they will give rise to further advances in PIC development. Tighter process control and small fabrication tolerances will permit improved performance of integrated power transistors and PICs in general. The relationship between on-state resistance and breakdown voltage, which restricts a device's current-handling capabilities, is being attacked on two fronts:

1. Improved device designs and finer fabrication processes to reduce on-state losses. The development of new device-simulation programs and other computer-aided design tools will enable engineers to construct more efficient high-voltage, high-current integrated transistors.

2. The introduction of integrated power devices in which current is conducted by minority and majority carriers, to substantially reduce the on-state resistance and consequently the chip size. The market share for these devices will grow if limitations in operating frequencies can be overcome.

Moreover, maximum breakdown voltages of the transistors defined by the one-dimensional rules may be improved by the introduction of more efficient two-dimensional design schemes—techniques like Resurf, for example. In fact, simulations show that lateral device configurations using the Resurf concept achieve higher breakdown voltages for a given length of silicon and for the same maximum value of the electric field.

There is also good reason to believe that gate oxide thicknesses in high-voltage MOS devices will in the near future be further decreased from 1000 angstroms to 400–500 angstroms. RCA has already marketed discrete devices with a gate oxide thickness of 500 angstroms, driven with 5 V at the gate. With the thin gate ox-

ide of MOS devices, integrated low-voltage devices will be scaled down to reach LSI transistor density per unit area. Should that occur, more analog and digital functions could be integrated on a chip, and circuit complexity might be dramatically increased.

By integrating further, researchers could create a PIC complete with sensing functions that would interface with analog devices—temperature sensors, Hall sensors, and photoreceptors, to mention a few. If sensing and power control were combined with signal processing capability, a stand-alone single-chip system or one interfaced to a central processor might be constructed. Low-level integration has already been achieved.

For example, optocoupling is used to switch high current in solid-state relays in place of the electromechanical switch. The International Rectifier's Crydom Division in El Segundo, Calif., is manufacturing solid-state relays with a light-emitting diode (LED) that can switch ac current as high as 1 A.

The next technological breakthrough in power conversion may come from the Massachusetts Institute of Technology in Cambridge. Scientists there have embarked on a three-year program aimed at developing a completely monolithic 90 percent efficient 50-W dc/dc converter that can deliver 5 V at 10 A from a 100-V source. This converter would be packaged in a 48-pin dual-in-line package (DIP) and would contain all components, including capacitors, magnetics, and power and control devices. Operating at 30 to 100 kHz, switching power converters are still bulky, however. As frequency increases, the size of the passive components will become smaller.

New thin-film materials are also being investigated for PICs. Here the passivation of high-voltage devices using semi-isolated oxygen- or nitrogen-rich polysilicon films would lead to more stable devices at lower cost. GE's high-voltage IC already uses this type of passivation. It allows the designers to simplify interconnections between low-voltage and high-voltage transistors on the chip, producing a smaller chip.

One thing is clear: interest in PICs has so widened in recent months that improvements appear inevitable.

To probe further

More information concerning PICs can be found in many papers published from 1979 to 1984 in the *Technical Digest* from the International Electron Devices Meeting, coordinated annually by the IEEE Electron Devices Society. The 1979 volume includes "High Voltage Thin Layer Devices (RESURF Devices)" by J.A. Appels and H.M.J. Vaes, pp. 238–41; and "A High Voltage Offset-Gate SOS/MOS Transistor" by M. Sakume et al., pp. 594–97. In the 1981 *Technical Digest*, dielectric-isolation technology is presented in "530 Volt Integrated Gated Diode Switch for Telecommunications" by A.R. Hartman et al., pp. 250–53; and a description of lateral-diffused MOS transistors is found in "Low Specific On-Resistance 400 V LDMOS" by E. Stupp, S. Colak, and J. Ni, pp. 426–28.

A paper presented by J. Tihani, "Integrated Power Devices," is found in the 1982 *Digest*, pp. 6–10. PIC technologies are compared in "Integrated Circuits for the Control of High Power" by R.S. Wrathall et al., 1983 *Digest*, pp. 408–11. A CMOS circuit with a shallow well is described in "Integrated High and Low Voltage CMOS Technology" by V. Rumennik and D.L. Heald, 1982 *Digest*, pp. 77–80. Lateral merged bipolar-MOS devices are discussed in "Comparison of High Voltage Devices for Power Integrated Circuits" by R. Jayaraman, V. Rumennik, B. Singer, and E. Stupp, 1984 *Digest*, pp. 258–61.

Various circuits made using PIC techniques were also covered in the 1985 International Solid State Circuits Conference, sponsored by the IEEE Solid State Circuits Council.

Power Integrated Circuits—A Brief Overview

B. JAYANT BALIGA, FELLOW, IEEE

Abstract—A brief overview of developments in power and high-voltage integrated circuits is presented. The technology can be classified into two types: 1) smart power devices that contain one or more common drain, vertical power transistors with control, and protective circuitry built on the same chip, and 2) high-voltage integrated circuits that combine lateral high-voltage with CMOS logic and analog bipolar circuits on the same chip. These technologies are being aimed at display drivers, telecommunications, motor drives, power supplies, and automotive electronics. A rapid growth in their application in the future can be expected.

I. INTRODUCTION

UNTIL A FEW years ago, power electronics and integrated circuits have taken separate routes. Power electronics has relied upon the implementation of circuits using discrete components. The major thrust in this area has been the development of power semiconductor devices with higher power handling capability. With the availability of microprocessors, the control system has been amenable to integration. However, the relatively high currents encountered in the gate drive circuits for bipolar transistors has required a discrete part implementation of these circuits.

During the last five years, a new class of MOS controlled power devices has emerged. Among these devices are the power MOSFET and power MOS-IGT [1]. These devices were developed because of their high-input impedance feature. The low-input gate currents required to control these devices makes the size of the components used in the gate drive circuits sufficiently small that these circuits are now amenable to integration. This has created the opportunity to obtain a large decrease in component count, resulting in a reduction in system cost, size, and weight. In addition, the smaller number of interconnects enhances system reliability. These features have created a resurgence in power electronic applications.

Power integrated-circuit technology can be partitioned into two broad categories: 1) "smart" discrete vertical power structures with sense or protection elements and logic or analog circuitry built into the same chip; and 2) high-voltage integrated circuits in which conventional logic and analog circuits are combined with high-voltage lateral devices. Considerable developmental effort is being undertaken in both categories. The smart discrete device effort is mainly targeted to automotive electronics, while the high-voltage integrated circuits are being developed

Manuscript received May 1, 1986; revised July 15, 1986.
The author is with the General Electric Corporate Research and Development Center, Schenectady, NY 12345.
IEEE Log Number 8610702.

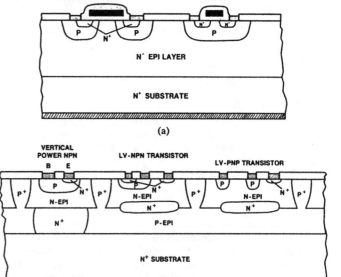

Fig. 1. (a) Discrete vertical double-diffused MOSFET structure with an n-MOS transistor integrated with it using a p-well technology. (b) Discrete vertical bipolar transistor integrated with lateral p-n-p transistor and vertical low-voltage n-p-n transistor using a double epitaxial layer technology with an n^+ plug.

for motor control, telecommunications, power supplies, displays, etc. The power spectrum over which this power technology can be applied ranges from 50 to 1200 V, with currents of 1 to 100 A.

II. SMART POWER TECHNOLOGY

The base of the smart power device technology is a discrete power device into whose structure other circuit elements are integrated to achieve an increase in functionality. Both discrete bipolar transistors and power MOSFET's have been used to create the desired smart power switches, as illustrated in Fig. 1. The power discrete devices are designed with vertical current flow by using a epitaxial drift layer grown on a highly doped substrate. The circuit elements can be integrated into the device by taking two approaches. In the first approach (Fig. 1(a)) a lightly doped p-well is diffused into the n-epitaxial layer and the lateral integrated elements built in the p-well [2]. In the second approach, a double epitaxial layer is utilized to achieve isolation [3]. In this case, an n^+ plug is diffused through the p^- epitaxial layer in order to create a vertical current path for the power transistor. In addition, n^+ buried layers are used for reducing the collector

Reprinted from *IEEE Trans. Electron Devices*, vol. ED-33, no. 12, pp. 1936–1939, Dec. 1986.

resistance of the n-p-n transistor and to increase the gain of the lateral p-n-p transistor.

This technology is limited to the integration of CMOS logic and analog sense-protection circuitry with either a single power transistor or an array of common drain power transistors. Such arrays are useful for implementation of a monolithic high side switch in automotive electronics. Complex chips combining CMOS logic for encode/decode functions and analog circuits for current and over-temperature protection with a power MOSFET have been reported [3]. In addition to the bipolar transistor illustrated in Fig. 1(b), several other vertical power structures have been used in this configuration. The power MOS-FET is a prime candidate for automotive electronics. The IGT is a candidate for high-voltage systems which require a smart switch with built-in self-protection features. The MOS-gated SCR [4] has also been used as the power device to create a crowbar chip for protection of other integrated circuits against adverse conditions, such as excessive temperature excursion [5].

III. HIGH-VOLTAGE INTEGRATED CIRCUITS

A variety of approaches have been developed to achieve a combination of high-voltage lateral transistors with logic and analog circuits. These technologies can be broadly classified into those based upon self-isolation, junction isolation, and dielectric isolation.

Self-Isolation: This technology utilizes the reverse-biased junction between the source–drain region and the body region to obtain isolation. An illustration of a self-isolated high-voltage device integrated with CMOS logic is provided in Fig. 2. In this process, the p⁻ substrates serve as the body region of the n⁻ channel FET's and an n-well is used to form the p-MOS transistors. It should be noted that the high-voltage transistor must be designed with an annular structure where the drain is completely surrounded by the gate–source regions. This limits the technology to common source high-voltage output devices. Breakdown voltages of up to 1000 V have been reported [6]. A typical example of an application for this HVIC approach is in display drivers.

Junction Isolation: This approach utilizes the ability of a reverse biased n⁻ epitaxial/p⁻ substrate junction to provide isolation. Within this context, two alternatives have been explored. In the first, a thick epitaxial layer is used, as shown in Fig. 3(a). This preserves a vertical high-voltage transistor structure that can be optimized for high current handling capability within the limitation of the resistance of the p⁺ buried layer and sinker diffusion [7]. The disadvantages of this approach are the poor performance of the low-voltage transistors due to the thick extended drain and the large area consumed by the deep p⁺ isolation diffusions and the deep n⁺ sinker diffusions.

In the second approach, a thin (5–8 μm) epitaxial layer is used, as shown in Fig. 3(b). Here, the n⁻ epitaxial layer is optimized to achieve high-performance low-voltage n-p-n and p-n-p transistors. The high-voltage transistor is achieved by using the "RESURF" principle [8]. The RE-

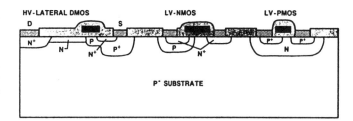

Fig. 2. Self-isolated high-voltage DMOS transistor integrated with CMOS logic components.

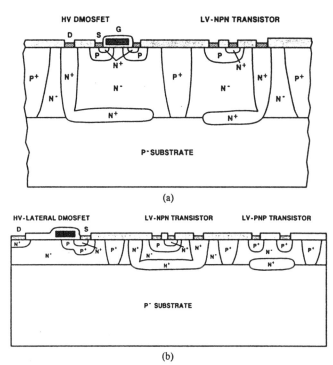

Fig. 3. (a) High-voltage DMOSFET integrated with a low-voltage n-p-n transistor by using thick-epitaxial layer technology. (b) High-voltage lateral DMOSFET integrated with low-voltage n-p-n and p-n-p transistors using the RESURF concept.

SURF concept is based upon using an optimized charge in the n⁻ epitaxial layer in the range of 0.5 to 1 × 10¹²/cm². This limited charge forces a two-dimensional redistribution of the electric field so that a high voltage can be supported laterally between the source and drain of the DMOSFET. An important advantage of this technology is that the breakdown voltage of the high-voltage devices can be scaled up by simply increasing the distance between the gate–source region and the drain region on the masks without any process alteration. This allows the use of a single manufacturing process for fabrication of a variety of high-voltage IC's suited to applications at different voltages. It even allows the fabrication of optimized high-voltage devices of different voltage ratings on a single chip. Due to the ability to form high-performance latchup-resistant CMOS circuitry and bipolar analog circuitry on the same chip with high-voltage lateral transistors, this technology can be used for a variety of applications, such as motor controls and power supplies [9].

Dielectric Isolation: The above isolation approaches cannot be used for the integration of all desirable com-

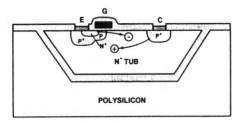

Fig. 4. A high-voltage lateral insulated gate transistor structure formed in a dielectrically isolated tub.

ponents and are prone to latchup failure at high temperatures. These problems can be overcome by using dielectric isolation. An example of a dielectrically isolated MOS bipolar transistor is shown in Fig. 4. In this example, an n-channel IGT is shown. In the on-state, the IGT operates with a high concentration of minority-carriers injected into the drift region [10]. This results in a high operating current density that can be utilized to raise the power handling capability of the power IC by an order of magnitude [11]. Such bipolar power devices cannot be implemented with junction isolation due to large substrate current flow. Dielectric isolation also provides a much higher packing density due to the smaller area taken up by the isolation region. This can offset the higher cost of the starting material [11].

Dielectrically isolated cross-point arrays are now being used in high volume in telecommunication systems [12]. Considerable effort is being undertaken to lower the cost of the starting material by developing alternate methods to produce dielectrically isolated tubs [13], [14]. As the cost of the starting material decreases, this technology can be expected to be favored for more and more high-voltage integrated circuits.

IV. Conclusions

Power and high-voltage integrated circuits are being developed for a wide variety of applications ranging from automotive electronics, home appliance control, motor drives, and computer power supplies at the higher power levels to cross-point arrays in telecommunications and display drivers at low power levels. A continual growth in the versatility of this technology can be anticipated. At the same time, there is a strong trend toward reducing cost because this technology is relatively new and will progress rapidly down the learning curve. In addition to im-

proved processing techniques and tighter design rules, the integration of MOS-controlled bipolar devices can be expected to boost the power handling capability by at least an order of magnitude. These technical developments are expected to result in a very rapid growth in the application of this technology. As the applications proliferate, computer-aided design (CAD) tools will be necessary to shorten the design cycle since most of the circuits must be customized to suit each application. With the increasing effort being devoted to both process/device technology and CAD tool development, a bright future can be predicted for these application specific integrated circuits (ASIC's) aimed at power control applications.

References

[1] B. J. Baliga and D. Y. Chen, *Power Transistors.* New York: IEEE Press, 1984.

[2] W. A. Lane and C. A. T. Salama, "Compatible VVMOS and NMOS technology for power MOS IC's," in *IEDM Tech. Dig.*, abstract 25.6, pp. 598–600, 1979.

[3] R. S. Wrathall, "The design of a high power solid state automotive switch in CMOS-VDMOS technology," in *IEEE Power Electron. Specialists Conf. Dig.*, pp. 229–233, 1985.

[4] B. J. Baliga, "Enhancement and depletion mode vertical channel MOS gated thyristors," *Electron. Lett.*, vol. 15, pp. 645–647, 1979.

[5] D. Zaremba and J. Mansmann, "Power integrated circuit makes board level overvoltage and overtemperature protection simple and inexpensive," *Power Conversion Int. Mag.*, pp. 14–20, Oct. 1985.

[6] T. Yamaguchi and S. Morimoto, "Process and device design of a 1000 V MOS IC," *IEEE Trans. Electron Devices*, vol. ED-29, pp. 1171–1178, 1982.

[7] B. Murari, "Power integrated circuits: Problems, tradeoffs, and solutions," *IEEE J. Solid-State Circuits*, vol. SC-13, pp. 307–319, 1978.

[8] J. A. Appels and H. M. J. Vaes, "High voltage thin layer devices (RESURF devices)," in *IEDM Tech. Dig.*, abstract 10.1, pp. 238–241, 1979.

[9] E. J. Wildi, T. P. Chow, M. S. Adler, M. E. Cornell, and G. C. Pifer, "New high voltage IC technology," in *IEDM Tech. Dig.*, Abstract 10.2, pp. 262–265, 1984.

[10] B. J. Baliga, M. S. Adler, R. P. Love, P. V. Gray, and N. D. Zommer, "The insulated gate transistor: A new three-terminal MOS-controlled bipolar power device," *IEEE Trans. Electron Devices*, vol. ED-31, pp. 821–828, 1984.

[11] H. W. Becke, "Approaches to isolation in high voltage integrated circuits," in *IEDM Tech. Dig.*, abstract 30.1, pp. 724–727, 1985.

[12] A. R. Hartman, J. E. Berthold, T. J. Riley, J. E. Kohl, Y-H Wong, H. T. Weston, and R. S. Scott, "530V integrated gated diode switch for telecommunications," in *IEDM Tech. Dig.*, abstract 11.1, pp. 250–253, 1981.

[13] C. Jaussaud, J. Stoemenos, J. Margail, M. Dupuy, B. Blanchard, and M. Bruel, "Microstructure of silicon implanted with high dose oxygen ions," *Appl. Phys. Lett.*, vol. 46, no. 11, pp. 1064–1066, 1985.

[14] S. Nakashima, Y. Maeda, and M. Akiya, "High voltage CMOS SIMOX technology and its application to a BSH-LSI," *IEEE Trans. Electron Devices*, vol. ED-33, pp. 126–132, 1986.

Power Integrated Circuits: Problems, Tradeoffs, and Solutions

BRUNO MURARI

Abstract–Current, voltage, and power tradeoffs will be presented together with circuits for protection in the case of short circuit, overvoltage, supply voltage reversal, and inductive load transients.

The future developments in power integrated circuits will be discussed.

Manuscript received November 4, 1977; revised January 30, 1978.
The author is with SGS-ATES Componenti Elettronici SpA, Castelletto di Settimo Milanese, Milan, Italy.

I. GENERAL CONSIDERATIONS

THE FIRST integrated circuits capable of supplying an output power of 1 or 2 W to the load appeared on the market about ten years ago. These were audio amplifiers and voltage regulators.

Market acceptance of these devices was originally poor due to fear that they might be more fragile than well-proven discrete component circuits using rugged power transistors.

However, power integrated circuits have now assumed great

Reprinted from *IEEE J. Solid-State Circuits*, vol. SC-13, pp. 307–319, June 1978.

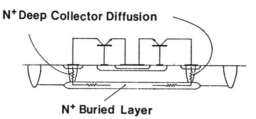

Fig. 1. Power integrated-circuit structure with deep-collector n⁺-diffusion.

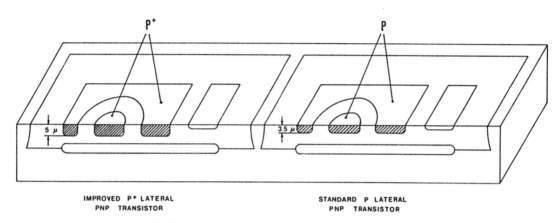

Fig. 2. p⁺ and p standard lateral p-n-p transistor structure.

importance and their range of applications is expanding continuously.

In the last ten years, there has been much progress in the technologies leading to higher current, voltage and power, and in the development of packages capable of meeting the heat-transfer requirements of more and more powerful chips.

II. TECHNOLOGIES FOR POWER INTEGRATED CIRCUITS

Since all the connections of a planar integrated circuit are on one surface, its structure is inferior to that of discrete transistors, especially as regards saturation voltage.

The introduction of a deep collector diffusion was the first major improvement in power IC technologies over small-signal IC technologies, the only ones available about ten years ago for the manufacture of op amps. This solution considerably reduces the saturation resistance of the output transistors. Fig. 1 shows a typical structure with a deep-collector n⁺-diffusion. The effect of the buried layer on the saturation resistance is also of some importance, particularly for low-voltage, high-current devices such as battery-supplied audio amplifiers for portable and car radios.

The solution lies in heavy doping of the buried layer and structural optimization of the emitter with deep-collector n⁺-diffusion around each finger to provide a further significant reduction in saturation resistance.

Another limitation of small-signal IC technology is the low current capability of the lateral p-n-p transistors realized during the same base diffusion. A second p⁺-diffusion has been introduced in order to realize the low-voltage Zener as well as lateral p-n-p transistors. This lateral p-n-p has a higher emitter charge and increased junction depth.

The higher emitter area in front of the collector, which is the result of deeper diffusion, improves the current capability, while the higher emitter charge in p⁺-diffusion increases the current gain referring to a standard p-n-p transistor. In this way, a power transistor capable of supplying 3 to 4 A in saturation can be driven directly by one of these 20-emitter, circular-structure, p-n-p devices which, at 100 mA, still have an h_{FE} of 10. Fig. 2 shows typical structures for two lateral p-n-p transistors, one realized using standard diffusion, and the other using a second p⁺-diffusion. Fig. 3 shows the h_{FE} as a function of I_c for both structures.

III. POWER-TRANSISTOR LIMITATIONS

Much progress has also been made in circuit design aimed at increasing the safety of devices under various types of overload conditions. In order to better understand the present state of the art, let us now consider the breakdown limits for a power transistor.

Fig. 4 shows the Safe Operating Area (SOA) of a typical integrated power transistor. The first limit, represented by line A-A', defines the maximum current which can be delivered by the device with a sufficient safety margin to avoid fusing the connecting wire between the chip and the pad. The second line, B-B', represents the limit of maximum dissipation

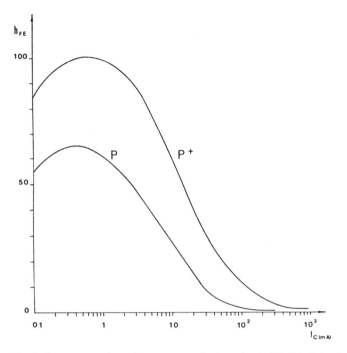

Fig. 3. h_{FE} comparison between standard and p⁺ 20-disk lateral p-n-p transistors.

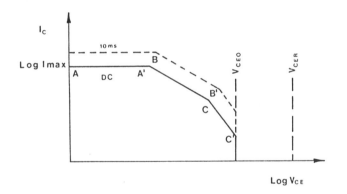

Fig. 4. Typical power transistors SOA curves.

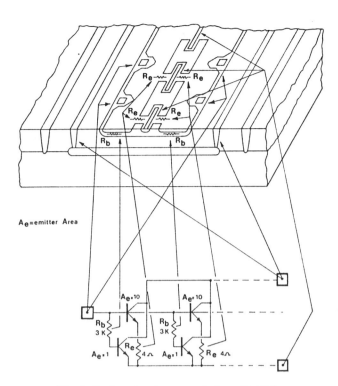

Fig. 5. Section showing power device with HES.

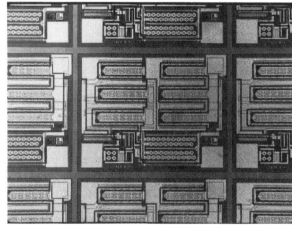

Fig. 6. Dual-Darlington power transistor with characteristic HES (TDA 1420).

for a junction temperature of 150°C. The third line, C-C', defines the safe limit in the high-voltage zones where problems of current localization with resulting "hot spots" exist. The V_{CEO} and V_{CER} lines represent, respectively, the breakdown voltage with base open, and with base short circuited to the emitter with a certain resistance.

In the last few years, most effort has been concentrated on improving the behavior of power transistors, particularly regarding current distribution in emitter fingers. The uniformity of current distribution has been improved by incorporating small ballast resistors which are taken directly from the emitter masks, thus involving no additional cost (Fig. 5). The result is a characteristic "H Emitter Structure" (HES) widely used in power integrated circuits. An example is shown in Fig. 6. This structure has allowed the collector-current range to be increased in proportion to the additional area of silicon used. The increased current uniformity per unit-emitter area has also allowed device ruggedness to be improved, as can be seen from the dc second breakdown curves shown in Fig. 7. Curve A in Fig. 7 refers to a standard transistor with continuous emitter fingers. Curve B refers to an improved version with ballast resistance produced with an H emitter structure on the same silicon surface.

IV. SHORT-CIRCUIT AND OVERVOLTAGE PROTECTION

It is well known that where power devices are concerned, it is very difficult to develop maximum power without destroying the device under certain overload conditions. One

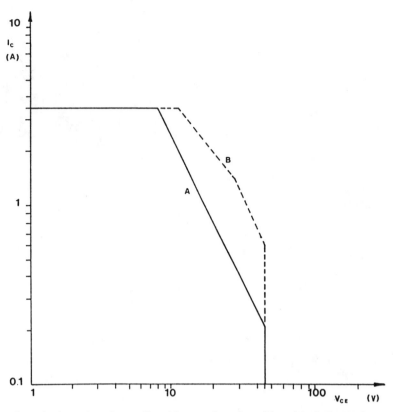

Fig. 7. SOA of standard transistor (curve *A*) and improved version with emitter ballast resistance (curve *B*).

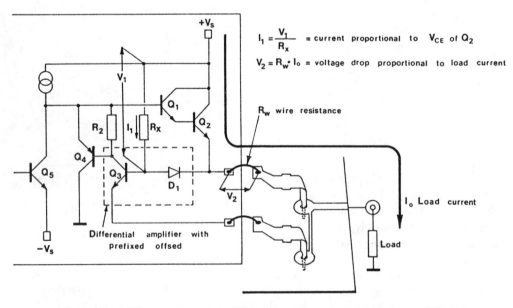

Fig. 8. TDA 2020 protection circuit with voltage and current continuously monitored.

of the most characteristic overloads for a power device is accidental or permanent short circuit of the load.

The first circuit to use the idea of protecting power devices by monitoring both the voltage and the current affecting each device, was the TCA 940 which was followed by the TDA 2020 (Fig. 8). The main aim, which was to avoid power loss when monitoring the current, was achieved by using the gold wire connecting the chip to the output pin. It must be emphasized that the protection circuit does not reduce the available output power since it is not necessary to add a resistance in series with the output transistors.

Transistors Q_3 and the diode-connected transistor D_1

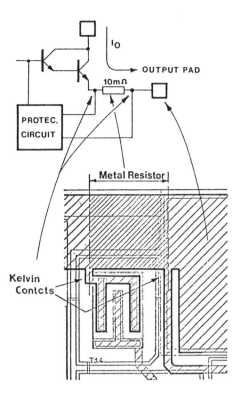

Fig. 9. Current-sensing resistance made with aluminum metallization mask.

together form a differential amplifier with a prefixed offset achieved by making the area of emitter D_1 ten times greater than that of Q_3. The collector current of Q_2 is given by the relationship

$$I_0 = \frac{KT}{q} \cdot \frac{1}{R_W} \cdot \frac{A_1/A_3 \cdot I_{c3} R_x}{V_{CE2} - V_{D1}}$$

where

I_0	load current;
K	Boltzmann's constant;
T	absolute temperature;
q	electron charge;
R_W	gold-wire resistance;
$A_1 ; A_3$	cathode and emitter area of D_1 and Q_3.

If I_{c3} becomes high enough to cause a voltage drop in R_2 greater than the turn-on voltage of the vertical p-n-p transistor Q_4 [i.e., $I_{c3} \geq (V_{BE4}/R_2)$], the drive to the final stage will be diverted through Q_4, inhibiting the output.

The gold wire represents a very well-calibrated shunt, but it creates a problem if the device is made available in alternative packages, since different packages have bond wires of different lengths. The solution to this problem was to use the resistance of the aluminum metallization which carries the emitter current: two Kelvin connections enable the emitter current to be measured with small spread (Fig. 9).

Another step forward was the introduction of a threshold circuit (Fig. 10) where, at a collector-to-emitter voltage higher than V_z, Q_2 is on and Q_1 base is short circuited to its emitter. In this condition, Q_1 is switched off and can with-

stand an overvoltage as high as V_{CER} (normally 20 to 30 V higher than V_{CEO}). Obviously, the other transistors in the circuit which are subjected to high voltages (load-dump conditions) must operate with the base grounded in order to easily withstand this overload.

The L 200, a programmable 5-pin voltage regulator in plastic package (Pentawatt®) incorporates all of these types of protection. Fig. 11 shows the output characteristics of the power Darlington of the L 200, from which the capacity of the device to withstand overvoltages can be noted. Fig. 12 shows the chip of the L 200 voltage regulator.

A 5-V, 5-A voltage regulator has recently appeared on the market in the United States. The new device, LAS 1905, is a standard design with resistances in each finger. In this case, the chip size is very large, 15 500 mil², which seems to be the present limit for high-price power-linear IC's.

Instantaneous protection in the safe operating area is not always necessary and can be substituted by simple thermal protection if the power device operates at relatively low voltage; i.e., lower than 15 V. Referring to Fig. 13, Q_1 is the thermal sensing element located on the chip very near to power transistor Q_3. During normal operation, Q_1 is off because its V_{BE} is driven by a fixed voltage V_R of only 400 mV. By increasing the temperature, the V_{BE} of Q_1 decreases by about 2 mV/°C and, at 150°C, Q_1 starts to conduct switching off the output power Darlington Q_2 and Q_3. An example of this type is the TDA 2002. In this device, both output transistors have practically no second-breakdown limits in

®Registered service mark of SGS-ATES Componenti Elettronici SpA.

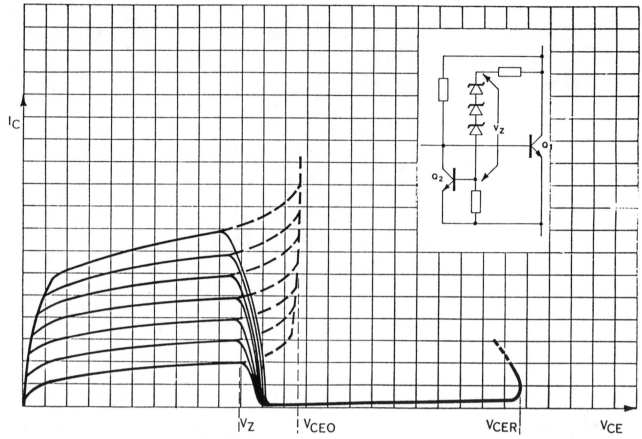

Fig. 10. Transistor with overvoltage circuit protection.

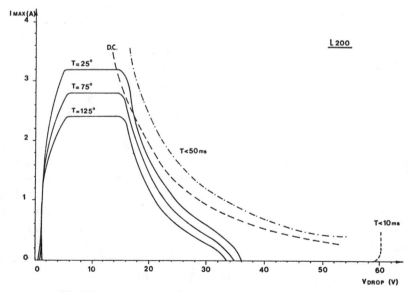

Fig. 11. Output characteristic of power pass transistor of L 200.

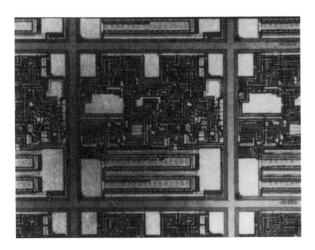

Fig. 12. L 200 voltage regulator.

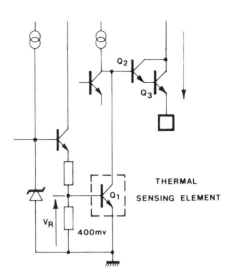

Fig. 13. Thermal-protection circuit.

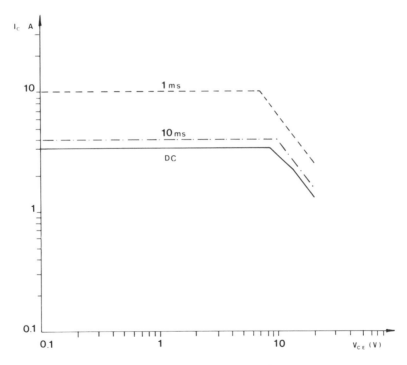

Fig. 14. SOA for output transistors of TDA 2002.

the operating voltage range, and can therefore use thermal shutdown also as a protection against short circuits (see Fig. 14).

It is important to note that the thermal sensing element must be located as near to the output transistors as possible in order to reduce the intervention delay time after overload. A further protection is required against load-dump conditions which arise due to supply-line transients. With a car radio,

for example, these conditions arise if the battery is disconnected while the alternator is supplying a high current. In this case, the alternator tries to maintain the current flow and, since the load impedance is much greater with the battery disconnected, a positive spike is produced. The portion of this spike which reaches the radio after being smoothed by the supply-line LC filter, reaches about 40 V. This is easily withstood by such devices as the TDA 2002, which incor-

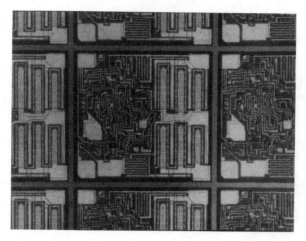

Fig. 15. TDA 2002 audio amplifier.

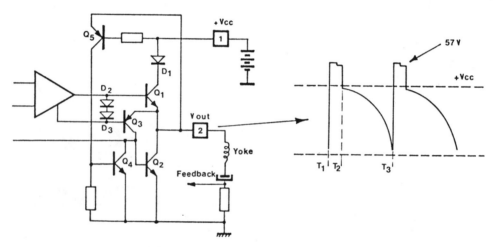

Fig. 16. TDA 1170 output stage with output transistor in V_{CER} condition during flyback.

porate an internal circuit to force the output transistors into V_{CER} instead of LV_{CEO} under those conditions (Fig. 10). The TDA 2002 audio amplifier die is shown in Fig. 15.

V. PROTECTION FOR INDUCTIVE LOADS

Power integrated devices often have to drive inductive loads; e.g., loudspeakers or solenoid relays in general. The switching of high currents in these loads gives rise to voltages which can exceed the supply, and fall below the ground value.

There are two possible solutions for inductive load protection: in the first case, we allow the overvoltage to fully develop, while in the second, we clamp it to $+V_{CC}$ by means of clamp diodes. The first solution has been used for the TDA 1170, vertical deflection circuit, which can withstand the flyback superimposed on supply voltages up to 57 V, even though the BV_{CEO} of the output transistors is only 40 V (see Fig. 16). Transistors Q_1, Q_2, and Q_3 are the final-stage class A–B operation of a power amplifier. This figure also shows the waveform at the output pin.

During the normal deflection time from T_2 to T_3, the current on the deflection-coil yoke changes slowly, driven by output power transistors Q_1 and Q_2 in normal class A–B operation. At time T_3, the input waveform changes rapidly, but the load is inductive and cannot follow a fast current change, so a positive overvoltage is developed by the yoke. This overvoltage at pin 2 is higher than $+V_{CC}$ (pin 1), so lateral p-n-p transistor Q_5 is switched on as is Q_4. In this situation, Q_2 is completely off with the base short circuited to its emitter, increasing its breakdown. Diode D_1 protects Q_1 during the overvoltage; Q_3 is a large channel p-n-p transistor easily able to withstand 80 V. The operating mode of the entire circuit is described in more detail in the work mentioned in [4].

In the second solution, which is used in audio circuits, the clamp diodes clamp overvoltages to one V_{BE} above $+V_{CC}$ and one V_{BE} below ground value. Negative overvoltages are automatically clamped by the substrate–collector isolation junction of the lower power transistor, which is always present in integrated circuits and of sufficient dimensions to carry

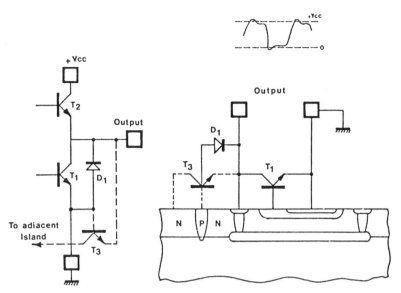

Fig. 17. Structure of lateral n-p-n parasitic transistor intrinsic in the output stage activated during negative spikes.

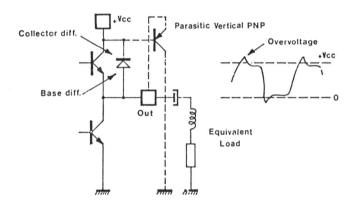

Fig. 18. Parasitic vertical p-n-p device intrinsic in the base–collector
diode activated during positive spikes.

the peak current. The only detail to be pointed out is that the chip layout must prevent undesired interference from the lateral n-p-n transistor; the emitter, base, and collector of this transistor are formed, respectively, by the collector of the power transistor, the insulation diffusion, and the epilayer of the adjacent island ($h_{FE} \cong 1$) (Fig. 17).

It is important to note that during negative overvoltage the parasitic lateral n-p-n, T_3, injects a current into the adjacent epitaxial islands and some parasitic Silicon Controlled Rectifiers (SCR's) may be fired with a possibility of latchup. To avoid this problem the position of each element, inserted close to the lower power transistor, must be considered to avoid SCR structure.

Protection against positive overvoltages arising at the output can be provided by simply connecting a diode between the output pad and $+ V_{CC}$ to withstand all supply voltages during normal operation and to clamp overvoltages to $V_{CC} + 1 \, V_{BE}$. Unfortunately, the integrated diode for overvoltage limiting has a vertical p-n-p parasitic transistor intrinsic in its structure

which injects carriers into the substrate. In fact, the base–collector junction, used to limit positive overvoltages, is simply the base–emitter junction of a parasitic vertical p-n-p (Fig. 18). It is therefore clear that during the positive transition, i.e., when the output pad is at a higher voltage than the V_{CC} pad, the vertical p-n-p conducts and dissipates in proportion to its h_{FE}.

The parasitic p-n-p transistor of a normal base–collector diode has an h_{FE} value around unity. It is easily understood that, for the parasitic transistor, more power is dissipated in the base–substrate junction than in the forward-biased base–emitter junction.

The results of an in-depth study have shown these losses to be greatly reduced, as can be seen from the parasitic p-n-p transistor gain curves in Fig. 19. The modified structure is shown in Fig. 20, and more details can be obtained from [5].

An integrated voltage regulator using these improved integrated diodes for line rectification has also been realized. This is the L 192 (see Figs. 21 and 22) which is mounted in a plastic

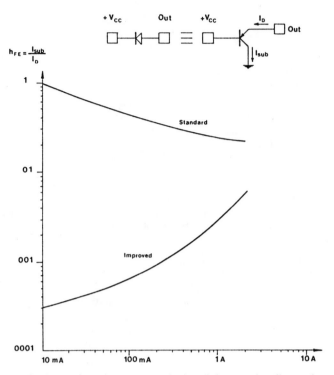

Fig. 19. Comparison between standard and improved collector–base diodes showing strong reduction of parasitic h_{FE}.

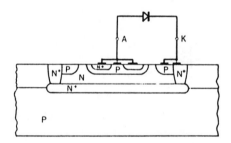

Fig. 20. Structure of improved diode.

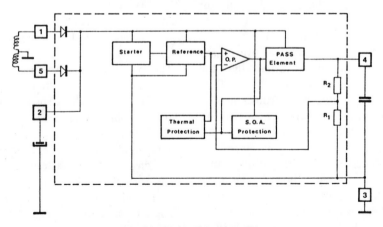

Fig. 21. Block diagram L 192.

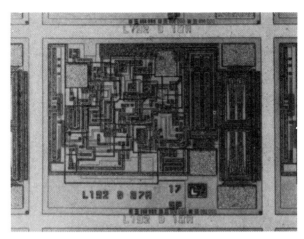

Fig. 22. Photograph of L 192 chip voltage regulator with rectifier diodes incorporated.

package (Pentawatt®) and can handle up to 250 mA at a stabilized voltage of 15 V. The rectification diodes can withstand surge current peaks in excess of 5 A for 5 ms and reverse bias of 80 V. The line and load regulation is comparable with that of similar 3-pin devices at present on the market. A future version with a fully integrated Graetz bridge is now under development.

VI. POLARITY INVERSION PROTECTION

In the event of supply voltage reversal, the collector of the upper output transistor is forward biased towards the substrate, and the gold bond wires for V_{CC} and ground pins are forced to carry about 6 A, which is limited by the substrate resistance. The wires must therefore be capable of withstanding this current for a longer period than the blowout time of the quick 1-A fuse, which is normally connected in series with the supply. The collector substrate diodes for the upper power transistor must also have sufficient area to carry this current.

VII. FUTURE DEVELOPMENTS

The TDA 2020 has now been on the market for several years, and only recently has a device with the same output power level been reported.

It seemed to some people that perhaps the limit for integrated Class B audio IC's had been reached. But this is not true, because today the limits are set only by questions of an economic nature because, although small areas of silicon can handle high voltages and currents (60 V and 4 A), they are severely limited in their ability to dissipate power. The present limit is, in fact, the intrinsic R_{TH} of the silicon which necessitates distribution of the power over much larger areas of silicon than are necessary to handle the voltage and current values required; for example, for a 30-W high-fidelity IC.

Great efforts are being concentrated at both package and chip technology levels in order to realize devices with this power which have reasonable chip dimensions and which are therefore cost effective.

VIII. HIGH-CURRENT AND HIGH-VOLTAGE TRENDS

In the switching device sector, the problem of dissipated power is less significant, so a great increase in activity by semiconductor manufacturers can be foreseen. An example of this type is the switching regulator realized for automobile alternators. Although it has never gone into production because similar solutions using discrete components are still more cost effective, it is nevertheless an excellent example of high-current integration.

Fig. 23 shows the output characteristics of the integrated Darlington which, without current protection, greatly exceeds 10 A in saturation with silicon areas of only 5000 mil². Fig. 24 shows the chip structure.

Good possibilities for development are also seen in the high-voltage IC sector. Here we must distinguish between devices that operate with base grounded, or in the V_{CER} switching mode, and those that operate in linear mode with base open. In fact, devices such as the 250-mA 7-Darlington IC, which withstands 80 V in off conditions, already exist, and soon devices with breakdown voltages of 120 V will be presented.

It has been necessary to carry out a long study on the surface conditions and MOS parasitic produced by the mobile carriers at the oxide–plastic interface in order to guarantee high enough breakdown voltages after thousands of hours of operation at high temperature [6] and [7]. As a result of the study, we are developing new solutions which include new technologies to replace the ones used at present for high-voltage linear devices. Devices operating at 80 V in the V_{CEO} condition and several hundred milliamperes, are now being developed in our research and development laboratories and will be announced next year.

IX. CONCLUSIONS

In the previous sections we have seen the limits reached today by linear integrated circuits: power over 20 W, breakdown voltages up to 80 V in the V_{CEO} or 120 V in V_{CER} conditions, and current up to 5 A.

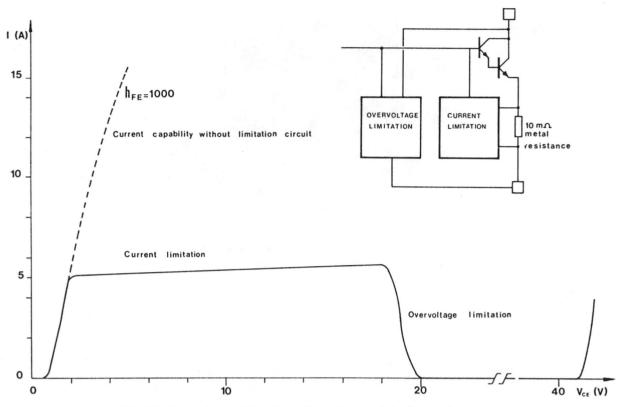

Fig. 23. Output characteristics of switching voltage regulator for car alternator.

Fig. 24. Switching voltage regulator for car alternator.

Further progress in devices operating in Class B will only be possible through better understanding and solution of dissipation problems, particularly within the chip itself. The use of new packages with greater power-handling capability than the present ones will also be necessary. In the field of devices operating in switching mode, the limits are not yet well known, but appear to be high; therefore, we can expect to see interfacing devices capable of driving very heavy loads, making use of the high-speed characteristics of planar technology.

ACKNOWLEDGMENT

The author wishes to thank all who have contributed in the development of the products and technologies described. The wealth of ideas and enthusiasm which have characterized the working environment of the SGS-ATES R&D Center have certainly accelerated the developments of recent years.

REFERENCES

[1] J. E. Solomon, "The monolithic op amp: A tutorial study," *IEEE J. Solid-State Circuits*, vol. SC-9, pp. 314–332, Dec. 1974.

[2] B. Murari, C. Cini, and V. Prestileo, "A high-power hi-fi monolithic amplifier," *IEEE Trans. Broadcast Telev. Receivers*, vol. BTR-20, pp. 311–321, Nov. 1974.

[3] E. L. Long and T. M. Frederiksen, "A high-gain 15-W monolithic power amplifier with internal fault protection," *IEEE J. Solid-State Circuits*, vol. SC-6, pp. 35–44, Feb. 1971.

[4] A. Romano and L. Venutti, "A monolithic integrated circuit for vertical deflection in television receivers," *IEEE Trans. Consumer Electron.*, vol. CE-21, pp. 85–94, Feb. 1975.

[5] F. Bertotti and S. D'Arrigo, "New voltage regulators integrate more functions, have wider applications fields," presented at the Chicago Fall Conf., 1977.

[6] V. Prestileo, "High voltage technology for display drivers," in *Electronic Information Displays*, 2nd Course, International School of Physic for Industry, presented at Erice, Italy, June 1977.

[7] P. Selini and G. Vignola, "Reliability Improvement Trough Design as Applied to a Family of Monolithic Linear Operational Amplifiers," presented at the Congresso di Varna, Bulgaria, Sept. 1977.

[8] S. Chou, "Small-signal characteristics of lateral transistors," *Solid-State Electron.*, vol. 15, 1972.

[9] ——, "An investigation of lateral transistors—D.C. characteristics," *Solid-State Electron.*, vol. 14, 1971.

[10] R. E. Blaha and W. R. Fahrner, "Passivation of high breakdown voltage p-n-p structures by thermal oxidation," *J. Electrochem. Soc.*, Apr. 1976.

THE most important aspect of high voltage integrated circuit technology is the incorporation of devices capable of supporting high voltages on a silicon chip containing analog and/or digital circuitry. Two types of devices are potential candidates for operation at high voltages. The first device is a transistor characterized by vertical current flow, i.e., current flow perpendicular to the surface of the silicon wafer. High voltage vertical transistor technology has been extensively used to form discrete devices. Both bipolar transistors and power MOSFETs have been fabricated with this structure. In order to support high voltages, these devices require a thick drift region. For a typical breakdown voltage of 500 volts, the drift region is about 50 microns in thickness. Consequently, to isolate these devices, it becomes necessary to perform very deep diffusions which are incompatible with integrated circuit processing. In addition, the low voltage devices fabricated in the thick epitaxial layer contain large series resistances which degrade their performance. For these reasons, the vertical high voltage device architecture that is optimal for discrete devices is found to be unattractive for high voltage integrated circuits.

It is highly desirable to form the high voltage devices using thin epitaxial layers. When thin epitaxial layers are utilized, the low voltage analog and digital devices can be optimally designed using the technology that is extensively applied for signal-level integrated circuits. The problem that had to be solved was to be able to support high voltages laterally in the thin epitaxial layers without severe degradation in the current handling capability. A major breakthrough in the development of high voltage devices that could be integrated into a thin epitaxial layer technology was the invention of the reduced surface field (RESURF) concept. Using the two-dimensional computer simulation of Poisson's equation, it was shown that high voltages could be supported in thin epitaxial layers with high doping concentrations by letting the depletion layer spread into a lightly doped substrate. This allowed the fabrication of high voltage transistors with reasonable current handling capability. Due to the compatibility of this technology with standard signal-level integrated circuit processing, it is expected that this approach will become predominant in the future.

This part on high voltage lateral devices contains 17 papers which describe various techniques to obtain both bipolar transistors and MOS devices suitable for integration. Although most of the papers deal with junction-isolation because it is the most commonly used process, the design and fabrication of devices suitable for dielectrically isolated circuits is also covered.

The first three papers in this part discuss the design of high voltage lateral bipolar transistors. The first of these papers describes an improved lateral PNP transistor structure in which a punch-through shield is formed around the emitter, and a deep graded diffusion is formed around the collector. These modifications of the conventional structure produce an improvement in the frequency response and Early voltage while maintaining a high current gain. The second paper discusses the integration of a high voltage, high speed vertical NPN transistor in a low voltage LSI bipolar process. This is achieved by the addition of a lightly doped buried layer in the high voltage transistor collector region. Breakdown voltages of over 100 volts have been achieved. By retaining the narrow base width used in the low voltage section of the circuit, these devices exhibit a high gain and good frequency response ($f_t = 1.2$ GHz). The third paper deals with second breakdown in lateral high voltage transistors. Since second breakdown is a destructive phenomenon, it limits the safe operating area and power handling capability of high voltage bipolar transistors. Improvements in the safe operating area of a power Darlington transistor are achieved by distributing the driver transistor, and by designing the emitter finger width optimally from the electrothermal point of view.

The next three papers in this part deal with high voltage MOS transistors. The first of these papers, by Yamaguchi and Morimoto, describes a silicon-gate isoplanar process in which 1000 volt lateral NMOS transistors have been integrated with low voltage NMOS LSI circuitry. The high voltage transistor is obtained by forming an annular structure with the drain in the middle. The drift layer of this transistor is formed by ion-implantation of phosphorus ions directly into a lightly doped p-type substrate. The second paper, by Rumennik and Heald, describes a method for achieving complementary high voltage MOS transistors in a low voltage CMOS process. The high voltage p-channel transistor is built in the n-well while the high voltage n-channel transistor is formed directly in the lightly doped p-type substrate. Breakdown voltages of 250 volts have been achieved. The third paper describes the effects of SIPOS passivation on the lateral high voltage NMOS transistors. An interesting observation is the reduction in the on-resistance due to the formation of a conductive accumulation layer at the surface of the drift region under the SIPOS layer. Although this may be beneficial in increasing the current handling capability, it should be noted that the SIPOS layer significantly reduces the switching speed.

These high voltage MOS transistors have a relatively long channel whose dimensions are determined by photolithographic processing limitations. This results in devices with poor transconductance and current handling capability. The next two papers describe a lateral high voltage transistor structure in which the channel length is determined by the difference in the diffusion depth of the p-base and n-emitter regions. The resulting devices have superior transconductance and current handling capability. Due to these features, the

DMOS structure is preferable for minimization of the die area as long as its implementation is compatible with the low voltage circuit processing.

Although high voltage transistors were shown to be achievable using CMOS-compatible processes, they tended to have a high on-resistance. An important breakthrough in reducing the on-resistance of high voltage lateral transistors was achieved by the introduction of the RESURF concept. The paper by Appels and Vaes discusses the results of two-dimensional modelling of breakdown in lateral high voltage transistors. It is shown that an optimal combination of the epitaxial (drift) layer charge and substrate doping can result in a greatly improved lateral field distribution. A drift region charge of 10^{12} per square cm is found to be optimal. This approach can be applied to form high voltage diodes, bipolar transistors, and JFETs as described in this paper, as well as high voltage DMOS transistors, as described in the following paper by Ludikhuize.

The power MOSFETs described in the previous papers exhibit relatively high on-resistances when compared with bipolar transistors. In order to obtain a high input impedance MOS device with low on-resistance, several structures that combine bipolar and MOS physics have been explored. Three examples are the lateral insulated gate transistor, the Schottky injection MOS gated transistor, and an insulated base transistor. As described in the next three papers, this merger of bipolar current conduction with MOS gate control can result in much better power handling capability than is possible with high voltage MOSFETs.

The last section of this part of the book focusses on high voltage devices formed in dielectrically isolated substrates. The first of these papers describes a process by which high voltage NPNs, PNPs, JFETs, and SCRs have been fabricated together with I²L logic circuitry. The following paper describes a V-groove dielectric isolation process used to form high voltage gated diode arrays for telecommunications. The gated diode is a unique device which is feasible only in this technology. The last paper, by Sugawara, describes the formation of high voltage complementary lateral MOS gated thyristors using a similar V-groove dielectric isolation technology. Devices capable of supporting 350 volts in both polarities have been achieved with the ability to handle 200 milliamperes of current.

REPRINT PAPERS

[1] J. D. Beasom, "A High Performance High Voltage Lateral PNP Structure," *IEEE Int. Electron Devices Meeting Digest,* Abst. 16.5, pp. 424–427, 1983.

[2] A. Y. Tang, R. Johnston, and P. J. Meza, "A Dual Buried Layer Technology for the Fabrication of High Voltage NPN Devices Compatible with a 1.5 Micron Epitaxial Bipolar Process," *IEEE Int. Electron Devices Meeting Digest,* Abst. 11.3, pp. 298–301, 1985.

[3] F. F. Villa, "Improved Second Breakdown of Integrated Bipolar Power Transistors," *IEEE Trans. Electron Devices,* vol. ED-33, pp. 1971–1976, 1986.

[4] T. Yamaguchi and S. Morimoto, "Process and Device Design of a 1000-V MOS IC," *IEEE Trans. Electron Devices,* vol. ED-29, pp. 1171–1178, 1982.

[5] V. Rumennik and D. L. Heald, "Integrated High and Low Voltage CMOS Technology," *IEEE Int. Electron Devices Meeting Digest,* Abst. 4.3, pp. 77–80, 1982.

[6] S. Mukherjee, C. J. Chou, K. Shaw, D. McArthur, and V. Rumennik, "The Effects of SIPOS Passivation on DC and Switching Performance of High Voltage MOS Transistors," *IEEE Int. Electron Devices Meeting Digest,* Abst. 28.4, pp. 646–649, 1986.

[7] M. J. Declercq and J. D. Plummer, "Avalanche Breakdown in High Voltage D-MOS Devices," *IEEE Trans. Electron Devices,* vol. ED-23, pp. 1–4, 1976.

[8] H. R. Claessen and P. Van der Zee, "An Accurate DC Model for High-Voltage Lateral DMOS Transistors Suited for CACD," *IEEE Trans. Electron Devices,* vol. ED-33, pp. 1964–1970, 1986.

[9] J. A. Appels and H. M. J. Vaes, "High Voltage Thin Layer Devices (RESURF DEVICES)," *IEEE Int. Electron Devices Meeting Digest,* Abst. 10.1, pp. 238–241, 1979.

[10] A. W. Ludikhuize, "High Voltage DMOS and PMOS in Analog ICs," *IEEE Int. Electron Devices Meeting Digest,* Abst. 4.4, pp. 81–84, 1982.

[11] D. N. Pattanayak, A. L. Robinson, T. P. Chow, M. S. Adler, B. J. Baliga, and E. J. Wildi, "n-Channel Lateral Insulated Gate Transistors: Part I—Steady State Characteristics," *IEEE Trans. Electron Devices,* vol. ED-33, pp. 1956–1963, 1986.

[12] J. K. O. Sin, C. A. T. Salama and L. Z. Hou, "The SINFET—A Schottky Injection MOS-Gated Power Transistor," *IEEE Trans. Electron Devices,* vol. ED-33, pp. 1940–1947, 1986.

[13] Z. Parpia, J. G. Mena, and C. A. T. Salama, "A Novel CMOS Compatible High Voltage Transistor Structure," *IEEE Trans. Electron Devices,* vol. ED-33, pp. 1948–1952, 1986.

[14] J. D. Beasom, "A 200V Complementary Vertical Bipolar Process with Compatible Logic," *IEEE Int. Electron Devices Meeting Digest,* Abst. 4.6, pp. 89–91, 1982.

[15] A. R. Hartman, J. E. Berthold, T. J. Riley, J. E. Kohl, Y. H. Wong, H. T. Weston, and R. S. Scott, "530V Integrated Gated Diode Switch for Telecommunications," *IEEE Int. Electron Devices Meeting Digest,* Abst. 11.1, pp. 250–253, 1981.

[16] Y. Sugawara, "High Voltage Complementary Gated MOS Thyristors," *IEEE Int. Electron Devices Meeting Digest,* Abstr. 9.5, pp. 226–229, 1986.

A HIGH PERFORMANCE HIGH VOLTAGE
LATERAL PNP STRUCTURE

James D. Beasom

Harris Semiconductor
Analog Products Division
Melbourne, Florida 32901

ABSTRACT

An improved high voltage lateral PNP
structure is described. Devices built with the
structure have H_{FE} and Early voltage as good as
quality discrete devices and maintain f_T greater
than 1.5 MHz at 350V. The process is simpler than
those previously described for production of complementary vertical devices. Experimental results
for a range of profiles and geometries are
presented.

INTRODUCTION

Many high voltage circuits require complementary bipolar devices. The conventional lateral
device structure usually used in low voltage IC
processes to provide the complement device has very
poor performance in high voltage applications due
to the lightly doped base regions. Gain bandwidth
(f_T) is low due to the wide base width required to
avoid collector to emitter punchthrough. Early
voltage is low because almost the entire base
collector depletion layer is in the lightly doped
base region.

Several processes which yield complementary
vertical devices have been described (1,2,3). The
performance of the complement devices in these
processes is excellent, however, the processes
required to produce them are very complex.

Processes which yield improved performance
lateral devices by use of a punchthrough shield
around the emitter (4) or a deep graded collector
region (5,6) have also been described. Such
processes yield devices with performance approaching that of a conventional vertical device with a
less complex process. Furthermore, these processes
do not introduce the latchup sensitive multilayer
structures which occur in complementary vertical
JI structures.

This paper presents results of an experimental
study of an improved lateral PNP which uses both a
punchthrough shield around the emitter and a deep
graded collector region. A range of profiles and
geometries are characterized and compared to a
conventional lateral structure illustrating the
significance of both the shield doping and the base
collector impurity gradient.

IMPROVED STRUCTURE

The improved structure is compared to the
conventional structure in fig. 1. The two modifications which constitute improvements are clearly
evident.

Both modifications in the improved structure
contribute to greater f_T at a given breakdown
voltage by allowing a smaller base width, thus
reducing base transit time which is the dominate
factor in f_T. The high (relative to N- base
region) doping of the shield prevents the base
collector depletion layer from reaching the
emitter at high base collector voltage. The
resulting electric field in the base is approximately the critical field across the entire N-
portion of the active base leading to high base
collector voltage at modest base width.

Peak base collector voltage at a given base
width is further increased by use of the low
gradient base collector junction. Such a junction absorbs a significant fraction of the applied
voltage leaving less to be absorbed in the active
base region.

The electric fields and voltages of the
reverse biased base collector junctions of conventional and improved structure devices of the
same base width are shown in fig. 2 and fig. 3.
Note the higher average field in the base of the
improved device compared to the punchthrough
limited conventional device and also the field

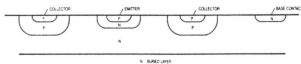

Figure 1. Lateral PNP structures

Reprinted from *IEEE 31st Int. Electron Devices Meeting*, pp. 298–301, 1985.

and voltage in the collector of the improved device.

The voltage blocking capabilities of the base regions of the two structures can be approximated by one dimensional Poisson equation solution along the surface. The resulting expressions are:

improved structure:

$$V_B = + E_c X_1 - \frac{q\ N_B\ X_1^2}{2\ \epsilon}$$

conventional structure:

$$V_B = \frac{q\ N_B\ X_1^2}{2\ \epsilon}$$

where E_c = critical field for avalanche
N_B = base impurity concentration
X_1 = collector-punchthrough shield space for improved structure
X_1 = base-collector spacing for conventional structure

An an example, evaluate the two expressions for the case

$E_c = 2 \times 10^5$ V/cm
$N_B = 3 \times 10^{14}$
$X_1 = 1.5 \times 10^{-3}$ cm

maximum base voltage improved structure = 249V

maximum base voltage conventional structure = 51V

The improvement due to use of the punchthrough shield is nearly five fold. The base width of the improved device is greater than that of the conventional one by the emitter-punchthrough shield edge spacing. That spacing can be held to a few microns so the improvement in voltage capability for a given base width remains substantial.

The improved structure has higher Early voltage than the conventional structure of equal base width because it has a much higher Gummel number due to the presence of the punchthrough shield. The shield typically remains largely undepleted even at maximum V_{CB}. Early voltage is further increased when the collector absorbs some of the applied voltage since less voltage must then be absorbed in the base and thus less base charge must be uncovered to sustain the applied voltage.

EXPERIMENTAL RESULTS

A number of experimental lots of devices were built in dielectrically isolated wafers with a range of punchthrough shield concentrations and base collector impurity grades to evaluate the performance of the improved structure. Full circular geometries with a wide range of base widths were used (shown in fig. 4). All devices have the same emitter and punchthrough shield geometries. Conventional lateral devices were made with the same masks to provide comparative results.

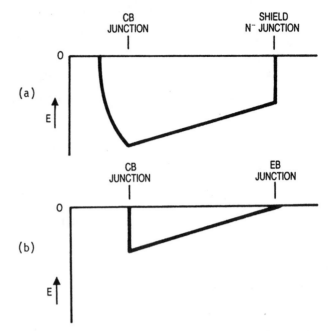

Figure 2. Electric field in improved (a) and conventional (b) geometries

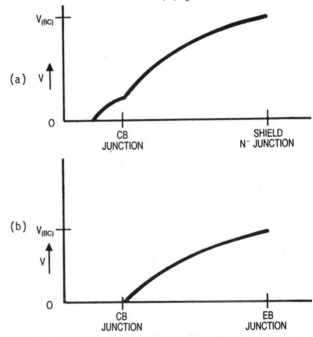

Figure 3. Voltage in improved (a) and conventional (b) geometries

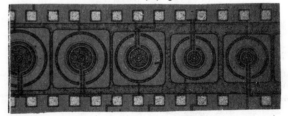

Figure 4. Photomicrograph of test geometries

Key process parameters and electrical results for a selected geometry in each process are presented in table 1.

TABLE 1

Parameter	Process					
	1	2	3	4	5	6
Collector-base grade (cm^{-4})	1.5×10^{19}	2.9×10^{18}	5.7×10^{17}	5.1×10^{17}	5.7×10^{17}	
Emitter shield surface concentration (ions/cm^3)	None	4×10^{15}	1×10^{18}	1×10^{18}	1×10^{18}	
Metallurgical base width (μ)	14	16	11	38	6	1.5
BV_{CES} (V)	120	220	225	450	350	250
f_T (MHz)	1.0	1.97	1.7	0.51	1.9	60
H_{FE}	59	166	70	71	40	100
Early voltage (V)	30	140	2000	623	500	200
V_{BE} (mV)	611	645	701	705	656	

Process 1 is a conventional lateral PNP process with 15Ωcm N- islands. Process 6 is a vertical complementary PNP from ref. 3. Processes 2 and 3 are in islands similar to process 1 but with various punchthrough shield and collector profiles. Process 5 is identical to process 3 except no buried layer is used. Process 5 is also a parallel stripe geometry unlike the circular geometries of the other processes.

The relative values of the parameters of process 2, which has the lowest shield doping, illustrate its effect on performance. Gummel number is lower than other shield devices as can be seen from the low V_{BE}. Tracking the low Gummel number is the low Early voltage. Also consistent with the low Gummel number is the high current gain.

Processes 3 and 5 have the lowest surface concentration collectors and thus can absorb a greater fraction of the applied voltage in the collector. This contributes to the high early voltages exhibited by the devices from these processes. Breakdown voltage in the process 3 device is limited by its collector and buried layer overlap.

The small base width which can be achieved at a given breakdown in processes 3 and 5 also arise in part from the relatively large fraction of base collector voltage absorbed in the low concentration collector.

Process 4 has a very low concentration N- (100Ωcm). It has islands twice the thickness of those of process 2. These two factors together lead to the higher breakdown voltage.

Common emitter characteristics of the devices from processes 1 through 4 are shown in fig. 5 to further illustrate the differing characteristics resulting from structure differences. The very low collector resistances exhibited by each of the devices is particularly noteworthy. This is a parameter for which lateral devices afford better performance than vertical devices.

Figure 6 illustrates the dependence of f_T on base width. Base width is taken as the minimum distance between collector and emitter in all cases. It is often less than the average distance over which carriers travel while passing from emitter to collector. The $f_T \propto \frac{1}{W^2}$ dependence indicates that base transport dominates f_T as would be expected for lateral devices.

Figure 7 illustrates the relationship between f_T and BV_{CES} for the various processes. The points for each process are for geometries with different base widths selected from the range in which base width sets BV_{CES}. An exception is the process 3 point for which no such geometry was available.

SUMMARY

An improved lateral PNP structure incorporating both a punchthrough shield around the emitter and a deep graded collector has been described. Devices with a range of structure parameters and base widths have been built and characterized to demonstrate the capability of the structure. Key results achieved include a device with 1.9MHz f_T and 350V BV_{CES} and a device with 2000V Early voltage.

REFERENCES

(1) T. Sakurai, K. Kato, Y. Inabe, T. Hayashi, "A 350V Complementary LSI Process Using Shallow Junctions," IEDM Tech. Digest, pp 793-795, Dec. 1982.

(2) D.W. Aull, D.A. Spires, P.C. Davis, S.F. Moyer, "A 60V IC for a Transformerless Trunk and Subscriber Line Interface," ISSCC Digest of Technical Papers, pp 246-247, Feb. 1981.

(3) J.D. Beasom, "A 200V Complementary Vertical Bipolar Process with Compatible Logic," IEDM Tech. Digest, pp 89-91, Dec. 1982.

(4) P.W. Shackle, A.R. Hartman, T.J. Riley, J.C. North, J.E. Berthold, "A 500V Monolithic Bidrictional 2x2 Crosspoint Array," ISSCC Digest of Technical Paper, pp 170-171, Feb. 1980.

(5) J.D. Beasom, "High Voltage Dielectric Isolation SCR Integrated Circuit Process," IEDM Tech. Digest, pp 178-180, Dec. 1977.

(6) S. Krishna, A. Ramde, "A Simple Technique for Improving Lateral PNP Transistor Performance," IEEE Journal of Solid State Circuits, pp 781-783, Vol. SC-17, Aug. 1982.

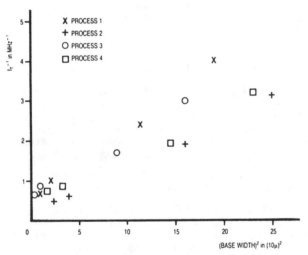

Figure 6.   Inverse frequency response vs. base width squared

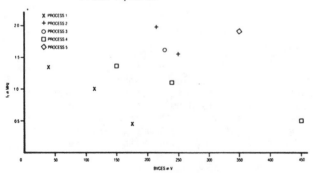

Figure 7.   Frequency response vs. BV_{CES}

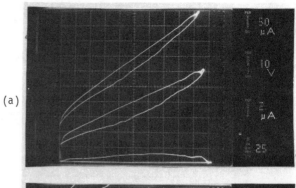

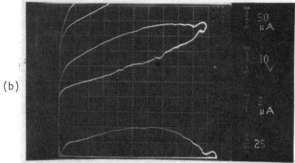

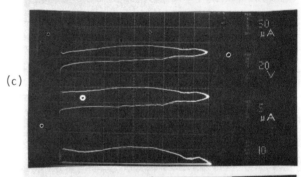

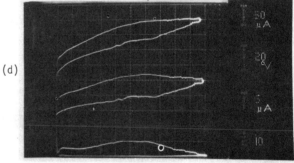

Figure 5.   Common emitter characteristics of devices from process 1 (a), process 2 (b), process 3 (c), and process 4 (d)

A DUAL BURIED LAYER TECHNOLOGY FOR THE FABRICATION OF HIGH VOLTAGE NPN DEVICES COMPATIBLE WITH A 1.5 MICRON EPITAXIAL BIPOLAR PROCESS

Alex Y. Tang, Roger Johnston and Peter J. Meza

Tektronix, Inc.

ABSTRACT

This paper presents a technique to integrate an optional high voltage high speed NPN transistor in a low voltage (LV) LSI bipolar process. The design approach of the LV process maximizes the device speed by forming a very narrow base width $(0.15\mu m)$ and a heavily doped buried layer $(\rho_S = 20\,\Omega/\square)$. LSI capability is achieved by using recessed oxide isolation on a $1.5\mu m$ thick epitaxial layer. This process architecture tends to limit LV_{CEO} and BV_{CBO} to about 10 and 20 volts respectively. The voltage capability can be expanded, however, without affecting the primary specifications of the LV process. This is achieved by the addition of a lightly doped buried layer. The feasibility of this concept is demonstrated by solving the Poisson equation. A high voltage (HV) device with a minimum LV_{CEO} of 45 volts and f_T of 1.2 Ghz has been fabricated. The narrow base width is sufficient to keep the HV device from punch through. Experimental results for a range of doping profiles are presented.

INTRODUCTION

Several techniques have been used to combine LV switching and HV analog devices on integrated circuits. Although these techniques increase breakdown voltage, there is an adverse affect on circuit speed and cost.

Most integrated circuits which combine high speed logic and high voltage switching are fabricated by an IC process specifically designed for the high voltage breakdown. Typically, only a few devices require such a capability. This leads to larger device area and unnecessarily complicating the manufacturing process, which both result in higher cost [1-4].

In some applications it is possible to extend the high voltage capability of a process by using "voltage sharing" between transistors such that no single device withstands voltages beyond its useful operating range [5-6], but the additional biasing circuitry increases parasitics.

Common base operation is used in an output stage to increase voltage performance to a limit of BV_{CBO}. In thin epitaxial ($1\mu m$ to $2\mu m$) bipolar processes, this technique does not improve the performance. Common base breakdown is usually several volts below BV_{CBO}.

This paper describes a simple way to fabricate HV and LV devices on the same thin epitaxial layer. Compatibility between high voltage analog and low voltage LSI logic devices is achieved.

DEVICE STRUCTURE

Figure 1 shows the schematic cross section of the LV and HV NPN devices. An extremely shallow and steep emitter-base junction is formed to optimize the cut off frequency (f_T) and to reduce the emitter time delay. The metallurgical base width is reduced to $0.15\mu m$ and the base doping is kept sufficiently high to achieve a reasonable Early voltage of 19 volts and safety from punch through. The f_T of the low voltage NPN has been measured to be 8.5 Ghz at $V_{CE} = 4V$. To assure the high speed capability of the HV NPN device, the same emitter-base profile is used. The minimum width emitter for both LV and HV devices is $1.5\mu m$.

The collector-base breakdown is increased by adding a lightly doped but deep N- buried layer (N-BL). The N- BL spacing between base and collector replicates the normally thick epitaxial layer required by an equivalent high voltage bipolar process. (Typically, a $9\mu m$ thick $2\,\Omega$-cm epi resistivity is required for 60 volts breakdown.)

The collector consists of three regions: a thin N type epitaxial layer which contains the collector-base junction, a diffused N- type well (N- BL) which conducts laterally, and an N+ doped collector contact which is composed of an N+ buried layer (N+ BL) and a deep collector sink.

The selection of epi resistivity is critical to the breakdown characteristics of the HV NPN and the f_T on the LV NPN. The epi resistivity used is $0.5\,\Omega$-cm, nearly the practical minimum. Poisson analysis indicates that if epi resistivity is reduced to $0.25\,\Omega$-cm, a sub-micron epi thickness is required to sustain a 45 volt breakdown. Increasing epi resistivity, though desirable for a HV device, will degrade the f_T and current handling capability of the LV NPN.

The N- BL is fabricated by phosphorous implant and diffusion, which must be carefully controlled to

Reprinted from *IEEE 31st Int. Electron Devices Meeting*, pp. 298-301, 1985.

assure uniformity. The surface concentration is critical to the HV characteristic, especially in the vicinity of $1 \times 10^{15}\ cm^{-3}$. This concentration will increase somewhat after epi deposition due to down diffusion of arsenic from the heavier doped epi layer. Although a low surface concentration is desirable, the total dopant must be enough to avoid excessive conductivity modulation from the collector-base and collector-substrate junctions. A high temperature drive (1250°C) is necessary to form a deep junction. Internal oxygen gettering is employed to improve the N- BL/substrate junction leakage.

Three other factors: a P+ guard ring, recessed oxide isolation, and channel stop mask are essential for fabrication of the HV device. In order to avoid the curvature effect on BV_{CBO}, a guard ring of P+ base contact and metal field plate is added to the HV NPN device. The recessed oxide wall is essential to isolate the base from the heavily doped collector contact and forces the depletion layer to spread into the N- BL. Poisson analysis indicates that a higher voltage can be sustained in the epi/N- BL region before critical field is reached at the collector-base junction. A channel stop mask separates the N+ BL from the P+ channel stop. This separation and the recessed oxide isolation forces the collector-substrate breakdown to occur at the N+ BL/P- substrate junction. The result is a high BV_{CS} of 160 volts, which is necessary for high voltage performance.

EXPERIMENTAL RESULTS

Figure 2a and 2b show the common emitter transfer curves of the LV and HV device on the same display scale. Both transistors have an emitter size of $1.5\mu m$ by $50\mu m$. The LV_{CEO} of the HV transistor is typically 45 volts for the nominal geometry spacing and N- BL profile. The optimal N- BL is formed by double ionized phosphorus implant and has a surface concentration of $1.1 \times 10^{15}\ cm^{-3}$. Figures 3a shows the common emitter transfer curves of a HV device fabricated with a heavier doped N- BL. This device exhibits an avalanche breakdown similar to the LV devices (11 volts). The avalanche current is limited by the voltage drop in the N- BL which in turn decreases collector bias. This limiting effect disappears if the implant dose exceeds $5 \times 10^{12}\ cm^{-2}$. If the N- BL implant dose is decreased as in figure 3b, LV_{CEO} is increased. LV_{CEO} can approach BV_{CBO}, exceeding 80 volts. However, the doping uniformity deteriorates rapidly and the N- BL sheet resistance can vary by 25% across the wafer. Also, the HV device saturates at less than 6mA.

Figure 4 shows the variation of forward gain (β_F) as a function of collector current (I_C) at $V_{CE}=7$ volts. The β_F of the HV device remains constant between 1 to 8 mA. As I_C approaches 10 mA, the device enters quasi saturation and β_F rolls off rapidly. The other factor that contributes to β_F roll off is collector-substrate bias voltage (V_{CS}). Figure 5 shows the variation of β_F as a function of I_C and V_{CS}; β_F is decreased as the bias voltage is increased. The current handling capability of the HV device is $80\mu A$ per micron of emitter length. For a high power device, a multiple interdigitated emitter-base-collector

configuration is desirable.

Figure 6 shows the forward Gummel plot a HV NPN device. I_C follows an almost ideal diode characteristic.

Figure 7 shows that a maximum operating voltage of 120 volts is achievable if the device is operated in the common base mode. The device in figure 7 has an increased base to collector contact spacing to allow for the depletion region spread. BV_{CBO} at $10\mu A$ is 130 volts.

Collector to emitter punch through voltage (BV_{CES}) is shown to be 120 volts in figure 8. The base width is narrow, but the collector-base junction depletion spread is almost entirely in the epi and N- BL, and punchthrough is prevented.

The deep P+ guard ring reduces the curvature effect of the active base implant. Several devices without this guard ring have been examined. Premature breakdown occurs in a device with a nominal N- BL. The gain of the parasitic PNP is reduced if the P+ guard ring is eliminated. However, potential latch up problems may still exist and therefore the device should not be saturated.

Figure 9 compares the f_T of a LV and HV device with identical emitter sizes ($1.5\mu m \times 50\mu m$). The f_T is fairly constant between 1mA and 8mA and does not vary much with V_{CE}. Although the peak f_T of the HV device is 1.2 Ghz, the frequency at which the maximum available power gain is unity (f_{MAX}) is 4.5 Ghz.

CONCLUSION

A high voltage high speed NPN transistor has been fabricated in an existing 1.5 micron 0.5Ω-cm epitaxial process. This device has an LV_{CEO} of 45 volts and an f_T of 1.2 Ghz. The frequency performance is compatible with the LV device. This combined LV and HV capability can be exploited in a circuit which is primarily digital but requires a large output voltage swing.

The dual layer buried layer technique is generally applicable to any thin epitaxial process with dielectric isolation. The doping profile of the N- BL can be tailored to voltage and current requirements. The technique can also be extended to poly-base and poly-emitter structures. Prototype circuits using this process are now being developed.

REFERENCES

[1] U. S. Davidsohn and F. Lee, Proc. IEE 57, pp. 1532-1537, Sept. 1969.

[2] J. D. Beezum, IEDM Technical Digest, p. 175, Dec. 1977.

[3] T. Okabe, M. Kimura, I. Shimizu, Y. Nagai and M. Nagata, IEDM Technical Digest, p.698, 1984.

[4] Y. Sugawara, T. Kamei, et. al., IEDM Technical Digest, p.412, Dec. 1983

[5] G. W. Haines and R. Genesi, ISSCC digest., p. 94, 1969.

[6] R. A. Blauschild, IEEE Journal of Solid-State Circuits, vol. SC-13, No.6, Dec., 1978.

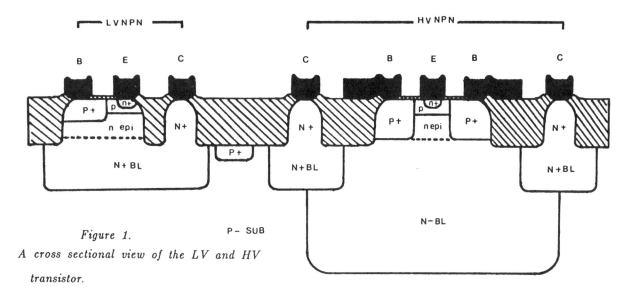

Figure 1.
A cross sectional view of the LV and HV transistor.

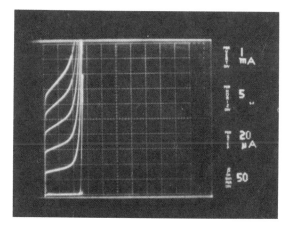

Figure 2a. LV NPN in common emitter mode.

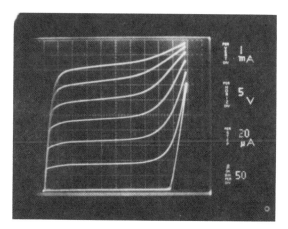

Figure 2b. HV NPN in common emitter mode.

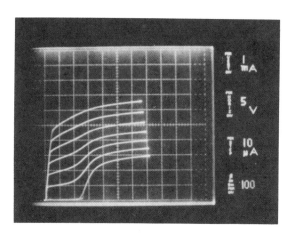

Figure 3a. HV NPN with heavier doped N- BL

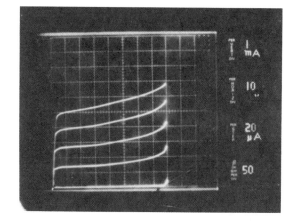

Figure 3b. HV NPN with lighter doped N- BL

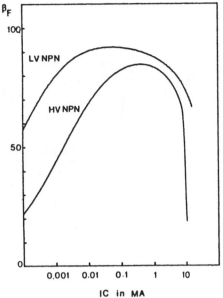

Figure 4. β_F vs. I_C for the LV and HV devices.

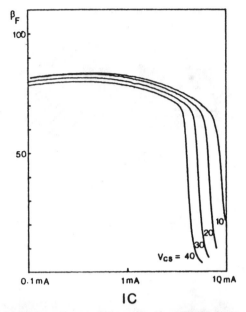

Figure 5. β_F vs. V_{CS} for the HV device.

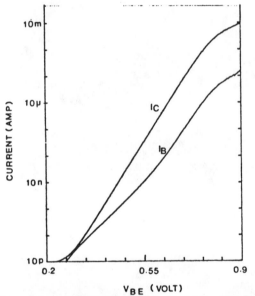

Figure 6.   Forward Gummel plot of the HV NPN at $V_{CE} = 7V$.

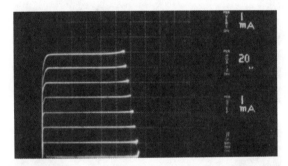

Figure 7.   HV NPN in common base mode.

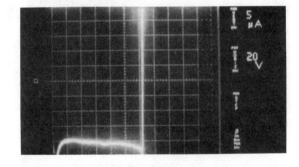

Figure 8. BV_{CES} of the HV NPN.

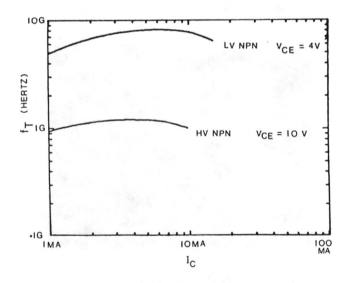

Figure 9. f_T vs. I_C for the LV and HV device.

Improved Second Breakdown of Integrated Bipolar Power Transistors

FLAVIO F. VILLA

Abstract—This paper presents two new power bipolar transistor structures with greatly increased forward second breakdown values without saturation voltage degradation. These structures, labeled $S1$ and $S2$, were obtained with slight modification of the output stages of an IC power amplifier and without complicating the standard IC process. The design concepts developed in this paper were applied to power transistors fabricated using two different processes already in production: process $A(V_{CEO(sus)} > 50$ V) and process $B(V_{CEO(sus)} > 80$ V). Measurements have shown that an improvement of three times for dc conditions and four times or more for single pulses duration of less than 1 ms can be obtained for structure $S1$ while structure $S2$ is able to achieve the proportionality between power silicon area and power levels. Experimental temperature distributions over emitter area and some theoretical calculations for the steady-state condition are given.

I. INTRODUCTION

A MAJOR PROBLEM associated with the application of bipolar power transistors, e.g., in IC power amplifiers, is forward biased secondary breakdown. Several studies indicate that the nature of this instability is purely thermal in origin. It derives from a large negative temperature coefficient of the base–emitter voltage: for a constant forward current, the voltage across the junction decreases linearly with temperature, at a rate of about 2 mV/°C; thus over the range of 30 to 200°C the collector current is increased by about 8 percent/°C.[1]

This tendency leads to the formation of a localized region with current density well in excess of the average value, until the silicon intrinsic temperature is reached. This is followed by a very rapid increase of current with consequent destruction of the transistor. The failure mechanism is shorting between the emitter and collector regions. The short circuits are produced by local melting of the Al–Si system, where the temperature reaches up to 577°C.

A number of corrective techniques can be used to improve the second breakdown characteristics. Some of them are aimed at controlling the hot spot temperature and to limit its effect on the silicon-metallization system and consist of:

1) The improvement of heat dissipation by reducing the silicon thickness. The thickness limit is defined by the production process and a minimum of 250 μm is required in order to avoid wafer breakage during handling. By this solution a junction-to-case thermal resistance of about 1.5°C/W can be obtained with a 10 000-mil² power transistor.

2) The improvement of heat dissipation by heat-sinking from the emitter side [1]. A junction-case thermal resistance $R_{\mathrm{th}j-c}$ of less than 1°C/W could be obtained in the conditions described at point 1. However, this solution requires a much more complex technology and has some limitation from the electrical point of view (e.g., the emitter must be grounded, parasitic capacitances are introduced, and so on).

3) The use of a barrier layer between silicon and aluminum in order to avoid the formation of Al–Si eutectic compounds, which melt at 577°C. Ti/W and Mo [2] are suggested as barrier metals. However, other drawbacks are met with this solution, related to contact resistivity instability and Al migration at high temperature.

Other solutions are oriented to obtain a uniform electrical conduction of the base–emitter junction, thus limiting the possibility of hot spot generation. Improvement of the emitter current uniformity can be obtained by dividing the large emitter of the device into a number of small insulated cells connected to the common emitter metallization through ballast resistors R_E [3]. These resistors are obtained by the emitter diffusion (Fig. 1(a)) and introduce no additional cost [4]. The result is the typical "H emitter structure" (HES) widely used in power integrated circuits. An example is shown in Fig. 1(b). The final power structures appear divided into a number of fingers (1, 2, $\cdots$, n), each composed of several cells (four or five), electrically circuited in parallel.

Nevertheless the principal drawback related to these standard structures concerns the optimum use of silicon area in raising voltage, current, and power levels. In fact, conventional structures do not allow the collector-current range to be increased in proportion to the additional area of silicon used. As shown later in Fig. 3(a), the second breakdown values (SOA area) do not depend on the number of power fingers [5].

Other drawbacks associated with standard H structures are related to:

1) saturation voltage degradation with a loss of useful output power and efficiency;
2) poor effectiveness of ballast resistors in high-voltage low-current conditions;

Manuscript received April 4, 1986; revised July 15, 1986.
The author is with SGS Research and Development Laboratories, Milan, Italy.
IEEE Log Number 8610536.

[1]More precisely, the collector current temperature coefficient depends on current density J (see Table I).

Reprinted from *IEEE Trans. Electron Devices*, vol. ED-33, pp. 1971–1976, Dec. 1986.

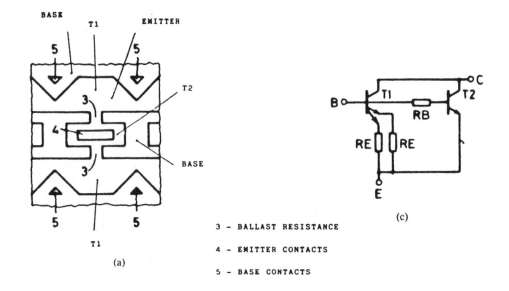

3 — BALLAST RESISTANCE

4 — EMITTER CONTACTS

5 — BASE CONTACTS

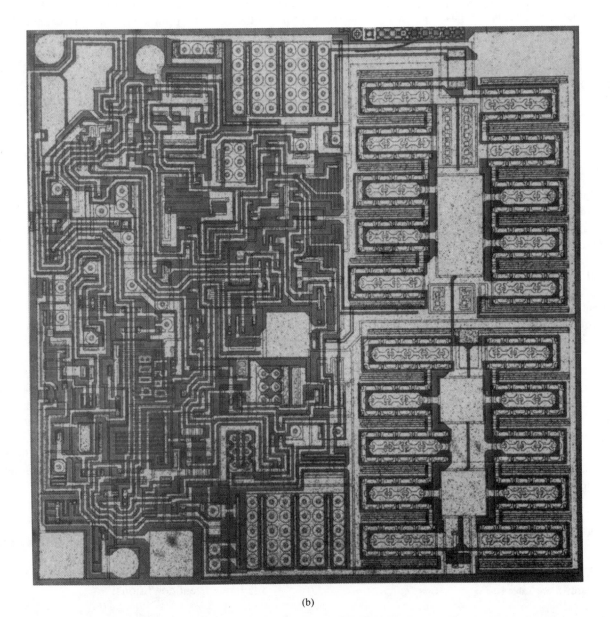

(b)

Fig. 1. (a) Typical *H* emitter cell. (b) Photograph of L260 audio amplifier (die size is 107 mils by 109 mils). (c) Cell equivalent circuit.

TABLE I

CURRENT DENSITY J	$\Delta I_C \left[V_{BE}(T) \right]$	$\Delta I_C \left[\Delta \beta(T) \right]$
mA/mils^2	%/°C	%/°C
0.4	10	0.4
8	7	−0.14 (*)
16	5	−0.1 (*)

(*) β decrease if T increases.

The process considered here is type A

−$\Delta I_C \left[V_{BE}(T) \right]$: variation of collector current ΔI_C due to base-emitter voltage temperature dependence for different current densities J.

−$\Delta I_C \left[\Delta \beta(T) \right]$: variation of collector current ΔI_C due to current-gain temperature dependence for different current densities J.

3) poor ruggedness of $T2$ transistor (Fig. 1(c)) due to the lack of emitter resistance; and
4) lower active emitter area, and then lower current capability at the same device area.

In this paper two structures are presented to achieve high forward second breakdown device performance without degradation of the saturation voltage and without complicating the standard IC process. Both structures are obtained with small modifications of output stages of IC power amplifiers and one of them is able to achieve the proportionality between power silicon area and power levels.

This paper reports the results obtained by applying these techniques to two different processes already in production, one for high-performance linear applications called $A(V_{CEO(sus)} > 50 \text{ V})$ and one named $B(V_{CEO(sus)} > 80 \text{ V})$ for higher voltage applications. Experimental temperature distributions over emitter fingers and some theoretical calculations are given for a five-finger transistor operating under steady-state conditions.

II. DEVICE ANALYSIS

The destructive secondary breakdown triggering energy of a power transistor, operating as a switch or amplifier, would be increased if the current-temperature sensitivity were decreased. Now the most damaging temperature-sensitive mechanism is the $V_{BE}(\text{ON})$ negative temperature coefficient, rather than the temperature sensitivity of current gain as shown in Table I. Therefore structures in which the current-temperature sensitivity only depends on the current gain temperature coefficient will have a higher value of forward second breakdown. The structures presented in this paper, labeled $S1$ and $S2$, had a double-diffused profile, were mounted in premolded multiwatt packages, and had conventional comb-like interdigitated geometry.

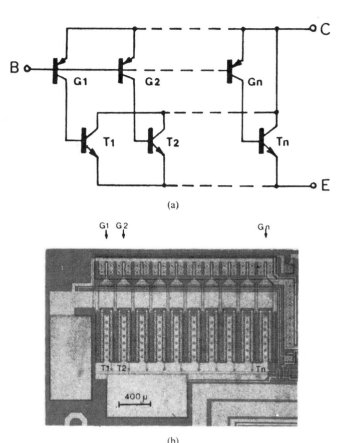

(a)

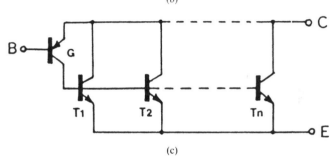

(b)

(c)

Fig. 2. (a) Equivalence circuit of structure $S1$. (b) Layout of $S1$ structure. (c) Conventional equivalent circuit of power amplifiers output stages.

III. DEVICE STRUCTURE $S1$

The first temperature desensitized structure, described in this paper, uses a Darlington power bipolar transistor in which the collector of the p-n-p driver (or emitter of the n-p-n driver) is split into several parts each connected to the base of each finger of the power n-p-n, as is shown in Fig. 2(a). Note that in a traditional output stage configuration the collector of the driver as a whole is connected to the base as a whole of power (Fig. 2(c)). Structure $S1$ may be realized without any wasted area. Its layout is represented in Fig. 2(b), and consists of multiple fingers $T1$, $T2$, $\cdots$, Tn ($n = 10$) connected in parallel using an aluminum metal layer and an identical number of current generators $G1$, $G2$, $\cdots$, Gn like four disk lateral p-n-p transistors each of which has the collector terminal connected to the base of a respective fingers of power by means of n$^+$ crossunders, realized inside the p-region.

As illustrated in Fig. 3, the SOA extension for a struc-

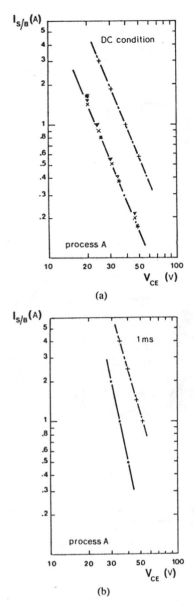

Fig. 3. (a)(———·———) SOA curve for structure $S1$ in dc condition and (b) for single pulse duration equal to 1 ms. The curves (———) obtained with conventional structures are given for comparison; ∇, *, ●, × are forward second breakdown values for one, two, three, and four power fingers, respectively.

ture of this type is significant. The increase of available power obtained is three times higher compared to that of the conventional structure for dc conditions (Fig. 3(a)) and four times greater or more for single pulse duration equal to 1 ms. (Fig. 3(b)). The maximum current gain is 4000 and the saturation voltage, corresponding to a collector current I_C of 5 A which halves the gain, is 1.5 V while the $V_{BE(SAT)}$ is about 1.2 V. The saturation voltages and gain indicated are the same as those of a traditional structure (Fig. 2(c)) in that the process and layout parameters that influence these values remain uncharged in the two structures compared. The only difference concerns the presence in structure $S1$ of n^+ crossunders with a resistance $R_{cu} = 2\Omega$, which introduces an additional voltage drop of $(I_B/n) \cdot R_{cu}$ (where n is the number of the crossunders) of roughly 30 mV. However, the use of these

crossunders is useful to obtain a uniform current density in the power transistor, even in a traditional structure, wherever a single level of metallization is used. Moreover, for the two structures examined, apart from the process spread, there is no appreciable variation in the ratio between $I_C(hFE/2)$ and the total emitter area which is 8 mA/mil². This is justified by the fact that the parameters that influence the reduction in gain of the transistor at high currents, such as the base charge Q_B, base width W_B, and the perimeter/area ratio of the emitter P_E/A_E, remain unchanged in the two structures.

IV. DEVICE STRUCTURE $S2$

Structure $S2$ is similar to the structure $S1$ but the transistor fingers are no longer arranged adjacent to one another but spaced 17 mil apart from one another (between the longitudinal symmetry axes of two adjacent fingers). It is experimentally found that when the power fingers are spaced by this amount the electrothermal interactions between the transistor fingers are eliminated. So the collector current range of a power transistor can be increased in proportion to the additional emitter area or number of fingers used. As an example, if the individual finger transistors forming the power transistor are limited by the forward secondary breakdown phenomenon to a given value, e.g., $I'_{S/B}$, the power transistor as a whole is able to withstand collector current values equal to $N \cdot I'_{S/B}$, N being the number of fingers forming the power transistor itself or

$$I_{S/B}(\text{power}) = N \cdot I'_{S/B}(\text{one finger}). \qquad (1)$$

In order to minimize the device area requirements, the space between any two adjacent transistor fingers is made to accommodate drive transistors operating as current sources or the finger transistors of the complementary stage where the device forms a class AB output stage, the two output transistors of which are switched on alternately.

In the case of the class AB output stage, the connections may be made on a single metal layer by means of suitable crossunders or by using two metal layers thus avoiding crossing in the connections. Fig. 4(a) and (b) shows the power capability of a five-finger 17-mil-spaced transistor. The results obtained are for two standard production processes A and B (see Table II) for different single pulse durations (1 and 10 ms) and for dc conditions. As can be seen from these figures, (1) is always true for each collector emitter voltage V_{CE} showing so the collector current is uniform on power area. For the same reasons indicated previously other parameters, such as $V_{CE(SAT)}$, $V_{BE(SAT)}$, and the ratio between $I_C(hFE/2)$ to total emitter area undergo no alterations.

V. CALCULATIONS AND THERMAL MEASUREMENTS

As an example of the part played by the spacing of the emitter fingers on thermal stability of a power transistor, the transistor steady-state temperature distribution was calculated for a cross section of a five-finger power tran-

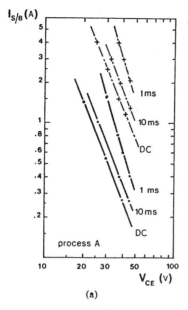

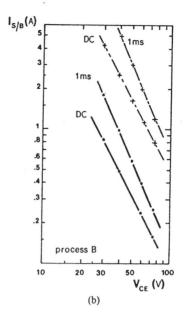

(a)

(b)

Fig. 4. (———·——) SOA curves for structure $S2$. The curves obtained with conventional structure (———) are given for comparison.

TABLE II
DATA COMPILATION SHOWING PROCESSES CHARACTERISTICS

PROCESS TYPE	BURIED LAYER SHEET RESISTIVITY	EPITAXIAL RESISTIVITY ρ_{EPI}	EPITAXIAL THICKNESS x_{EPI}	BASE SHEET RESISTIVITY ρ_{sb}	EMITTER SHEET RESISTIVITY ρ_{se}	BASE JUNCTION DEPTH x_{jb}	EMITTER JUNCTION DEPTH x_{je}	J_C at h_{FE} MAX	J_C at $h_{FE} = \frac{1}{2}h_{FE}$ MAX	V_{CEO} (SUS) at $I_C = 1mA$	V_{CBO} at $I_C = 100\mu A$
	$\Omega/\square$	Ω-cm	μm	$\Omega/\square$	$\Omega/\square$	μm	μm	mA/mils^2	mA/mils^2	(V)	(V)
PROCESS A	20	4+6	15+17	100	3	4.5	3.5	1	8	50	80
PROCESS B	20	6+10	18+22	100	3	4.5	3.2	0.6	6	80	100

sistor assuming uniform current flow in each finger (Fig. 5(a)). The assumptions made in this analysis are summarized as follows:

1) uniform current density distribution in the emitters,
2) homogeneous and isotropic thermal conductivity,
3) end effects are neglected,
4) heat is generated only along the collector–base junction $y = W$, and
5) temperature at $y = 0$ is uniform at T_S where T_S is the temperature of the heat sink

In this way the differential equation governing this process is

$$\partial^2 T/\partial x^2 + \partial^2 T/\partial y^2 = 0 \qquad (2)$$

and the boundary conditions are

$$\text{at} \quad x = 0 \qquad \partial T/\partial x = 0$$
$$\text{at} \quad x = (a + b)/2 \qquad \partial T/\partial x = 0$$
$$\text{at} \quad y = W \qquad -K\partial T/\partial y = \begin{cases} Q/a & \text{for } 0 \leq x \leq a/2 \\ 0 & \text{for } a/2 < x \leq (a + b)/2 \end{cases}$$
$$\text{at} \quad y = 0 \qquad T = T_S$$

where Q is the heat liberated at each emitter per unit length of emitter (e.g., watts per centimeter), a is the emitter width, K is the thermal conductivity (e.g., watts per centimeter times degrees Kelvin), b is the emitter spacing, and W is the chip thickness. The junction temperature $T(x, W)$ obtained solving (2) for a five-finger power transistor [5] is

$$\frac{K(T - T_S)}{P_0 L} = 5\left(\frac{W}{L}\right)\left(\frac{a}{L}\right) + \sum_{n=1}^{\infty} \frac{1}{n^2\pi^2} \sin n\pi \left(\frac{a}{L}\right)$$
$$\cdot tgh\, 2n\pi\left(\frac{W}{L}\right)\left[1 + 4\cos n\pi\left(\frac{a + b}{L}\right)\right.$$
$$\left. \cdot \cos 3n\pi\left(\frac{a + b}{L}\right)\right]\cos 2n\pi\left(\frac{x}{L}\right).$$

65

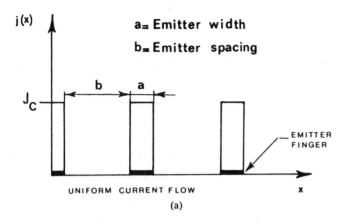

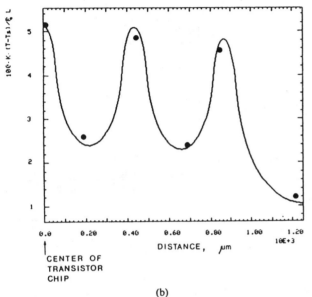

Fig. 5. (a) Assumed distribution of current density in the transistor emitter representing the cases of uniform current flow. (b) Steady-state emitter temperature distribution calculated for five-finger interdigitated structure. The emitter width is 115 μm, emitter spacing 320 μm, chip thickness 320 μm, and chip width is 2500 μm. The power density P_0 is calculated by multiplying the collector voltage times total collector current divided by the total emitter area. Here $P = 15$ W.

Here P_0 is the uncrowded collector power density (collector junction voltage times total collector current divided by the total emitter area) and L is the total transistor chip width.

The result of this calculation is shown in Fig. 5(b) for $a = 115$ μm, $b = 320$ μm, $W = 320$ μm, $L = 2500$ μm, and $T_S = 300°$K. The result was compared with the experimental thermal profile obtained with infrared microradiometer (IRM). The device was mounted on water-cooled dissipator and tested in dc conditions. The power P applied to it was 15 W ($V_{CE} = 30$ V; $I_C = 0.5$ A). The agreement between calculated and measured profiles is a further evidence both that the $S2$ structure examined eliminates completely electrothermal interaction between the emitter fingers and the validity (1).

VI. CONCLUSIONS

Measurements have shown that the thermal instability of bipolar power transistors can be drastically reduced. Slight modification of the output stages of an IC power amplifier allows the proportionality between power silicon area and power levels to be achieved.

The agreement between experimental and calculated temperature distribution in steady-state condition further confirms these results.

ACKNOWLEDGMENT

The author wishes to thank B. Murari, F. Bertotti, and C. Cognetti for helpful discussion. He also would like to thank U. Mastromatteo for device fabrication, G. Siepe for analytical calculation work, and A. Sorbo for layout work. Special thanks are due to A. Torazzina for technical assistance and measurements.

REFERENCES

[1] D. Navon and E. A. Miller, *Solid-State Electron.*, vol. 12, pp. 69–78, 1969.
[2] E. B. Hakim, *IEEE Trans. Reliabil.*, vol. R-17, no. 1, Mar. 1968.
[3] D. Stolnitz, *IEEE Trans. Electron Devices*, vol. ED-13, no. 8/9, pp. 643–648, 1966.
[4] B. Murari, *IEEE J. Solid-State Circuits*, vol. SC-13, no. 3, June 1978.
[5] F. F. Villa, private communication, CIL/66/VLF/zrm, 1981.
[6] W. R. Wilcox, *IEEE Trans. Electron Devices*, vol. ED-10, p. 308, 1963.

Process and Device Design of a 1000-V MOS IC

TADANORI YAMAGUCHI AND SEIICHI MORIMOTO

Abstract—High-voltage MOS devices and logic N-MOS circuits have been integrated on the same chip by using a silicon-gate isoplanar process that is compatible with present N-MOS LSI technology. The electrical characteristics of high-voltage MOS devices are modeled and characterized in terms of channel length, drift-layer length, drift-layer ion dose, and extended source field-plate effect. The theoretical calculations of on-resistance, saturation drain current, and pinchoff voltage agree well with the experimental results. Based on the experimental and theoretical results, the device structure and the process parameters are optimized to obtain maximum drain saturation current with a low on-resistance and a drain breakdown of 1000 V. The optimized high-voltage MOS device can perform with a saturation drain current as high as 84 mA with an on-resistance as low as 300 Ω within an area of 520 μm $\times$ 1320 μm while maintaining a drain breakdown of 1000 V.

LIST OF SYMBOLS

L Channel length.
W Channel width.
W_p Channel width of parallel portion in race-track pattern.

T_{ox} Gate-oxide thickness.
T_F Field-oxide thickness.
ϵ_0 Permittivity of free space.
ϵ_{si} Dielectric constant of silicon.
ϵ_{ox} Dielectric constant of silicon dioxide.
C_{ox} Gate-oxide capacitance.
X_{jd} Drift-layer depth.
N_{do} Drift-layer ion dose.
L_d Drift-layer length.
R_D Drain radius.
V_{GS} Gate-bias voltage.
V_{DS} Drain-bias voltage.
V_{SB} Substrate-bias voltage.
q Electronic charge.
ϕ_f Fermi potential.
ϕ'_{MS} Work function difference.
μ_{so} Maximum surface-electron mobility.
μ_d Electron mobility in drift layer.
N_{SS} Silicon-interface charge density.
V_X $V_X = 2\phi_f + \phi'_{MS} - qN_{SS}/C_{ox}$.
γ $\gamma = (2\epsilon_0 \epsilon_{si} q N_{SB})^{1/2}/C_{ox}$.

Manuscript received July 27, 1981; revised October 19, 1981.
The authors are with the Technology Group, Tektronix, Inc., Beaverton, OR 97077.

Reprinted from *IEEE Trans. Electron Devices*, vol. ED-29, pp. 1171–1178, Aug. 1982.

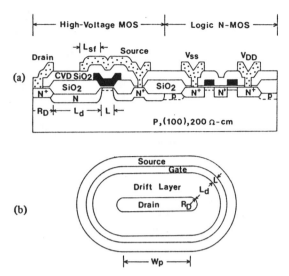

Fig. 1. (a) High-voltage MOS IC device structure. (b) High-voltage MOS device pattern.

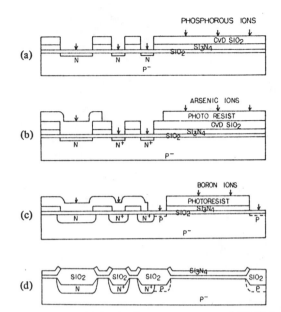

Fig. 2. The major wafer-fabrication process steps. (a) Drift layer ion implantation. (b) Source ion implantation. (c) Field ion implantation. (d) Local oxidation.

I. INTRODUCTION

THE TWO basically different approaches to making high-voltage MOSFET's are to use either a vertical MOS structure [1]–[3] or a horizontal MOS structure with a pinched resistor [4]. Recently, high-voltage MOS integrated circuits are becoming important as driver devices in various display applications. In order to integrate high-voltage MOS devices and logic circuits on the same chip, the vertical MOS structure requires an epitaxial layer with a deep isolation layer [5]. In this case, drain breakdown voltage is often limited by the epitaxial layer and the isolation layer.

On the other hand, several authors have demonstrated high-voltage MOS IC's [6]–[9] that use a horizontal device structure. However, the process technology is rather complicated, and the drain breakdown voltage is often limited by the surface avalanche breakdown associated with the impact ionization currents. It has been demonstrated that the source field plate effectively improves this surface avalanche breakdown voltage [10].

This paper describes an advanced high-voltage MOS IC technology that uses a silicon-gate isoplanar process that is compatible with present N-MOS LSI technology. The device structure and the process parameters are optimized to provide a 1000-V drain-breakdown voltage with maximum drain current and minimum on-resistance.

II. DEVICE STRUCTURE AND PROCESS DESIGN

Fig. 1(a) shows the cross-sectional view of the high-voltage MOS IC using a silicon-gate isoplanar structure. The high-voltage MOS device consists of source, channel, drift layer, and drain regions forming a horizontal structure with an extended source field plate. The source region of the high-voltage MOS device extends to the field region of the logic N-MOS circuit, which consists of conventional silicon-gate enhancement- and depletion-mode MOS devices. Because a recessed oxide technology is employed in the high-voltage MOS device, the channel region is self-aligned not only with the source region but also with the drift-layer region, which in

turn is self-aligned with the drain region. In this high-voltage MOS device, the drain is always surrounded by the source; therefore, the high-voltage MOS device has either a circle or a race-track pattern, as shown in Fig. 1(b).

Fig. 2 shows the major process steps. The starting material is p-type bulk silicon. The first step is to grow a thin SiO_2 film followed by a chemical-vapor deposition of Si_3N_4 and SiO_2 films. The source and drift-layer regions are patterned at the same time in a CVD SiO_2 film and a Si_3N_4 film. Phosphorus ions are then implanted into the drift-layer region. Arsenic-ion implantation is done for the source region using a photoresist as a masking material. After these two ion-implantation steps, the arsenic and phosphorus impurities are diffused. The active device regions of the logic circuits are then defined in the Si_3N_4 film that was deposited initially. Boron ions are implanted into the field regions of the logic devices. After the field boron-ion implantation, a thick SiO_2 film is grown selectively in the source and drift-layer regions of the high-voltage MOS device and in the field region of the logic devices as shown in Fig. 2(d). At this point, note that in the high-voltage MOS device area that the channel region is self-aligned with the source and drift-layer regions and that the drift-layer region is self-aligned with the drain region. The rest of the process steps are the same as for conventional silicon-gate N-MOS LSI's.

III. HIGH-VOLTAGE MOS DEVICE MODEL

In this high-voltage MOS device, there are basically four different operating regions. Fig. 3 shows schematically the device model and the drain characteristics for each operating region. A gate-bias voltage higher than the channel threshold voltage is assumed. As shown in Fig. 3(a), drain current first increases almost linearly with the drain-bias voltage. The on-resistance R_{on} is given by

$$R_{on} = R_{ch} + R_d \qquad (1)$$

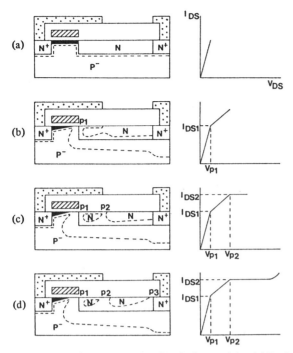

Fig. 3. Schematic of high-voltage MOS device model. (a) Region 1. (b) Region 2. (c) Region 3. (d) Region 4.

where R_{ch} is the channel resistance and R_d is the drift-layer resistance. In the case of the race-track pattern shown in Fig. 1(b), R_d is given by

$$R_d = \left[\frac{2\pi q \mu_d N_d}{\ln(1 + L_d/R_D)} + \frac{2q\mu_d N_d W_p}{L_d} \right]^{-1}. \tag{2}$$

In this equation, N_d represents the total mobile carrier density in the drift layer. If it is assumed that the drift layer has a uniform impurity distribution and is reverse biased by a drain voltage and a substrate voltage, then N_d is given by

$$N_d = N_{d0} - N_a \left[\frac{2\epsilon_0\epsilon_{si}(V_{DS} + V_{SB})}{q} \frac{N_{SB}}{N_a} \frac{1}{(N_a + N_{SB})} \right]^{1/2} \tag{3}$$

where

$$N_a = \frac{N_{d0}}{X_{jd}}. \tag{4}$$

In order to calculate R_{ch} at zero drain-bias voltage, the surface electron mobility μ_s is modeled by

$$\mu_s = \mu_{s0} \left[\frac{\epsilon_{si} E_{CM} T_{ox}}{\epsilon_{ox}(V_{GS} - V_{TH})} \right]^C \tag{5}$$

where E_{CM} and C are empirical constants.

As the drain voltage is increased, the channel region that is close to the drift layer (p_1) is pinched off as shown in Fig. 3(b). This first pinchoff voltage V_{p1} is given by

$$V_{p1} = V_{DSAT} + I_{DS1}R_{d1} \tag{6}$$

where V_{DSAT} is the channel pinchoff voltage, R_{d1} is the drift-layer resistance at the drain voltage of V_{p1}, and I_{DS1} is the channel pinchoff current. I_{DS1} is given by

$$I_{DS1} = \frac{W}{L} C_{ox} \mu_s \left\{ (V_{GS} - V_X)V_{DSAT} - \frac{1}{2} V_{DSAT}^2 \right.$$

$$- \frac{2}{3} \gamma \left[(V_{DSAT} + V_{SB} + 2\phi_f)^{3/2} \right.$$

$$\left. - (V_{SB} + 2\phi_f)^{3/2} \right] \right\}. \tag{7}$$

When the drain voltage is further increased, the increased drain voltage is dropped across the first pinchoff region. This voltage drop causes channel-length modulation and increased drain current. The drain-current increase ΔI_{DS}, due to the channel-length modulation, is expressed by

$$\Delta I_{DS} = I_{DS1} \frac{\Delta L}{L - \Delta L} \tag{8}$$

where ΔL is the channel shrinkage due to the channel-length modulation. Using the same concept introduced by Frohman-Bentchkowsky et al. [11], we can express ΔL empirically by

$$\Delta L = \frac{(1 - \delta)V_{DS} - V_{DSAT}}{E_1 + E_2 + E_3} \tag{9}$$

where δ is an empirical constant to approximate the potential voltage at the drift-layer edge close to the channel pinchoff point. $E_1, E_2,$ and E_3 are given by

$$E_1 = \left\{ \frac{qN_{SB}}{2\epsilon_0\epsilon_{si}} [(1 - \delta)V_{DS} - V_{DSAT}] \right\}^{1/2} \tag{10}$$

$$E_2 = \alpha \left(\frac{\epsilon_{ox}}{\epsilon_{si}} \right) \left[\frac{(1 - \delta)V_{DS} - V_{GS} + qN_{SS}/C_{ox}}{T_{ox}} \right] \tag{11}$$

$$E_3 = \beta \left(\frac{\epsilon_{ox}}{\epsilon_{si}} \right) \left(\frac{V_{GS} + qN_{SS}/C_{ox} - V_{DSAT}}{T_{ox}} \right) \tag{12}$$

where α and β are empirical constants.

When the drain voltage is further increased, the region p_2 is pinched off before the surface electric field in the first pinch-off region reaches a critical avalanche electric field ($\cong 3 \times 10^5$ V/cm), as shown in Fig. 3(c). Once the region p_2 is pinched off, the increased drain voltage is dropped across the second pinchoff region and is no longer applied to the first pinchoff region. Therefore, the electric field in the first pinchoff region no longer increases. As a result, the surface avalanche break-down happening at the first pinchoff region can be prevented; furthermore, the channel-length modulation no longer pro-gresses. Therefore, the drain current saturates completely at the second pinchoff voltage. The saturation drain current I_{DS2} is given by

$$I_{DS2} = I_{DS1} \frac{L}{L - \Delta L_2} \tag{13}$$

where ΔL_2 is the channel shrinkage at the drain voltage of V_{p2}. The second pinchoff voltage V_{p2} is given by

$$V_{p2} = V_{p20} + I_{DS2}R_{d2} \tag{14}$$

where V_{p20} is the second pinchoff voltage at zero gate-bias voltage and R_{d2} is the drift-layer resistance at the drain

69

voltage of V_{p2}. In order to calculate R_{d2}, the drift-layer length L_d in (2) has to be replaced by $L_d - L_{sf}$, where L_{sf} is the extended-source field-plate length measured from the drift-layer edge. V_{p20} is calculated as

$$V_{p20} = \frac{q(N_a + N_{SB})}{2\epsilon_0\epsilon_{si}}$$

$$\cdot \left\{ \left[X_{jd} + \frac{\epsilon_{si}}{\epsilon_{ox}} T_F \frac{N_{SB}}{N_a} + X_{jd}^2 + 2\frac{\epsilon_{si}}{\epsilon_{ox}} T_F X_{jd} \right]^{1/2} \right.$$

$$\left. - \left(X_{jd} + \frac{\epsilon_{si}}{\epsilon_{ox}} T_F \right) \left(\frac{N_{SB}}{N_a} \right)^{1/2} \right\}^2. \quad (15)$$

When the drain voltage is further increased, finally the region p_3 close to the n^+ drain junction is pinched off. For the same reason mentioned before, this third pinchoff region sustains the drain-voltage increase until the surface avalanche breakdown occurs at the third pinchoff region or until the bulk junction breakdown takes place. The third pinchoff voltage V_{p3} is given by

$$V_{p3} = \frac{q}{2\epsilon_0\epsilon_{si}} \frac{N_{d0}}{N_{SB}} (X_{jd}N_{SB} + N_{d0}). \quad (16)$$

IV. Experimental Results

High-voltage MOS devices and N-MOS logic circuits have been integrated on the same chip by using the process described in the previous section. The starting material was p-type bulk silicon with $\langle 100 \rangle$ surface orientation and 200-$\Omega \cdot$ cm resistivity. The gate-oxide and field-oxide thicknesses between the extended-source field plate and the drift layer were 1050 Å and 2.0 μm, respectively. Phosphorus-doped polysilicon was used as a gate-electrode material. In order to make the gate threshold voltage adjusted to 1.0 V, boron ions were implanted into the channel region at an ion dose of 3×10^{11} cm^{-2} with an energy of 40 keV. The drain n^+ junction depth was 1.5 μm. In this experiment, a circle pattern with a drain radius of 50 μm was used for the high-voltage MOS device. In order to investigate the electrical characteristics of the high-voltage MOS device, the drift-layer ion dose was varied from 4×10^{11} cm^{-2} to 2×10^{12} cm^{-2} at an implantation energy of 150 keV. The drift-layer depth was 2.0 μm. As device geometrical parameters, the channel and drift-layer lengths were ranged from 6 to 16 μm and from 50 to 200 μm, respectively.

Fig. 4 shows the typical drain characteristics of a high-voltage MOS device with a 200-μm drift-layer length and a 16-μm channel length. The drain breakdown voltage at zero gate-bias voltage is greater than 1000 V with drain leakage current less than 30 nA. At a gate bias of 4 V, no surface avalanche current was observed for drain voltages up to 800 V.

Fig. 5 shows the drain breakdown voltage as a function of gate-bias voltage for two different devices. One device has an extended-source field plate of 30 μm; the other does not have an extended-source field plate. There is a significant difference in breakdown voltage between the two devices—approximately 200 to 250 V. This difference is due to the existence of a

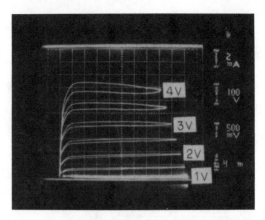

Fig. 4. Typical drain characteristics of high-voltage MOS device with $N_{d0} = 1 \times 10^{12}$ cm^{-2}, $L_{sf} = 30$ μm.

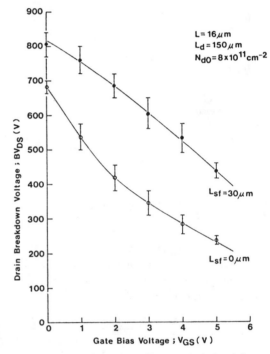

Fig. 5. Extended-source field-plate effect on drain-breakdown voltage.

second pinchoff voltage. In the case of $L_{sf} = 0$, the surface electric field in the first pinchoff region increases continuously until the third pinchoff occurs. This high electric field in the first pinchoff region generates a lot of impact ionization currents and results in surface avalanche breakdown at relatively low drain voltage. The drain breakdown voltage dependence on drift-layer length is shown in Fig. 6. The longer drift layer results in a higher drain-breakdown voltage. As for the drift layer, there is an optimum ion dose for maximum drain breakdown voltage. Based on the two-dimensional computer analysis [10], the maximum drain breakdown voltage can be expected if the surface electric field is equalized among the first, second, and third pinchoff regions. In this experiment, it was found that the optimum drift-layer ion dose was 1.0×10^{12} cm^{-2}.

As shown in Fig. 7, there is significant drain leakage current

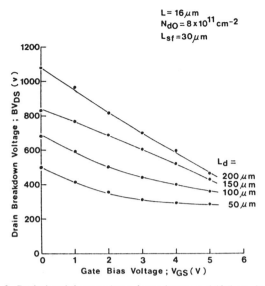

Fig. 6. Drain-breakdown voltage dependence on drift layer length.

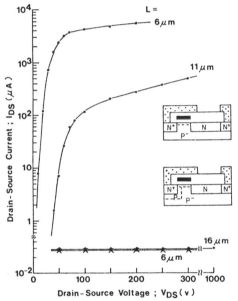

Fig. 7. Drain leakage currents for different channel-length devices with $L_d = 100\,\mu$m, $N_{d0} = 1 \times 10^{12}$ cm^{-2}, and $L_{sf} = 30\,\mu$m. (a) ——•——, (b) ——×——.

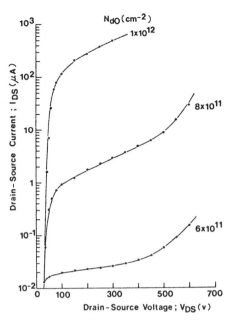

Fig. 8. Drain leakage current dependence on drift layer ion dose. $L = 11\,\mu$m, $L_d = 100\,\mu$m, $L_{sf} = 30\,\mu$m.

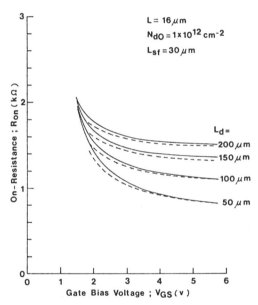

Fig. 9. On-resistance for different drift layer length devices. ——experimental; ————theoretical.

observed for 6- and 11-μm channel devices at zero gate-bias voltage. However, at a 16-μm channel length, the drain leakage current was less than 30 nA even with the drain at 1000 V. This drain leakage current is caused by punchthrough current in the channel region. This punchthrough current can be suppressed if the second pinchoff occurs before the potential barrier in the channel region is lowered. This effect suggests that the lower second pinchoff voltage or the higher impurity concentration in the channel region allows the shorter channel length without punchthrough leakage current. In order to reduce the second pinchoff voltage at zero gate-bias voltage, it is suggested from (15) that either the drift-layer ion dose or the field-oxide thickness has to be reduced. Fig. 8 demonstrates the punchthrough leakage current dependence on the drift-layer ion dose. At the drift-layer ion dose of 6×10^{11} cm^{-2},

the punchthrough leakage current was less than 30 nA in the 11-μm channel device. However, in this case, the surface avalanche current was observed for a drain voltage of over 400 V, and the drain breakdown voltage at zero gate-bias voltage was limited at 650 V.

Another approach to suppress the punchthrough leakage current for short-channel devices is to use an additional p-type layer surrounding the source region, as shown in Fig. 7. With p-type surface concentration of 1×10^{16} cm^{-3}, the punchthrough leakage current was controlled to less than 30 nA in the 6-μm channel device.

The on-resistance was measured at a 50-mV drain voltage. Fig. 9 shows the on-resistance as a function of gate-bias voltage

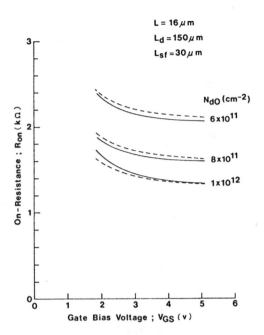

Fig. 10. On-resistance for different drift layer ion doses. ——— experimental; ---- theoretical.

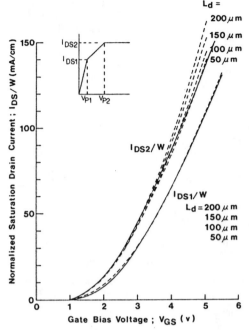

Fig. 11. Normalized saturation drain current for different drift layer length devices. ——— experimental; ---- theoretical; $L = 16$ μm, $N_{d0} = 1 \times 10^{12}$ cm^{-2}, $L_{sf} = 30$ μm.

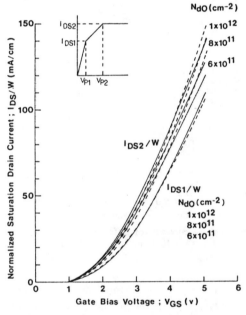

Fig. 12. Normalized saturation drain-current dependence on drift layer ion dose. ——— experimental; ---- theoretical; $L = 16$ μm, $L_d = 100$ μm, $L_{sf} = 30$ μm.

for different drift layer lengths. It is obvious that the longer drift layer results in a higher on-resistance. The on-resistance saturates as the gate-bias voltage is increased. This saturated on-resistance depends very little on channel length because the channel resistance becomes negligible compared with the drift layer resistance as the gate-bias voltage is increased. Fig. 10 shows the on-resistance dependence on drift layer ion dose. The on-resistance is inversely proportional to the drift layer ion dose, as is expected from (1) and (2).

The saturation drain currents at the first and second pinch-off voltages were normalized by the total channel width. Figs. 11 and 12 show the normalized saturation drain currents measured in devices with different drift layer lengths and with different drift layer ion doses. The normalized saturation drain current at the first pinchoff voltage does not depend at all on drift layer length or ion dose but is determined only by channel length and gate-bias voltage. At the second pinchoff voltage, however, the normalized saturation drain current depends a little on drift layer length and ion dose. This dependence is due to the dependences of the first and second pinchoff voltages on the drift layer length and ion dose, as shown in Figs. 13 and 14.

The pinchoff voltage depends on three device parameters: 1) drift layer length; 2) drift layer ion dose, and 3) channel length. The following three paragraphs describe these dependences in detail.

In Fig. 13, the longer drift layer results in larger first and second pinchoff voltages, and also the first and second pinch-off voltages increase as the gate-bias voltage is increased. These dependences can be explained by the fact that the longer drift layer results in a larger drift layer resistance, and the larger gate-bias voltage results in a larger drain current. These effects lead to a larger voltage drop across the drift layer resistance, as indicated by the second term in (6) and (14).

As shown in Fig. 14, the lower drift layer ion dose results in

a larger first pinchoff voltage for a given gate-bias voltage. This effect is also due to the larger voltage drop across the larger drift layer resistance. On the other hand, the lower drift layer ion dose results in a lower second pinchoff voltage at zero gate-bias voltage. However, the lower drift layer ion dose gives rise to a larger rate of increase in the second pinch-off voltage with respect to the gate-bias voltage. This effect results because the lower drift layer ion dose is responsible for the larger voltage drop across the drift layer resistance.

The first pinchoff voltage is inversely proportional to the

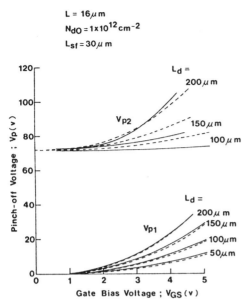

Fig. 13. Pinchoff voltage dependence on drift layer length. ——experimental; ‒‒‒‒ theoretical.

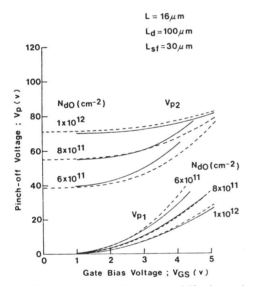

Fig. 14. Pinchoff voltage dependence on drift layer ion dose. ——experimental; ‒‒‒‒ theoretical.

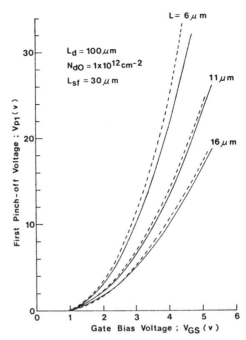

Fig. 15. First pinchoff voltage dependence on channel length. ——experimental; ‒‒‒‒ theoretical.

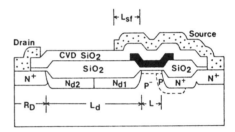

Fig. 16. Optimized high-voltage MOS-device structure.

$E_{CM} = 2.3 \times 10^4$ V/cm, $C = 0.25$, and $\mu_{S0} = 1050$ cm^2/V · s. N_{SS} was measured by a $C-V$ curve at 8×10^{10} cm^{-2}. μ_d was assumed to be 1150 cm^2/V · s. The theoretical calculations of the on-resistance, the saturation drain current, and the pinch-off voltage were in good agreement with the experimental results.

V. Discussion

In order to maximize the saturation drain current capability while maintaining a 1000-V drain breakdown, the channel length must be minimized by keeping the drift layer length larger than 150 μm and the drift-layer ion dose at 1×10^{12} cm^{-2}. However, the short-channel length and the high drift layer ion dose result in drain punchthrough leakage current. It was demonstrated in Figs. 7 and 8 that either the additional p-type region surrounding the source region or the lower drift layer ion dose effectively prevented the punchthrough leakage current. On the other hand, the higher drift layer ion dose is necessary in order to obtain a low on-resistance. The optimized high-voltage MOS-device structure shown in Fig. 16 takes these factors into account in order to obtain the maximum drain-current capability with low on-resistance while maintaining a 1000-V drain breakdown. The source region is surrounded by an additional p-type region that has a surface-

channel length, as is shown in Fig. 15. This relationship can be explained by the fact that the channel pinchoff current I_{DS1} in (6) changes in inverse proportion to the channel length. It was difficult to measure the third pinchoff voltage because the drain current was completely saturated at the second pinchoff voltage. In the case of a drift layer ion dose of 1×10^{12} cm^{-2}, the third pinchoff voltage was estimated to be about 500 V, if a uniform impurity distribution with a density of 5×10^{15} cm^{-3} and a depth of 2 μm in the drift layer were assumed.

In order to calculate the on-resistance, the saturation drain current, and the pinchoff voltage, the empirical constants α, β, and δ were determined by curve fitting with the experimental results. The best fit was obtained at $\alpha = 0.01$, $\beta = 0.6$, and $\delta = 0.75$. The comparison between experimental and calculated results on surface electron mobility determined impurity concentration of 1×10^{16} cm^{-3}. The gate-threshold voltage is adjusted at 1.0 V by a channel boron-ion implantation. The drift layer is composed of two regions, N_{d_1} and N_{d_2}. N_{d_1} has an ion dose of 6×10^{11} cm^{-2}. This lightly doped first drift layer region provides a low second pinchoff voltage to suppress the punchthrough leakage current. The second drift layer region N_{d_2} has an ion dose of 1×10^{12} cm^{-2}, which provides the maximum drain-breakdown voltage and reduces the on-resistance. The optimized high-voltage MOS device, which had a circle pattern with $R_D = 50$ μm, $L = 6$ μm, and $L_d = 200$ μm, demonstrated drain breakdown voltage as high as 1000 V with drain leakage current less than 30 nA, on-resistance of 1700 Ω, and normalized saturation drain current of 260 mA/cm at a 5-V gate bias. In this device, the on-resistance can be reduced to 300 Ω by using a race-track pattern with $W_p = 800$ μm and $R_D = 100$ μm.

VI. Conclusions

High-voltage MOS devices and logic N-MOS circuits have been integrated on the same chip by using a silicon-gate iso-planar process that is compatible with present N-MOS LSI technology. The electrical characteristics of the high-voltage MOS device were modeled and characterized in terms of channel length, drift layer length, drift layer ion dose, and extended-source field-plate effect. The theoretical calculations of on-resistance, saturation drain current, and pinchoff voltage were in good agreement with the experimental results. It was concluded that the optimum high-voltage MOS-device structure uses a p-type region surrounding a source region with a double drift layer structure in order to obtain the maximum drain-current capability with a low on-resistance while maintaining a 1000-V drain breakdown. Based on the experimental results and the theoretical calculations, it was demonstrated that the optimized high-voltage MOS device achieved drain breakdown voltage as high as 1000 V with drain leakage current less than 30 nA, on-resistance as low as 300 Ω, and saturation drain current up to 84 mA within an area of 520 μm $\times$ 1320 μm.

References

[1] K. P. Lisiak and J. Berger, "Optimization of nonplanar power MOS transistors," *IEEE Trans. Electron Devices*, vol. ED-25, p. 1229, 1978.

[2] V.A.K. Templer, R. P. Love, and P. V. Gray, "A 600-volt MOSFET designed for low on-resistance," *IEEE Trans. Electron. Devices*, vol. ED-27, p. 343, 1980.

[3] R. W. Coen, D. W. Tsang, and K. P. Lisiak, "A high-performance planar power MOSFET," *IEEE Trans. Electron Devices*, vol. ED-27, p. 340, 1980.

[4] I. Yoshida, T. Masuhara, M. Kubo, and T. Tokuyama, "Device design of an ion implanted high voltage MOSFET," in *Proc. 6th Conf. Solid State Devices*, (Tokyo, Japan), p. 249, 1974.

[5] J. D. Plummer, "Monolithic MOS high voltage integrated circuits," in *IEDM Tech. Dig.*, p. 70, 1980.

[6] K. Fujii, Y. Torimaru, K. Nakagawa, T. Fujimoto, and Y. Aoki, "400-V MOS-IC for EL display," in *ISSCC Dig. Tech. Papers*, p. 46, 1981.

[7] M. Pomper, L. Leipold, J. Tihanyi, and H. Longo, "High voltage DIMOS driver circuit," *IEEE J. Solid-State Circuits*, vol. SC-15, p. 328, 1980.

[8] D. Sharma, J. Gautier, and G. Merckel, "A high voltage circuit for driving liquid crystal displays," *IEEE J. Solid-State Circuits*, vol. SC-13, p. 375, 1978.

[9] T. Suzuki, T. Kuriyama, and H. Sakuma, "A high voltage high frequency SOS/CMOS pulse generator," in *IEDM Tech. Dig.*, p. 264, 1980.

[10] T. Okabe, I. Yoshida, S. Ochi, S. Nishida, and M. Nagata, "A complementary pair of planarpower MOSFET's," *IEEE Trans. Electron Devices*, vol. ED-27, p. 334, 1980.

[11] D. Frohman-Bentchkowsky and A. S. Grove, "Conductance of MOS transistors in saturation," *IEEE Trans. Electron Devices*, vol. ED-16, p. 108, 1969.

INTEGRATED HIGH AND LOW VOLTAGE CMOS TECHNOLOGY

Vladimir Rumennik*, David L. Heald
Microelectronics Center, Xerox Corporation
El Segundo, CA 90245

ABSTRACT

Novel, complementary high- and low-voltage MOS transistors are described. The high-voltage CMOS transistors were designed and fabricated using the same shallow well as that of low-voltage CMOS transistors, thus enabling integration of the devices without the use of dielectric isolation. The high voltage p-channel transistor is built inside of the n-type well and the p-type offset channel is used to separate the drain area from the gate, which has the same oxide thickness and threshold voltage as a low-voltage p-channel transistor. The high-voltage n-channel devices are built in the high resistivity p-type substrate, using an n-type offset channel to separate the N^+-drain and the gate. The high- and low-voltage CMOS transistors were fabricated using 55-75 ohmcm, p-type substrate with a minimum channel length of 8 microns for the high-voltage and 2 microns for the low-voltage transistors. Drain to source breakdown voltages above 250V and above 25V have been demonstrated for the high-voltage and low-voltage transistors respectively.

INTRODUCTION

High-voltage integrated transistors have found various applications as analog and switching devices. The integrated high-voltage and low-voltage CMOS technology offers circuit performance advantages over N-channel technology in terms of power dissipation and speed, and also offers some additional flexibility in circuit design unavailable otherwise. Several efforts have been made to develop an integrated high- and low-voltage CMOS technology (1-3). A high- and low-voltage SOS/CMOS technology has been described in (1). Integrated bulk silicon CMOS devices (2,3) have been fabricated by utilizing deep impurity diffusion which creates isolated wells of opposite dopant to the substrate. The drain depletion region in such a design expands vertically and the breakdown voltage is thus limited by the depth of the diffused well.

In this paper a shallow well concept is described for the fabrication of high- and low-voltage CMOS transistors in bulk silicon. The p-channel high-voltage transistors are built inside an identical well as that for the low-voltage transistors. The vertical expansion of the depletion region is transformed into horizontal expansion by utilizing the offset channel, which is in turn depleted prior to the gate oxide breakdown. A depleted region, free of carriers, supports high, drain-to-source breakdown voltage. The

high-voltage n-channel transistors are built in the high resistivity p-type substrate, utilizing the offset channel to provide high drain-to-source breakdown voltage. The low-voltage p- and n-channel transistors have the same gate oxide thickness and threshold voltage as the high voltage transistors.

DEVICE STRUCTURE

The high-voltage p- and n-channel transistors have an enclosed circular structure with the drain in the center of the device. The p-channel devices are built inside of an n-well, which is about 5 microns deep. The well has a polysilicon field plate to enhance the well to substrate breakdown voltage. The n-channel transistors are built in the high resistivity p-type substrate. The heavily doped drain area is separated from the gate by an offset channel, Figure 1. When the transistors are turned on, current flows from source through the gate channel and the offset, low-doped channel to the drain as it does in a conventional MOS transistor. When the devices are turned off and the voltage is applied between source and drain the p- and n-channel transistors behave somewhat differently. In the p-channel transistor, the offset channel depletes and simultaneously depletes the well underneath. The entire well region between drain and gate becomes depleted at a certain voltage below the gate-oxide rupture voltage, and any additionally applied voltage then drops across that region, which then behaves as an insulator. When the well and offset channel are totally depleted the electric field becomes largely horizontal and the device must be treated as a two-dimensional structure. The simulations show that the maximum horizontal electric field is a function of the doping level in the offset channel and well and is sensitive to the charge mismatch between them. In the n-channel transistor during turn-off, the offset channel and the region of the substrate underneath is depleted providing a region free of carriers, which then supports high drain voltage.

The low-voltage n- and p-channel transistors are self aligned to their gates.

FABRICATION PROCESS

The fabrication process developed for an integrated high- and low-voltage CMOS transistor has 11 masking steps and utilizes (100) oriented, 55-75 ohmcm resistivity, p-type silicon.

The initial oxide film is grown and the wafers are patterned for the well. Phosphorus is implanted, driven at high temperature to a depth of 5 microns and then the

---

*Vladimir Rumennik is an independent consultant; 7742 Redlands St., #H2031, Playa del Rey, CA 90291.

Reprinted from *IEEE 28th Int. Electron Devices Meeting*, pp. 77-80, 1982.

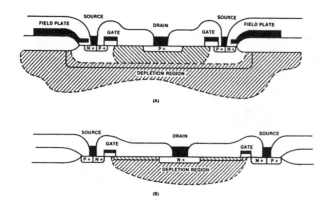

Figure 1. (a) High voltage p-channel structure;
(b) High voltage n-channel structure.

wafers are oxidized. An Si_3N_4 film is deposited and patterned, followed by patterning and implanting with boron for the channel stop areas. A thick oxide is grown selectively in the field area. Then the Si_3N_4 film and the initial oxide underneath is removed and the gate oxide of 1000 Å thick is grown. The threshold voltage of the n-channel transistors is adjusted by patterning and implanting boron in the gate areas. The polysilicon film is deposited, doped, patterned and etched. The p-type offset channel is formed by implanting boron followed by patterning and implanting phosphorus for the n-type offset channel. The heavily doped P^+-source and drain areas are formed by implanting BF_2 into photoresist patterned wafers. Then the thin oxide film is grown to protect implanted areas and the new photoresist pattern is printed and etched for the N^+ source and drain. The N^+ areas are formed either by As-implant or by outdiffusion from the phosphorus rich CVD SiO_2 film which is deposited and reflowed at high temperature. Contacts are etched and the interconnections are formed by patterning an Al film. The protective phosphorus-doped SiO_2 film is deposited and pad areas are defined.

EXPERIMENTAL RESULTS

In this series of the experiments for the development of the integrated high- and low-voltage CMOS transistors the shallow well concept was verified. Although the reported results are satisfactory for the purpose for which they have been developed, it is expected that higher breakdown voltages can be achieved by further optimizing the process parameters.

The typical drain characteristics of the high-voltage n-channel transistors are shown in Figure 2. The drain breakdown voltage at zero biased gate is in excess of 400V, exhibiting almost linear dependence on the offset channel length. The drain leakage current is less than 1 nA. The typical characteristics of the p-channel transistors are shown in Figure 3, when the drain is connected to the substrate and the source is connected to the field plate. The drain breakdown voltage is over 225V, and the

drain leakage current is less than 1 nA at zero gate bias voltage. The well-to-substrate breakdown voltage is in excess of 400V for the 30-micron wide field plate. Both high-voltage transistors are stable at high temperature. Punch-through between source and drain is not observed for channel gate lengths as small as 8 microns.

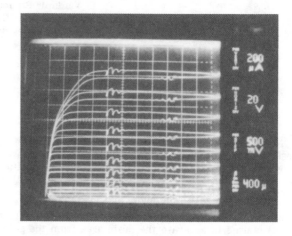

Figure 2. Typical drain characteristics of high-voltage p-channel device with the offset channel 40 microns long.

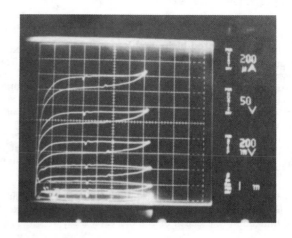

Figure 3. Typical drain characteristics of high-voltage n-channel device with the offset channel 70 microns long.

The low-voltage p- and n-channel transistors as well as the high-voltage transistors have a threshold voltage of -2.5V and +1V respectively. The typical drain characteristics of low-voltage p- and n-channel transistors of 50 x 50 microns are shown in Figures 4 and 5. The non-symmetrical values of the threshold voltage for the p- and n-channel transistors are dictated by the specific circuit requirements. The drain breakdown voltage at zero gate-to-source voltage exceeds 25V for both types of transistors. The short channel effects such as source to drain punch-through and the threshold voltage changes are depicted in Figures 6 and 7. The threshold voltage changes are small for the p-channel transistors with channel length as small as 2 microns. However, the n-channel transistors have more pronounced changes of the device parameters at much longer channels due to the high resistivity substrate. The short channel effect is significantly reduced in the experiments with the "twin tub" process (curve 3), when the second p-type tub is diffused in the area of the n-channel transistors and the impurity concentration is higher than in the substrate.

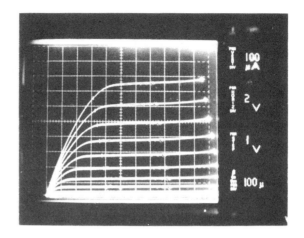

Figure 5. Typical drain characteristics of low-voltage n-channel device.

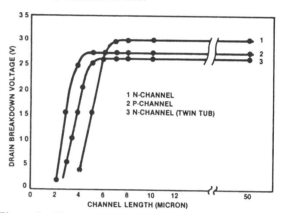

Figure 6. The source to drain breakdown voltage vs. channel length.

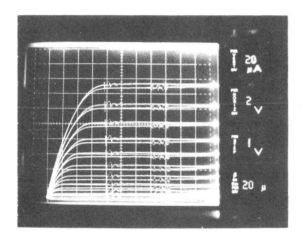

Figure 4. Typical drain characteristics of low-voltage p-channel device.

Although the SCR-type of trigger (latch-up) between different circuit components has not been completely eliminated, the regenerative effect was noticeably suppressed by shorting the sources of the devices to the silicon underneath and the SCR-type of latch-up was not observed, in the operating current range.

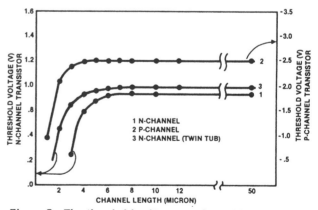

Figure 7. The threshold voltage vs. channel length.

CONCLUSION

A new concept of the integrated high- and low-voltage CMOS transistors has been developed and verified. High-voltage transistors of a circular geometry are built in a high resistivity substrate together with low-voltage transistors. The blocking capabilities of the high-voltage transistors are in excess of 250V and show stable operation at high temperature.

ACKNOWLEDGEMENTS

The authors are grateful to all of the people at Xerox Microelectronics Center, who contributed to this project and special thanks to Joan Hack for her wafer processing effort.

REFERENCES

1. T. Suzuki, T. Kuniyama and H. Sakuma, "A high voltage - high frequency SOS/CMOS pulse generator," IEDM Technical Digest, p. 264, 1980.

2. J.D. Plummer and T.D. Meindl, "A monilitic 200-V CMOS analog switch," IEEE J. Solid-State Circuits, Vol. 11, No. 6, pp. 809-817, Dec. 1976.

3. E. Habebotte, B. Hoefflinger, W. Renker, G. Zimmer, "A Coplanar CMOS Power Switch," IEEE J. Solid-State Circuits, Vol. SC-16, No. 3, pp. 212-225.

THE EFFECTS OF SIPOS PASSIVATION ON DC AND SWITCHING PERFORMANCE OF HIGH VOLTAGE MOS TRANSISTORS

S.Mukherjee, C.J.Chou, K.Shaw, D.McArthur and V.Rumennik
Philips Laboratories,
North American Philips Corporation,
345 Scarborough Road,
Briarcliff Manor, N.Y. 10510.

ABSTRACT

For long term stability of high voltage NMOS transistors the application of a SIPOS passivation layer over the drift regions has been studied. This has been found to change the device characteristics both for steady state and switching. This paper describes the mechanism of interaction of the SIPOS layer and the drift region of the device and presents 2-dimensional simulation results together with experimental data. An analytical 1-dimensional model is outlined and shown to agree well with the 2-dimensional simulation results.

1. INTRODUCTION

In power integrated circuits, employing lateral high voltage devices, passivation of the drift regions is an important consideration both in terms of device performance and long term stability. The application of semi-insulating polycrystalline silicon (SIPOS) as a passivation layer in integrated circuits has been extensively studied [1,2] primarily because of shielding properties against external electric fields. Additionally, under proper growth conditions SIPOS layers have been found to be resilient to mobile ionic contamination.

Therefore, SIPOS passivation of high voltage devices has been of interest for some time. The electrical properties of SIPOS has been extensively studied and several conductivity models have been proposed [3,4]. To date, all published work on SIPOS passivated devices have dealt with the effects of SIPOS on the D.C. and long term reliability characteristics of the passivated devices. This has been considered adequate in applications where the passivation does not play any active role in the current conducting paths of the active devices. As a result of this, little attention has been focussed in the literature to correlate device performance (transient and steady state) and the properties of the SIPOS layer.

The objective of this work is to develop a comprehensive understanding of the mechanism of interaction produced by SIPOS field plate on the DC and switching characteristics of high voltage NMOS devices.

2. DEVICE STRUCTURE

A cross-section schematic of a high voltage NMOS transistor with and without SIPOS field plate are shown in Figure-1(b) and (a) respectively. In the passivated device the SIPOS layer is provided on top of the drift region with an interface oxide layer to electrically isolate the field plate from the drift region. The SIPOS layer is connected on the two ends to the gate and drain electrodes to provide an uniform potential drop.

3. INTERACTION OF SIPOS FIELD PLATE AND UNDERLYING DRIFT REGION

According to [4], SIPOS closely represents single crystal silicon islands with trap centers in the band gap, and surrounded by oxide layer. The conduction proceeds by electron tunneling through the oxide barriers. In the present application, for simplicity and qualitative understanding, SIPOS is treated as silicon with overall low carrier mobility. This suffices as long as the SIPOS layer operates in the accumulation mode, which is the case for the n-doped SIPOS field plate in high voltage NMOS transistors.

Figure-2(a) shows a section of the drift region of high voltage NMOS transistor with the interface oxide and SIPOS field plate. This structure can be considered as a combination of the structures shown in Figure-2(b) and (c). In Figure-2(b), the potential and charge distribution in the silicon (drift region) is determined by the voltage applied to the metal gate. Similarly, the potential in the SIPOS layer in Figure-2(c) is determined by the applied potential on the metal gate. However, when the SIPOS field plate and the silicon drift region are combined (Figure-2(a)), the two layers interact. Depending on the coupling between the drift region and the SIPOS layer (a function of the interface oxide thickness) and the conductivity of the SIPOS the potential distribution in the SIPOS is altered to follow that of the drift region. Assuming SIPOS to behave similarly to silicon, the equilibrium charge distribution in the two layers is such that the electric field in the silicon is minimum and charge neutrality is maintained throughout.

Reprinted from *IEEE 1986 Int. Electron Devices Meeting*, pp. 646–649, 1986.

4. STEADY STATE CHARACTERISTICS

Referring to Figure-1(a), it is well known that the operation of this device is that of an n-channel MOS transistor with an extended drain. The entire drift region is depleted for the maximum applied voltage so that the surface field is minimized and the breakdown voltage is as close as possible to that of a planar junction.

With a SIPOS field plate on the drift region (Figure-1(b)), the depletion condition is altered. For a given drain voltage, with the device in the OFF state, a potential distribution is attained on the surface of the drift region, and the SIPOS layer. Figure-3(b) shows that the potential on the surface of the drift region is more positive than that in the SIPOS layer. This causes an accumulation of electrons in the n-doped SIPOS layer at the interface. This accumulation layer in the SIPOS causes the formation of a depletion layer at the drift region surface for charge neutrality. The expected equilibrium charge distribution in the high voltage NMOS device, with SIPOS field plate is shown in Figure-3(a).

Clearly Figure-3(a) shows that the charge equilibrium condition is altered in comparison with standard silicon dioxide passivated device. The charge in the SIPOS helps to deplete the drift region from the surface thereby enhancing the depletion process. Therefore, a larger amount of drift region charge can be provided without degrading the breakdown voltage. In other words with the SIPOS field plate, a lower ON resistance can be achieved without reducing the breakdown voltage.

D.C. on resistance as a function of breakdown voltage measured on high voltage N-channel MOS devices with and without SIPOS passivation are shown in Figure-4. As pointed out above, this plot illustrates that, the SIPOS field plate enables one to obtain a lower on resistance for the same breakdown voltage as compared to silicon dioxide passivated devices.

In the ON state the gate voltage is high and this reverses the potential difference between the SIPOS field plate and the drift region. Here, the potential in the SIPOS field plate is more positive than that in the drift region surface. This causes an accumulation layer to form on the drift region surface, causing an additional reduction in the ON resistance, compared to conventional device.

5. TRANSIENT SWITCHING CHARACTERISTICS

As pointed out above, the SIPOS field plate produces a surface depletion layer in the drift region in the OFF state in equilibrium (D.C. Case). Now let us consider the case when the device (shown in Figure-1) is connected with a load resistor on the drain to a high voltage, and is turned ON by applying a high voltage on the gate, instantaneously. As soon as the device is turned on, electrons injected from the source cause a drain current, which in turn causes the drain potential to drop. This in turn collapses the depletion region between the drift region and the p-substrate. However, the charge accumulated in the SIPOS, creating the surface depletion region, cannot respond instantaneously because of its low conductivity. Initially, the surface resides in deep depletion condition corresponding to the initial potential difference between the drift region and the SIPOS field plate. This manifests as high ON resistance initially compared to steady state (D.C.). A typical transient response is shown in Figure-5. Note here that, the response can be associated with two parameters, causing it to differ from ideal square wave response. These parameters are denoted as Delta-R (the effective on resistance increase at turn on compared to D.C. case) and Td (the time taken to reach the steady state ON resistance value).

From the physical picture of the switching process described above, it follows that the two perturbation parameters of the transient response shown in Figure-5, are related to physical parameters as follows. The Delta-R is a function of the amount of charge accumulated in SIPOS, causing deep depletion at turn on. This in turn is determined by :

(1) The type and amount of doping of the SIPOS layer.

(2) The potential barrier between the drift region and the channel region.

(3) The total doping of the drift region.

(4) Thickness of the SIPOS layer.

(5) Interface dielectric thickness.

Similarly, the other parameter, Td is determined by:

(1) The conductivity of the SIPOS layer determining the RC time constant of the discharge process.

(2) Minority carrier lifetime in the drift region.

(3) Photogeneration of carriers, when the device is exposed to light during switching.

(4) Tunneling current across the interface dielectric, for thin interface dielectrics.

(5) Interface dielectric thickness.

To minimize the switching delay, one can vary the physical parameters to minimize either or both Delta-R and Td.

As explained earlier, the deep depletion condition in the drift region should be sensitive to the minority carrier generation caused by photon radiation and the transient switching response is expected to depend on ambient light during switching. Figure-5 shows the drain voltage waveform for different intensities of light on the device. Clearly, with increasing light intensity the delay time decreases without altering Delta-R. This is because Delta-R is a function of the drift region surface depletion layer thickness in the OFF state, which is determined by the amount of charge stored in the SIPOS field plate. This charge is not expected to change significantly with light intensity. The time delay changes because at turn on, the surface of the drift region resides in the deep depletion condition, and the delay time is determined by the rate at which this deep depletion collapses either because of photogenerated carriers or the discharge of the SIPOS charge. The SIPOS discharge time is long because of the low conductivity and consequently high RC time constant of the SIPOS layer. Therefore, the Td results shown in Figure-5, are dominated by photogeneration of carriers in the deep depletion region. As expected, devices without SIPOS field plate do not show any light dependence.

As pointed out earlier, the interface oxide thickness also influences the transient response. Measured Delta-R variation with interface oxide thickness is shown in Figure-6. The thicker the interface oxide, the smaller the value of Delta-R. This is indeed the case for interface oxide thicker than 500 angstroms. However, for thinner interface oxide (125 angstrom) Delta-R is seen to decrease. This is caused by the increased coupling between the drift region and the SIPOS layer forcing the potential distribution in the two regions to closely match each other, thereby reducing the depletion layer thickness in the drift region in the OFF state.

6. MODELING AND SIMULATION RESULTS

To gain a complete understanding of the effects of SIPOS field plate on the characteristics of high voltage NMOS devices, 2-dimensional modeling and simulations have been carried out using HECTOR.

The OFF state electron concentration distribution of a SIPOS (n-doped) field plated high voltage NMOS transistor drift region is shown in Figure-7(b), in a three dimensional plot. It is clear from this plot that, for the applied drain bias (80 volts), the drift region is depleted both from the surface as well as the p-substrate and p-channel regions. Figure-7(a) shows the same result for a device without SIPOS field plate. Here, because of the absence of field plate, the depletion layer appears at the drift to p-substrate junction and drift to channel diffusion junction, as expected.

An analytical one-dimensional model has been developed to determine the depletion layer width in the drift region for SIPOS passivated high voltage NMOS transistors in the OFF state. Some simplifying assumptions have been made without sacrificing accuracy. These assumptions include defining the device in terms of rectangular boundaries, and decoupling the electric fields in the lateral and vertical directions of the device. This reduces the problem to the solution of the one-dimensional Poisson equation in the vertical and lateral direction of the device separately. The depletion layer depth in the drift region calculated using the analytic model is shown in Figure-8 together with that calculated

using two-dimensional simulation. The small discrepancy is caused by the 1-D approximation of the electric field.

7. CONCLUSION

The mechanism of operation of SIPOS passivated high voltage NMOS transistors has been described both for steady state (ON and OFF condition) and transient switching. The device parameters influencing the switching delay and increased ON resistance have been discussed. Two-dimensional numerical and one dimensional analytic modeling results have been presented and shown to be in agreement.

ACKNOWLEDGMENTS

We wish to acknowledge the support and technical discussions with B.Singer and the clean room staff for processing silicon.

REFERENCES:

(1) T.Matsushita, et al., Jpn. J.Appl. Phys. Suppl. Vol.15, 1976, pp.35.

(2) Hidenobu Mochizuki,et al., Jpn. J. Appl. Phys. Suppl.Vol.15,1976 pp.41.

(3) M.L.Tarng, J. Appl. Phys. 49,4069,1978.

(4) J.Ni, and E.Arnold, Appl. Phys. Lett. 7, 554, 1981.

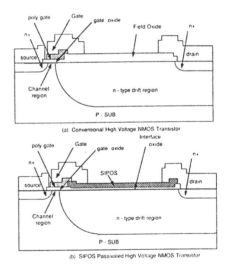

(a) Conventional High Voltage NMOS Transistor

(b) SIPOS Passivated High Voltage NMOS Transistor

Figure-1. Cross-sectional schematic of high voltage NMOS transistor.

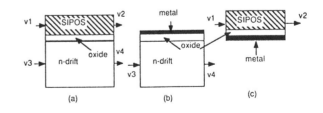

(a)   (b)   (c)

Figure-2. Section of drift region with SIPOS.

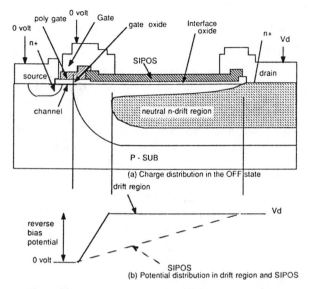

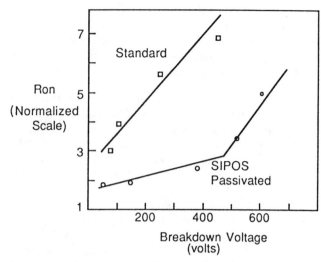

Figure-3. Potential and charge distribution in the device.

Figure-4. Breakdown voltage vs Ron for Standard and SIPOS passivated NMOS transistor.

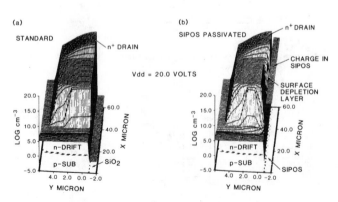

Figure-5. Switching characteristics of SIPOS passivated NMOS transistor.

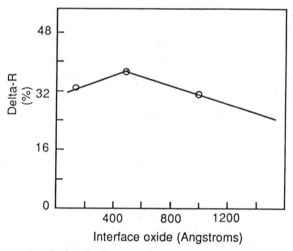

Figure-6. Delta-R during switching vs interface oxide thickness.

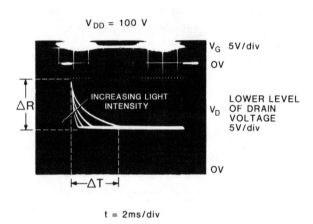

Figure-7. Two dimensional simulation of electron concentration in the OFF state.

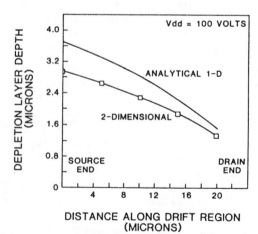

Figure-8. Computed surface depletion layer depth along drift region.

Avalanche Breakdown in High-Voltage D-MOS Devices

MICHEL J. DECLERCQ AND JAMES D. PLUMMER

Abstract—A new type of voltage breakdown occurring in high-voltage D-MOS transistors is described. This effect severely reduces the high-voltage capability of these devices when the gate field plate is extended through the drift region toward overlapping the n$^+$ drain contact region. The breakdown is shown to be due to an avalanche phenomenon appearing close to the n$^+$ region, due to the very high field induced in this MOS structure in nonequilibrium. A first-order theory is developed to confirm the conclusions of the experimental study.

INTRODUCTION

SINCE their first presentation of a few years ago [1], D-MOS transistors have been used in several types of applications, most particularly as microwave devices [2], [3], high-voltage switches [4], and in high-speed logic [5].

One interesting feature of the device is its ability to achieve high-voltage operation and short channel lengths at the same time. This behavior has been attributed to the graded channel and to the field plate covering the weakly doped drift region [3], [6].

In a study of the optimal structure of the device for high-voltage performance, it has been observed that the breakdown voltage is severely reduced when the field plate is extended toward the n$^+$ drain contact region. Explanation of this behavior is the purpose of this paper.

EXPERIMENTAL EVIDENCE OF THE PHENOMENON

The basic structure of the D-MOS device to be considered in this paper is shown in Fig. 1. These high-voltage devices were fabricated in the Stanford Integrated Circuits Laboratory in n$^-$ epitaxial material. Their principal parameters are:

n$^-$ epitaxy	25 μm, 5 $\Omega \cdot$cm
channel length	$L = 3$ μm
drift region length	$L' = 25$ μm
source junction depth	2 μm
gate oxide thickness	0.3 μm
field oxide thickness	1.3 μm
channel threshold voltage	5 V $\pm$ 1 V.

A more complete description of these devices and the reasons for the above parameters may be found in [7].

Manuscript received June 13, 1974; revised August 8, 1975.
M. J. Declercq was with Stanford University, Stanford, CA 94305. He is now with the Laboratoire de Microélectronique, Université Catholique de Louvain, Bâtiment Maxwell, B-1348 Louvain-La-Neuve, Belgium.
J. D. Plummer is with Stanford Electronics Laboratories, Stanford University, Stanford, CA 94305.

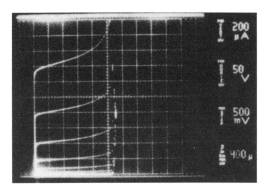

Fig. 1. Cross section of D-MOS transistors fabricated in n$^-$ epitaxial material at Stanford.

Fig. 2. Typical breakdown characteristic of device with field plate (gate metal) kept 10 μm away from n$^+$ drain contact region, as in Fig. 1.

When the edge of the field plate (gate metal) covering the n$^-$ drift region over the 1.3 μm oxide is kept at 10 μm or more away from the n$^+$ diffused drain region, the drain-to-source breakdown voltage with shorted gate BV$_{\text{DSS}}$ reaches a value of 270 V. This breakdown voltage is associated with the double diffused region of the device and can be due to a) avalanching of the p-n$^-$ source to drain diode, or b) punchthrough of the p-n$^-$ depletion layer through the p-channel diffusion to the n$^+$ source contact. For the particular devices considered in this study, the characteristics show a typical punchthrough behavior b) where the breakdown voltage is reduced with increasing gate voltages (Fig. 2).

When the gate metal of the same device is extended until it overlaps the n$^+$ drain region, the breakdown voltage falls to about 150 V with the curves presenting a sharp knee at the breakdown point (Fig. 3(a)). The difference between these new characteristics and the previous breakdown shown in Fig. 2 is illustrated more clearly in Fig. 3(b), which shows a 10$\times$ magnification of the breakdown knee for various gate voltages.

Increasing the gate voltage over a wide range yields a similar increase in the breakdown voltage, according to the equation

$$\text{BV}_{\text{DS}} = \text{BV}_{\text{DSS}} + mV_G \qquad (1)$$

with $m \simeq 1$. This behavior is typical of an avalanche

Reprinted from *IEEE Trans. Electron Devices*, vol. ED-23, pp. 1–4, Jan. 1976.

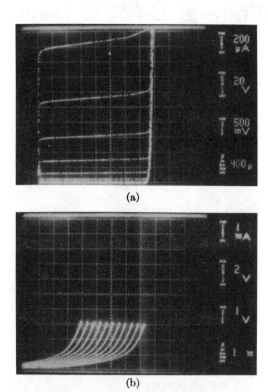

(a)

(b)

Fig. 3. Typical breakdown characteristic of device with gate field plate overlapping n^+ drain contact region. (a) Complete I_D–V_{DS} characteristic. (b) Magnification around BV_{DSS}.

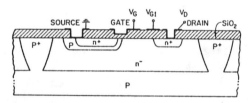

Fig. 4. Cross section of D-MOS device with separate field plate over n^+ drain region.

phenomenon and is similar to the breakdown characteristic previously observed in p-n junctions covered by a field plate [8].

In the case of these D-MOS devices, however, the range of the gate voltage is such that covering the p-n^- junction by the gate metal plate does not lower the surface breakdown of the junction, but helps to increase it by reducing the surface electric field in this region. Since the breakdown voltage is severely reduced only when the field plate is extended toward the n^+ drain contact region, it can be assumed that the origin of the breakdown is localized in this n^--n^+ graded region.

In order to verify this assumption, a modified structure has been built where the gate electrode has been kept away from the n^+ region, but a separate field plate covers the n^--n^+ transition region (Fig. 4). Modifying the voltage V_{G1} of this new field plate while keeping V_G constant yields exactly the same low breakdown characteristics as shown in Fig. 3(a) and (b) and as given by (1), but the breakdown is controlled this time by V_{G1} instead of V_G.

This effect can be explained by an avalanche phenomenon occurring in the surface of the semiconductor near the n^+ drain contact region, due to the high field induced in this region by the field plate.

Since this MOS capacitor is in nonequilibrium due to the proximity of the p-n junction [9], the carriers generated by avalanche cannot be absorbed by creating a stable surface inversion layer. These carriers are, therefore, injected toward source and drain and give rise to the abrupt breakdown observed.

Connecting the field plate to the drain n^+ diffusion removes the high electric field in this region and yields the same high breakdown characteristic of about 270 V that was observed on devices with a short field plate (Fig. 2).

FIRST-ORDER THEORY

In order to develop a first-order theory of the MOS avalanche breakdown in D-MOS transistors, it will be assumed that the nonequilibrium conditions existing in the depletion region of the reverse-biased p-n junction still hold at the end of the n^- drift region, close to the n^+ drain contact. This first-order approximation is justified by the fact that the length of the drift region is 25 μm, which is much smaller than the expected value of the diffusion length, which is related to the variation of the quasi-Fermi levels.

Assuming this condition, the surface under the field plate will be strongly depleted for large values of V_D, but will never reach inversion for $V_{G1} \geq 0$. Let us first assume the classical case of an MOS structure with a constant substrate doping N_D and a one-dimensional field. Calling:

ϕ_s — voltage drop between the silicon surface and the bulk,

V_o — voltage drop across the oxide in the absence of interface charges,

$V_{G'} = \phi_s + V_o$ total voltage in the absence of interface charges and contact potentials,

E_s — electric field in the silicon at the Si/SiO_2 interface,

E_o — electric field in the oxide,

ϵ_{ox} — permittivity of the oxide,

ϵ_s — permittivity of the silicon,

q — elementary charge of an electron,

x_o — oxide thickness,

x_d — depletion layer width,

$C_0 = \epsilon_{ox}/x_0$ — oxide capacitance per unit area,

we obtain by 2 successive integrations of Poisson's equation

$$|E_s| = \frac{qN_Dx_d}{\epsilon_s} \qquad (2)$$

$$|\phi_s| = \frac{qN_Dx_d^2}{2\epsilon_s}. \qquad (3)$$

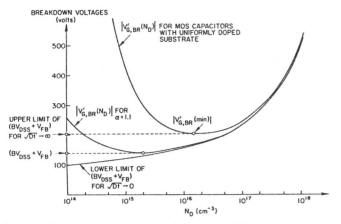

Fig. 5. Avalanche breakdown voltages of MOS structures in non-equilibrium conditions. Values are given for oxide thickness $x_o = 1.3$ μm.

Using the continuity condition on the electric field at the interface, the voltage drop across the oxide can be written, using (2), as

$$| V_o | = | E_o | x_o = \frac{q N_D x_d x_o}{\epsilon_{ox}}. \tag{4}$$

Noting that $V_G' = \phi_s + V_o$ and then eliminating x_d from (3) and (4), using (2) we obtain

$$| E_s | = q N_D \left\{ \left[\left(\frac{1}{C_o} \right)^2 + \frac{2 | V_G' |}{\epsilon_s q N_D} \right]^{1/2} - \frac{1}{C_o} \right\}. \tag{5}$$

The avalanche breakdown voltage $V_{G,BR}'$ can be deduced from (5) in which E_s is replaced by the value of the critical field $E_{s,cr}(N_D)$ at which avalanche occurs:

$$| V_{G,BR}' | = \epsilon_s E_{s,cr}(N_D) \left[\frac{E_{s,cr}(N_D)}{2 q N_D} + \frac{1}{C_o} \right]. \tag{6}$$

Taking for $E_{s,cr}(N_D)$ the values published by Sze for avalanche in p-n junctions [10] and confirmed by Goetzberger for avalanche in MOS capacitors [11], this breakdown voltage has been calculated as a function of the doping N_D. The result is plotted in Fig. 5 for $x_o = 1.3$ μm and is the upper curve in the figure. It appears from this figure that the lowest breakdown voltage is $V_{G,BR}' = 207$ V, and occurs for $N_D \simeq 1.5 \times 10^{16}$ cm^{-3}.

This one-dimensional theory does not apply exactly to the D-MOS breakdown being considered here because the n$^+$ drain contact diffusion causes an impurity gradient (n$^-$ to n$^+$) to exist in the substrate rather than the uniformly doped substrate assumed in the above analysis. We can, however, consider the limiting case in which the diffusion length $(Dt)^{1/2}$ of the n$^+$ diffusion is assumed to be so large that the curvature of the electric field due to the impurity gradient along the Y direction can be neglected. In this case, the electric field lines remain vertical, and the structure may be modeled simply as a number of MOS capacitors in parallel, each having a uniformly doped substrate and with the range of substrate dopings spanning between n$^-$ and n$^+$.

V_G' can be related to the D-MOS drain voltage V_D in this case by the expression

$$V_D = | V_G' | + V_{G1} - V_{FB} \tag{7}$$

with

V_{G1} voltage applied on the D-MOS field-plate,
V_{FB} flat-band voltage in the field-plate region.

The BV$_{DSS}$ value of a D-MOS device in which the gate metal is extended to the drain contact and in which the n$^+$ diffusion $(DT)^{1/2} \to \infty$ is, therefore, given by replacing V_G' in (7) by the minimum value reached by the $V_{G,BR}'$ curve in Fig. 5:

$$\text{BV}_{DSS} = | V_{G,BR}' (\text{min}) | - V_{FB}. \tag{8}$$

The opposite limiting case is reached in the D-MOS when the profile of the drain diffusion can be considered as a step function. Under this condition, the breakdown voltage is given by

$$\text{BV}_{DSS} + V_{FB} = E_{s,cr}(N_D) \frac{x_o \epsilon_s}{\epsilon_{ox}} \tag{9}$$

with N_D the doping density of the n$^-$ drift region. A plot of this function is shown as the lowest curve in Fig. 5. This curve represents the lower limit of the avalanche breakdown voltage of the D-MOS.

In the real case where the $(Dt)^{1/2}$ factor of the n$^+$ diffusion has an intermediate value, an exact solution of the breakdown voltage would involve a two-dimensional solution of Poisson's equation in the graded surface MOS capacitor. A simple approximation can, however, be used to take into account the curvature of the electric field from the surface toward the heavier doped n$^+$ region.

Due to this curvature, an electric field line starting from a doping density $N_D(y)$ in the interface region will extend into the bulk through higher doped zones toward the limit of the depletion region. This effect can simply be taken into account for the computation of the surface field $E_s(y)$ by assuming that the electric field lines extend vertically through a space charge region having a mean doping density of $N_D(y) \cdot 10^\alpha$, with $\alpha > 0$. The breakdown voltage $V_{G,BR}'$ will be reached when the resulting surface field $E_s(y)$ reaches the value of $E_{s,cr}[N_D(y)]$, corresponding to the true surface doping density $N_D(y)$ at this point. Under these assumptions, the one-dimensional theory can be immediately applied, with (5) and (6) becoming

$$| E_s | = q N_D 10^\alpha \left\{ \left[\left(\frac{1}{C_o} \right)^2 + \frac{2 | V_G' |}{\epsilon_s q N_D 10^\alpha} \right]^{1/2} - \frac{1}{C_o} \right\} \tag{10}$$

$$| V_{G,BR}' | = \text{BV}_{DSS} + V_{FB} = \epsilon_s E_{s,cr}(N_D)$$
$$\cdot \left[\frac{E_{s,cr}(N_D)}{2 q N_D 10^\alpha} + \frac{1}{C_o} \right]. \tag{11}$$

It is immediately verified that (11) tends toward its upper or lower limits, respectively, (6) and (9), for the extreme values of α. This coefficient α is essentially a function of the parameters of the n^+ diffusion. Its experimental value for the transistors studied in this paper is $\alpha = 1.1$, which is derived from the observed breakdown voltage $BV_{DSS} = 150$ V.

Keeping the gate field plate away from the n^+ region makes α tend quickly toward zero, in which case the avalanche breakdown voltage is given by the point corresponding to the n^- substrate doping on the upper curve of Fig. 5. This value is generally much larger than the other breakdown limits of the transistor.

It should be noted that the only breakdown phenomenon described in Fig. 5 is that associated with the n^--n^+ drain region of the device. For n^- doping levels of greater than $\approx 10^{16}$, the overall transistor breakdown BV_{DSS} will be limited not by this n^--n^+ breakdown phenomenon but rather by avalanching of the p-n^- source to drain junction.

CONCLUSION

It has been shown that besides channel punchthrough and avalanching of the drain-substrate or drain-source junctions, a third breakdown phenomenon can appear in some MOS devices. This new breakdown, which is typical for D-MOS transistors fabricated in n^- material, is due to the avalanche appearing under the gate field plate at the end of the drift region. The phenomenon severely limits the high-voltage behavior of the devices when the field plate is extended toward overlapping the n^+ drain contact region.

This breakdown limitation can be avoided either by keeping the edge of the gate field-plate a few microns away from the n^+ drain region or by covering this region by a separate field-plate electrically connected to the drain.

It is also obvious from these conclusions that high-voltage D-MOS devices are not compatible with a self-alignment process where the gate field plate is used for the delineation of the n^+ drain contact region.

REFERENCES

[1] Y. Tarui, Y. Hayashi, and T. Sekigawa, "Diffusion self-aligned MOST: A new approach for high-speed devices," *Proc. 1st Conf. Solid State Devices*, pp. 105–110, 1969.
[2] T. P. Cauge, J. Kocsis, H. J. Sigg, and G. D. Vendelin, "Double-diffused MOS transistor achieves microwave gain," *Electronics*, pp. 99–104, Feb. 15, 1971.
[3] H. J. Sigg, G. D. Vendelin, T. P. Cauge, and J. Kocsis, "D-MOS transistor for microwave applications," *IEEE Trans. Electron Devices*, vol. ED-19, pp. 45–53, Jan. 1972.
[4] J. D. Plummer, J. D. Meindl, and M. G. Maginness, "An ultrasonic imaging system for real-time cardiac imaging," *Int. Solid State Circuits Conf.*, pp. 162–163, Feb. 1974.
[5] Y. Tarui, Y. Hayashi, and T. Sekigawa, "Diffusion self-aligned enhance-depletion MOS-IC," *Proc. 2nd Conf. Solid State Devices*, pp. 193–198, 1970.
[6] G. A. McLintock, R. E. Thomas, and R. S. Cobbold, "Modeling of double-diffused MOS transistors with self-aligned gates," *Int. Electron Devices Meeting*, Dec. 1972.
[7] M. D. Pocha, A. G. Gonzalez, and R. W. Dutton, "Threshold voltage controllability in double-diffused-MOS transistors," *IEEE Trans. Electron Devices*, vol. ED-21, pp. 778–784, Dec. 1974.
[8] A. S. Grove, O. Leistiko, and W. W. Hooper, "Effect of surface fields on the breakdown voltage of planar silicon P-N junctions," *IEEE Trans. Electron Devices*, vol. ED-14, p. 157, Mar. 1967.
[9] A. S. Grove and D. J. Fitzgerald, "Surface effects on P-N junctions-characteristics of surface space-charge regions under nonequilibrium conditions," *Solid State Electron.*, vol. 9, p. 783, 1966.
[10] S. M. Sze, *Physics of Semiconductor Devices*. New York: Wiley, 1969.
[11] A. Goetzberger and E. H. Nicollian, "Transient voltage breakdown due to avalanche in MIS capacitors," *Applied Phys. Lett.*, vol. 9, p. 444, 1966.

An Accurate DC Model for High-Voltage Lateral DMOS Transistors Suited for CACD

H. RENE CLAESSEN AND PIET VAN DER ZEE

Abstract—Double-diffused lateral MOS transistors with a drain–source breakdown voltage larger than 280 V have been integrated in an epitaxial junction isolated IC process. For these devices a four-component dc model suited for computer-aided circuit design (CACD) is developed based upon 2-D device simulation. The nonhomogeneously doped backgate is well described by two cascoded MOS transistors with different threshold voltages and gain factors. In the drift region the nonlinear dependence of the electron drift velocity on the applied electrical field is taken into account, and modulation of the on-resistance caused by a varying substrate voltage is incorporated properly. In order to model the characteristics in the entire range of operation, 10 parameters have to be optimized. The method for the parameter extraction is discussed, and a comparison between measured *I–V* characteristics and calculated values according to the model is given.

I. INTRODUCTION

INTEGRATED CIRCUITS using the DMOST structure have successfully been designed and processed in a new high-voltage IC process. An 8-MHz video amplifier has been integrated and is in preparation for production [1]. The DMOST structure that has been used is shown in Fig. 1. Source–substrate potentials up to 280 V are allowed for this structure.

This paper presents 2-D device simulation results and an accurate compact dc model suitable for CACD for the lateral DMOST.

Previous investigations on high-voltage lateral DMOST's have mostly dealt with the modeling of the on-resistance as described by Sun and Plummer [2] and Colak [3]. Unlike the model of Pocha and Dutton [4], the presented model takes into account the effect of nonhomogeneous doping concentration of the backgate and modulation of the drift region resistance as a function of drain–source and drain–substrate voltage. As a consequence the dependence of the drain current on the gate–source, the drain–source, and the source–substrate voltage is accurately modeled in the entire range of operation.

Owing to the fact that in each specific mode of operation the electric behavior is described by a limited number of model parameters, optimization of these parameters is straightforward and unambiguous.

In Section II, the basic operation of the device and some important 2-D simulation results are discussed. Section III describes the derivation of the model equations, and

Manuscript received April 4, 1986; revised July 20, 1986.
The authors are with Philips Research Laboratories Eindhoven, Eindhoven, The Netherlands.
IEEE Log Number 8610703.

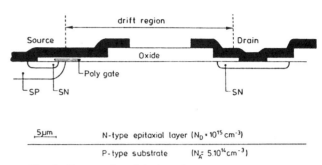

Fig. 1. Cross section of the investigated DMOST structure.

Section IV presents the incorporation of the current saturation in the drift region into the formulas. In Section V, the aspect of parameter determination will be elucidated, and finally in Section VI a model simulation of the complete *I–V* characteristics is compared with experimental data.

II. DEVICE SATURATION AND 2-D SIMULATION

In the cross-sectional view (Fig. 1) we can distinguish an n^+ source (SN), a p-backgate (SP), a polysilicon gate located on thin oxide, an extension of the aluminum source contact known as field plate, and an n^- epilayer with n^+ drain contact (SN). The active gate-controlled transistor region is formed by the difference in lateral diffusion of the p-backgate and the n^+ source. The function of the drift region is to accomplish a high source-to-drain breakdown voltage. By choosing a lightly doped epitaxial material combined with a field plate, the potential difference between drain and source is divided gradually over the epilayer. This means that punchthrough, gate corner breakdown, and avalanche multiplication will occur only at large biasing conditions. It is evident that a tradeoff between a high drain–source breakdown voltage and a low drift region series resistance must lead to optimum device performance. Some relevant process and geometry data of the examined structure are listed in Table I.

The DMOST is an n-channel MOSFET. This implies that under normal operation the drain will be at positive potential with respect to the source. When we apply a gate bias, an electron inversion channel arises in the p-backgate above a certain positive gate–source voltage. Under normal operation this will lead to the injection of electrons originating from the n^+ source into the epilayer. The injected electrons will drift towards the positively biased

Reprinted from *IEEE Trans. Electron Devices*, vol. ED-33, pp. 1964–1970, Dec. 1976.

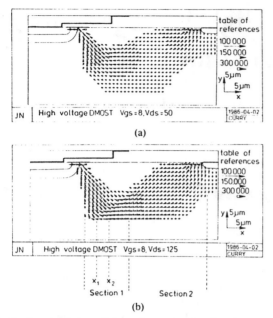

Fig. 2. Device simulation of the epilayer showing the electron current. The arrows indicate direction and magnitude of the electric current density. Three intervals to specify the current density in a certain region are used. As indicated the arrows distinguish current densities between 100 and 150 A/cm², between 150 and 300 A/cm², and above 300 A/cm². In both situations (for V_{ds} = 50 V and V_{ds} = 125 V), the substrate was connected to the source.

TABLE I

gate oxide thickness	1000 Å
length of field plate on 1 μm oxide (covering the drift region)	9.5 μm
length of field plate on 3 μm oxide	5.0 μm
oxide thickness under field plate	1.0 μm and 3.0 μm
epilayer thickness (D)	17 μm
width of the structure (W)	250 μm
total gate length	6.0 μm
— source overlap	1.0 μm
— drift region overlap	3.5 μm
— effective channel length	1.5 μm
distance between p backgate and n⁺ drain implantation	32 μm

drain through the resistive drift region, and the drain-source current is controlled by the applied gate bias.

Device simulation results produced with the 2-D device simulator CURRY [5] clearly show the current flow in the drift region for two different drain–source voltages; see Fig. 2. From these results we can conclude that due to the depletion region caused by the potential difference between field plate and epilayer, the electron current is pushed downwards into the epitaxial material. The depletion region in the epilayer caused by the reverse biased epi-substrate junction limits the effective cross section through which the electrons can flow. This effect is particularly clear for high drain–source voltages. When we consider Fig. 2(b) (device simulation for V_{ds} = 125 V),

it can be seen that the effective cross section is almost halved with respect to Fig. 2(a) (device simulation for V_{ds} = 50 V).

III. PHYSICAL EFFECTS AND THEIR MODEL EQUATIONS

We will now first pay attention to the modeling of the active MOST region in the p-backgate, and then deal with the drift region.

A. Active MOST Region

It is a well-known phenomenon that for a DMOST the gain factor (β) varies with gate biasing conditions. The observed change in the gain factor is caused by a constant variation of the electrical channel length, which is a result of the nonhomogeneous doping profile under the gate. Therefore it is not possible to describe a DMOST as a conventional MOS transistor with a fixed threshold voltage and a fixed channel length. As a consequence, a DMOST should be considered to be a series configuration of a large number of conventional MOS transistors with different threshold voltages corresponding with the local doping concentration under the gate. This, of course, yields no practical solution for modeling purposes. Efficient modeling of the active MOST region is based upon an investigation concerning the consequences of the lateral impurity profile on the electrical characteristics.

First the vertical boron-doping profile of the backgate has been obtained with SUPREM II. Because this profile showed a Gaussian distribution, we used the complementary error function to determine the lateral profile. Based on this lateral profile the conductance of the active MOST region as a function of gate–source voltage has been calculated using the device simulator CURRY. With the circuit simulator PHILPAC (an internal Philips development comparable with ESPICE), it has been verified that the gradual change in the gain factor as a function of gate bias could be modeled adequately by two MOS transistors in a series configuration, each having a different gain factor β and a different threshold voltage V_T. Let us now consider Fig. 3. In this figure transistor 1 represents the active region under the gate with the highest doping concentration (near the source) and transistor 2 represents the region where the concentration is lower. As a result V_{T1} will be larger than V_{T2} (in fact the peak doping concentration in the channel determines V_{T1}).

For both devices the well known enhancement MOST model equations can be used [6]. As the p-backgate is connected to the source, the body effect has been neglected. In order to incorporate the effect of static feedback on the electron channel under the gate, we have defined the active gate bias to depend on the drain voltage of transistor 2(V_{d2}) according to [6]. This leads to the following equations:

$$I_{ds} = \beta \frac{(V_{g's} - V_T - \frac{1}{2}V_x)V_x}{(1 + \theta_a(V_{g's} - V_T))(1 + \theta_c V_x)}$$

$$V_x = V_{ds}, \quad \text{for } 0 < V_{ds} \leq V_{dss}$$

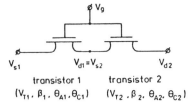

Fig. 3. The electrical behavior of the p-backgate is modeled using a two-transistor configuration to account for the nonhomogeneous-doping concentration in lateral direction.

$$V_x = V_{dss}, \quad \text{for } V_{ds} > V_{dss}$$

$$V_{dss} = \frac{1}{\theta_c} \sqrt{(1 + 2\theta_c(V_{g's} - V_T))} - 1. \quad (1)$$

The active gate bias of each transistor is defined by

$$V_{g's} = V_{gs} + \gamma V_{d2} \frac{(V_{gs} - V_{T1})^2}{z^2 + (V_{gs} - V_{T1})^2}$$

where

β	is the gain factor,
θ_a	is the mobility reduction factor to account for the effect of the normal field in the channel,
θ_c	is the mobility reduction factor to account for velocity saturation in the channel,
V_T	is the threshold voltage,
γ	is the static feedback factor,
z	= 0.65 V (modeling constant), and

$\dfrac{(V_{gs} - V_{T1})^2}{z^2 + (V_{gs} - V_{T1})^2}$ represents a smoothing factor to make the transition from weak inversion to strong inversion.

For each transistor we have four parametes β, V_T, θ_a, θ_c, and, furthermore, the parameter γ.

B. Drift Region

In order to describe the electrical behavior of the drift region, it is convenient to divide this region into two sections as depicted in Fig. 2(b): one section for which the electron current is affected by both depletion regions originating from the epilayer–substrate junction and the field plate (section 1), and one section for which the influence of the field plate can be neglected (section 2). For each section a current voltage relation will be derived based on a number of assumptions: the epi–substrate junction is considered to be abrupt (especially for large reverse biasing conditions this assumption yields accurate results for calculation of the depletion layer width [7]), the gradual channel approximation is assumed to be valid in the entire drift region, the dependence of the electron drift velocity on the electrical field is given by (2); see also Fig. 4 [8], [9].

$$v = v_{\text{Sat}} \frac{-E}{E_c + |E|} \quad (2)$$

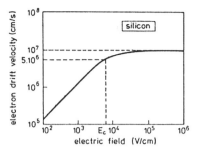

Fig. 4. Electron drift velocity versus electric field in silicon.

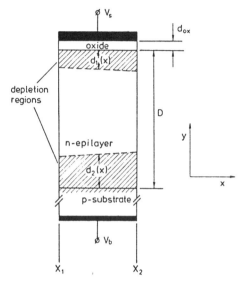

Fig. 5. Typical structure of a part of the drift region above which a field plate is present. The depletion regions in the epilayer are sketched assuming a positively biased n-epilayer with a small potential gradient in the x-direction.

where

v_{Sat}	is the scattering limited velocity of the electrons,
E	is the electrical field, and
E_c	is the field characterizing velocity saturation.

When part of the drift region (between x_1 and x_2) is extracted from Fig. 2, we observe the typical structure given in Fig. 5. The width of the depletion layer caused by the potential difference between the undepleted epilayer and the field plate is indicated as $d_1(x)$, and the depletion layer width originating from the epilayer–substrate junction is denoted as $d_2(x)$. Similar to the derivation of the junction FET equations [8], we will assume that in the depleted region the lateral electric field is small compared with the vertical field (gradual channel approximation).

Let us now consider an elemental section dx of Fig. 5. The electron current I_d through the elemental section can be written as

$$I_d(x) = N_d q v(x) h(x) W \quad (3)$$

where

N_d	is the donor doping concentration,
q	is the electron charge,
$v(x)$	is the electron drift velocity,
$h(x)$	is the effective thickness, and
W	is the width of the structure.

The effective epilayer thickness is given by

$$h(x) = D - d_1(x) - d_2(x) \qquad (4)$$

with D the total thickness of the epilayer.

This equation is valid when the carrier density does not exceed the doping concentration. From Fig. 4 it is apparent that a maximum value for $v(x)$ equals 10^7 cm/s. This implies that (3) can be used for current densities not exceeding 1600 A/cm^2. CURRY simulations showed that in the epilayer this condition is satisfied.

Let $V(x)$ be the local potential in the epilayer. For $d_1(x)$ and $d_2(x)$ we can find

$$d_1(x) = \sqrt{\frac{2\epsilon_{si}N_a(V(x) - V_b)}{q(N_a + N_d)N_d}} \qquad (5)$$

$$d_2(x) = \frac{\epsilon_{si}}{\epsilon_{ox}}\left(-d_{ox} + \sqrt{d_{ox}^2 + 2\epsilon_{ox}^2\frac{V(x) - V_s}{q\epsilon_{si}N_d}}\right) \qquad (6)$$

where

ϵ_{si} is the permittivity of silicon,
ϵ_{ox} is the permittivity of silicon oxide,
N_a is the acceptor concentration in the substrate, and
d_{ox} is the thickness of the oxide under the field plate.

Combining (2)–(6) and at the same time replacing $E(x)$ by $-dV(x)/dx$ yields

$$I_d(x) = N_d q v_{Sat} W \frac{dV(x)/dx}{E_c + |dV(x)/dx|}\left[D + \frac{\epsilon_{si}}{\epsilon_{ox}}d_{ox}\right.$$
$$- \sqrt{\frac{2\epsilon_{si}N_a}{q(N_a + N_d)N_d}(V(x) - V_b)}$$
$$\left. - \frac{\epsilon_{si}}{\epsilon_{ox}}\sqrt{d_{ox}^2 + 2\frac{\epsilon_{ox}^2}{qN_d\epsilon_{si}}(V(x) - V_s)}\right]. \qquad (7)$$

It must be noted that (4) has its limitations. Considering (4)–(6) it can be understood that for sufficiently large values of $d_1(x)$ and $d_2(x)$ the effective thickness $h(x)$ can become zero or negative. The validity range of (4) will be discussed in Section IV.

Integration of $I_d(x)$ over section 1 leads to

$$I_d = \frac{I_m}{E_cL_1 + V_2 - V_1}\left[\left(D + \frac{\epsilon_{si}}{\epsilon_{ox}}d_{ox}\right)(V_2 - V_1)\right.$$
$$- \frac{2}{3}R_s((V_2 - V_b)^{1.5} - (V_1 - V_b)^{1.5})$$
$$\left. - \frac{2}{3}R_f((V_2 + V_O - V_s)^{1.5} - (V_1 + V_O - V_s)^{1.5})\right] \qquad (8)$$

with

$$R_s = \sqrt{\frac{2\epsilon_{si}N_a}{q(N_a + N_d)N_d}} \qquad (9)$$

$$R_f = \sqrt{\frac{2\epsilon_{si}}{qN_d}} = \sqrt{\frac{N_a + N_d}{N_a}}R_s \qquad (10)$$

$$V_O = \frac{qN_d\epsilon_{si}}{2}\left(\frac{d_{ox}}{\epsilon_{ox}}\right)^2 \qquad (11)$$

$$I_m = N_d q v_{Sat} W \qquad (12)$$

where

L_1 is the length of section 1, and
V_1, V_2 are the electric potentials at the beginning and end of section 1, respectively.

It will be clear that we have now derived the current–voltage relation of that part of the drift region above which a field plate is present. The oxide layer thickness between field plate and epitaxial material is supposed to be constant in the derivation. This implies that the step of the field plate on thicker oxide, as present in Fig. 2, has not been taken into account. However, device simulation results have shown that the stepped field plate can be approximated by an equivalent (shorter) flat field plate.

As the polysilicon gate overlapping the drift region has minor effects on the electrical characteristics of the device, this has not been modeled separately.

For section 2 we need only put $d_1(x)$ to zero in the derivation in order to obtain the desired dependence of the current on the applied voltages. This leads to

$$I_d = \frac{I_m}{E_cL_2 + V_d - V_2}\left[D(V_d - V_2)\right.$$
$$\left. - \frac{2}{3}R_s((V_d - V_b)^{1.5} - (V_2 - V_b)^{1.5})\right] \qquad (13)$$

with L_2 length of section 2.

When the doping concentration of the epilayer and substrate are known, it is possible to express R_f in R_s (see (10)). This substitution leads to five free parameters for the drift region:

I_m Maximum current per unit epilayer thickness.

E_cL_1, E_cL_2 Voltage drop characterizing the onset for velocity saturation effects in section 1 and section 2, respectively.

R_s Factor describing the influence of the substrate potential.

V_O Correction voltage to account for the effect of the oxide thickness on the depletion layer width caused by the field plate.

C. Entire DC Model

The complete dc model consists of the composition of the modeled drift region and the active MOST-region. In Fig. 6, the equivalent-circuit diagram is drawn indicating the biasing voltages that have to be used in the specified equations.

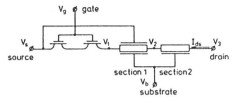

Fig. 6. Complete four-element dc model.

IV. CURRENT SATURATION IN THE DRIFT REGION

As mentioned in Section III-B the model equations derived for the drift region are not always valid. For a certain current the thickness $h(x)$ has a minimum value unequal to zero due to the fact that the electron drift velocity is limited by scattering. In the situation that $h(x)$ in (4) drops below this minimum value, (4) is not valid anymore. Physically this means that the current in the drift region saturates. The gradual channel approximation no longer holds in this situation. This effect also occurs in the JFET and is described by Grove [7] and Sze [8]. As current saturation in section 2 of the drift region occurs at nonpractical currents and voltages, this effect is only discussed for section 1.

The model equations (8) and (13) are based upon (3), which describes the local drain current $I_d(x)$. As the current is constant throughout the drift region, the product $v(x) h(x)$ has to be constant as well. When there is no avalanche multiplication, (14) holds

$$v(x) h(x) = \frac{I_d}{q N_d W}. \qquad (14)$$

In the positive x-direction the potential in the drift region is monotonically increasing and as a consequence the effective thickness $h(x)$ is decreasing with increasing x; see (4)–(6). This means that in this model the minimum thickness occurs at the end of the drift region ($x = L_1$). As the maximum electron velocity is limited by scattering to the saturation velocity v_{sat}, the thickness of the undepleted epilayer has a minimum which is a function of the drain current

$$h(L_1)_{\text{min}} = \frac{I_d}{q N_d W v_{\text{sat}}}. \qquad (15)$$

This equation, together with (9)–(12), enables us to find a maximum value V_m for the potential V_2 at the end of the drift region from (4)

$$D + \frac{\epsilon_{\text{si}}}{\epsilon_{\text{ox}}} d_{\text{ox}} - R_s \sqrt{V_m - V_b}$$

$$- R_f \sqrt{V_m + V_O - V_s} = \frac{I_d}{I_m}. \qquad (16)$$

In the situation that $V_2 < V_m$, no saturation effects occur in the drift region and (8) gives a valid description of the current–voltage behavior. For $V_2 = V_m$, (8) still holds and I_d can be written as a function of V_m. In doing so, an implicit expression for the maximum voltage V_m is obtained

$$D + \frac{\epsilon_{\text{si}}}{\epsilon_{\text{ox}}} d_{\text{ox}} - R_s \sqrt{V_m - V_b} - R_f \sqrt{V_m + V_O - V_s}$$

$$= \frac{1}{E_c L_1 + V_m - V_1} \left[\left(D + \frac{\epsilon_{\text{si}}}{\epsilon_{\text{ox}}} d_{\text{ox}} \right) (V_m - V_1) \right.$$

$$- \frac{2}{3} R_s ((V_m - V_b)^{1.5} - (V_1 - V_b)^{1.5})$$

$$\left. - \frac{2}{3} R_f ((V_m + V_O - V_s)^{1.5} - (V_1 + V_O - V_s)^{1.5}) \right]. \qquad (17)$$

This maximum voltage V_m characterizes the onset of saturation in section 1. The same expression is obtained by determining the maximum in the model equation for I_d from differentiation of I_d with respect to V_2. With this in mind an extension of the model beyond V_m is possible by keeping the drain current I_d constant at the value obtained with $V_2 = V_m$. This approach implies an infinite output impedance for V_2 exceeding V_m.

The result above is obtained assuming that the velocity of the electrons at the end of the drift region equals v_{Sat}. With the v–E dependence proposed in Section III (2) this velocity corresponds to an infinitely strong electrical field E_m. The field E_m, however, will have a finite strength and therefore the electrons at the end of the first section will have a velocity smaller than v_{Sat}. When $v(L_1)$ is expressed as a function of E_m, (18) gives a more accurate determination of the maximum for V_2, now assigned with V_p

$$D + \frac{\epsilon_{\text{si}}}{\epsilon_{\text{ox}}} d_{\text{ox}} - R_s \sqrt{V_p - V_b} - R_f \sqrt{V_p + V_O - V_s}$$

$$= \frac{1 + E_c/E_m}{E_c L_1 + V_p - V_1} \left[\left(D + \frac{\epsilon_{\text{si}}}{\epsilon_{\text{ox}}} d_{\text{ox}} \right) (V_p - V_1) \right.$$

$$- \frac{2}{3} R_s ((V_p - V_b)^{1.5} - (V_1 - V_b)^{1.5}$$

$$\left. - \frac{2}{3} R_f ((V_p + V_O - V_s)^{1.5} - (V_1 + V_O - V_s)^{1.5}) \right]. \qquad (18)$$

As V_p is smaller than V_m, dI_d/dV_2 at $V_2 = V_p$ has a positive value. Therefore a linear extrapolation of I_d with respect to V_2 for values of V_2 exceeding V_p results in a finite output impedance, which can be optimized with E_m.

V. PARAMETER DETERMINATION

Parameter determination is generally based upon an optimization routine minimizing the sum of relative errors between a model calculation and the corresponding electrical measurement. In order to use such a method with success it is inevitable to distinguish several areas in the electrical characteristics that are specifically sensitive to

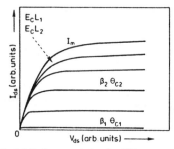

Fig. 7. Hypothetical *I–V* characteristics for different gate–source voltages. For some parameters the important regions for the parameter extraction are indicated.

changes in only a few parameters. Only then an independent parameter determination procedure is possible.

Fig. 7 indicates the areas to be optimized with a corresponding parameter. The parameters left will be discussed separately.

As can be understood from Section III, the threshold voltage of transistor 1 (see Fig. 5) actually represents the turn-on voltage of the entire high-voltage DMOST. Therefore, V_{T1} can directly be measured and gives no problem. Unlike V_{T1}, V_{T2} has a far less pronounced effect on the electrical characteristics of the model. As a consequence, an unambiguous determination of V_{T2} is quite difficult. Model calculations showed that the value of V_{T2} is not critical. Based on 2-D device simulations with the program CURRY, a value of 0.4 V was found offering good results for our structure.

The factor θ_a incorporates the effect of mobility reduction due to a strong transversal field in the electron channel. A commonly used value for θ_a is 0.03/V.

The parameter R_s describes the influence of the depletion layer width caused by the substrate to epilayer junction on the current. As a consequence R_s can be determined by investigating the dependence of the total drain current on the applied source to substrate bias at high gate-to-source voltages.

V_O incorporates the influence of the oxide thickness on the depletion layer width caused by the potential difference between field plate and epilayer. Optimization of V_O is possible, but calculation of V_O with process data (N_d and d_{ox}) yields a value sufficiently accurate to be used in the model equations.

Table II shows the optimized values of the parameters together with some calculated values based upon geometry and process parameters.

VI. COMPLETE *I–V* CHARACTERISTICS

Evaluation of a transistor model should be performed over a wide range of current and voltage operating conditions. For the discussed high-voltage power transistor this leads to a relatively large power dissipation under certain biasing conditions. Therefore we used pulsed-mode measurements techniques to avoid unacceptable thermal heating of the crystal. Nevertheless we could not effectively eliminate high-temperature effects for a dissipation exceeding 1.5 W. For that reason, most of the model evaluation has been carried out below this boundary.

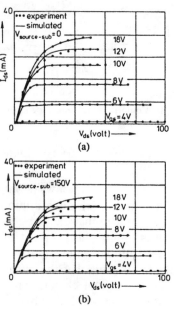

(a)

(b)

Fig. 8. Comparison of simulations from the model with experimental high-voltage DMOST *I–V* characteristics.

TABLE II

parameter	optimized value		calculated value from the geometry and the process
V_{T1}	3.1 V		
V_{T2}	0.4 V	(default)	
θ_{a1}	0.03 V^{-1}	(default)	
θ_{a2}	0.03 V^{-1}	(default)	
θ_{c1}	0.3 V^{-1}		
θ_{c2}	0.7 V^{-1}		
β_1	2.95 mA/V^2		4.60 mA/V^2
β_2	4.59 mA/V^2		4.60 mA/V^2
γ	2.3 10^{-4} V^{-1}		
R_S	3.9 10^{-7} M/$\sqrt{V}$		6.6 10^{-7} M/$\sqrt{V}$
V_O			6.9 V
R_f			$\sqrt{3}\ R_S$
I_m	3.3 10^3 A/M		4.0 10^3 A/M
$E_c l_1$	6.9 V		11.2 V
$E_c l_2$	14.0 V		14.4 V

The calculated values follow from :

β = W/L μ_n C_{OX}, with

electron mobility in the channel	μ_n	= 400	cm^2 / Vs
oxide capacitance per unit area	C_{OX}	= 3.5 10^{-8}	F/cm^2
effective channel lenght	L	= 0.75	μm
width of the device	W	= 250	μm

E_c = 8.0 10^3 V/ cm   (see fig. 4)

L_1 = 14 μm   (see fig. 1)

L_2 = 18 μm   (see fig. 1)

Comparison of experimental and calculated results shows a good agreement in a large range of operating conditions (Fig. 8). For our structure the modeling of the on-resistance was accurate within 6 percent for different source–substrate voltages. In the low-current and high-voltage region, the dependence of I_{ds} on V_{gs} has been modeled within 2 percent. High currents are modeled with an accuracy better than 5 percent.

VII. DISCUSSION

In this paper we have extensively discussed the operation and the modeling of a high-voltage lateral DMOST structure. Based on insight gained by 2-D device simulation results we have been able to develop a four component dc transistor model for use in computer-aided circuit design. It has been shown that in a wide range of operating conditions the model calculations are very accurate.

When transistors operate within limited areas, circuit simulations with only part of the model are possible. This greatly reduces simulation time and may yield results of comparable accuracy. As an example we mention the use of the equivalent-circuit diagram given in Fig. 3, extended with a fixed series resistor for modeling low-current (high-voltage) applications. Omitting one MOS transistor in Fig. 6 might give good simulation results for switching applications.

ACKNOWLEDGMENT

The authors would like to thank Prof. F. M. Klaassen and A. W. Ludikhuize for interesting discussions and critical remarks concerning the model.

REFERENCES

[1] P. G. Blanken and P. van der Zee, "An integrated 8-MHz video output amplifier," *IEEE Trans. Consumer Electron.*, vol. CE-31, no. 3, pp. 109–118, Aug. 1985.

[2] S. C. Sun and J. D. Plummer, "Modeling of the on-resistance of LDMOS, VDMOS, and VMOS power transistors," *IEEE Trans. Electron Devices*, vol. ED-27, no. 2, pp. 356–367, Feb. 1980.

[3] S. Colak, "Effects of drift region parameters on the static properties of power LDMOST," *IEEE Trans. Electron Devices*, vol. ED-28, no. 12, pp. 51–53, Dec. 1981.

[4] M. D. Pocha and R. W. Dutton, "A computer-aided design model for high-voltage lateral Double Diffused MOS (DMOS) Transistors," *IEEE J. Solid-State Circuits*, vol. SC-11, no. 5, pp. 718–726, Oct. 1976.

[5] S. J. Polak, C. den Heijer, W. Schilders, P. Markowich, "Semiconductor device modeling from the numerical point of view," *Int. J. Numerical Methods Engin.*, to be published.

[6] F. M. Klaassen and W. C. J. de Groot, "Modeling of scaled-down transistors," *Solid-State Electron.*, vol. 23, pp. 237–242, 1980.

[7] A. S. Grove, *Physics and Technology of Semiconductor Devices.* New York: Wiley, 1967.

[8] S. M. Sze, *Physics of Semiconductor Devices.* New York: Wiley, 1981.

[9] W. E. Beadle, J. C. C. Tsai, and R. D. Plummer, *Quick Reference Manual for Silicon-Integrated Circuit Technology.* New York: Wiley, 1985.

HIGH VOLTAGE THIN LAYER DEVICES (RESURF DEVICES)

J.A. Appels and H.M.J. Vaes

Philips Research Laboratories
Eindhoven - The Netherlands

ABSTRACT

The application of a somewhat unusual diode structure opens the possibility to make novel kinds of high voltage devices even with very thin epitaxial or implanted layers. In the new structures crucial changes in the electric field distribution take place at or at least near the surface. The acronym RESURF (REduced SURface Field) was chosen.

BASIC STRUCTURE

The basic structure consists of a high-ohmic P^-substrate with an epitaxial N^-layer on it, which is laterally bounded by a P^+ diffusion[1]. The diode thus formed consists of two parts: one horizontal P^-N junction and a vertical P^+N junction. Considering these parts as one-dimensional junctions, the vertical one has the lower breakdown voltage, which is determined by the doping concentration of the epitaxial layer (e.g. 370 V for $N_{epi} = 6.10^{14}$). The breakdown voltage of the horizontal junction is considerably higher due to the high-ohmic substrate (1150 V for the example of fig. 1).

For thick epitaxial layers the depletion at the surface of the vertical P^+N junction is not influenced by the horizontal junction and hence breakdown voltage is determined by the P^+N junction. The electric field pattern along the surface and the axis of symmetry for this case is given in fig. 1a. Going to thinner layers however, the depletion of the vertical P^+N junction becomes more and more reinforced by the horizontal junction. Consequently at the same applied voltage, the depletion stretches along the surface over a much longer distance than would be expected according to a simple one-dimensional calculation. Now the electric field at the surface is far below the critical field (Fig. 1b) and a much higher voltage can be applied before breakdown occurs. Beneath a certain thickness of the epitaxial layer, this REduced SURface Field will not reach the critical value not even at high voltages and hence

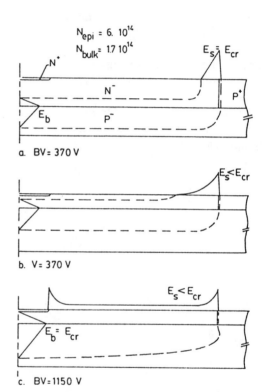

Fig. 1. Representation of the electric field distribution.
   a. for a thick epitaxial layer (370 V),
   b. for a thin epitaxial layer (370 V),
   c. for a thin epitaxial layer (1150 V).

surface breakdown has been eliminated. Now the breakdown of the diode is determined by the horizontal junction and thus the ideal bulk breakdown can be reached. (Fig. 1c). However, since the epitaxial layer is fully depleted a new effect arises. Due to the curvature of the N^+ contact the electric field will strongly increase. For very thin epitaxial layers the effect becomes so pronounced that

Reprinted from *IEEE 25th Int. Electron Devices Meeting*, pp. 238–241, 1979.

the electric field peak at the edge
of the N⁺ region is larger than the field
in the bulk.
Now corner breakdown will occur at a
voltage which is lower than the ideal bulk
breakdown voltage. Two-dimensional numerical calculations show that a symmetrical electric field distribution at the
surface is obtained, when $N_{epi} \cdot d_{epi} =$
10^{12} at/cm², where N_{epi} and d_{epi} are
the doping concentration and the thickness of the epitaxial layer, respectively.
For the structure as discussed so far, a
plot of breakdown voltage versus epitaxial
layer thickness is given.

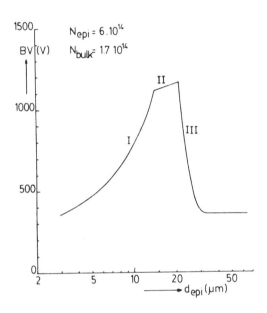

Fig. 2. Breakdown voltage as a function
of epitaxial layer thickness.
In region II breakdown takes
place at the horizontal junction.
In region I and III breakdown
takes place at the N⁺ or P⁺ regions, respectively.

LATERAL BIPOLAR TRANSISTOR

A minor change in the diode structure
leads to a high voltage bipolar transistor. Simply by introducing an N⁺ emitter
diffusion in the P⁺ isolation region, a
transistor is obtained. (Fig. 3). To make
transistor action more efficient, it
is preferred to enlarge the P⁺ region
by a shallow P⁺ base diffusion.

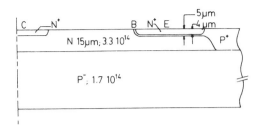

Fig. 3. Cross-section of a lateral
bipolar transistor.

The high-ohmic N⁻ region together with
the N⁺ contact diffusion forms the
collector zone of the transistor.
The transistor action itself mainly takes
place in the top-layer of the structure.
By increasing the resistivity of the substrate, high emitter-collector breakdown
voltages can be obtained. The P⁺ base-
diffusion need not necessarily be connected to the isolation region but can
also be made as a floating island in
the N⁻ layer.
Fig. 4 presents the current-voltage
characteristics of an NPN lateral transistor made in an epitaxial layer with a
thickness of 15 /um.

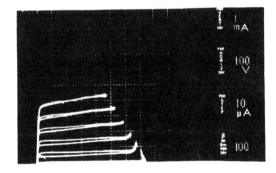

Fig. 4. Common emitter output characteristics of a lateral bipolar transistor. BV_{CEO} = 730 V BV_{CBO} = 850 V.

VERTICAL BIPOLAR TRANSISTOR

Fig. 5 shows a cross-section of a vertical PNP transistor. The only difference
with a conventional structure is an additional N⁻ layer which is laterally
bounded by a P⁺ diffusion.

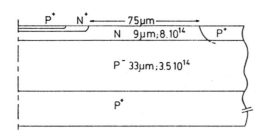

Fig. 5. Cross-section of a vertical bipolar PNP transistor.

In contrast with the lateral transistor, the Resurf N⁻ layer, is now a part of the base region. By a proper choice of dimensions and doping concentration of the N⁻ layer, the electric field distribution at the surface can be such that breakdown will take place at the horizontal N⁻P⁻ junction. In this way even with shallow base diffusions very high collector-base breakdown voltages can be obtained.

Fig. 6 shows the measured I-V characteristics of such a PNP transistor.

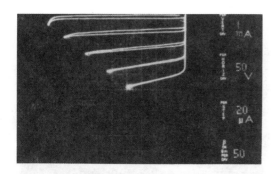

Fig. 6. Vertical PNP Resurf transistor made according to the principle described. BV_{CEO} = 470 V; BV_{CBO} = 520 V.

JUNCTION FET

In conventionally fabricated J-Fets a high gate-to-drain breakdown voltage is inherently coupled with a thick high-ohmic layer in order to be able to accommodate the applied reverse voltage at the drain end.

The use of Resurf layers opens the possibility of making high-voltage J-Fets with a low pinch-off voltage and a high current-carrying capability, in relatively thin epitaxial or implanted layers.

Fig. 7 shows a cross-section of a thin layer Resurf J-Fet.

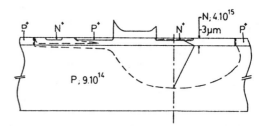

Fig. 7. Cross-section of a Resurf J-Fet.

The extension of the depletion layer in the substrate as well as the electric field distribution in the bulk and at the surface of the drain end are depicted. I-V characteristics of some experimental samples made with non-optimized photo masks are shown in Figs. 8 and 9.

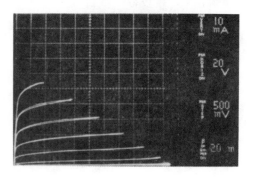

Fig. 8. Resurf J-Fet made in 3 μm thick epitaxial layer. $BV_{S-D} \le$ 230 V.

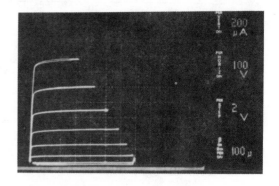

Fig. 9. Resurf J-Fet made in a 15 μm thick epitaxial layer.

CONCLUSION

The use of high-ohmic substrates with relatively thin epitaxial layers on them, which meet the requirements mentioned in this paper (i.e. $N_{epi} \times d_{epi} \cong 10^{12}$ at/cm²) opens the possibility of making high-voltage devices whose structure and operation, in particular the electric field distribution, differ essentially from those of conventional devices.

Ref.
1) Late News Paper, ESSDERC '79 München.

HIGH-VOLTAGE DMOS AND PMOS IN ANALOG IC'S

A.W. Ludikhuize

Philips Research Laboratories
Eindhoven - The Netherlands

ABSTRACT

A lateral 300V DMOS device is described
which can be integrated in a standard
bipolar IC process. The device, applicable as a high voltage source follower
for analog circuits, is based upon the
"double-acting resurf" principle; a modification with an interrupted p- top
layer or with a stepped field plate is
used. The p- layer improves the intercon-
nection-induced breakdown and can be
used in the extended drain of a 280 V
PMOST.

INTRODUCTION

For functions like driving transducers
or CRT's and for analog switches, high
voltage analog stages of over 250 V may
be needed on the chip. Vertical bipolars
are less suitable because of the required
thick epi-layers and even integration of
vertical DMOS devices in a standard IC
process is rather difficult. High voltage
lateral MOS devices of over 500 V, using
thin layer extended drain or "resurf"
techniques (1-3), can easily be incorporated, but a high voltage source follower is
impossible. Source followers using lateral
DMOS devices and 25-30 µm epi have been
reported (4); here 200 V is considered the
limit for junction isolated devices because of deep isolation diffusions and
parasitic bulk and surface effects (5).
Recently a "double-acting resurf" technique has been reported (6); compared to
"resurf" as mentioned above, it not only
offers better lateral conduction but also
prevention of substrate punch-through in
follower applications. Owing to a higher
doping content of the n layer (about
2.10^{12} cm^{-2}), the depletion layer at source
(back gate)-to-substrate breakdown does
not extend to the surface diffusion (as
shown by the left-hand shaded area in fig.
1) and no punch-through occurs. At high
voltage on the n$^+$ drain with the other
terminals grounded, a high field would
occur at the source edge. By using a p-top
layer, depletion of the n layer is obtained from the top and the bottom (right-
hand shaded areas in fig. 1) causing a

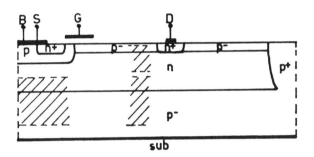

Fig.1. A double-acting resurf structure.

smooth voltage decrease over the lateral
distance between source and drain; at
high drain voltage this p- top layer has
to be depleted too. The effect was demonstrated on JFET and lateral bipolar devices (6); the p- and n layers were opti-
mized at $0.5 \ 10^{12}$ cm^{-2} and $1.8 \ 10^{12}$ cm^{-2}
respectively.

LATERAL DMOST

For proper functioning of a lateral DMOST
(LDMOST), the design of fig. 1 has to be
adapted. In fig. 2 a window is shown, made
locally in the p-layer at the source side;
electrons from the gate-controlled surface
channel now pass through a vertical JFET
which limits the current capability and
increases the on-resistance. The window
dimensions are therefore a compromise between on-resistance and breakdown.

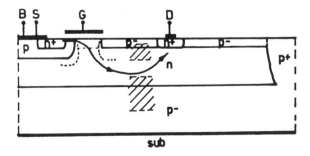

Fig.2. LDMOST with interrupted p-layer.

Reprinted from *IEEE 28th Int. Electron Devices Meeting*, pp. 81-84, 1982.

Instead of a p-top layer also a stepped
field plate, connected to gate or source,
can be applied in order to obtain depletion from the surface, as shown in fig. 3.

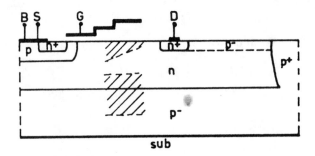

Fig.3. LDMOST with stepped field plate.

The pinching effect on the n layer is
much less, lowering the breakdown voltage,
but now the entire epi-layer with local
accumulation contributes to a low on-resistance.

Computer calculations using our 2D Poisson-
program "Semmy" were performed on the
structure depicted in fig. 4 for several
combinations of p-layer and field plates,
cf. table 1. A 19 μm 5Ωcm n-type epilayer as used in a 50-60 V standard bipolar process is applied on a 30Ωcm p-
substrate. The 3 μm p-layer, assumed
without a window here, has a net dose of
$1.6 \cdot 10^{12}$ cm^{-2}; this high value improves
the current capability of an extended
drain PMOST as will be discussed later on,

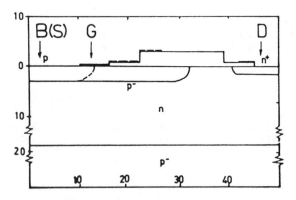

Fig.4. LDMOST structure; dimensions in μm.

but delays pinch off and requires the p-
layer to be withdrawn from the n$^+$ drain
in order to prevent low breakdown values.
The gate-oxide is 0.1 μm; the field plates
(dashed) step on 0.8 and 3.0 μm oxide. The
punch-through voltage to the substrate is
calculated to be 600V; spreading of epi
dope and thickness may decrease this value
to 300 V.

In figs. 5 and 6 equipotential and equifield lines at 300 V drain voltage are
shown for a device with a p-layer; the

co-operation of top and bottom depletion
is visible on the left in fig. 5. The
highest field of 23.2 V/μm, obtained at
the p-diffusion curvature, does not cause
breakdown (avalanche integral <1).

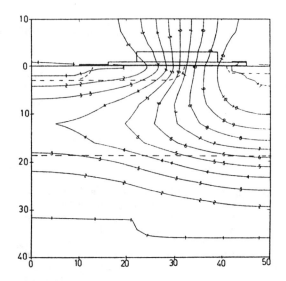

Fig.5. LDMOST equipotential lines at V d-s
= 300V; per step 30V, step l=0V.

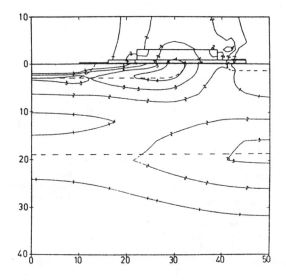

Fig.6. LDMOST equifield lines at V d-s
= 300V; per step 5V/μm, step l=5V/μm.

Table 1 E max (in V/μm) at V d-s=300V;
epi, p-layer and field plates (F.P.) as
in fig. 4.

substr.	p-	F.P.	E_{maxSi}	B.V.	E_{maxox}
n	yes	yés	32.0	<300	56
p-	no	no	63.5	<<300	177
p-	yes	no	23.2	>300	22.7
p-	no	yes	28.7	>300	95
p-	yes	yes	24.5	>300	35

Fig.7. shows an actual device with a stepped field plate connected to the source; the layout corners are bevelled. At the connection of the polysilicon gate th e field plate had to be interrupted as single-layer metallization is used and a local p-layer is applied. The active gate width is 500 μm, the channel length is approx. 2.0 μm. The drain surrounds the back gate and prevents parasitic PMOS action from back gate to isolation when the source is at high voltage. As crossing interconnection over shallow n^+ shows only 200V breakdown on 3.0 μm oxide, the shallow n^+ drain has been locally omitted underneath this metallization. A collector wall diffusion

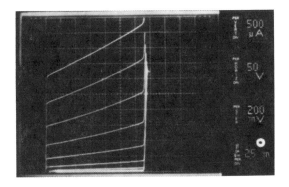

Fig.7.   LDMOST for 300V; gate and source with field plate in the centre, n^+ drain 3/4 around as a stopper; drain pitch 90 μm.

or a buried polysilicon field shield can be used here; this way a breakdown >300 V is obtained. At the isolation diffusion edge a p-layer is applied (withdrawn from the n^+ drain), which improves breakdown noticeably in the case of crossing (drain) interconnection and avoids walk-out phenomena below 300V.

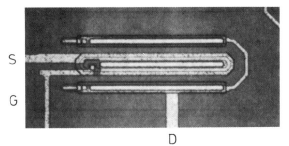

Fig.8. LDMOST BV drain-to-source; the substrate is connected to the source.

A source-to-substrate breakdown of over 300V was obtained limited by the drain-to-isolation distance. Drain-to-source breakdown (substrate is at source potential) is shown in fig. 8 to be over 300V; breakdown generally occurs at the bevelled

back gate corners.

Fig. 9 shows the low-voltage on-characteristics. V_T is about 2.4V and $\beta_0 = 16$ μA/V^2; R_{on} is 300 Ω corresponding with 6.7 Ω-mm^2 for the active area. Owing to partial depletion of the epi-layer, R_{on} increases at 300 V s-sub to 450 Ω and I_{max}^{on} (10V d-s) becomes 18mA. For a variant according to fig. 2 with a p-ring and 10 μm local windows R_{on} was found to be 450-600 Ω .

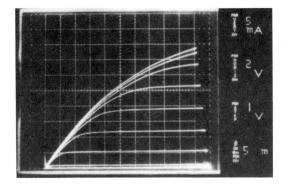

Fig.9. LDMOS on-characteristics.

Experiments in plastic encapsulation showed good stability in dry ambient at 150°C. In wet ambient instabilities are sometimes observed at the drain. Simulation with a field plate at V_{surf} on 1 μm nitride on top of the structure indicated the drain configuration of fig. 4 to be poor; a field plate overlapping the n^+ drain edge is sufficient.

EXTENDED DRAIN PMOST

In the same process a complementary high-voltage extended drain PMOST (EPMOST) has been made; the extension is pinched between the epi-layer and a stepped field plate connected to source or gate (cf. ref.7). For better gradual pinching and less Early effect in the PMOS channel, a buried n^+ layer is applied locally as shown in fig. 10. Source and back gate are

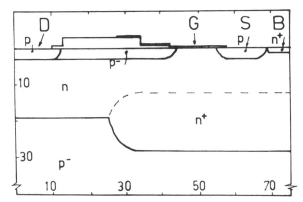

Fig.10. Extended drain PMOST structure.

situated on the right, drain and p- extension on the left. The effective channel length is about 11 µm, but lower values with more Early-effect are possible. A computer calculation with 300V on source and gate shows equipotential and equifield lines (figs.11 and 12); the maxi-

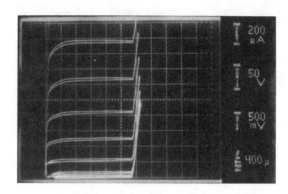

Fig.14. EPMOST BV drain-to-source; the substrate is connected to the drain.

vice acts as a stopper for parasitic PMOS action.

The measured drain-to-source breakdown is shown in fig. 14 to be 280V; this breakdown occurs at the small-radius end of the drain. The active gate width is about 550 µm; $V_T=1.5V$, g_m max $(10V_{d-s})=1.4mA/V$ and $\beta_0=7\mu A/V^2$. R_{on} is 900 Ω, corresponding with $30\Omega mm^2$ for the active area.

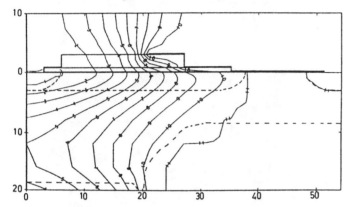

Fig.11. EPMOST equipotential lines at V s, g-d, sub=300V; per step 30V, step 1=0V.

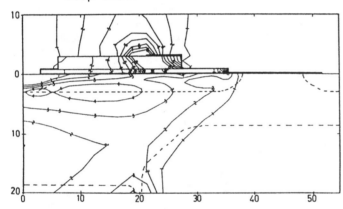

Fig.12. EPMOST equifield lines at V s, g-d, sub=300V; per step 5V/µm, step 1=5V/µm.

mum field of 23V/µm does not cause breakdown. An actual EPMOST is shown in fig. 13; the p drain is in the centre and the n^+ backgate contact on the outside of the de-

CONCLUSION

By using a modification of the "double-acting resurf" principle, a lateral DMOST for 300V analog applications can be integrated with standard bipolar components. The use of a p- implanted layer allows interconnections to over 300V on 3 µm oxide. The same p-layer has been used in an extended drain PMOST of 280V.

ACKNOWLEDGEMENT

The author wishes to thank his colleagues for their stimulating co-operation and particularly W. Ruis and R. Bonne for preparation of the samples.

REFERENCES

1) J.A. Appels, H.M.J. Vaes, Proc. IEDM, pp. 238-241 (1979)
2) S. Colak, B. Singer, E. Stupp, IEEE El. Dev. Lett. EDL-1, pp. 51-53 (1980)
3) S. Colak, IEEE Tr. El. Dev ED-28, pp. 1455-1466 (1981).
4) J.D. Plummer, J.D. Meindl, IEEE J. Sol. St. Circ. SC-11, pp. 809-817 (1976).
5) J.D. Plummer, Proc. IEDM, pp. 70-74, (1980).
6) H.M.J. Vaes, J.A. Appels, Proc. IEDM, pp. 87-90 (1980).
7) T. Okabe et al, IEEE Tr. El. Dev. ED-27, pp. 334-339 (1980).

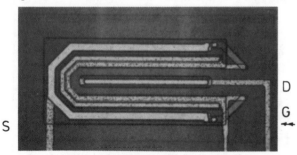

Fig.13. EPMOST with central drain and gate, source and back gate 3/4 around; the n^+ back gate acts as a stopper; scale as fig. 7.

n-Channel Lateral Insulated Gate Transistors: Part I—Steady-State Characteristics

DEVA N. PATTANAYAK, MEMBER, IEEE, A. L. ROBINSON, T. PAUL CHOW, MEMBER, IEEE, MICHAEL S. ADLER, FELLOW, IEEE, B. JAYANT BALIGA, FELLOW, IEEE, AND ERIC J. WILDI, MEMBER, IEEE

Abstract—The basic physics of the steady-state characteristics of the lateral insulated gate transistor (LIGT) is discussed. Results from a two-dimensional computer simulation of representative LIGT structures are presented. Several structural and process enhancements to the basic LIGT structure to increase the current handling capability and suppress latchup are pointed out. Experimental results of the steady-state characteristics of a variety of LIGT test structures are presented and analyzed. The static latching aspect of LIGT is discussed in some detail. LIGT devices employing either a buried layer or surface shorts are shown to current limit rather than latching up.

I. INTRODUCTION

A LATERAL insulated gate transistor (LIGT) [1]-[3] is an integrable MOS controlled power switch, whose on resistance is about an order of magnitude lower than the corresponding lateral DMOS transistor. However, like the vertical IGT [4],[1] lateral IGT's can exhibit latch up resulting in loss of gate control at current levels large enough to trigger the parasitic thyristor element inherent in the device. New LIGT structures with very high latching current levels or with current limiting features have been reported recently [5]. In this paper, a comprehensive account of the steady-state behavior of LIGT's with different structural and process modifications to improve forward conduction and latching level is presented. The basic physics of operation of the LIGT is discussed briefly, followed by modeling results obtained from two-dimensional numerical solution of the semiconductor equations. This is followed by a description of the test device design and process sequence used for fabrication of the lateral IGT structures. Key experimental results are presented and analyzed.

II. BASIC PHYSICS OF OPERATION OF AN LIGT

The basic structure of an n-channel LIGT is shown schematically in Fig. 1. The main difference between this structure and a lateral DMOS structure is that the p^+ anode becomes the n^+ drain for the DMOS structure. Generally, the substrate is electrically tied to the source contact. When a positive gate voltage above threshold voltage is applied with respect to the source, an inversion channel is formed that connects the n^+ cathode to the n^- epi region. If a positive voltage is now applied between the p^+ anode and the cathode, most of the voltage appears across the emitter junction (J_1), until the junction becomes sufficiently forward biased. Any additional increase in voltage then appears mainly across the channel and drift regions. The holes are injected into the n^- epi region from the anode and electrons flow into the same region from the n^+ source via the inversion channel. The n^- epi region becomes conductivity modulated. With a further increase in the p^+ emitter voltage, more voltage appears across the inversion channel and the electron current increases to compensate for the increased hole current. Most of the holes are collected at the substrate, but some holes flow through the p-base region and are collected at the contact. In accordance with Kirchoff's law, the anode current is balanced by the hole current flowing into the p^+ substrate, the electron current flowing into the n^+ source, and hole current flowing through the p-base into the common contact of n^+ source and p-base. The junction J_3 is shorted by the common source contact and does not take part in carrier injection until the lateral hole current flowing in the p-base is sufficient to locally forward bias the J_3 junction. When this happens, both the p^+ anode and the n^+ source simultaneously inject, which increases their injection efficiency in a regenerative way leading to a very low impedance path between the p^+ anode and the n^+ source. This low-impedance p-n-p-n parasitic path causes the device to conduct high amounts of current similar to a thyristor, and the gate control is lost. The device now cannot be turned off by mere removal of the gate voltage. When this happens the device is said to be latched. Reversal of the emitter voltage to bring the

Manuscript received July 25, 1986.

D. N. Pattanayak, T. P. Chow, M. S. Adler, B. J. Baliga, and E. J. Wildi are with General Electric Corporate Research and Development, Schenectady, NY 12301.

A. L. Robinson was with General Electric Corporation Research and Development, Schenectady, NY 12301. He is now with the Department of Electrical Engineering, University of Michigan, Ann Arbor, MI 48109.

IEEE Log Number 8610951.

[1]J. P. Russell, A. M. Goodman, L. A. Goodman, and J. M. Nielson, "The COMFET—A new high conductance MOS-gated device," *IEEE Electron Device Lett.*, vol. EDL-4, no. 3, p. 63, 1983. See also, M. F. Chang, G. C. Pifer, B. J. Baliga, M. S. Adler, and P. V. Gray, "25 amp, 500 volt insulated gate rectifier," in *IEDM Tech. Dig.*, p. 83, 1983; L. A. Goodman, "Recent advances in discrete power transistors," in *IEDM Tech. Dig.*, p. 270, 1984; H. Yilmaz, W. R. Van Dell, K. Owyang, and M. F. Chang, "Insulated gate transistor modeling and optimization," in *IEDM Tech. Dig.*, p. 274, 1984; and A. Nakagawa, Y. Yamaguchi, K. Watanabe, H. Ohashi, and M. Kurata, "Experimental and numerical study of non-latchup bipolar mode MOSFET characteristics," in *IEDM Tech. Dig.*, p. 150, 1985.

Reprinted from *IEEE Trans. Electron Devices*, vol. ED-33, pp. 1956-1963, Dec. 1986.

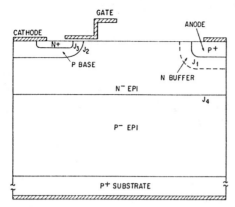

Fig. 1. Schematic diagram of a lateral IGT.

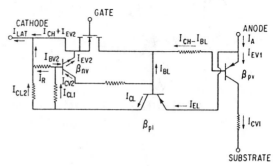

Fig. 2. Equivalent circuit of a lateral IGT.

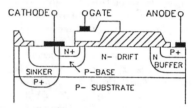

Fig. 3. LIGT structure showing p⁺ sinker (type C).

device current below the holding current of the p-n-p-n path is necessary to switch the device to its unlatched state.

III. EQUIVALENT CIRCUIT FOR AN LIGT

Clearly the LIGT is a compound device. It can be thought of as a combination of a lateral DMOS element, a vertical bipolar element, a lateral bipolar element, and a lateral parasitic thyristor element. When the MOS gate is biased above the threshold voltage, the source of the DMOS acts like the base electrode for both the lateral and vertical bipolar transistors. The base current for the lateral and vertical bipolar transistors in LIGT flows from the source via the MOS inversion channel and increases as the gate to source voltage is increased. As the base current increases so does the emitter current by the transistor action. A simple equivalent circuit for an LIGT is shown in Fig. 2. The various current components with obvious interpretation are also shown in the figure. From a straightforward application of Kirchoff's law it follows that the anode current can be represented as

$$I_A = I_{ch} + I_{CV1} + I_{CL2} - \beta_{nv} \cdot I_R$$
$$+ (\beta_{nv} + 1) \frac{(\beta_{PL}\beta_{nv}I_R + I_{CL2} - \beta_{PL}I_{BL2})}{\beta_{PL}\beta_{nv} - 1}. \quad (1)$$

Equation (1) contains a lot of information. Let us consider the situation when $\beta_{nv} \approx 0$, as will be the case when the vertical n-p-n transistor is very well shunted at the emitter–base junction. In that case, (1) becomes

$$I_A \cong I_{ch} + I_{CV1} + I_{CL2}. \quad (2)$$

In this case, the equivalent circuit consists mainly of the DMOS component and the lateral and vertical bipolar transistors whose bases are driven by the MOS channel. Assuming a fraction f_1 of channel current is driving the lateral p-n-p bipolar, with the rest of the channel current driving the vertical p-n-p bipolar current, one obtains

$$I_A \cong I_{ch}[1 + f_1\beta_{PL} + (1 - f_1)\beta_{PV}]. \quad (3)$$

Due to the two-dimensional and inhomogeneous doping profiles, it is rather difficult to find analytical expressions for the various quantities on the left-hand side of (3). However, (3) shows that prior to latchup the LIGT device current is controlled by the MOS channel.

If, however, β_{nv} is not negligible and the product $\beta_{nv}\beta_{p1} \cong 1$, then (1) can be written as

$$I_A \simeq \frac{(\beta_{nv} + 1)(I_R + I_{CL2} - \beta_{PL}I_{BL})}{(\beta_{PL}\beta_{nv} - 1)}. \quad (4)$$

Now even if the MOS channel is switched off, i.e., $I_{BL} = 0$, the device current is non-zero, implying the loss of MOS control of the device operation. To a first order, the LIGT will latch when the emitter–base junction of the vertical n-p-n transistor is sufficiently forward biased for this junction to inject and the beta products are greater than 1. Denoting this junction bias to be V_j, we find from the equivalent circuit

$$V_J \simeq (I_{CL1} - I_{BV2})R_J \quad (5)$$

where R_J is the resistance of the path connecting the base of the vertical n-p-n transistor to its emitter, and I_{BV2} is the base current of vertical n-p-n transistor as shown in Fig. 2. The value of V_J can be kept low by either decreasing R_J or I_{CL1} or both. For the same total device current, if the vertical bipolar current I_{CV} is increased, then I_{CL1} is correspondingly decreased. This is, in fact, what is achieved by employing a substrate consisting of a p⁻ epitaxial layer on a p⁺ wafer. The thickness of the p⁻ layer is chosen to support the required voltage. The other solution to improve latching characteristics of an LIGT is to decrease R_J. This can be done by means of a p⁺ sinker diffusion (as shown in Fig. 3), which reduces the resistance of the p-base underneath the n⁺ emitter diffusion. Yet another solution to the latchup problem is to increase I_{CL2}. This is done in two ways. The first method is by means of a buried layer as shown in Fig. 4. In this case, current is diverted away from the p-base into the buried layer and gets collected at the source contact. The second method is to periodically interrupt the n⁺ source, leaving regions of p-base without n⁺ source in them and then diffusing p⁺ at these regions. This amounts to increasing the I_{CL2} component of the current, thus increasing the latch-

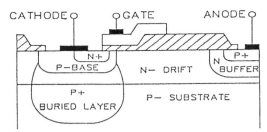

Fig. 4. LIGT structure showing p$^+$ buried layer (type D).

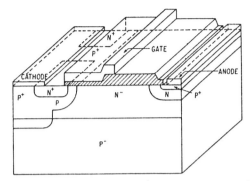

Fig. 5. LIGT structure showing p$^+$ surface shorts (type G).

TABLE I
LIGT DEVICE TYPES

Device Type	Substrate	p$^+$ Sinker	p$^+$ Buried Layer	p$^+$ Surface Shorts
A	P- epi	No	No	No
B	P- epi on P$^+$	No	No	No
C	P- epi	Yes	No	No
D	P- epi	No	Yes	No
E	P- epi on P$^+$	Yes	No	No
F	P- epi on P$^+$	No	Yes	No
G	P- epi	No	No	Yes
H	P- epi on P$^+$	No	No	Yes

ing current level of the device, as this component of current does not trigger the parasitic four-layer path. A schematic diagram of this LIGT is shown in Fig. 5. The various LIGT structures fabricated are called device types A through H and are identified in Table I.

Prior to latching, the LIGT can be turned off by removing the gate-to-source voltage. When the gate bias is removed, base drives for the vertical and lateral p-n-p transistors disappear since the MOS channel current feeds the bipolar bases. The lateral and vertical bipolar transistor components then turn off through recombination and sweeping out of the excess carriers. The LIGT turn-off is not treated here and will be presented elsewhere [6]. After the excess carriers are removed, the voltage mainly appears across junctions J_2 and J_4 (of Fig. 1). The n$^-$ epi layer becomes depleted of mobile carriers and the surface electric field assumes nearly a constant value (as in LCC and RESURF diodes [7], [8]). Punchthrough breakdown is avoided by means of an n-buffer layer surrounding the p$^+$ emitter.

From the above description of the various LIGT structures and device physics, it is clear that the device current and carrier distributions are two-dimensional in nature.

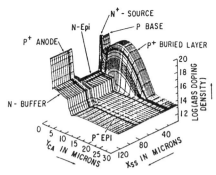

Fig. 6. Doping distribution used for simulating type F LIGT structure.

Simple analytical expressions for the degree of conductivity modulation and current–voltage relationships while providing a useful insight into the device behavior are rather difficult to obtain without introducing arbitrary parameters. We have solved the full set of semiconductor equations and the appropriate boundary conditions by numerical means, the results of which will be discussed in the next section.

IV. MODELING RESULTS

An exact two-dimensional computer program [9], [10] that employs a finite difference technique to solve the set of semiconductor equations simultaneously on a nonuniform grid is used to determine the carrier and potential distributions inside the LIGT for any given dc bias point. It employs well-known physical models for the various transport parameters and carrier generation and recombination processes. In order to elucidate the LIGT device behavior the simulation results for a type F LIGT (see Fig. 4) will be discussed in some detail. The doping density used for simulation of the type F LIGT is shown in Fig. 6. The doping distributions are chosen so that the breakdown voltage of the LIGT is greater than 500 V. The threshold voltage of the device is about 6.5 V.

The carrier distributions are shown in Figs. 7 and 8, when the LIGT is biased to a gate voltage of 20 V and drain voltage of 2.3 V. The drift region is well modulated by carriers with carrier density of the order of 10^{16} per cm^{-3}, well above the background level of 2.10^{13} cm^{-3}. The electron and hole densities are nearly equal in the drift region as is to be expected in high-level injection. This conductivity modulation is the reason why the LIGT has a lower forward voltage drop compared to the LDMOSFET.

The electron distribution near the DMOS section of the LIGT is shown in Fig. 9. The p-base region surrounding the n$^+$ source is not injecting carriers because it is effectively shorted with the p-base by the surface contact. The potential distribution is shown in Fig. 10. As can be seen from it, most of the potential drops across the channel and at the collector region. The larger drop of voltage across the channel is a reflection of the fact that the drift region is heavily modulated.

The current paths inside the device can be easily determined, once the stream function is calculated. Following the method described in [11], the total stream function is calculated from the knowledge of the total current densities. The current lines are shown in Fig. 11 for the case

103

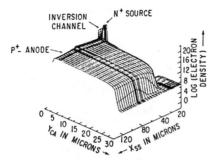

Fig. 7. Electron density distribution inside the type F LIGT at bias point; $V_{GS} = 20$ V and $V_{DS} = 2.3$ V. The substrate is at the source potential.

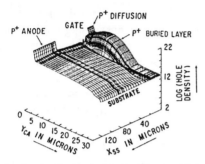

Fig. 8. Hole density distribution inside the type F LIGT for the same bias point as in Fig. 7.

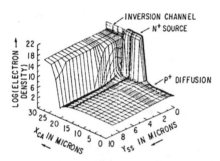

Fig. 9. Close-up of the electron distribution shown in Fig. 7.

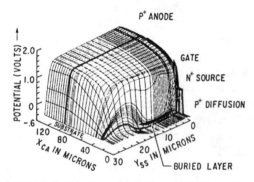

Fig. 10. Potential distribution inside the type F LIGT for the same bias point as in Fig. 7.

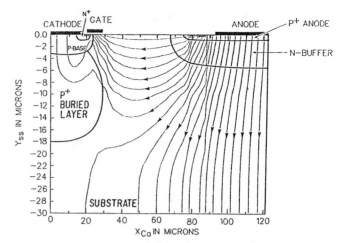

Fig. 11. Current distribution inside the type F LIGT. The bias point is same as in Fig. 7.

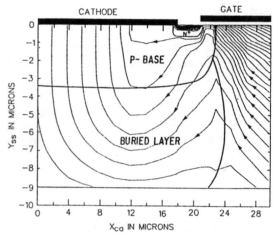

Fig. 12. Close-up of current distribution near the DMOS section of the LIGT, whose current distribution is shown in Fig. 11.

when the gate is at 20 V and the drain is at 2.3 V with respect to the cathode. The substrate is tied to the cathode and is at zero potential. Equal amounts of current, in this case about 4.6 A/cm², flows between any two adjacent lines. The current from the anode streams vertically into the substrate and laterally into the channel and the p⁺ buried layer and p-base region. At this bias point, about 60 percent of the current is flowing into the substrate and the rest is flowing laterally out of which two-thirds flows into the channel and the rest (one-third) flows into the p-base,

p⁺ buried layer. An expanded view of current flow around the p⁺ buried layer is shown in Fig. 12. The current flows into the p⁺ buried layer region, away from the p-base underneath the n⁺ source. Since the current component that does not pass through the p-base region does not contribute to forward biasing the source p-base junction, the latching current level is increased, as discussed earlier.

The current lines inside a type B LIGT on p⁻ epitaxial on p⁺ substrate is shown in Fig. 13(a). In this case all the current lines pass through the p-base region before being collected at the cathode contact as is seen in the close up shown in Fig. 13(b). As a result, type B LIGT's latch at a lower current level, compared to type F LIGT's.

The calculated I–V characteristic of the type F LIGT is shown in Fig. 14, including the various current components. The ratio between the vertical and lateral current component decreases with increased forward bias. This is due to the vertical p-n-p transistor current becoming saturated at higher anode voltage. For the voltage range shown in Fig. 14, the device has not latched, the maximum junction drop across the n⁺ source and p-base junction is about 0.38 V. As it appears, for the design parameters used in this simulation, the device will current limit. The ratio of the substrate current to the lateral current depends upon the particular design. For example, with a dif-

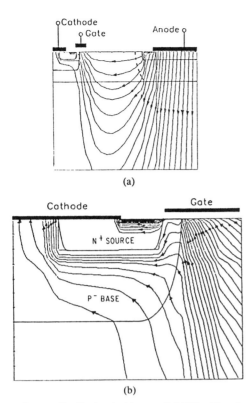

(a)

(b)

Fig. 13. (a) Current distribution inside type *B* LIGT with gate voltage = 20 V and anode voltage of 2 V. (b) Close-up of current lines near the DMOS section, corresponding to (a).

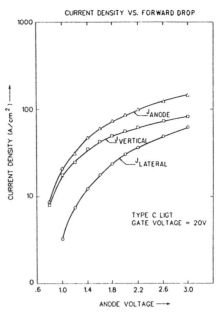

Fig. 14. Calculated current density versus forward drop for type *F* LIGT.

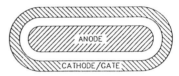

Fig. 15. Schematic representation of device layout.

ferent design the lateral current can be made to exceed the vertical or the substrate current. Based on the simulation results and the understanding of the internal current flow, carrier, and potential distributions at various bias points, several test structures have been designed and fabricated. The test devices along with the process sequences to fabricate them are discussed in the next sections.

V. TEST DEVICE DESCRIPTION

Regardless of the specific configuration, all of the test devices were designed with radial symmetry. The cathode and gate completely surround the anode, making the device self-isolating.

A schematic representation of the layout for most of the test devices is illustrated in Fig. 15; we refer to this as a "racetrack" configuration. While the computer models assume a strictly two-dimensional device, the actual device is three-dimensional; the semicircular ends are required for isolation. Because of the difference between the radii of curvature of the cathode/gate region and that of the anode, the ends behave differently from the linear portion. This complicates the issue of comparing measured and simulated performance of the LIGT structures.

VI. PROCESS DESCRIPTION

The processing sequence used for fabrication was identical for all test devices, except as necessary to implement the various device modifications described earlier. Two types of starting wafers were used: 1) 60–90 $\Omega \cdot$ cm $\langle 100 \rangle$ oriented boron-doped silicon substrates, and 2) 35μm-thick 60–90 $\Omega \cdot$ cm boron-doped epitaxial layers on p$^+$

substrates. p$^+$ buried layers for type *D* and *F* devices were formed prior to growth of the 4–8-μm-thick phosphorus-doped epitaxial layers.

The total charge in the n-epi was chosen for a minimum breakdown voltage of 500 V for the devices with drift region lengths of 35 μm. The n-epi was grown lightly doped; the majority of the dopants were introduced through ion implantation, in accordance with the LCC technique.

A deep boron diffusion was used to form the p$^+$ isolation sinkers. The gate oxide thickness was 100 nm, while that of the field oxide was 1 μm. The polysilicon gate electrode layer was deposited by low-pressure chemical vapor deposition (LPCVD), then heavily doped with phosphorus. The cathode region, consisting of the p-base and the n$^+$ source diffusions self-aligned to the polysilicon gate electrode, was formed by the conventional double-diffused method. The p$^+$ anode region was formed in the n-buffer diffusion, which prevents punchthrough of the vertical p-n-p component of the LIGT under high anode voltage conditions. The process was completed with conventional processing to etch contact openings, and to deposit and pattern the metallization layer.

VII. EXPERIMENTAL RESULTS

A. I–V Characteristics

The current density at different forward[2] drops for LIGT devices with different designs are shown in Fig. 16. As

[2]These results have already been presented in [6] and are reproduced here for the sake of completeness.

105

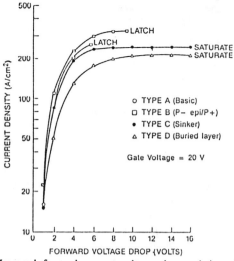

Fig. 16. Measured forward current-voltage characteristics of different LIGT structures.

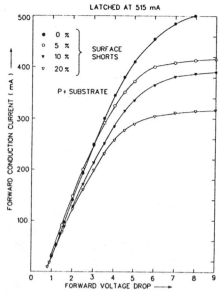

Fig. 18. Measured forward current-voltage characteristics of type *H* LIGT.

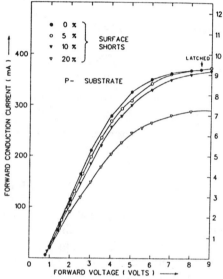

Fig. 17. Measured forward current-voltage characteristics of type *G* LIGT.

expected, the current densities of LIGT's made over p^- epitaxial layer on p^+ substrates are higher than LIGT's made over p^- substates. However, both of these types of devices latch, the former having a higher latching current than the latter. The LIGT devices that employ a sinker diffusion to reduce the p-base resistance (types *C* and *E*) as well as LIGT structures with a buried layer to divert holes away from the p-base region (types *D* and *F*) current limit before latching. The type *D* and *F* LIGT's, however, show higher forward drops at the same current density, due to a lower level of conductivity modulation in the drift region.

The current-voltage characteristics of type *G* LIGT's on p^- substrates, whose n^+ source diffusion is interrupted orthogonally by p^+ diffusions (see Fig. 5) at periodic intervals are shown in Fig. 17. The p^+ surface diffusions are called surface shorts. Type *A* devices without surface short latched at an anode current of 350 mA, and type *B* devices without surface short latched at an anode current of 515 mA. In contrast, all devices with surface shorts exhibit current limiting rather than latching. This is as expected because surface shorts like buried layers provide alternate paths for hole currents to flow to the cathode

terminal without going through the p-base junction. The increase in forward drop due to the effect of the surface shorts on the forward voltage drop is small at typical operating current levels (100–150 mA). With an increasing percentage of the density of surface shorts, the anode current decreases, due to the loss of MOS channel. The current-voltage characteristics of type *H* LIGT's on p^- epitaxial on p^+ substrates with various density of surface shorts are shown in Fig. 18. While these sets of curves are similar in nature to those described in Fig. 17, it is to be noted that the anode currents are substantially higher for type *H* LIGT's fabricated on p^- epitaxial on p^+ substrates than type *G* LIGT's, which are fabricated on p^- epitaxial substrates. Another point to note is that the saturation current levels of the type *G* and *H* LIGT's decrease with the percentage increase of the surface short area to the total device area. This can be explained as follows. With the increase of surface short, the effective width of the MOS channels is decreased along with a proportional decrease of the MOS current, and in accordance with (3) the device current decreases.

B. Substrate and Lateral Current Components

The measured substrate current densities for different types of LIGT at a gate bias of 20 V are shown as a function of anode voltage in Fig. 19. The substrate currents are generally an order of magnitude smaller for devices made on p^- substrates compared to those made on p^- epitaxial on p^+ substrates. The measured lateral current densities for different types of LIGT's for the same gate bias of 20 V are shown as a function of anode voltage in Fig. 20. The simulated results for type *F* LIGT's are also shown in Figs. 19 and 20 for comparison. The fit between simulation and experiment is fairly good in view of the fact that no attempt was made to exactly correlate the structural and doping profiles of the tested device. The lateral current in the LIGT is the sum of electron current flowing in the MOS channel and the hole current collected at the source contact, which is the collector current of the lateral bipolar transistor. The lateral current component of the devices shown here which are fabricated on p^- sub-

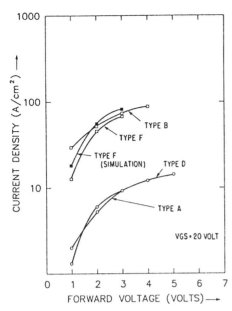

Fig. 19. Substrate current density versus forward drop for different types of LIGT's at gate voltage of 20 V. Simulated result for type *F* is shown for comparison.

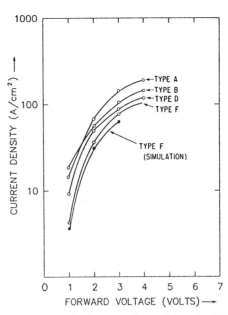

Fig. 20. Lateral current density versus forward drop for different types of LIGT's at gate voltage of 20 V. Simulated result for type *F* is shown for comparison.

strates are higher than those fabricated on p⁻ epitaxial on p⁺ substrates. This is due to the fact that more current is flowing into the collector of the lateral bipolar transistor than to the vertical bipolar transistor, due to the large substrate resistance, for devices fabricated on p⁻ substrates. The fraction of current that goes to the substrate as opposed to that collected laterally is a function of several design parameters and can be varied to suit one's need. However, substrate currents could potentially interfere with the operation of other devices in a power IC by raising the potential of the substrate near the n-epi/p-junction. This is especially true for circuits where a large fraction of the total area is used by LIGT's, as compared with those where the LIGT's take up a smaller part of the total area. However, for equivalent devices the voltage drop across the p⁻ substrate is substantially greater than for p-epi/p⁺ substrate; the effective substrate resistance of the latter is orders of magnitude smaller than that of the former, while the substrate current increases by about a factor of five. Thus, for common-source applications where the substrate and cathode are at the same potential, the p-epi/p⁺ substrate is probably the better choice. Also, power IC technologies can be made effectively immune to substrate potentials of several volts by proper protection of the low-voltage components[3] [12].

VIII. Summary

The physics of steady-state behavior of junction-isolated LIGT's have been discussed both analytically and through computer simulation. Various structural and process enhancements have been developed to increase the current handling capability of LIGT's as well as suppressing latchup. Different LIGT structures have been fabricated, tested and analyzed. Current limiting LIGT's, i.e., LIGT's that do not latch, have been fabricated. It is shown

in particular that replacing the substrate p⁻ with a p⁻ epitaxial layer on a p⁺ substrate significantly enhances the forward current density at a given forward drop. Buried-layer and surface short LIGT devices have been fabricated that current limit rather than latch at high current levels. These devices, because of their low forward drop at high current densities, are ideally suited for use as power switches and can be easily integrated in applications involving common source configurations. These devices, since they employ thin epitaxial layers and have a lateral geometry, can also be easily integrated with low-voltage logic circuitry.

References

[1] M. Darwish and K. Board, "Lateral resurfed COMFET," *Electron. Lett.*, vol. 20, p. 520, 1984.
[2] R. Jayaraman, V. Rumennik, B. Singer, and E. H. Stupp, "Comparison of high voltage devices for power integrated circuits," in *IEDM Tech Dig.*, p. 258, 1984.
[3] D. N. Pattanayak and M. S. Adler, "Analysis of current flow in lateral insulated gate transistors," in *Proc. 43rd Annual Device Research Conf.* (Boulder, CO), paper 6B5, June 17-19, 1985.
[4] B. J. Baliga, M. S. Adler, P. V. Gray, R. P. Love, and N. Zommer, "The insulated gate rectifier (IGR): A new power switching device," in *IEDM Tech. Dig.*, p. 264, 1982.
[5] A. L. Robinson, D. N. Pattanayak, M. S. Adler, B. J. Baliga, and E. J. Wildi, "Lateral insulated gate transistors with improved latching characteristics," in *IEDM Tech. Dig.*, p. 744, 1985.
[6] Unpublished.
[7] J. A. Appels and H. M. J. Vaes, "High voltage thin layer devices (RESURF devices)," in *IEDM Tech. Dig.*, p. 238, 1979.
[8] E. J. Wildi, P. V. Gray, T. P. Chow, H. R. Chang, "Modeling and process implementation of implanted RESURF type devices," in *IEDM Tech. Dig.*, p. 268, 1982.
[9] M. S. Adler, "A method for achieving and choosing variable density grids in finite difference formulations and the importance of degeneracy and band gap narrowing in device modeling," in *Proc. NASECODE I Conf.* Dublin, Ireland: Boole Press, no. 3-30.
[10] ——, "A method for terminating mesh lines in finite difference formulations of the semiconductor device equations," *Solid-State Electron.*, vol. 23, pp. 845-853, 1980.
[11] D. N. Pattanayak, "Current paths in semiconductor devices," General Electric TIS Rep. 85CRD141, 1985.
[12] E. J. Wildi, T. P. Chow, M. S. Adler, M. E. Cornell, and G. C. Pifer, "New high voltage IC technology," in *IEDM Tech. Dig.*, p. 262, 1984.

---

[3]For a discussion on this subject of integrated power devices, see V. Rumennik, "Power devices are in the chips," *IEEE Spectrum*, p. 42, July 1985.

The SINFET—A Schottky Injection MOS-Gated Power Transistor

JOHNNY K. O. SIN, STUDENT MEMBER, IEEE, C. ANDRE T. SALAMA, SENIOR MEMBER, IEEE, AND LI-ZHANG HOU

Abstract—A new MOS-gated power device, the Schottky injection FET (SINFET), is described in this paper. The device offers 6 times higher current handling capability than conventional n-channel power LDMOS transistors of comparable size and voltage capability and still maintains a comparable switching speed. The low on-resistance is obtained by conductivity modulation of the high-resistivity n^- drift region using a Schottky injector. Since only a small number of minority carriers are injected, the speed of the device is not degraded substantially and high latchup resistance is achieved. Breakdown voltages and specific on-resistance observed on typical devices are 170 V and 0.01 Ω · cm^2, respectively. Gate-turn off times are of the order of 30 ns. Two-dimensional simulation and experimental results comparing the SIN-FET with the LDMOST and lateral insulated gate transistor (LIGT) are presented.

I. Introduction

THE MOST COMMON MOS transistor structure used in high-voltage integrated circuit (HVIC) applications is the LDMOST. One of the major drawbacks of the structure is the high on-resistance that limits the current handling capability of the device. Recently, new vertical structures such as the IGT [1], [2] or COMFET [3], [4] and lateral structures such as the LIGT [5]–[9], which combine MOS and bipolar transistors, have been proposed. These structures use conductivity modulation of the drift region to reduce the on-resistance. However, since a large quantity of minority carriers are injected into the drift region, a serious degradation in switching speed results. In this paper, a new lateral high-voltage MOS-FET structure, called the Schottky injection FET (SIN-FET) [10] is described in detail. The structure is suitable for high-voltage IC applications and provides high input impedance, low on-resistance, and most importantly switching speeds comparable to conventional n-channel LDMOST's. In addition, it is fairly latchup proof and offers low substrate leakage currents.

To demonstrate the operation and characteristics of the SINFET, two-dimensional simulations and experimental results are presented. A comparison between the SIN-FET, LDMOST, and LIGT is also given.

Manuscript received April 15, 1986; revised July 31, 1986. This work was supported by the Natural Sciences and Engineering Research Council of Canada.

J. K. O. Sin and C. A. T. Salama are with the Department of Electrical Engineering, University of Toronto, Toronto, Canada M5S 1A4.

L. Z. Hou is on leave with the Department of Electrical Engineering, University of Toronto, Toronto, Ontario, Canada M5S 1A4. He is with the Hebei Semiconductor Research Institute, Shijiazhuang, Hebei, China.

IEEE Log Number 8610814.

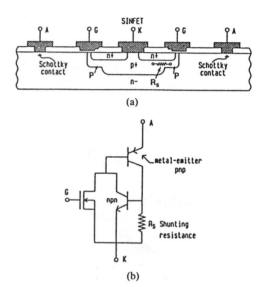

Fig. 1. (a) Cross section and (b) model of the SINFET.

II. Device Structure and Operation

A cross section and circuit model of the n-channel SIN-FET are illustrated in Figs. 1(a) and (b), respectively. The device structure is similar to that of an LDMOS transistor except that a Schottky barrier is used instead of a high-low (n^+-n^-) "ohmic" contact at the anode (drain). The resistivity of the n^- drift region in the device is modulated by injection of minority carriers from the anode resulting in a significant reduction in the on-resistance as in the case of the IGT. However, the present device differs in a fundamental way from the LIGT in the fact that the injecting contact is a Schottky diode which is traditionally only thought to inject majority carriers efficiently. However, as has been recently verified experimentally [11], Schottky barriers under high-level injection can operate in a bipolar mode and inject minority carriers efficiently enough to cause conductivity modulation, but in small enough quantities[1] not to cause significant minority-carrier storage effects, which can slow down the device.

Operation of the SINFET is similar to that of the LIGT except that the Schottky barrier at the anode causes the SINFET to turn-on at a lower forward voltage than the LIGT.

---

[1]Instead of controlling minority carrier injection level, alternatives such as controlling the carrier lifetime by irradiation have been proposed [2], [4]. However, these techniques are not practical in an IC environment.

Reprinted from *IEEE Trans. Electron Devices*, vol. ED-33, pp. 1940–1947, Dec. 1986.

As shown in Fig. 1(b), the model for the SINFET structure consists of a MOSFET and a four-layer p-n-p-n thyristor like device but with a metal emitter p-n-p transistor. During normal operation, current flowing through the shunting resistance R_S of the n-p-n transistor is very small, keeping the current gain of the n-p-n transistor very low. The equivalent circuit in this mode of operation can be simplified to a metal-emitter p-n-p transistor driven by a MOSFET with the n-p-n transistor omitted. At high operating current level, the parasitic thyristor may latch on. This occurs when the sum of the current gain of the metal-emitter p-n-p transistor ($\alpha_{\text{p-n-p}}$) and the current gain of the n-p-n transistor ($\alpha_{\text{n-p-n}}$) is greater than or equal to unity. Turning off the device, in this case, may have to be done by lowering the anode current below the holding current value of the parasitic thyristor or reversing the anode voltage and commutating the structure. Since the current gain of the metal-emitter p-n-p transistor is much lower than that of a conventional p-n-p transistor, latchup current level in the SINFET is higher than in the LIGT.

In addition, in monolithic high-voltage devices such as the LIGT, significant substrate current leakage is observed. This leakage is due to the parasitic vertical p-n-p transistor formed by the anode, the n⁻ base and the p-substrate. In junction isolated SINFET structure, this parasitic p-n-p transistor is formed by the anode metal contact, the n⁻ base and the p-substrate; thus, its current gain is much smaller than in conventional vertical p-n-p transistor resulting in significantly less leakage currents.

The design of the SINFET is critically dependent on the ability of the Schottky barrier to inject minority carriers. For a Schottky contact to provide efficient injection, the barrier height ϕ_h for minority carriers (holes) must be low. A low barrier height can be obtained by choosing the proper metal–semiconductor combination and controlling the density of surface states at the metal–semiconductor interface [12]. To obtain high minority-carrier injection efficiency, surface states at that interface must be minimized so that ϕ_h will be effectively determined by the metal work function and electron affinity of the semiconductor. The injection efficiency of the Schottky barrier is also dependent on the geometry and doping concentration of the neutral semiconductor region. Amemiya and Mizushima [11] found that optimum design of high-speed high-blocking-voltage low on-resistance Schottky diodes requires: 1) ϕ_h to be between 0.2 and 0.35 eV and 2) the neutral semiconductor region thickness and resistivity to be less than 20 μm and larger than 10 Ω · cm, respectively.

III. Two-Dimensional Device Modeling

Numerical modeling offers a useful method of providing insight into the physics of device operation as well as accurate quantitative predictions of device characteristics for complex structures such as the SINFET.

The objectives of the simulations are to investigate the conductivity modulation effects in the SINFET and to compare the forward conduction characteristics of the SINFET, the LIGT, and the LDMOST. Correlation be-

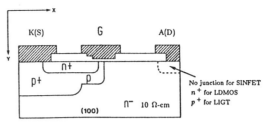

Fig. 2. Cross section of the structures used in the numerical simulations.

tween the simulations and experimental results are presented.

The numerical simulator used in the present investigation is PISCES-IIB, a two-dimensional simulator developed at Stanford University by Dutton and his co-workers [13]. It solves the Poisson and continuity equations and includes Schottky boundary conditions at both low- and high-level injections.

The Schottky-barrier model used is the one implemented in PISCES IIB [14]. This model accounts for the work function of the electrode metal, the surface recombination velocity, the barrier lowering mechanisms arising from image forces and the surface state density at the metal–semiconductor interface [15]. Furthermore, mechanisms such as Shockley–Read–Hall recombination, Auger recombination, and concentration-dependent mobility are also considered in the model to account for moderate and high injection level effects. The model parameters used in the simulations were extracted from both experimental and theoretical data [13], [14]. Simulations indicate that the most important of these parameters are the work function (4.77 eV), electron affinity (4.05 eV), and barrier height lowering coefficient [14] (2×10^{-7} cm), which determine the final barrier height for hole injection in the diode ($\phi_h = 0.4$ eV in our case).

A cross section of the three structures used in the simulations is shown in Fig. 2. In this figure, the anode of the SINFET is an aluminum–n⁻ silicon Schottky barrier, the drain of the LDMOST is an aluminum–n⁺-n⁻ high-low junction and the anode of the LIGT is an aluminum–p⁺-n⁻ diode. The relevant dimensions and doping profiles are defined from processing parameters through SU-PREM III [16], which acts as an input interface to PISCES IIB. For illustration purposes, the simulations presented here were performed with a gate to source (cathode) voltage of 20 V and with the source (cathode) connected to ground.

Figs. 3 and 4 show the simulation results for the two-dimensional hole and electron concentrations respectively in the SINFET structure at an anode voltage of 1.5 V. As can be seen from Fig. 3, holes injected from the anode are present in the n⁻ drift region. A portion of these injected holes flow through the shunting resistance R_S and are collected by the cathode, and the rest recombine with the electrons flowing from the channel. The injected hole concentration in the drift region is about an order of magnitude higher than the n⁻ substrate doping concentration. These injected carriers are responsible for modulating the conductivity of the high-resistivity drift region. It is worth

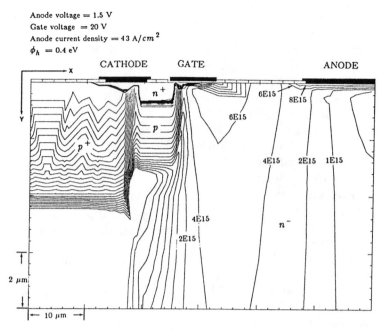

Anode voltage = 1.5 V
Gate voltage = 20 V
Anode current density = 43 A/cm^2
ϕ_h = 0.4 eV

Fig. 3. Hole concentration in the SINFET structure at a forward voltage of 1.5 V.

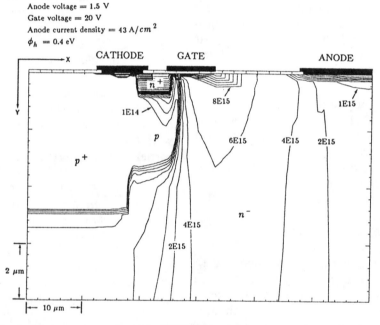

Anode voltage = 1.5 V
Gate voltage = 20 V
Anode current density = 43 A/cm^2
ϕ_h = 0.4 eV

Fig. 4. Electron concentration in the SINFET structure at a forward voltage of 1.5 V.

pointing out that the hole concentration near the electron accumulation region under the gate electrode is higher than the hole concentration in the drift region. This is due to the fact that the current transport mechanism of minority carriers originating from Schottky contact at high forward bias is mainly governed by drift rather than diffusion as is the case in a p-n junction. Holes injected from the anode are swept through the drift region by the electric field and pile up because the accumulation region acts as a reflecting barrier [17].

As can be seen from Fig. 4, electron concentration in the drift region is also about an order of magnitude higher than the original doping concentration. Thus, as far as the

on-state is concerned, the effective substrate doping concentration is about an order of magnitude higher than it was originally before modulation resulting in a substantial increase in the current handling capability of the SINFET.

Again from Fig. 4, one observes that the electron concentration in the p-channel region below the n^+ cathode is low but finite. These electrons originate from the n^+ region and are due to the slight forward biasing of the n^+-p junction that results from the lateral hole current flowing through the shunting resistance R_S. This effect is shown more prominently in Fig. 5, in which the SINFET structure is simulated with an anode voltage of 3 V. At this bias voltage, a much higher hole current density is

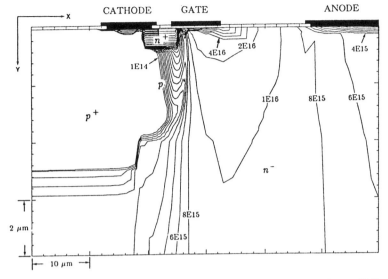

Anode voltage = 3 V
Gate voltage = 20 V
Anode current density = 183 A/cm^2
ϕ_h = 0.4 eV

Fig. 5. Electron concentration in the SINFET structure at a forward voltage of 3 V.

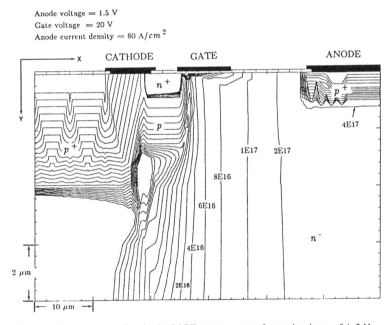

Anode voltage = 1.5 V
Gate voltage = 20 V
Anode current density = 80 A/cm^2

Fig. 6. Hole concentration in the LIGT structure at a forward voltage of 1.5 V.

flowing through the shunting resistance R_S causing further forward biasing of the n^+-p junction. Electrons are now concentrated at the right corner of the n^+ region. Any further increase in anode forward bias can cause the n^+–p-channel junction to become significantly forward biased and results in high electron injection from the n^+ region into the p-channel region, forcing the structure to latch. When the structure latches on, it operates in a thyristor-like conducting mode. In this mode of operation most of the electron current flows through the p-channel region instead of the inversion channel and gate control is lost. The simulated current density prior to latchup was found

to be approximately 210 A/cm^2 at a forward anode voltage of 3.4 V for the structure under investigation.

For comparison purposes, the two-dimensional hole concentration in an equivalent LIGT structure is shown in Fig. 6. The simulation was performed at an anode voltage of 1.5 V. From the figure, it can be seen that the amount of minority carriers (holes) injected from the anode of the LIGT is about two orders of magnitude higher than the original substrate doping and an order of magnitude higher than the amount injected by the SINFET under the same biasing condition. In fact, the anode injection efficiency, defined as the ratio of the hole current to the total current,

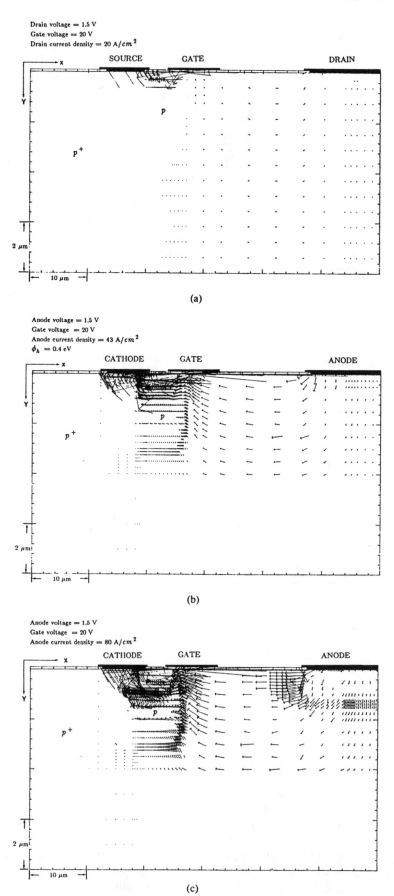

Fig. 7. Total current vectors for (a) LDMOST, (b) SINFET, and (c) LIGT.

was calculated to be approximately 21 and 90 percent for the SINFET and LIGT, respectively. For forward anode voltages higher than 1.5 V, the LIGT latches on. The current density simulated prior to latchup is approximately 80 A/cm^2.

The latchup current density of both the SINFET and LIGT are dependent upon the amount of minority carriers flowing through the p-base resistance. Since the minority-carrier injection efficiency of the Schottky contact in the SINFET is very low, less minority carriers flow through the shunting resistance, and the device can be operated at a higher forward bias and at higher operating current levels. However, in the case of the LIGT, a significant amount of minority carriers is injected by the p$^+$ anode even at a low forward bias, causing the structure to latchup at a low current level. To improve the latching characteristics in both structures, the shunting resistance R_S must be reduced such that higher current density can flow through it without causing a significant voltage drop. This can be achieved by moving the p$^+$ diffusion closer to the outer edge of the p-channel region, thereby reducing the distance between the outer edge of the p-channel region and the cathode short [9].

The total current vectors through the LDMOST, SINFET, and LIGT are shown in Fig. 7(a), (b), and (c). In these figures, the length of the vectors represent the magnitude of the current, and the arrows indicate the direction of current flow. Fig. 7(a) shows the current vectors for the LDMOST biased at a drain voltage of 1.5 V. The current is uniformly distributed and flows deep into the bulk. It can also be seen that in this case there are no current vectors in the p-channel region (no conductivity modulation). Fig. 7(b) shows the current vectors for the SINFET structure also biased at 1.5-V anode voltage. The current flows closer to the surface due to conductivity modulation and splits into two paths, one flowing towards the inversion channel and the other toward the p-channel region. Current vectors are present in the p-channel region and are due to minority carriers injected by the anode and flowing through the shunting resistance. In Fig. 7(c), the current in the LIGT flows again in a similar manner as in the SINFET. However, more current vectors are present in the p-channel region due to higher injection levels in that structure. The current densities, in the cases under consideration, were calculated to be 20, 43, and 80 A/cm^2 for the LDMOST, SINFET, and LIGT, respectively.

The forward conduction characteristics of the three structures, obtained by simulating the current through the drain (anode) electrode for a set of applied voltage using PISCES IIB, are shown in Fig. 8. The LIGT has the highest current handling capability at forward bias beyond 0.9 V and latches on at voltage higher than 1.5 V. The SINFET has higher current density than the LDMOST at forward voltage greater than 1 V and eventually latches on at voltage above 3.4 V.

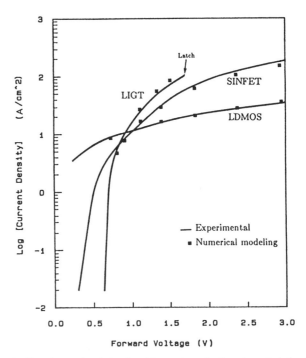

Fig. 8. Experimental and simulated forward conduction characteristics for the LDMOST, SINFET, and LIGT.

IV. DEVICE FABRICATION

A 6-μm linewidth and 3-μm alignment tolerance process was used to fabricate the experimental SINFET devices on 10-$\Omega \cdot$ cm n-type 100-orientation Si substrates. The gate oxide thickness was 900 Å. The channel length, drift region length and channel width were 1.5 μm, 20 μm, and 0.4 cm, respectively. The total active device area was 0.3 mm^2. The Schottky-barrier contact in the SINFET structure was fabricated using aluminum on n-type silicon. The minority-carrier barrier height for this type of Schottky diode is approximately 0.4 eV.

For the sake of comparison, standard n-channel LDMOST's and LIGT's with exactly the same dimensions were fabricated simultaneously with the SINFET's on the same substrates. A comparison on the dc and transient performance of the three types of devices will be given in the next section.

V. EXPERIMENTAL RESULTS

The typical *I–V* characteristics of the SINFET are illustrated in Fig. 9. At zero gate bias, the forward and reverse blocking voltages of the SINFET are 170 and 80 V, respectively. By comparison, the forward and reverse blocking voltages of the LIGT are 170 and 90 V, respectively, and the breakdown voltage of the LDMOST is 170 V. The threshold voltages for all the devices are typically 2 V. The experimental forward conduction characteristics of the LDMOST, SINFET, and LIGT are also shown in Fig. 8 and compared to the two-dimensional simulation results. Very good agreement was obtained between experimental and simulated results. For forward drops be-

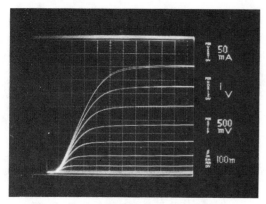

Fig. 9. Typical SINFET *I–V* characteristics.

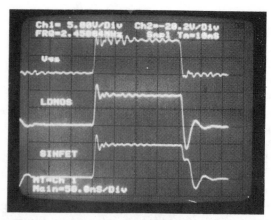

Fig. 10. Switching waveforms for the LDMOST and SINFET. Top: gate voltage, 5 V/div. Middle: LDMOST current waveform, 100 mA/div. Bottom: SINFET current waveform, 100 mA/div. Time scale: 50 ns/div.

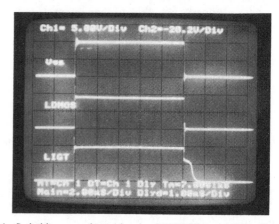

Fig. 11. Switching waveforms for the LDMOST and LIGT. Top: gate voltage, 5 V/div. Middle: LDMOST current waveform, 100 mA/div. Bottom: LIGT current waveform, 100 mA/div. Time scale: 2 μs/div.

low 0.3 V, the LDMOST is conducting appreciably, while the SINFET is just beginning to conduct. Above this voltage, the SINFET shows a factor of 6 improvement in current density over the LDMOST for the same forward voltage ($V_F = 3$ V). On the other hand, the LIGT starts to conduct at about 0.7 V and has about 5 times higher current handling capability than the LDMOST at $V_F = 1.7$ V. The specific on-resistances of the SINFET, LDMOST, and LIGT were measured to be 0.01, 0.09, and 0.008 Ω · cm^2, respectively.

The latchup current density for the SINFET was measured to be 225 A/cm^2 at $V_F = 3.3$ V, which agrees closely with the simulated result. By comparison, the LIGT latches on at forward voltage of 1.7 V which is close to the simulated value of 1.5 V. The latchup current density at that voltage is approximately 100 A/cm^2. This confirms experimentally that the parasitic metal–emitter p-n-p transistor in the SINFET has a lower current gain than the conventional lateral p-n-p transistor in the LIGT. Due to the low injection efficiency at the anode and high substrate resistivity, the substrate current in junction isolated SINFET devices was found to be 3 percent of the anode current.

The transient characteristics of the three types of devices were investigated. The measurements were carried out using a resistive load connected between the anode and the power supply with the cathode connected to ground. A gate drive of 10 V and a load current of 200 mA (65 A/cm^2) were used. The resulting anode current switching waveforms are shown in Figs. 10 and 11. Fig. 10 shows the drain and anode current waveforms of the LDMOST and SINFET. The turn-on time for both devices is 10 ns, while the turn-off time of the SINFET (30 ns) is slightly longer than the LDMOST (10 ns), as expected. This confirms that the injection level in the Schottky contact is indeed low enough not to affect the switching performance appreciably. In Fig. 11, the drain and anode current waveforms of the LDMOST and LIGT are shown. The turn-on time of the LIGT is comparable to the LDMOST; however, the turn-off time of the LIGT is about 1.5 μs due to the large quantity of minority carriers stored in the drift region, which has to be removed via recombination.

VI. DISCUSSION AND CONCLUSION

A new power transistor, called the Schottky injection FET (SINFET), was described in this paper. This transistor uses a Schottky injector to achieve conductivity modulation of the high-resistivity drift region. It provides 6 times higher current handling capability than conventional n-channel LDMOS transistors while still maintaining a comparable switching speed. In addition to low on-resistance and fast switching, the SINFET devices also provide high forward and reverse blocking capability, high latchup current density, and low substrate leakage current when junction isolation is used.

The experimental results reported here were obtained on nonoptimized devices as far as forward and reverse blocking voltages are concerned. To improve the forward blocking voltage, RESURF [18] techniques should be used. The reverse blocking voltage of the SINFET is sustained by the Schottky contact at the anode. At high reverse bias, the high field intensity at that contact gives rise to low breakdown voltage and excess leakage current. This electrode sharp-edge effect can be reduced by guarding the Schottky contact with a p$^+$ diffused guard ring [19], [20].

From the results of the theoretical and experimental comparisons of the various structures, it can be concluded that for low current applications in which switching speed is very critical, the LDMOS transistors are advantageous. However, for high-current and low-frequency applications, the LIGT's are most suitable. The SINFET are very promising in applications that require medium switching speeds and current densities.

REFERENCES

[1] B. J. Baliga, M. S. Adler, P. V. Gray, R. P. Love, and N. Zommer, "The insulated gate rectifier: A new power switching device," in *IEDM Tech. Dig.*, pp. 264–267, 1982.

[2] M. F. Cheng, G. C. Pifer, B. J. Baliga, M. S. Adler, and P. V. Gray, "25 amp, 500 volt insulated gate transistor," in *IEDM Tech. Dig.*, pp. 83–86, 1983.

[3] J. P. Russell, A. M. Goodman, L. A. Goodman, and J. M. Neilson, "The COMFET—A new high-conductance MOS-gated device," *IEEE Electron Device Lett.*, vol. EDL-4, pp. 63–65, 1983.

[4] A. M. Goodman, J. P. Russell, L. A. Goodman, C. J. Nuese, and J. M. Neilson, "Improved COMFET with fast switching speed and high current capability," in *IEDM Tech. Dig.*, pp. 79–82, 1983.

[5] M. Darwish and K. Board, "Lateral resurfed comfet," *Electron. Lett.*, vol. 20, no. 12, pp. 519–520, 1984.

[6] R. Jayaraman, V. Rumennik, B. Singer, and E. H. Stupp, "Comparison of high voltage devices for power integrated circuits," in *IEDM Tech. Dig.*, pp. 258–261, 1984.

[7] D. Pattanayak and M. Adler, "Analysis of current flow in lateral insulated gate transistors," in *Proc. Device Research Conf.*, p. VIB-5, 1985.

[8] M. R. Simpson, P. A. Gough, F. I. Hshieh, and V. Rumennik, "Analysis of the lateral insulated gate transistor," in *IEDM Tech. Dig.*, pp. 740–743, 1985.

[9] A. L. Robinson, D. N. Pattanayak, M. S. Adler, B. J. Baliga, and E. J. Wildi, "Lateral insulated gate transistors with improved latching characteristics," in *IEDM Tech. Dig.*, pp. 744–747, 1985.

[10] J. K. O. Sin and C. A. T. Salama, "The SINFET: A new high conductance, high switching speed MOS-gated transistor," *Electron. Lett.*, vol. 21, no. 24, pp. 1134–1136, 1985.

[11] Y. Amemiya and Y. Mizushima, "Bipolar-mode Schottky contact and applications to high-speed diodes," *IEEE Trans. Electron Devices*, vol. ED-31, pp. 35–42, 1984.

[12] S. M. Sze, *Physics of Semiconductor Devices*, 2nd ed. New York: Wiley, 1981.

[13] M. R. Pinto, C. S. Rafferty, H. R. Yeager, and R. W. Dutton, "PISCES-IIB," Stanford Electronics Lab., Dept. of Electrical Eng., Stanford Univ., 1985.

[14] E. Sangiorgi, C. Rafferty, M. Pinto, and R. Dutton, "Non-planar Schottky device analysis and applications," in *Proc. Int. Conf. Simulation of Semiconductor Devices and Processes* (Swansea, U.K.), pp. 164–171, July 1984.

[15] K. Shenai, E. Sangiorgi, K. C. Saraswat, R. M. Swanson, and R. W. Dutton, "Accurate barrier modeling of metal and silicide contacts," *IEEE Electron Device Lett.*, vol. EDL-5, pp. 145–147, 1984.

[16] S. E. Hansen, *SUPREM-III User's Manual*, Stanford Univ., 1985.

[17] D. L. Scharfetter, "Minority carrier injection and charge storage in epitaxial Schottky barrier diodes," *Solid-State Electron.*, vol. 8, pp. 299–311, 1965.

[18] J. A. Appels and H. M. J. Vaes, "High voltage thin layer devices," in *IEDM Tech. Dig.*, pp. 238–241, 1979.

[19] J. K. O. Sin and C. A. T. Salama, to be published.

[20] J. L. Saltich and L. E. Clark, "Use of a double-diffused guard ring to obtain near ideal *I–V* characteristics in Schottky barrier diode," *Solid-State Electron.*, vol. 13, pp. 857–863, 1970.

A Novel CMOS-Compatible High-Voltage Transistor Structure

ZAHIR PARPIA, STUDENT MEMBER, IEEE, JOSÉ G. MENA, STUDENT MEMBER, IEEE, AND C. ANDRE T. SALAMA, SENIOR MEMBER, IEEE

Abstract—A novel high-voltage transistor structure, the insulated base transistor (IBT), based on a merged MOS-bipolar concept, is described. This device, which can be implemented using a standard CMOS process, is capable of handling high current densities without latching. The IBT exhibits a fivefold increase in current density compared to the lateral DMOS. A simple technique by which the switching speeds of the IBT can be improved by almost an order of magnitude without significantly compromising its current carrying capability is also presented.

I. INTRODUCTION

A VARIETY of applications in the telecommunications and display areas require high-voltage driver transistors with breakdown voltages in the 100 V range. In these circuits, the high-voltage transistors are generally used only at the outputs, while the rest of the system consists of low-voltage analog or digital control circuits. In order to achieve cost and area savings, the high-voltage transistors must be integrated on the same chip as the low-voltage circuitry. In many such monolithic applications, high-voltage MOS transistors, because of their simplified drive circuitry, are preferred to bipolar transistors. However, the disadvantage of high-voltage MOS transistors is that they offer relatively inferior current handling capabilities as compared to their bipolar counterparts.

The lateral DMOS transistor (LDMOS) is an example of a MOS transistor, suitable for implementation in high-voltage integrated circuits (HVIC's). The cross section of a structure[1] similar to that of the double-diffused MOS transistor and fabricated using a p-well polysilicon gate CMOS process, is shown on Fig. 1(a). The source and the channel region are in the p-well, while a relatively low doped drift (n-substrate) region, (which can be modeled as a resistor R_D) separates the n^+ drain contact from the channel. The breakdown voltage of the device is determined by the concentration and the length of the drift region. As a general rule, the lower the drift region concen-

Manuscript received April 15, 1986; revised July 31, 1986. This work was supported in part by the Natural Sciences and Engineering Research Council of Canada.

Z. Parpia and C. A. T. Salama are with the Department of Electrical Engineering University of Toronto, Toronto, Ontario, Canada, M5S 1A4.

J. G. Mena was with the Department of Electrical Engineering, University of Toronto, Toronto, Ontario, Canada, M5S 1A4. He is now with AT&T Bell Laboratories, Reading, PA.

IEEE Log Number 8610815.

[1]This structure is not fabricated using the conventional double diffused process but will still be designated as an LDMOS in this paper.

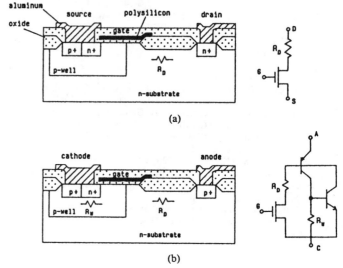

Fig. 1. Device cross sections and equivalent circuits. (a) Lateral DMOS. (b) Lateral IGT.

tration, the higher is the LDMOS breakdown voltage. However, the low drift region concentrations also mean higher on-resistances. Thus, a trade-off between on-resistance and breakdown voltage exists.

A structure that combines MOS and bipolar transistors to achieve high current densities, while simultaneously maintaining high input impedance, has recently been proposed. This device, called the insulated gate transistor (IGT) [1], or alternatively the conductivity-modulated FET (COMFET) [2], depends on conductivity modulation of the drift region to dramatically reduce the on-resistance. Lateral IGT (LIGT) structures, proposed and analyzed by various authors [3]–[7], show similar improvements in the on-resistance. A cross section of a LIGT, fabricated using a standard CMOS process, is shown on Fig. 1(b). The LIGT has virtually the same structure as the LDMOS, except that the n^+ drain in the LDMOS has been replaced by a p^+ diffusion. As its equivalent circuit shows, the LIGT can be modeled as a MOS-gated SCR. During normal operation, the n-p-n transistor is off, and the circuit reduces to that of a MOS-gated p-n-p transistor. However, if the current flowing through the shunt resistor R_W is large enough, the n-p-n will turn on and the LIGT will latch up and gate control will be lost. Another shortcoming of the LIGT is that it has slower turn-off times [4] than the LDMOS because

Reprinted from *IEEE Trans. Electron Devices*, vol. ED-33, pp. 1948–1952, Dec. 1986.

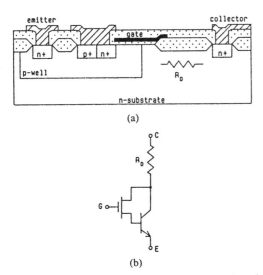

(a)

(b)

Fig. 2. The insulated base transistor. (a) Device cross section. (b) Equivalent circuit.

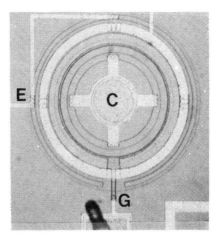

Fig. 3. Photomicrograph of the IBT.

the excess carriers in the base of the p-n-p can only be removed through recombination.

In this paper, a novel high-voltage power transistor, that can be easily integrated with low-voltage CMOS circuitry is described. The device is based on a merged MOS-bipolar concept, with the bipolar base current controlled by a MOS gate, hence the acronym IBT (insulated base transistor). The IBT is capable of operating at high current densities, and in contrast to the IGT is latchup free. A simple technique to reduce the turn-off times in the IBT as well improve its breakdown voltage, without significantly compromising its current carrying capability, is also presented. Because this device can be fabricated using a standard CMOS process, high-density analog/digital circuitry as well as high-voltage drivers can be implemented on the same chip.

II. IBT STRUCTURE AND OPERATION

A cross section of the IBT is shown on Fig. 2(a). The device uses a similar structure to that of the LDMOS, with the exception that an extra n^+ diffusion is added inside the p-well. This diffusion forms the emitter of a vertical n-p-n bipolar transistor. The p-well and the n-substrate form the respective base and collector of this transistor. The circuit model of the IBT is shown in Fig. 2(b). In this figure, R_D is the drift region resistance.

In normal operation, the collector terminal C is held at a higher voltage than the emitter E and the device current is controlled by the voltage at the gate terminal G. In order for the IBT to conduct current, both the MOS and the bipolar transistors must turn on. In the case of the MOS transistor, its gate-to-source voltage has to exceed its threshold voltage V_{TM} while for the n-p-n transistor, its base–emitter junction must be forward biased. Thus the effective turn-on voltage of the IBT is given by

$$V_T = V_{TM} + V_{BE(on)} \qquad (1)$$

where $V_{BE(on)}$ is the turn-on voltage of the n-p-n base–emitter junction.

When the gate to emitter voltage V_{GE} is greater than V_T, the MOS starts conducting current. This current forms the base current of the bipolar transistor, which in turn is amplified and the resulting collector current I_C is given by

$$I_C = (\beta + 1)I_{MOS} \qquad (2)$$

where I_{MOS} is the MOS current at a given gate voltage and β is the common emitter current gain of the n-p-n transistor. Thus, assuming $V_{GE} \gg V_{BE(on)}$, the IBT will conduct $(\beta + 1)$ times the current of a comparable LDMOS.

III. EXPERIMENTAL RESULTS

In order to compare device characteristics, LDMOS, LIGT, and IBT high-voltage structures were fabricated using a 5-μm analog/digital CMOS process.[2] Since no process changes are required to implement the high-voltage devices, the performance of the low-voltage CMOS devices is not affected.

The MOS transistors inherent in all three structures were implemented using identical channel lengths, channel widths, and drift regions. As the photomicrograph of the IBT in Fig. 3 shows, the devices use a circular enclosed collector structure. In order to avoid premature punch-through breakdown in the MOS transistor, a 15-μm channel length was used. The effective channel width was 750 μm. The drift region length (length of the n-substrate underneath the field oxide), was 24 μm. Because of the extra n^+ diffusion, the IBT requires approximately 30 percent more area than the LDMOS.

The threshold voltages of the LDMOS and the LIGT are identical to that of the low-voltage n-channel transistors (≈ 1 V) because they are all fabricated in the same p-well. The IBT has a turn-on voltage of 1.5 V. The I–V characteristics of the IBT are shown on Fig. 4. These exhibit an offset from the origin, which is necessary to for-

[2]In this process, devices are fabricated on a 5-$\Omega \cdot$ cm n-type substrate. An implanted p-well is used for the fabrication of the low-voltage n-channel transistors. Isolation between devices is provided by a 1-μm LOCOS field oxide. The process uses 850-Å gate oxides and n^+ polysilicon gates. The magnitude of the threshold voltage for both the n- and p-channel transistors is 1 V.

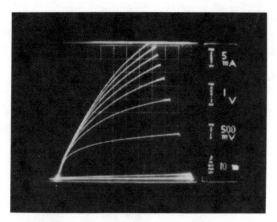

Fig. 4. *I-V* characteristics of the IBT.

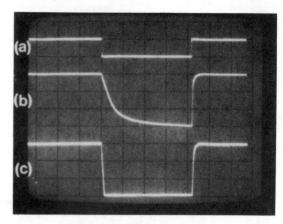

Fig. 6. Transient response of the IBT (2 μs/div horizontal). Curve (*a*) Gate input (5 V/div vertical). Curve (*b*) IBT collector current (20 mA/div vertical). Curve (*c*) Collector current of the improved IBT (20 mA/div vertical).

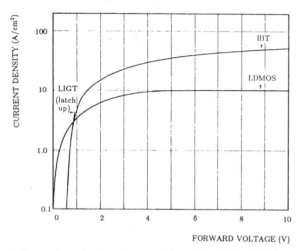

Fig. 5. Forward conduction characteristics of the IBT, LDMOS, and LIGT.

ward bias the bipolar base–emitter junction, and is inherent in all merged MOS-bipolar devices.

The forward conduction characteristics of the three devices, biased at gate voltages of 5 V, are shown on Fig. 5. The current density is calculated by dividing the current in each device by the active device area [4]. For forward voltages exceeding 0.7 V, the IBT exhibits superior current handling capabilities than the LDMOS. In fact, at a forward voltage of 10 V, the IBT exhibits a fivefold increase in current density as compared to the LDMOS.

At low anode currents, the LIGT shows similar forward conduction characteristics to the IBT. However, at anode current densities higher than 4 A/cm² (in this case, at a current of 2.9 mA), the LIGT latches up. In contrast to the LIGT, neither the IBT nor the LDMOS latch up. The very low value of the LIGT latching current is primarily due to the high sheet resistance of the p-well in this process. Because high-resistivity wells are common to most CMOS processes, the LIGT is not attractive in CMOS-based HVIC's.

The breakdown voltages of the IBT and the LIGT are limited by the common emitter breakdown voltage of the bipolar transistors (BV_{CEO}). Thus, they are expected to have lower breakdown voltages than the LDMOS transis-

tor. In this case, while the LDMOS breaks down at 190 V, the LIGT breakdown voltage is 80 V and the IBT breakdown voltages is 70 V.

The switching characteristics of the IBT were investigated under pulsed gate voltage operation. The output current of the device in response to a square wave gate voltage pulse is shown on Fig. 6(b). While the turn-on time of the IBT is relatively short (in the order of 200 ns), it suffers (in common with the LIGT) from long turn-off times. In this case, the 90- to 10-percent turn-off time is approximately 2.2 μs. By comparison, the LDMOS had turn-on and turn-off times of 180 ns. The turn-off transient of the IBT is composed of two stages. The first is an initial fast drop followed by a slow exponential drop. This phenomenon is similar to that observed in the IGT, and has been analyzed by Kuo *et al.* [8]. The fast drop results from the cutoff of the MOS current. After the MOS channel disappears, the n-p-n transistor undergoes open-base turn-off, with the collector current dropping exponentially with time, as the excess carriers in the base decay through recombination. Recombination lifetime control by electron irradiation or heavy metal doping can be used to reduce the fall times. These techniques, however, cannot be applied to the IBT because they can lead to irreparable damage to the low-voltage transistors fabricated on the same chip.

IV. AN IMPROVED IBT STRUCTURE

A simple technique to improve the turn-off time of the IBT can easily be implemented. It does not require additional processing steps and consists of reducing the effective carrier lifetime in the base of the bipolar transistor (when the MOS is turned off). This is achieved by placing a shunt resistor *R* between the bipolar base and emitter, as shown in Fig. 7. Because the bipolar base in the IBT is easily accessible and is also a low-voltage node, a p-well resistor shown in Fig. 7(b) can be used. Since relatively low values of *R* are required, this resistor can be fabricated adjacent to the IBT without significantly in-

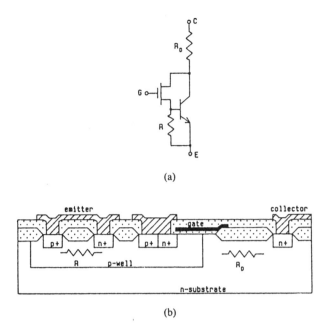

(a)

(b)

Fig. 7. Improved IBT structure. (a) Equivalent circuit. (b) Device cross section.

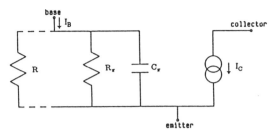

Fig. 8. Circuit used to model the IBT turn-off.

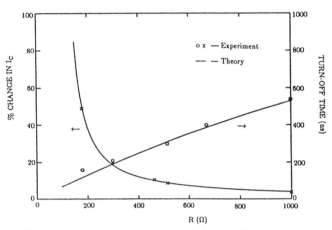

Fig. 9. Change in the collector current and the turn-off time as a function of the shunt resistor R.

creasing the device area. For example, a 500-Ω resistor requires less than 1 percent of the IBT active area.

One drawback of this technique is that it reduces the current-carrying capability of the overall device, since the shunt resistor R lowers the effective current gain of the composite transistor (consisting of the bipolar transistor and the shunt resistor) [9]. Therefore, high-speed operation is achieved at the expense of decreased current density. The IBT current, in the absence of the resistor, is given by (2). Adding resistor R, the overall current becomes

$$I_C = (\beta + 1)I_{MOS} - \frac{\beta V_{BE}}{R} \qquad (3)$$

where V_{BE} is the base–emitter voltage of the n-p-n transistor.

The turn-off time of the IBT can be analyzed using the equivalent circuit of Fig. 8. This circuit, which models the base–emitter junction of the bipolar transistor by a parallel resistor–capacitor combination, can be used to model the charge in the base region during turn-off. The differential equation describing the relation between V_{BE} and the base current I_B is

$$C_\pi \frac{dV_{BE}}{dt} + \frac{V_{BE}}{R_\pi \| R} = I_B(t) \qquad (4)$$

where R_π and C_π are the respective input resistance and base-charging capacitance of the n-p-n transistor. While both R_π and C_π are a function of V_{BE}, they will be assumed constant in order to simplify the following analysis. Defining the base charge $Q_B = C_\pi V_{BE}$ and $\tau = C_\pi(R_\pi \| R)$, (4) can be rewritten as

$$\frac{dQ_B}{dt} + \frac{Q_B}{\tau} = I_B(t). \qquad (5)$$

When the MOS transistor is turned off, $I_B = 0$ and $Q_B(t)$ can be obtained from (5) as

$$Q_B(t) = Q_B(0)e^{-t/\tau} \qquad (6)$$

where τ is assumed constant and $Q_B(0)$ is the base charge right after the initial fast drop. The effect of R is to reduce the time constant τ, resulting in a faster discharge of the base region.

By setting $R_\pi C_\pi = \beta \tau_B$, where τ_B is the base transit time, the above expression for the base charge $Q_B(t)$ reduces to that developed by Kuo *et al.* [8] for the case where $R = \infty$. The time constant τ can then be expressed as

$$\tau(R) = \frac{R}{R + R_\pi} R_\pi C_\pi = \frac{R}{R + R_\pi} \beta \tau_B. \qquad (7)$$

The total device current I_C can be expressed as [8]

$$I_C(t) = \frac{Q_B(t)}{\tau_B} = I_C(0)e^{-t/\tau} \qquad (8)$$

where $I_C(0)$ is the collector current right after the initial fast drop. Using (7) and (8), the 90–10-percent current turn-off time t_f can be written as

$$t_f = 2.2 \frac{R}{R + R_\pi} \beta \tau_B. \qquad (9)$$

The concept of adding R to reduce the turn-off time was applied to the fabricated IBT's. The percentage change in the collector current and the turn-off time, as a function of R, are shown on Fig. 9. Note that the device current

119

and the turn off times are as predicted in (3) and (9). The improvement in the turn-off times is significant; for example, for $R = 500$ Ω, the fall time is reduced by almost an order of magnitude, at the expense of only an 8-percent decrease in device current. The transient response of the improved IBT, with a 500-Ω shunt resistor is shown in Fig. 6(c). In this case, the turn-off time is reduced from 2.2 μs to 300 ns, while the turn-on time is virtually unchanged. Another advantage of the shunt resistor is that it improves the BV_{CEO} breakdown of the bipolar transistor. In the case of the 500-Ω resistor, the IBT breakdown more than doubles from 70 to 160 V.

V. Conclusions

A novel high-voltage transistor structure, the insulated base transistor (IBT), was proposed and implemented. The device, which was fabricated using a standard CMOS process, offers higher current densities than comparable LDMOS transistors and better reliability than comparable LIGT's because of its latchup-proof structure. One other advantage of the IBT is that the bipolar transistor and the LDMOS parameters can be varied independently of each other, thus the IBT current density can be further improved by optimizing the design of these transistors. A simple technique for reducing the turn-off time of the IBT, while at the same time increasing it's breakdown voltage, was also demonstrated. This improved IBT structure has breakdown voltages and switching speeds comparable to the LDMOS, while at the same time maintaining high current density operation.

Acknowledgment

The devices were fabricated under the auspices of the Canadian Microelectronics Corporation.

References

[1] B. J. Baliga, M. S. Adler, P. V. Gray, and R. P. Love, "The insulated gate rectifier (IGR): A new power device," in *IEDM Tech. Dig.*, pp. 264–267, 1982.

[2] J. P. Russell, A. M. Goodman, L. A. Goodman, and J. M. Nelson, "The COMFET—A new high conductance MOS-gated device," *IEEE Electron Device Lett.*, vol. EDL-4, pp. 63–65, 1983.

[3] M. Darwish and K. Board, "Lateral resurfed comfet," *Electron. Lett.*, vol. 20, pp. 519–520, June 1984.

[4] R. Jayaraman, V. Rumennik, B. Singer, and E. H. Stupp, "Comparison of high voltage devices for power integrated circuits," in *IEDM Tech. Dig.*, pp. 258–261, 1984.

[5] D. Pattanayak and M. Adler, "Analysis of current flow in lateral insulated gate transistors," in *Proc. Device Research Conf.*, pp. VIB-5, 1985.

[6] M. R. Simpson, P. A. Gough, F. I. Hshieh, and V. Rumennik, "Analysis of the lateral insulated gate transistor," in *IEDM Tech. Dig.*, pp. 740–743, 1985.

[7] A. L. Robinson, D. N. Pattanayak, M. S. Adler, B. J. Baliga, and E. J. Wildi, "Lateral insulated gate transistors with improved latching characteristics," in *IEDM Tech. Dig.*, pp. 744–747, 1985.

[8] D.-S. Kuo, J.-Y. Choi, D. Giandomenico, C. Hu, S. P. Sapp, K. A. Sassaman, and R. Bregar, "Modeling the turn-off characteristics of the bipolar-MOS transistor," *IEEE Electron Device Lett.*, vol. EDL-6, pp. 211–214, 1985.

[9] S. K. Ghandhi, *Semiconductor Power Devices*. New York: Wiley, 1977.

A 200V COMPLEMENTARY VERTICAL BIPOLAR PROCESS WITH COMPATIBLE LOGIC

James D. Beasom

Harris Semiconductor
Analog Products Division
Melbourne, Florida 32901

ABSTRACT

A 200V BV_{CBO} complementary vertical bipolar process utilizing dielectric isolation is described. The process is designed for telecommunications applications. Compatible I^2L gates achieve a propagation delay of 180ns. Structure and characteristics of 200V NJFET's and SCR's which can be made with the process are described.

INTRODUCTION

Telecommunication applications such as SLIC's, cross point switches and test access have spurred much interest in IC processes which can operate to voltages much higher than the 50V required by most classic linear and data acquisition circuits. A wide variety of processes with voltage capability to 700V have been described (1,2,3). These processes provide various combinations of MOSFET's and of JFETS or SCR's with one polarity of vertical bipolar.

Complementary vertical bipolar devices are required for some applications such as SLIC's. The highest reported voltage capability for such processes in both DI and JI is about 100V (4,5).

The process described in this paper provides complementary vertical bipolars with $BV_{CBO} > 200V$. High density logic is achieved by use of a compatible I^2L structure.

SCR's and NJFET's are also available and can be used for high current and low offset switches among other applications. Dielectric isolation is used to eliminate parasitic isolation devices and to allow use of SCR's without concern for substrate collection of a fraction of device current.

COMPLEMENTARY ISLAND FABRICATION

The P type regions required for PNP collectors are formed by a long P type diffusion into an N type substrate. The junction depth is made greater than the final DI island thickness of 37μ and the DI isolation is aligned to overlap the periphery of the diffusion so that the finished islands are entirely P type.

Selective P and N type buried layers are formed by conventional masking and diffusion techniques. After collector and buried layer diffusions are done, the wafers are isolated with the standard single poly DI process.

BIPOLAR DEVICES

The bipolar devices are formed in the complementary islands by a sequence of four diffusions: PNP base, NPN base, PNP emitter and NPN emitter. Corners are rounded and base metallization is extended over the collector region as a field plate to maximize BV_{CBO}.

Common emitter characteristics for small geometry devices (A_E PNP = 0.31 mil^2, A_E NPN = 0.76 mil^2) are shown in fig. 1. BV_{CBO}'s for the same devices are shown in fig. 2. Key typical electrical characteristics are presented in table 1.

(a)

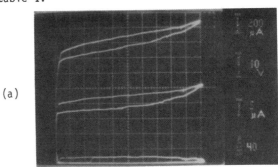

(b)

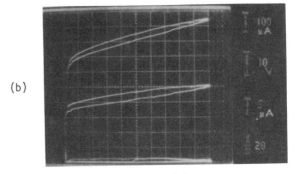

Figure 1. NPN (a) and PNP (b)
Common Emitter characteristics

Reprinted from *IEEE 28th Int. Electron Devices Meeting*, pp. 89–91, 1982.

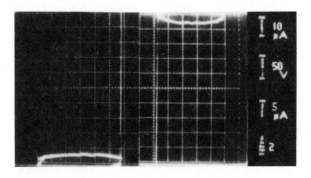

Figure 2. NPN (left) and PNP (right) BV_{CBO}

TABLE 1

Parameter	NPN	PNP
H_{FE}	250	100
BV_{CBO} (V)	250	250
BV_{CEO} (V)	130	150
V_A (V)	300	200
f_T (MHz)	260	60

SCR

The SCR is made using the usual IC structure of merged vertical NPN and lateral PNP. Lateral PNP base-width is large enough (95μ) that punch through does not limit breakdown. The resulting forward and reverse breakdowns, shown in fig. 3, are the same as NPN BV_{CBO}. Other characteristics of the SCR with cathode area of 0.5 mil^2 are on resistance of 9Ω at 30ma and V_F of 1.8V at 100ma.

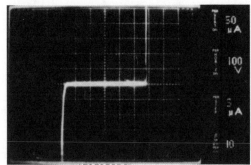

Figure 3. SCR forward and reverse blocking voltage.

NJFET

The structure of the JFET is shown in fig. 4. The P collector diffusion which penetrates completely through the island is used to connect the top and bottom gates. The top gate is formed by the NPN base diffusion. The bottom gate is formed by the P buried layer diffusion.

Breakdown voltage is increased by terminating the edges of the buried layer diffusion in the isolation diffusion so that only the plane part of the buried layer is part of the final gate channel PN junction. Using this structure, device breakdown is limited to the NPN base to collector breakdown.

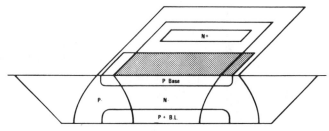

Figure 4. NJFET Cross-section.

Common source characteristics to the initiation of breakdown are shown in fig. 5 for a device with $\frac{W}{L} \approx 1$. Pinch off voltage is about 11V.

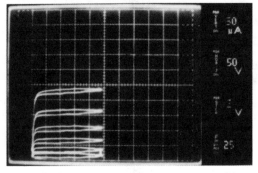

Figure 5. NJFET common source characteristics.

Variations in island thickness are absorbed in the channel thickness of the FET, consequently the process yields a rather broad range of pinch offs. The spread of V_p observed over several runs is 5 to 25V.

I^{2}L

I^{2}L is an attractive logic form because it has high density and is compatible with basic bipolar processing. Achieving I^{2}L functionality in a high voltage process is difficult. An approach used by several is to selectively increase the doping of the I^{2}L islands which improves both margin for functionality and speed (6,7).

Two types of I^{2}L gates have been realized in this process using selectively doped I^{2}L islands. In both cases, the islands are doped by a back side N type diffusion driven by the Dt product used for the P collector. In one case, the doping of the N collector is chosen high enough that it compensates enough of the base charge of the normal NPN's to make them suitable for I^{2}L devices. In the other case, a special I^{2}L base diffusion is combined with the N collector to achieve a very low Gummel number for the I^{2}L devices without constraining the high voltage NPN's. One of the gates is illustrated in fig. 6.

Figure 6. 4 Output I²L gate.

Characteristics of four collector end injector gates are given in table 2. The two collector β is determined by connecting two collectors of a four collector gate in parallel. The four collector βu for the N collector gate is at best marginal, however, it should be possible to improve it by increasing the N collector doping to achieve greater compensation of the base.

The difference in speed, measured on ring counters made from 4 collector gates, between the two structures arises from two factors. The N collector has about a factor of 10 higher doping in the N collector only devices considerably reducing hole storage in the emitter. The very low Gummel number of the I²L + N collector devices result in H_{FE} roll off at very low injector currents leading to cessation of functionality at much lower current density for those devices.

TABLE 2

Parameter	N collector only process	N collector + I²L base process
βu 4 collector	3.5	9
βu 2 collector	8	17
βd I²L	425	2000
βd normal NPN	150	200
β PNP	1.5	1.5
I²L pinch base	30KΩ/□	150KΩ/□
Normal NPN pinch base	5KΩ/□	5KΩ/□
τpd	180ns	480ns

The N collector, which may be two orders of magnitude higher in concentration than the N starting material, can be used as a very effective deep contact diffusion for high voltage NPN's. A comparison of identical geometries with and without N collector diffusion beneath the collector contact is shown in fig. 7. Collector resistance is reduced about a factor of two by use of the N collector as deep contact diffusion for this geometry.

SUMMARY

Structure and resulting component characteristics of a complementary vertical bipolar process have been described. 200V compatible I²L structures have been demonstrated. High voltage SCR's and JFET's which can be built with the process are characterized.

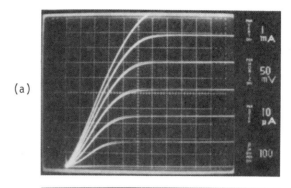

(a)

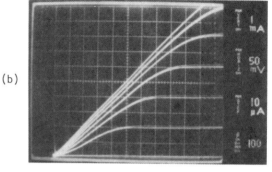

(b)

Figure 7. NPN common emitter characteristics with (a) and without (b) deep contact.

REFERENCES

(1) W.H.A. Matthews, "400V Switches for Subscriber Line Interface," ISSCC Digest of Technical Papers, pp. 238-240:Feb. 1981.

(2) A.R. Hartman, J.E. Berthold, T.J. Riley, J.E. Kohl, Y.H. Wong, H.T. Weston, R.S. Scott, "530V Integrated Gated Diode Switch for Telecommunications," IEDM Technical Digest, pp. 250-253:Dec. 1981.

(3) T. Kami, "High Voltage Integrated Circuits for Telecommunications," IEDM Technical Digest, p. 254:Dec. 1981.

(4) D.W. Aull, D.A. Spires, P.C. Davis, S.F. Moyer, "A 60V IC for a Transformerless Trunk and Subscriber Line Interface," ISSCC Digest of Technical Papers, pp. 246-247: Feb. 1981.

(5) D.P. Laude, "A Monolithic Subscriber Line Interface," ISSCC Digest of Technical Papers, pp. 248-249:Feb. 1981.

(6) D.J. Allstot, S.K. Tui, T.S. Wei, P.R. Gray, R.G. Meyer, "A New High-Voltage Analog Compatible I²L Process," IEEE J. Solid State Circuits, Vol. SC-13, pp. 479-482:Aug. 1978.

(7) L. Halbo, T.A. Hansen, "I²L and High Voltage Analog Circuitry on the Same Chip: A Comparison Between Various Combination Processes," IEEE J. Solid State Circuits, Vol. SC-14, pp. 666-671:Aug. 1979.

530V INTEGRATED GATED DIODE SWITCH FOR TELECOMMUNICATIONS

Adrian R. Hartman, Joseph E. Berthold, Terence J. Riley, James E. Kohl, Yiu-Huen Wong,
Harry T. Weston, Robert Steven Scott

Bell Laboratories
Murray Hill, New Jersey 07974
Reading, Pennsylvania 19603

ABSTRACT

The objective of this work is to develop a new solid state crosspoint switch for telecommunications circuits. The switch is fully integrated into 580V monolithic circuits with appropriate control circuitry. Integrated arrays, packaged in hermetic chip carriers, perform the high level line circuit switching functions previously realized with arrays of electro-mechanical crosspoints.

The Gated Diode Switch (GDS) is a dielectrically isolated lateral $P^+\pi PN^+$ diode with a diffused gate on the planar surface and an MOS gate (consisting of the isolation oxide and polycrystalline substrate) on the lower boundary. With the center gate structure it achieves 530V bilateral blocking, very low crosstalk, insensitivity to transients and full current break capability. Two switches, each 0.15mm^2, can be connected in antiparallel to realize a bidirectional current capability of 120mA DC and 500mA surge. Electron and hole injection produces conductivity modulation in the π-type tub to realize an incremental on resistance of 18 ohms and a forward voltage of 1.7V at 30mA.

The paper describes the properties of the GDS when it is maintaining the off state, turning on and breaking current. The paper also establishes the requirements this switch places on its integrated control circuit. Integrated arrays containing four pairs of bilateral crosspoint switches have been developed for the subscriber line interface circuits of a large digital electronic switching system, #5 ESS.

INTRODUCTION

Telephone switching systems, serving local subscriber loops, must provide relatively high voltage functions such as battery feed (50-100V), ringing (90V RMS), and high voltage signaling and testing (150V). In large electronic switching systems it is desirable to concentrate the expensive line circuit and digital interface functions. A concentrator switching matrix, which previously was realized with electromechanical switches, can now be fabricated with high voltage integrated circuits having dielectrically isolated crosspoint switches and control circuits. The crosspoint

switch or pass element can be a thyristor (1) or gated diode switch (2). This paper discusses the properties of the gated diode switch and the requirements it places on its associated control circuitry.

GATED DIODE SWITCH-GDS

Shown in Figure 1 is a cross-section of a dielectrically isolated gated diode switch. The GDS is formed in a tub (or well) of single crystal material which is isolated from a polycrystalline substrate by a wrap-around silicon dioxide layer. It has a center gate between the anode and cathode contacts of a $P^+\pi PN^+$ diode. The cathode is surrounded by a punch through shield or p base region which allows the cathode and gate to be relatively closely spaced.

GATED DIODE SWITCH (GDS)

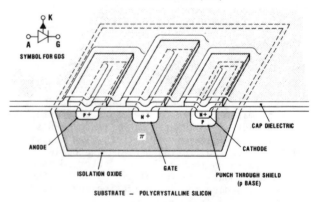

Fig. 1 Gated Diode Switch in Dielectrically Isolated Wafer

The GDS uses the gating and switching principles of the static induction thyristor, gridistor, field-terminated diode and field-controlled thyristor. Unlike these devices the GDS has a center gate planar structure and realizes bilateral blocking since both the gate to anode and gate to cathode breakdown voltages are large. This high gate breakdown voltage allows GDS's to be connected in antiparallel with common gates to provide bidirectional current capability.

Reprinted from *IEEE 27th Int. Electron Devices Meeting*, pp. 250-253, 1981.

Appropriate gate voltages and currents are supplied through a control circuit which is illustrated in block diagram form in Figure 2. The circuit performs three functions: (1) it sources leakage currents for off state maintenance; (2) it sinks currents for turn on; and (3) it sources substantial currents for breaking direct currents during turn off. Each of these conditions will be described in the following sections.

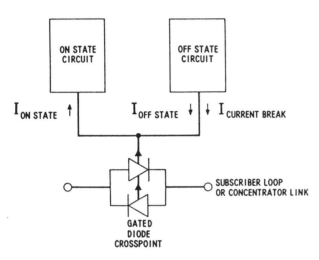

Fig. 2   GDS Control Circuit Block Diagram

OFF STATE MAINTENANCE

When the gate of the GDS is raised to a large positive potential (+315V), the diodes between the gate and anode and between the gate and p shield are reverse biased and the π material is depleted. The substrate is held at this same high positive potential, and, because of the combined influence of the diffused top gate and the MOS bottom gate (isolation oxide and substrate conductor), a potential barrier to hole flow is formed in the region below the diffused gate. The anode and cathode are then isolated from each other. Both switch terminals can assume any voltage above -265V (avalanche breakdown limited) and below +265V. The 50V difference between the gate voltage and the maximum switch terminal voltage is provided to maintain the potential barrier and thus the off state of the switch. The center gate of the GDS serves as an AC ground in the off state, and consequently the crosstalk between the switch terminals is negligible. Two antiparallel GDS's form a gated diode crosspoint and in subscriber loop circuits a pair of crosspoints (tip and ring) is switched with one control circuit.

To maintain the off state the control circuit must provide the leakage current of the gate to anode and gate to cathode junctions. Because of the compact geometry of the GDS, these leakages are relatively small as shown in Figure 3. Plotted here is the gate leakage of one GDS. Its gate is held at +315V and the anode and cathode are shorted together and held at lower potentials.

The leakage current increases with an activation energy of typically 0.8eV over the range of 25°C to 90°C. The circuit must also supply any voltage transients on the line which are capacitively coupled to the gate. Because the π material in the GDS is largely depleted in the off state, the capacitances are relatively small, and the resulting transient currents are readily supplied by the control circuit.

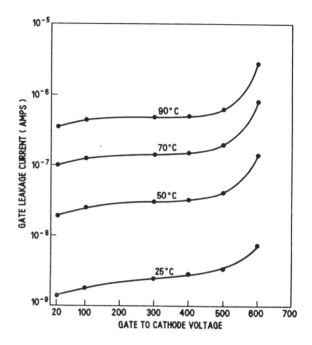

Fig. 3   GDS Gate Leakage Current versus Gate To Cathode Voltage (with anode and cathode shorted)

The normal operation range of the GDS is ±200V or 400V blocking. The switch must also sustain ±265V on a transient basis. This margin in voltage is required for operation of the protection circuits. Therefore, normal off state maintenance currents at 70°C are typically a few μA's, and the transient (worst case) maintenance currents at 70°C are a few 10's of μA's for a crosspoint pair consisting of 4 GDS's. The DC maintenance currents are negligible for a device operating between 25 and 40°C, which is a more typical operation temperature in a central office environment.

GDS TURN ON CHARACTERISTICS

In order to switch the GDS from the off to the on state, it is necessary to reduce the gate potential until the difference between the gate and the anode (or cathode) potential is less than the voltage required to maintain the off state. This voltage for a typical GDS is 20V. The transient in gate voltage from 315V to within 20V of the maximum terminal voltage is determined by the gate capacitance and the control circuit turn on current. As the crosspoint begins to turn on, currents flow in the GDS (of the pair) that is forward biased by an external power supply (such as the line circuit connected to the concentrator). Electrons and holes are injected into the π material from the cathode and anode, respectively. Since the external supply is of much lower impedance than the control circuit, the gate is rapidly pulled down to approximately 0.7V below the anode potential, and the switching transient is completed.

The gate current sunk into the on state control circuit should be relatively small. In effect that current constitutes an on state leakage between the control circuit and the crosspoint terminals.

In Figure 4 is plotted the turn on time of the GDS as a function of the inverse gate current. The required switching time for the crosspoint circuit is determined by the instruction cycle time of the processor controlling the concentrator. In general, turn on times of $\lesssim$1000µs are adequate. This performance can be achieved in the GDS with gate currents of typically 4µA. The turn on time is inversely proportional to gate current, and it is directly proportional to the voltage difference between the positive supply and the more positive of the GDS terminals. These linear relationships are observed because the gate capacitance is nearly independent of voltage under most operating conditions, and therefore $\Delta T = (C/I_G) \Delta V$. The capacitance between the gate and the anode or cathode is relatively small (<0.1pF), however the gate to substrate capacitance is significant. As the gate is pulled down below the positive supply potential (315V) electrons are injected from the gate to form an inversion layer on a portion of the tub/isolation oxide boundary. The inversion layer must form since the polycrystalline substrate is held at the most positive potential and the gate, which is a source of electrons, is pulled below it in potential. Other devices in the control circuit connected to the gate terminal can also contribute to the inversion layer capacitance. Once the inversion layer is formed the capacitance is independent of voltage, since it only depends on the area of the inversion layer and the thickness of the isolation oxide.

Once the GDS is turned on it exhibits the forward voltage characteristics of a $P^+\pi PN^+$ diode. It has a typical incremental resistance of 18Ω and a forward voltage of 1.7V at 30mA. No power is required to maintain the on state, since the GDS is a "normally on" crosspoint. The current drawn from the gate is insignificant relative to the typical anode to cathode currents of 60mA DC.

The turn on time of the GDS can be reduced to 5-10µs by sinking sufficient gate current into the on state control circuit during the switching transient.

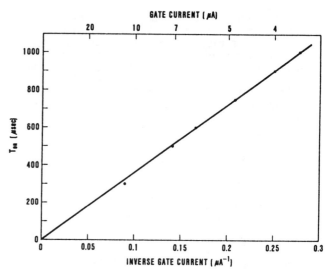

Fig. 4   GDS Turn On Time versus Inverse Gate Current

CURRENT BREAK REQUIREMENTS

The gated diode switch has direct current break capability. It can interrupt direct currents as large as its full direct current capacity without sustaining any degradation. This contrasts sharply with the REMREED electromechanical switches it replaces which are degraded by contact erosion after a small number of full current break operations.

To provide the turn off capability the internal resistance of the GDS gate must be relatively small. Additionally the off state control circuit must provide a gate current pulse that is comparable to the anode-to-cathode current. The turn off time of the GDS is given in Figure 5 as a function of the peak gate current with initial anode current as a parameter. In this measurement the gate current pulse is provided by a constant current source with a compliance voltage of 110V. The anode is loaded with the appropriate resistor to establish the desired anode current from a 50V supply. As the peak gate current is increased the turn off time, or the time to effect current break, is reduced to approximately 5µs.

Inherent to the GDS structure (Figure 1) is an npn transistor with the cathode as the emitter, the gate as the collector and the anode as the base. To effect current break it is necessary to pull this npn transistor out of saturation and to raise the collector (or gate) to the voltage required to put the GDS into a blocking state. The amount of pulsed gate current required is proportional to the gain (β) of the npn transistor in the anode load case (grounded emitter). If instead the load resistor is placed in the cathode (grounded base), then the gate current required is proportional to the transistor's α. At low currents in the GDS where β is greater than 1.0, it is more difficult to turn off the anode loaded GDS. This effect can be seen clearly in Figure 6 where the peak gate current is plotted as a function of the initial anode-to-cathode (or pass) current. For this figure the anode and cathode loaded GDS turn off times were chosen to be 100µs and 25µs, respectively. At high pass currents of 120mA the gate current approaches 35mA for both loading conditions. At these higher currents the npn transistor is operating well into the gain roll off region, and β and α are comparable and both less than unity.

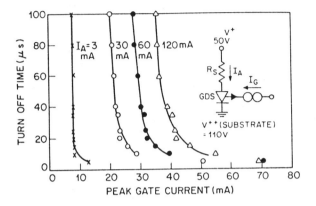

Fig. 5   GDS Turn Off Time versus Peak Gate Current with Initial Anode Current As A Parameter (anode load)

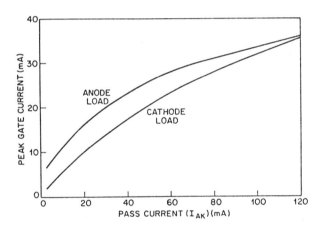

Fig. 6   GDS Peak Gate Current versus Initial Anode-to-Cathode Current During Current Break (chosen turn off times of 100µs for anode load and 25µs for cathode load)

In an analogy to the gate turn off thyristor, one can define a turn off gain as the ratio of the initial anode-to-cathode current to the peak gate current required for turn off. Over the typical range of pass currents the GDS realizes turn off gains of 2 to 3.

The physical mechanism during turn off can be described as a collection of electrons by the gate, which produces a pulsed gate current load on the control circuit. The electrons in the conductivity modulated π region are efficiently collected by the gate, and the local potential in the gate region is pulled up by the control circuit. When the potential barrier is once again established on the anode side of the gate region, the flow of holes from the anode is blocked, and no additional electron injection from the cathode occurs. Equivalently, raising the gate potential pinches off the base current to the npn transistor, and the emitter current drops to leakage current levels.

SUMMARY

A new high voltage semiconductor tele-communications device, the gated diode switch (GDS), has been developed for use in the high level concentrator of a large digital electronic switching system (3). This device has been integrated with control circuits on dielectrically isolated substrates to form a 2x2 matrix of pairs of switches having 530V blocking capability.

ACKNOWLEDGEMENTS

Many individuals at Bell Laboratories in Murray Hill, NJ, Reading, PA and Naperville, IL have contributed to the development of this solid state switch. In particular we are indebted to the guidance of A. U. Mac Rae, B. T. Murphy, C. G. B. Garrett and J. Godfrey. Technical contributions were made by J. Anidjar, J. P. Ballantyne, J. C. Gammel, R. A. Furnanage, R. T. Kraetsch, W. F. MacPherson, R. A. Nordin, C. E. Reid, T. J. Robe, M. Robinson, P. W. Shackle and M. A. Shibib.

REFERENCES

(1) M. Tokunaga, T. Kamei, I. Ishi and M. Kawanami, "Development of Integrated Semiconductor Crosspoint Switches and a Fully Electronic Switching System," Proc. Intn. Switching Symp., Kyoto, Japan, paper 221-4 Oct. 26, 1976.

(2) P. W. Shackle, A. R. Hartman, T. J. Riley, J. C. North and J. E. Berthold, "A 500V Monolithic Bidirectional 2x2 Crosspoint Array," ISSCC Digest of Technical Papers, San Francisco, CA, p. 170, 171, Feb. 14, 1980.

(3) H. L. Bosco, R. K. Eisenhart, F. A. Saal and W. G. Scheerer, "No. 5 ESS - Hardware Design," Proc. Intn. Switching Symp., Montreal, Session 31A, Paper 3, Sept. 24, 1981.

High Voltage Complementary Gated MOS Thyristors

Y. Sugawara

Hitachi Research Laboratory of Hitachi, Ltd.,
Hitachi, Ibaraki, 319-12, Japan

ABSTRACT

A new lateral thyristor, the COGMOS (Complementary Gated MOS) thyristor was developed for analog digital compatible power IC's. It is a BiMOS composite device in which six elements, such as pnp and npn transistors, p and n channel MOSFET's and two diodes, are merged. The fabricated COGMOS thyristor has a high bidirectional blocking voltage ($\geq\pm350V$), low triggering MOS gate voltage ($\sim 5V$) and high MOS gate isolation voltage ($>500V$). It can be driven under a floating bias condition by a constant low supply voltage and can be isolated electrically from an input circuit, as same as relays, transformers and photocoupled semiconductor devices.

INTRODUCTION

To make electronic equipments which are more efficient, compacter, cheaper and more reliable, hybrid power IC's and power modules are widely used and monolithic power IC's have begun to develop [1, 2, 3]. Since the surge voltage and the surge current become very large in these devices as compared to conventional IC's, electrical isolation between an input circuit and an output power circuit is very important to reduce electric interference between them. For this purpose, relays, transformers and photocoupled semiconductor devices are used commonly, but these devices cannot be integrated into an IC chip. On the other hand, MOS and BiMOS [4, 5] devices can be integrated into the IC chip, but they cannot be driven under a floating bias condition and the gate breakdown voltages needed for isolation between the input and output circuits are very low. Capacitor coupled devices [6, 7] can be integrated into the chip and can be driven under the floating bias condition, but they cannot be driven by DC drive signals and they dissipate large drive powers. To overcome these problems, a novel semiconductor device has been developed.

DEVICE STRUCTURE AND OPERATION MECHANISM

Figure 1 shows an equivalent circuit of a COGMOS (Complementary Gated MOS) thyristor which is composed of six elements, pnp and npn transistors, p and n channel MOSFET's and two diodes. The COGMOS thyristor and its drive circuit are isolated by the gate oxides of the p and n channel MOSFET's. When an input signal is given to the control terminal C, the supply voltage Vs is applied to the gate electrodes of the MOSFET's Q3 and Q4. Under a forward bias condition, the thyristor, which is composed of pnp and npn transistors, is triggered by the p channel MOSFET Q3 when the potential Vk of its cathode electrode K is higher than that of the drive circuit Vs, and it is triggered by the n channel MOSFET Q4 when the potential V_A of its anode electrode A is lower than that of the drive circuit. Thus, the COGMOS thyristor can be driven under the floating bias condition by the drive circuit with a constant low supply voltage Vs.

Figure 2 shows the structure of the COGMOS thyristor which is fabricated by an EPIC (Epitaxial Passivated IC) process. The cell size is $325\mu m \times 280\mu m$ and cell size reduction techniques [8] are utilized. The six elements shown in Figure 1 are merged in one device. The lateral p channel MOSFET and the vertical n channel MOSFET are fabricated in parallel with the lateral pnp transistor and the vertical npn transistor by making MOS gate electrodes on the $n_{\bar{B}}$ base and the p_B base, respectively. By connecting an n contact of an $n_{\bar{B}}$ base to the gate electrode Ga, p_E emitter and p_B base junctions are utilized as diodes D1 and D2, respectively. The n_E and p_B of the vertical n channel MOSFET under the MOS gate electrode Gk are fabricated with a self-aligned technique to obtain high transconductance and a low threshold voltage. To achieve high blocking voltage, the junction termination extension technique [9] is used under the gate electrodes, so that, the lateral p channel MOSFET has double offset gates not only on the side of the p_E source but also on the side of the p_B drain. The field plate technique is used except under the gate electrodes.

By utilizing a two-dimensional analysis of the breakdown voltage, the structures of the field plate and the p^- layer for the junction termination extention are optimized and it is confirmed that the p^- layer can reduce the electric field of the junction in the same way the field plate can. The minimum triggering MOS gate

Reprinted from *IEEE 1986 Int. Electron Devices Meeting*, pp. 226–229, 1986.

voltage needed to latch up the COGMOS thyristor is also analyzed. The structure parameters of the COGMOS thyristor are decided by using the results of these analyses.

BLOCKING VOLTAGE AND TRIGGERING MOS GATE VOLTAGE

In conventional lateral power MOS devices, high forward blocking voltages are realized by sacrificing the reverse blocking voltages. In the COGMOS thyristor, both good forward and reverse blocking voltages must be realized. Therefore, a new method using short diodes, D1 and D2 has been developed.

Figure 3(a) shows output characteristics of the COGMOS thyristor without the short diodes. Both forward and reverse blocking voltages are about 60V. The low blocking voltage is attributed to the gate electrode Ga which is electrified when a high voltage is applied to the COGMOS thyristor and a channel is generated under the gate electrode. By connecting the contact of the n_E^- to the gate electrode, p_E emitter and p_B base junctions of the thyristor act as short diodes, and the potential of the gate electrode is automatically fixed to the highest potential by these diodes and generation of a channel under the gate is reduced. Thus, high bidirectional blocking voltages of about 350V are achieved as shown in Figure 3(b).

Figure 4 shows experimental relationships between blocking voltage and length of the p^- layer of the COGMOS thyristor with the short diodes. The distance between the p^- layer of the p_E emitter and that of the p_B base is $35\mu m$. The blocking voltage increases with a longer p^- layer because the electric field reduction effect due to the p^- layer is increased. The reverse blocking voltages become constant at the p^- layer length of more than $25\mu m$. This is due to the blocking voltage being limited by the electric field, not at the junction of p_E, p_B or p^- layer, but at the n^+ buried channel stopper under the interconnection [10].

Figure 5 shows experimental relationships of the blocking voltage and the triggering MOS gate voltage vs. n_E diffusion time. According to the increase in n_E diffusion time, not only the triggering n channel MOS gate voltage, but also the forward blocking voltage decrease. The reason for the former is the increased transconductance and the reason for the latter is the increased leakage current due to the increase in the $n_E p_B n_B^-$ transistor's h_{FE}, because the self-aligned lateral p_B width of the $n_E p_B n_B^-$ transistor decreases and the surface impurity concentration under the gate electrode decreases by increase of the n_E diffusion time. This is also the reason for the forward blocking voltage being lower than the reverse one in Figure 4.

Figure 6 shows experimental relationships of isolation voltage and the triggering MOS gate voltage vs. thickness of the gate oxide film. Although the gate oxide film is composed of three kinds of oxide films, the isolation voltage and the triggering MOS gate voltages become larger in proportion to the increased thickness. When the thickness of the oxide film is $0.7\mu m$, p and n

channel triggering MOS gate voltages of about 5V and isolation voltages of more than 500V can be realized at the same time. Table 1 lists typical electrical properties of the COGMOS thyristor. A resistor of $5.6k\Omega$ is connected between the p_B base and n_E emitter in all the measured COGMOS thyristors in Figures 3-6 and Table 1.

FLOATING BIAS OPERATION

For the fabricated COGMOS thyristor, the circuit shown in Figure 1 is used and the floating bias operation is examined experimentally. The drive circuit is a flip-flop type and is composed of the high voltage p and n channel MOSFET's which have the same structure as those of the COGMOS thyristor.

Figure 7 shows the floating bias operation of the COGMOS thyristor. Although the voltage of the cathode is changed from $-$ 250V to $+$ 250V, the COGMOS thyristor can be turned on, and the floating bias operation is realized. The main electrodes A or K and electrodes of the drive circuit S, C or E are isolated electrically by the gate oxides of both p and n channel MOSFET's Q3 and Q4, the diodes, and the MOSFET's of the drive circuit. The isolation voltage of more than 350V is realized between the COGMOS thyristor and the terminals of the drive circuit.

For telecommunications uses, linearity of output characteristics before latching and a large latching current are needed in addition to the electrical characteristics described above. As shown in Figure 8, the necessary good linearity is realized and the latching currents are controlled by the resistance between the p gate and the cathode, R_{GK} and that between the n gate and the anode, R_{GA}.

These electrical properties of the COGMOS thyristor make its use possible in place of photo and capacitor coupled devices, relays and transformers for many applications.

The concept of this COGMOS thyristor can be applied widely, and other COGMOS devices, such as COGMOS transistors, are fabricated also.

SUMMARY

A new lateral BiMOS device, a COGMOS thyristor was developed. A high bidirectional blocking voltage ($\geq\pm350V$) was achieved by preventing the MOS gate electrification with using short diodes and by reducing the electric field with using a composite technique for the junction termination extension and field plate. Both low triggering MOS gate voltage ($\sim5V$) and high isolation voltage ($>500V$) were achieved by structure optimization of the self-aligned vertical n channel MOSFET and the lateral p channel MOSFET with double offset gates. Using the COGMOS thyristor, floating bias operation with a constant low input voltage and electrical isolation between output and input circuits were realized, just as in relays, transformers and photocoupled semiconductor devices.

ACKNOWLEDGMENTS

The authors wish to thank Drs. Y. Kawamoto and T. Kariya, and Messers, K. Miyata, T. Yatsuo and J. Kitano for their continuous encouragement and guidance. Appreciation is also expressed to members of the IC Fabrication Group, especially to Messers. T. Shirasawa and S. Kawahata.

REFERENCES

1) Y. Sugawara, K. Miyata and M. Okamura : IEDM Technical Digest, p.728, 1985.

2) B. G. Bynum and D. L. Cave : ISSCC Digest of Technical Papers, p.290, 1984.

3) I. Wacyk, M. Amato, and V. Rumennick : ISSCC Digest of Technical Papers, p.16, 1986.

4) A. L. Robinson, D. N. Pattanayak, M. S. Adler, B. J. Baliga and E. J. Wildi : IEDM Technical Digest, p.744, 1985.

5) J. D. Plummer and B. W. Scharf : IEEE Trans. Electron. Dev., vol. ED-27, p380, 1980.

6) W. H. A. Mattheus : ISSCC Digest of Tech. Paper, p.238, 1981.

7) G. Remmerie and L. D. Bossche : IEEE J. Solid State Circuits, vol. SC-19, 1984.

8) Y. Sugawara, T. Kamei Y. Hosokawa and M. Okamura : IEDM Technical Digest, p.412, 1983.

9) V. A. K. Temple : IEDM Technical Digest, p.423, 1977.

10) Y. Sugawara, T. Kamei and Y. Hosokawa : 14th (1982 International) Conf. on Solid State Devices, Tokyo, 1982.

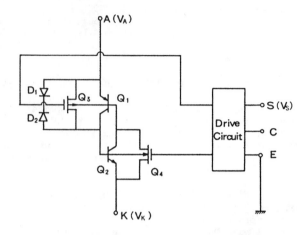

Fig. 1. Equivalent circuit corresponding to COGMOS thyristor.

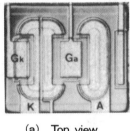

(a) Top view

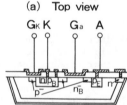

(b) Cross-sectional view

Fig. 2. Structure of COGMOS thyristor.

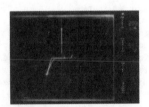

(a) Without short diodes

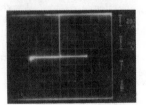

(b) With short diodes

Fig. 3. Output characteristics of COGMOS thyristors.

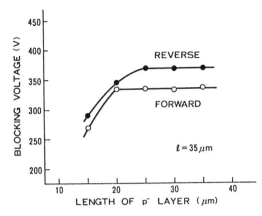

Fig. 4. Experimental relationships between blocking voltage of COGMOS thyristor and length of p⁻ layer.

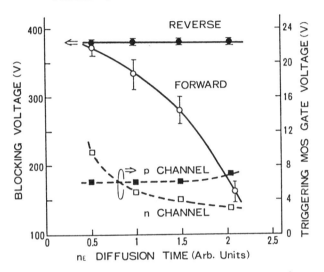

Fig. 5. Experimental relationships of blocking voltage and triggering MOS gate voltage vs. n_E diffusion time.

Table 1. Electrical properties of typical COGMOS thyristor

Blocking voltage	Forward	350 V
	Reverse	370 V
Average current		200 mA
Triggering MOS gate voltage	p channel	6 V
	n channel	5 V
Forward voltage drop		1.8 V
On resistance		7 Ω
Dv/dt capability		>1000 V/μs
Isolation voltage		550 V

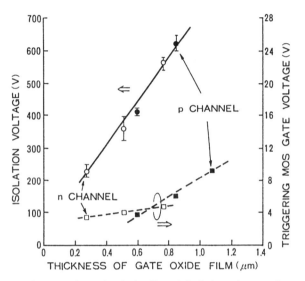

Fig. 6. Experimental relationships of isolation voltage and triggering MOS gate voltage vs. thickness of gate oxide film.

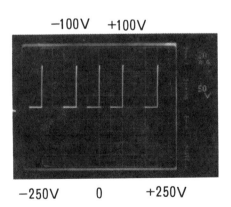

Fig. 7. Floating bias-operation.

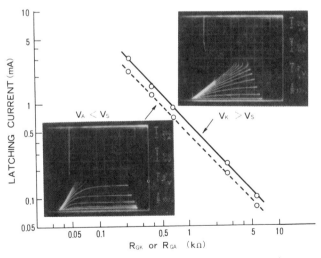

Fig. 8. Experimental relationships of latching current vs. resistance between p gate and cathode, R_{GK} or resistance between n gate and anode, R_{GA}.

Part III
HVIC Process Technology

WITH the increasing interest in high voltage integrated circuit technology, various processes have been explored for the integration of high voltage bipolar and MOS transistors with analog and digital circuitry. The process for the fabrication of these high voltage integrated circuits can be generated by either starting with a high voltage device technology and trying to include the low voltage circuit elements into it, or by starting with low voltage logic or analog circuitry and trying to form high voltage transistors. Since the bulk of the integrated circuit industry is based upon low voltage digital integrated circuit technology, most of the high voltage integrated circuit processes have been developed by starting from this strong base.

This part of the book contains seven papers that emphasize processing aspects of the high voltage integrated circuits. The first two papers use a standard linear bipolar process as the base. By the addition of only a few additional steps it has been possible to form high voltage analog circuits with I^2L logic circuitry.

The next three papers in this part deal with high voltage integrated circuits formed by starting with low voltage CMOS processes as the base. The first of these papers, by Plummer and Meindl, describes the formation of high voltage n-channel DMOS and p-channel lateral MOSFETs in a CMOS process technology. Using this process, a monolithic quad CMOS analog switch has been fabricated for ultrasonic imaging with 200 volt, 0.3 ampere drivers. The following paper by Dolny *et al.* demonstrates that it is possible to form 60 volt lateral n-channel and p-channel MOSFETs by the addition of an extended drain to conventional low voltage CMOS transistors. The last of these papers discusses the design and formation of a high voltage DMOS transistor by starting with a metal gate CMOS process. The DMOSFETs have a breakdown voltage of up to 150 volts.

The final two papers describe processes that were created to optimize the integration of low voltage CMOS logic, analog bipolar circuits, and high voltage MOS transistors. In the first of these papers, an epitaxial technology with the RESURF concept is utilized to realize lateral DMOSFETs and bipolar transistors with breakdown voltages as high as 1200 volts. The technology described in this paper allows the fabrication of CMOS logic circuits and low voltage analog circuits. The analog portion of the chip is fabricated using lateral PNP transistors and vertical NPN transistors. A 1200 volt half bridge circuit has been implemented with this circuit to drive insulated gate transistors in a high power motor drive circuit. The last paper in this part discusses a process that can be used in either junction or dielectric isolation. The high voltage elements consist of lateral high voltage n-channel DMOSFETs and lateral p-channel MOS transistors capable of operating off a 60 volt power supply. An eight channel multiplexer chip has been fabricated for use in high voltage testers.

REPRINT PAPERS

[1] D. J. Allstot, S. K. Lui, T. S. T. Wei, P. R. Gray, and R. G. Meyer, "A New High-Voltage Analog-Compatible I^2L Process," *IEEE J. Solid-State Circuits,* vol. SC-13, pp. 479–483, 1978.

[2] L. Halbo and T. A. Hansen, "I^2L and High-Voltage Analog Circuitry on the Same Chip: A Comparison Between Various Combination Processes," *IEEE J. Solid-State Circuits,* vol. SC-14, pp. 666–671, 1979.

[3] J. D. Plummer and J. D. Meindl, "A Monolithic 200-V CMOS Analog Switch," *IEEE J. Solid-State Circuits,* vol. SC-11, pp. 809–817, 1976.

[4] G. M. Dolny, O. H. Schade, B. Goldsmith, and L. A. Goodman, "Enhanced CMOS for Analog-Digital Power IC Applications," *IEEE Trans. Electron Devices,* vol. ED-33, pp. 1985–1991, 1986.

[5] S. Krishna, J. Kuo, and I. S. Gaeta, "An Analog Technology Integrates Bipolar, CMOS, and High-Voltage DMOS Transistors," *IEEE Trans. Electron Devices,* vol. ED-31, pp. 89–95, 1984.

[6] M. F. Chang, G. Pifer, H. Yilmaz, E. J. Wildi, R. G. Hodgins, K. Owyang, and M. S. Adler, "Lateral HVIC with 1200-V Bipolar and Field-Effect Devices," *IEEE Trans. Electron Devices,* vol. ED-33, pp. 1992–2001, 1986.

[7] R. Williams, L. Sevilla, E. Ruetz, and J. D. Plummer, "A DI/JI Compatible Monolithic High Voltage Multiplexer," *IEEE Trans. Electron Devices,* vol. ED-33, pp. 1977–1984, 1986.

A New High-Voltage Analog-Compatible I²L Process

DAVID J. ALLSTOT, STUDENT MEMBER, IEEE, SIK K. LUI, STUDENT MEMBER, IEEE, TOM S. T. WEI,
PAUL R. GRAY, SENIOR MEMBER, IEEE, AND ROBERT G. MEYER, SENIOR MEMBER, IEEE

Abstract—A new technique for realizing high-performance I²L circuits simultaneously with high-voltage analog circuits is described. The method is flexible and may be used with any standard linear bipolar process. Only one additional noncritical masking step and one phosphorous implant are required to form the I²L n-wells.

Experimental results are presented which show I²L betas of greater than eight per collector with the I²L BV_{CEO} exceeding 3 V. The measured minimum average propagation delay is 40 ns using a 14 μm thick, 5 Ω · cm epitaxial layer, while the analog BV_{CEO} exceeds 50 V.

LIST OF SYMBOLS

A_B	I²L base region area.
A_C	I²L collector area.
B_{down}	Analog n-p-n forward (down) current gain.
$\beta_{p\text{-}n\text{-}p}$	Lateral p-n-p injector current gain.
β_{up}	I²L n-p-n reverse (upward) current gain.
D_n	Diffusivity of electrons.
F	Fan-out of I²L gate.
N_{epi}	Epitaxial doping concentration.
Q_B'	Intrinsic n-p-n base Gummel number.
Q_B	Extrinsic n-p-n base Gummel number.
Q_{imp}	n-well phosphorous implant dose.
s_p	Effective hole recombination velocity in epi.
t_{del}	Average I²L gate delay.
W_{epi}	Thickness of epi layer under base region.

I. INTRODUCTION AND OBJECTIVES

FOR large-scale integrated systems, it is often desirable to fabricate both analog and digital circuitry on the same chip using the same processing schedule. Analog compatibility was one of the main promises of I²L when it was introduced in 1972 [1]–[2]. This claim was based on the fact that I²L was a new circuit technique rather than a new process. Unfortunately, there are fundamental process tradeoffs between analog breakdown voltage and I²L performance which have impeded the development of bipolar analog/digital LSI circuits.

One solution to this problem is to juggle the epitaxial (epi) thickness and resistivity in an attempt to obtain satisfactory device characteristics [3]. This approach comprises both the analog and digital performance and, in addition, an extra masking step and deep n⁺ diffusion are usually required to form the I²L guard rings. This technique is not suitable

Manuscript received February 7, 1978; revised March 30, 1978. This research was supported by the Joint Services Electronics Program under Contract F44620-76-C-0100. D. J. Allstot was supported in part by an IBM Doctoral Fellowship. This paper was presented in part at the International Electron Devices Meeting, Washington, DC, December 1977.

The authors are with the Department of Electrical Engineering and Computer Sciences and the Electronics Research Laboratory, University of California, Berkeley, CA 94720.

where both high-voltage analog and high-speed I²L circuits are required.

A super-β process may also be used to gain analog compatibility [4]. This approach realizes excellent I²L dc performance, but only moderate ac performance is achieved due to excessive hole storage in the lightly doped epi. Control presents a problem since a small intrinsic base doping must be obtained in the presence of a high-resistivity epi region which is itself subject to large variations in doping.

Another method, poly I²L, uses a completely new process which has shown excellent I²L performance with moderately high analog breakdown voltages [5]. The main disadvantage of this approach is that it is so different from standard processes that it is difficult to incorporate into existing process schedules.

The goals of this work were to develop high-performance I²L on the same IC chip with high-voltage analog circuits while maintaining the process simplicity required for LSI capability. To achieve these goals, it was decided to modify a standard high-voltage linear bipolar process subject to the following assumptions: 1) a single epitaxial layer would be used with its parameters determined strictly by the analog breakdown voltage requirements; 2) any additional masking steps would be sufficiently noncritical so that the overall yield would not be significantly reduced, and 3) any additional doping steps would be performed by ion implantation to maintain controllability. Furthermore, it was required that the I²L performance be determined independently of variations in the epi layer thickness and starting resistivity. n-well I²L was conceived as a method for meeting these objectives.

II. PROCESS DESCRIPTION

A. Analog Processing Requirements

As mentioned above, the characteristics of the epitaxial layer were determined by the analog breakdown voltage requirements. A 5 Ω · cm, 14 μm thick epi layer was chosen to give analog n-p-n down betas of about 200 with a BV_{CEO} of greater than 50 V as shown in Fig. 1. This analog performance is obtained independently of the additional processing steps required to form the I²L transistors.

B. Digital I²L Processing Requirements

The epi characteristics directly affect the I²L performance. The I²L up beta is given in terms of processing parameters as [6]

$$\beta_{up} = \left(\frac{A_C}{A_B}\right) \frac{1}{\left[1 + F\left(1 - \frac{A_C}{A_B}\right)\right] \frac{Q_B'}{Q_B} + \frac{(F+1)s_p Q_B'}{D_n N_{epi}}}. \quad (1)$$

Reprinted from *IEEE J. Solid-State Circuits*, vol. SC-13, no. 4, pp. 479–483, Aug. 1978.

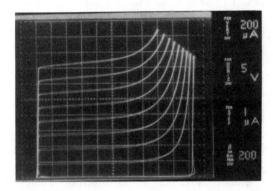

Fig. 1. Analog n-p-n transistor characteristics.

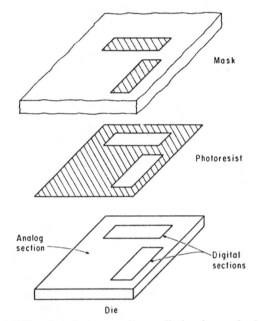

Fig. 2. Additional mask step permits n-well phosphorous implant only in I^2L digital sections of the chip.

Hence, for high β_{up}, large epi concentration and a small intrinsic base Gummel number are required. Similarly, the I^2L minority carrier storage delay is given in terms of processing parameters as

$$t_{del} = \left(\frac{A_B}{A_C}\right) \frac{(F+1)\,W_{epi}Q_B'}{D_n N_{epi}}. \qquad (2)$$

Again, small Q_B' and large N_{epi} are desirable. These requirements are opposite to those which achieve high analog breakdown voltage. Therefore, process modification is necessary to meet these objectives simultaneously, assuming that w_{epi} is fixed by analog breakdown requirements.

C. Process Modifications

In applications requiring combined analog/digital functions, it is usually possible to partition the chip into several separate analog and digital sections. This partitioning allows definition of a new masking step as shown in Fig. 2. This mask permits modification of the I^2L epi regions, while the analog epi regions remain unchanged in order to preserve the desired analog parameters.

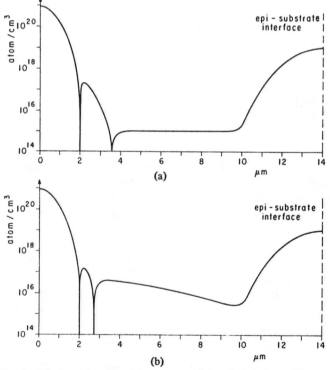

Fig. 3. n-well I^2L process flowchart.

Fig. 4. Calculated profiles for n-p-n transistors in (a) the analog sections, and (b) the n-well digital I^2L sections of the chip.

In order to increase N_{epi} and reduce Q_B' in the I^2L sections, the new mask defines a photoresist pattern which permits phosphorous implantation only in the I^2L regions. This masking step and implantation are performed after the epi growth, but before the isolation diffusion, as shown in the process flowchart of Fig. 3. During the subsequent high temperature cycles, the implanted phosphorous is driven into the I²L epi regions, forming an n-well. This n-well step improves the I²L performance in two ways: 1) the effective epi resistivity in the I²L region is decreased from 5 to about 0.2 Ω · cm, and 2) simultaneously, the intrinsic base Gummel number is reduced to about 1×10^{12} cm^{-2} due to base charge cancellation. Hence, this single processing step improves both the I²L ac and dc performance, while the n-p-n transistors in the analog regions are unaffected, thus preserving their high-voltage capability. Fig. 4 shows the calculated n-p-n profiles in both the analog and n-well regions.

Since the n-well is formed from the surface, variations in epi thickness have little effect on the I²L performance. In addition, the n-well resistivity (which is defined by ion implantation) is well controlled.

III. RESULTING PERFORMANCE

The performance of the n-well I²L devices was measured using the test chip shown in Fig. 5.

A. DC Performance

Fig. 6 shows the I²L betas for a four collector gate versus collector current for an implant dose of 2.34×10^{13} ions/cm². The dc up beta is greater than eight per collector for a device perpendicular to the injector, while the up beta remains greater than two for collector currents less than 200 µA. For these test devices, the lateral p-n-p mask-defined base width was 0.4 mils. In addition, a grounded p-ring surrounded the test devices to simulate injection losses under the shallow n⁺ isolation rings to adjacent gates. Fig. 7 shows a typical set of I²L n-p-n common-emitter characteristics.

Table I gives the n-p-n up beta as a function of injector base width for an array of one-collector I²L gates, and also the lateral p-n-p injector beta versus $W_{\text{p-n-p}}$ for the same array of transistors.

B. AC Performance

The I²L ac performance was measured using a nine-stage, four collectors/gate ring oscillator with the results plotted in Fig. 8. The minimum average propagation delay is 40 ns at a gate current of 200 µA. The resulting power–delay product of 1.8 pJ could be improved by reducing the lateral p-n-p base-width which was 0.4 mils. The unused collectors were left floating during the measurement to simulate a worst case speed condition.

C. Comparison to Other Techniques

Table II compares the analog BV_{CBO} and digital ring oscillator performance parameters for the n-well process and the other three approaches mentioned earlier. It can be seen that only the n-well process combines high-voltage linear circuitry with high-speed I²L circuits.

D. Variations with n-Well Implant Dose

Since the n-well doping effectively determines the I²L performance, it is necessary to investigate parameter changes relative to phosphorous implant variations. Table III shows the I²L up beta versus n-well implant dose. It can be seen

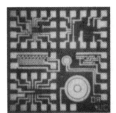

Fig. 5. Die photo of experimental test chip.

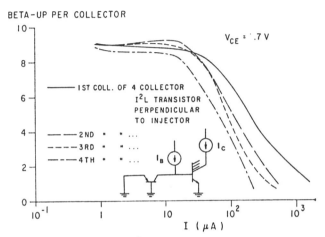

Fig. 6. Measured I²L β_{up} versus collector current.

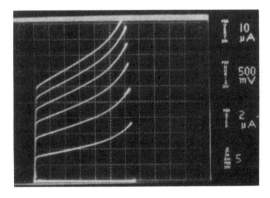

Fig. 7. I²L n-p-n characteristics for one collector of a four-collector transistor.

TABLE I
MEASURED β VARIATIONS WITH INJECTOR BASE WIDTH FOR ONE-COLLECTOR I²L GATES

$W_{\text{p-n-p}}$ (mils)	$\beta_{\text{p-n-p}}$	$\beta_{\mu p}$
0.4	0.28	20
0.5	0.24	22
0.6	0.20	23
0.7	0.16	24

that large variations in implant dose can be tolerated while still maintaining a beta of at least two per collector. Table III also shows the I²L breakdown voltage versus implant dose. Again, large changes in Q_{imp} can be tolerated with an I²L BV_{CEO} of at least 2 V.

137

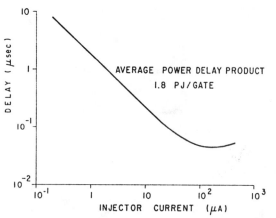

Fig. 8. Measured power–delay performance for a nine-stage ring oscillator with four collectors/gate.

TABLE II
COMPARISON FOR ANALOG AND RING OSCILLATOR PARAMETERS FOR DIFFERENT APPROACHES

Approach	BV_{CBO}	t_{min} (ns)	F (Ring Oscillator Fanout)
Epi Tradeoff [3]			
$2\,\Omega \cdot cm, 12\,\mu m$	70	100	1
Super-β [4]	70	35	1
Poly I^2L [5]	40	5	1
n-well I^2L	80	40	4

TABLE III
I^2L PARAMETERS VARIATIONS VERSUS n-WELL IMPLANT DOSE

Q_{imp} (ions/cm^2)	β_{up}	BV_{CEO} ($I_c = 10\,\mu A$)
0	0.3	7.5
7.81×10^{12}	3	4.2
2.34×10^{13}	7	2.8
3.91×10^{13}	6	1.5

IV. CONCLUSIONS

n-well I^2L achieves high-performance I^2L gates on the same chip with high breakdown voltage analog transistors. For the process described in this paper, I^2L betas of eight per collector were realized with propagation delays of 40 ns. These parameters were obtained simultaneously with analog transistors having a BV_{CBO} exceeding 80 V. The simplicity and flexibility of this process along with its complete analog/digital compatibility make it ideal for bipolar LSI system applications.

ACKNOWLEDGMENT

The measurement assistance of R. Kaneshiro is appreciated. Signetics, Inc. and Precision Monolithics, Inc. supplied the wafers. The authors also wish to acknowledge the contributions to this project of F. Ademic of Signetics, Inc.

REFERENCES

[1] H. H. Berger and S. K. Wiedmann, "Merged transistor logic—A low-cost bipolar logic concept," *IEEE J. Solid-State Circuits*, vol. SC-7, pp. 340–345, Oct. 1972.

[2] K. Hart and A. Slob, "Integrated injection logic: A new approach to LSI," *IEEE J. Solid-State Circuits*, vol. SC-7, pp. 346–351, Oct. 1972.

[3] J. Saltich, W. George, and J. Soderberg, "Processing technology and AC/DC characteristics of linear compatible I^2L," *IEEE J. Solid-State Circuits*, vol. SC-11, pp. 478–485, Aug. 1976.

[4] G. Bergmann, "Linear compatible I^2L technology with high voltage transistors," *IEEE J. Solid-State Circuits*, vol. SC-12, pp. 566–572, Oct. 1977.

[5] R. D. Davies and J. D. Meindl, "Poly I^2L—A high-speed linear-compatible structure," *IEEE J. Solid-State Circuits*, vol. SC-12, pp. 367–375, Aug. 1977.

[6] F. M. Klassen, "Device physics of integrated injection logic," *IEEE Trans. Electron Devices*, vol. ED-22, pp. 145–152, Mar. 1975.

I^2L and High-Voltage Analog Circuitry on the Same Chip: A Comparison Between Various Combination Processes

LEIF HALBO AND TROND A. HANSEN

Abstract—Various simple processes are possible for obtaining a combination of I^2L and high-voltage analog functions on the same IC chip. The simplest methods involve the introduction of one extra process step which affects only the I^2L part, in addition to the analog process.

In this paper comparative experiments are presented for the I^2L properties of: method *A*) a standard 25 V BV_{CE} analog process; method *B*) a modification of the same process with an extra N^+ diffusion giving deeper I^2L collectors; method *C*) a modification giving a more shallow I^2L base; and methods *D*) two modifications involving a selective doping of the epi layer in the I^2L part. Aside from the additional step in each method all process parameters, as well as the I^2L gate geometry, are kept the same.

It is found that processes *D* give significantly higher effective gain for the n-p-n switching transistor than the other methods. The optimum speed is also higher for these processes, but the other methods have a lower power-delay product at low current level. The reasons for the differences are analyzed.

For one of the processes *D* the effect of a shallow versus deep N^+ guard ring is discussed, and the sensitivity to variations in process parameters is commented on.

I. INTRODUCTION

FOR many purposes it is advantageous to combine logic and high-voltage ($BV_{CE} \sim 20$–50 V) analog circuitry on one monolithic IC chip. Integrated injection logic (I^2L) is a dense bipolar logic with great flexibility in power requirements, etc., and is particularly well suited for such a combination.

Among the many possible uses of such a combination are: A/D converters, logic and op amps for a standard ±15 V supply, sensors with logic for signal handling, logic and output driver-stages (for example, for audible telephone ringer signals), and automatic controls.

When a process is to be developed for combining I^2L and high-voltage analog circuitry (hereafter referred to as a combination process), the properties of the analog part must be considered given, based on the optimization of the n-p-n transistor. This severely limits the performance of the I^2L unless one accepts additional process steps and a more complex and costly process.

Manuscript received October 23, 1978; revised January 2, 1979. This work was supported by the Royal Norwegian Council for Scientific and Industrial Research. This paper is based in part on a paper presented at the Fourth European Solid-State Circuits Conference, Amsterdam, The Netherlands, September 18–21, 1978.

The authors are with the Central Institute for Industrial Research, Blindern, Oslo, Norway.

The I^2L properties obtained in unmodified analog processes, corresponding to various breakdown voltages, were investigated by Saltich *et al.* [1]. For $BV_{CE} > 20$ V they found poor I^2L driving capability and fan-out limited to $\leqslant 3$. The minimum delay for two-collector gates in a 30 V process was $\gtrsim 100$ ns/gate, which is very slow compared to optimized I^2L.

The reasons for this poor I^2L performance are that the high analog breakdown voltage requires 1) high active base integral doping in the n-p-n transistor (Gummel number G), 2) thick epitaxial layer with 3) low doping. These requirements cause in the I^2L n-p-n switching transistor a low β_{up} and a high value of I_{po}/I_{no} [2]. Thus, a very low n-p-n effective up gain β_{eff} is obtained. Storage of much hole diffusion charge in the thick, lowly doped n-p-n emitter gives long delay times at high current levels.

An improved combination process, which can be used with existing high-voltage analog processes with a minimum of change, is highly desirable. Several principles for combination processes have been suggested. However, in most cases, few details have been given for the analog starting process, the I^2L gate geometry used, and the electrical data obtained. Thus, it is not possible to make a direct comparison of the qualities of the different processes.

In this paper we wish to present and compare experimental results obtained for the I^2L properties of various simple combination processes based on the same analog process. Each combination process is realized by introducing one extra mask and process step in addition to the analog process. The additional step is optimized with respect to the I^2L properties but does not affect the analog part.

By using such a combination process one gets I^2L with a shallow N^+ guard ring. Better properties are obtained if one is willing to add one more masking step for a deep N^+ diffusion. The merit of deep versus shallow N^+ will be discussed for one of the processes.

II. SIMPLE COMBINATION PROCESSES

In all the methods to be compared the main purpose of the additional process step is to reduce the base Gummel number in the I^2L n-p-n transistor. This is indicated schematically in Fig. 1. The cross section of an I^2L gate produced by a standard analog process is shown on the left in *A*. The corresponding doping profiles are fully drawn in the figure to the right.

In (*B*) the N^+ diffusion for the I^2L collectors is made in a

Reprinted from *IEEE J. Solid-State Circuits*, vol. SC-14, no. 4, pp. 666–671, Aug. 1979.

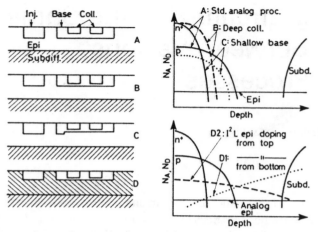

Fig. 1. I^2L obtained by various methods: *A*) Standard analog process. *B*) Deep N^+ diffusion for I^2L collectors. *C*) Shallow p diffusion for I^2L base. *D*) Enhancement of epi doping from below or above. Schematic cross sections are shown to the left and doping profiles to the right.

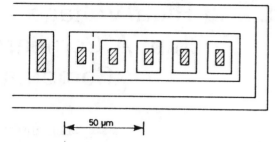

Fig. 2. Layout of four-collector I^2L gate. In process *C* the base area to the right of the dashed line is lightly doped.

separate step [3], and these collectors are deeper than the analog emitter. The new N^+ profile is dashed in the figure to the right. Thus, the active base thickness is reduced, as well as the active base integral doping.

In (*C*) a similar reduction in active base thickness is obtained by making the I^2L active base in a separate process step of lighter doping and more shallow drive-in [4]. The corresponding doping profile is dotted.

Finally, in (*D*) a heavier doping is introduced through the whole depth of the epi layer in the I^2L part of the chip, whereas the base and collector diffusions are the same as in the analog part. This doping may be introduced as an extra phosphorus buried layer which is diffused up through the epi layer, *D1* [5], or it may be introduced after epi growth and diffused down, *D2* [6].

The effect of these changes on the static I^2L properties can be seen from the expression for β_{eff} [2]:

$$\beta_{eff} = [1/\beta_{up} + I_{po}/I_{no}]^{-1}.$$

Here

$$\beta_{up} = I_C/I_B, \quad I_C = I_{no} \exp(qV_{EB}/kT),$$
$$I_{no} = S_C q n_i^2 D_n/G, \quad \text{and}$$
$$I_{po} = S_{inj} q n_i^2 D_p/(N_{epi} w_{p\text{-}n\text{-}p}).$$

The symbols have their usual meaning [2].

By a reduction of the n-p-n base Gummel number $G \equiv \int N_B' \, dx$, I_{no} and β_{up} are increased in all processes *B–D*. For processes *D*, I_{po} is simultaneously reduced due to the higher epi doping. For processes *D*, I_B is also reduced, as will be shown later.

The big thickness of the epi underneath the base remains essentially unaltered despite the modifications. The stored charge here [2] remains large for *B* and *C*, but is reduced in *D* due to the higher doping.

Other methods for I^2L/high-voltage analog combinations have been proposed [7]-[9]. However, they involve greater

modifications of standard processes and will not be further discussed here.

III. EXPERIMENTAL RESULTS

A. Process Details

The different processes *B–D* have been realized as modifications to our conventional 25 V BV_{CE} analog process. In order to get the most direct comparison between the methods, the same geometrical layout of the I^2L gates is used in all cases, as shown in Fig. 2. For method *C* the base area to the right of the dashed line is lightly doped. Dynamic measurements are made on nine-stage ring oscillators with output buffer and coupling to the collector farthest from the injector. This gives the longest delay for that geometry and is a very conservative measure of the four-collector gate speed.

The processes are adjusted to give $BV_{CE} = 3$ V for the I^2L gates to give some margin of safety in case of variations of processing parameters. The epi layers have $\rho = 2 \, \Omega \cdot cm$ $t = 12$ μm after growth, and the analog process gives $BV_{CE} \approx 30$ V, $\beta_{n\text{-}p\text{-}n} \approx 200$. I^2L made in the unmodified analog process *A* is included in the following for comparison.

The combined processes are obtained in the following way. In process *B*, the deep collector process, an N^+ predeposition of 5 $\Omega/\square$ (same as the analog emitter diffusion) is made for the I^2L collectors and driven partly in. Then the analog emitter diffusion is predeposited and the drive-in is completed. In process *C*, the shallow base process, the ordinary base is first predeposited. The lightly doped base is implanted with a dose of $8 \times 10^{14} \, cm^{-2}$ and drive-in of both is done. Process *D1*, the selective epi doping from below, is made by implanting $5 \times 10^{14} \, cm^{-2}$ phosphorus into the substrate after drive-in of the regular arsenic buried layer. In process *D2* a dose of $2 \times 10^{13} \, cm^{-2}$ phosphorus is implanted as the first step after epi growth. A deep N^+ guard ring of 5 $\Omega/\square$ predeposition is used.

The process parameters for the I^2L part are shown in Table I. The depths are measured by groove-and-stain and are not accurate. Also, the active base sheet resistivity R_p is only approximate.

B. Static Properties

Fig. 3 shows the measured β_{eff} versus I_C for processes *A*, *B*, *C*, and *D2*. *D1* gave results very similar to *D2* and is not shown in the figure.

It will be noted that the selective epi doping processes *D* give by far the highest β_{eff} at all current levels. At low currents

TABLE I
PROCESS PARAMETERS. W_b IS ACTIVE BASE THICKNESS, R_p IS ACTIVE BASE SHEET RESISTIVITY

Parameter	A Std. analog	B Deep coll.	C Shallow base	D1 Epi up	D2 Epi down
ρ_{epi} (Ωcm) average	2.0	2.0	2.0	0.2	0.25
N_{epi} ($\times 10^{15}$cm^{-3}) average	2.5	2.5	2.5	40	25
W_{epi} (μm) net (under base)	4.5	4.5	4.5/4.7	4.9	4.9
R_B ($\Omega/\square$)	120	120	120/200	120	120
W_B (μm)	3.6	3.6	3.6/3.4	3.2	3.2
W_B' (μm) approx.	~0.8	~0.6	~0.6	~0.4	~0.4
R_p ($\Omega/\square$) approx.	~10k	~100k	~100k	~40k	~40k
BV_{CE}(V) I^{2}L	7.5	3	3	3	3

TABLE II
CURRENT MEASURED IN ONE- AND FOUR-COLLECTOR I^{2}L GATES, AT V_{BE} = 650 mV. FOR THE FOUR-COLLECTOR GATES THE NEAREST COLLECTOR IS USED. UNIT μA

Process	1-coll. gate			4-coll. gate		
	I_C	$I_B(V_{inj}=0)$	$I_B(I_{inj}=0)$	I_C	$I_B(V_{inj}=0)$	$I_B(I_{inj}=0)$
A	34	13.5	7.2	36	16.2	8.6
B	141	13.7	8.5	154	17.1	11.3
C	122	15.5	7.5	132	17.4	8.4
D1	120	2.6	2.5	137	4.9	4.9
D2	100	2.2	2.1	103	4.2	4.1

TABLE III
APPROXIMATE BASE CURRENT COMPONENTS IN FOUR-COLLECTOR GATES AT V_{BE} = 650 mV CALCULATED FROM DATA OF TABLE II. UNIT μA

Process	I_{met}	I_B'	I_{rev}
A	6	2.5	7
B	6	5	6
C	7	2	9
D1	~0.9	4	~0.1
D2	~0.7	4	~0.1

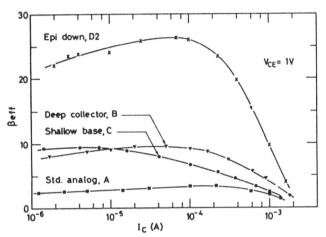

Fig. 3. Effective n-p-n gain versus collector current for four-collector gates for each process. The collector farthest from the base contact is used, the other collectors are floating.

processes B and C give nearly the same gain, but for B the gain starts dropping at a considerably lower current due to the higher base series resistance. Finally, the standard analog process A gives β_{eff} which is only slightly above 1. The common emitter gain of the p-n-p, β_{p-n-p}, is 4–5 for methods A–C, and ~1.0 for D1 and D2.

To analyze the static behavior in detail, measurements on special test structures should be made. Here we shall limit ourselves to a comparison of data for one-collector gates and four-collector gates. Table II gives collector current, and base current with injector grounded or floating, at V_{BE} = 650 mV. For the four-collector gates the nearest collector is used to minimize effects of base series resistance.

The most important components of the n-p-n base current I_B are [10]–[12]

$$I_B = I_{rev} + I_{met} + I_{ox} + I_{bl} + I_{str} \qquad (1)$$

where I_{rev} represents reverse injection of holes to injector, and I_{met} and I_{ox} are electron recombination in the metal covered and oxide covered base, respectively. I_{bl} is hole recombination in the buried layer and the N$^+$ ring, and I_{str} is leakage current to the substrate.

Since the current densities are nearly independent of gate

geometry, I_{rev} and I_{met} are approximately the same for one- and four-collector gates. The remaining components are proportional to their respective areas. As a fair approximation we take the area ratio for four- and one-collector gates to be 2.5 for each of these current components. Also we neglect the difference in recombination in the predeposited and implanted parts of the base of method C. It is then possible to find approximate values of I_{met}, I_{rev}, and the sum of the remaining base current components $I_B' \equiv I_{ox} + I_{bl} + I_{str}$. The results are given in Table III.

The low collector current value of process A is related to the large Gummel number and is the reason for the much lower β_{eff} of A than of B and C. Processes A, B, and C have similar values of the base current components, as might be expected. Processes D have much lower base current than the other processes, with injector floating as well as grounded. Table III indicates the reason for this to be lower I_{rev} as well as lower I_{met}. The low I_{rev} is due to the high epi concentration. But the generally accepted expression for I_{met} [11], [12],

$$I_{met} = S_{met} \frac{q n_i^2 D_n}{\int N_B dx} \exp(q V_{BE}/kT),$$

does not predict any dependence on epi doping. The two most likely explanations for our data seem to be 1) the effective surface recombination velocity under the metal [13] is smaller for methods D than for the other methods, or 2) equation (1) is incomplete and additional recombination is of importance. This would make the magnitudes in Table III inaccurate. Detailed measurements on test structures [10]–[12] are in progress and will be discussed in a future paper.

To get sufficient driving capability and noise margin for I^{2}L it is desirable to have $\beta_{eff} \gtrsim 10$ for four-collector gates for the whole range of currents and temperatures of interest. At low

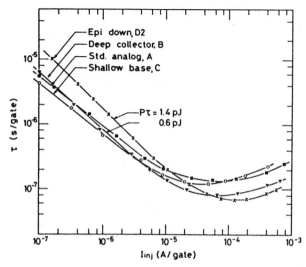

Fig. 4. Delay time versus injector current for four-collector gates for each process measured by nine-stage ring oscillators. The collector farthest from the injector drives the next stage.

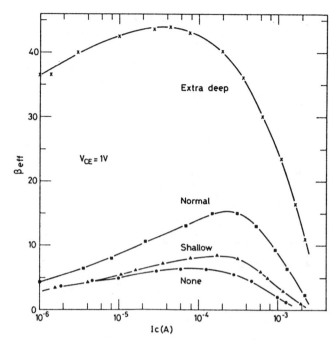

Fig. 5. Effective gain versus collector current for four-collector I^2L gates, process $D2$, with different depths of the N^+ guard ring.

temperatures β_{eff} is reduced [12]. Also, if a shallow N^+ guard ring is used, instead of the present deep N^+, β_{eff} is reduced by about a factor 2 (Section IV below). The data presented here show that the selective epi doping methods have static properties much superior to the other methods, giving flexibility in use of shallow/deep N^+ guard and use of geometrically unfavorable gates with several crossovers, etc.

C. Dynamic Properties

Fig. 4 shows four-collector gate delay time versus injector current for processes A, B, C, and $D2$. The data for method $D1$ are very similar to those for $D2$. It should be emphasized that four-collector gates of method A only operate marginally: from a number of wafers processed only a few ring oscillators worked at all. For all methods one-collector gates have approximately a factor 2 shorter delay at low currents and a factor 3 shorter at high currents.

Methods A, B, and C give low delay and are very similar at low currents, with a power-delay product at 1 μA/gate of $\sim$0.6 pJ. Methods D have a power-delay product which is twice as high. The difference is caused by the increased charge storage in the n-p-n emitter-base depletion region for methods D, due to high epi doping [2].

At high currents methods D are best with a minimum four-collector gate delay $\lesssim$70 ns/gate compared to 80 for B, 110 for C, and 140 for A. The superiority of methods D is due to less diffusion charge storage in the more highly doped epi layer [2]. The improvement is not as great as the epi concentration ratio alone would predict, because for a given injector current V_{BE} is higher for the methods with high epi doping.

The difference between methods A and B is due to the charge in the thicker active base of method A. The poor minimum delay of method C is due to the high base series resistance, which causes debiasing at lower currents for this method than for the other methods (cf. Fig. 3).

IV. ADDITIONAL PROPERTIES OF THE SELECTIVE EPI DOPING PROCESS $D2$

In view of the superior performance of the selective epi doping processes we shall present some additional results on method $D2$.

In some combined circuits parts of the analog circuitry require low collector series resistance and a deep N^+ diffusion. In that case the normal, deep I^2L guard ring is automatically available. Most often there is no such need in the analog part, and the deep N^+ process step is saved if the I^2L can do with only shallow N^+ guard.

To see the importance of deep versus shallow N^+ we have processed wafers with both types by method $D2$. (See [14] for analogous results for conventional I^2L process.) The use of no N^+ at all has been included for comparison, as well as an extra deep N^+ which makes certain that the concentration is high even where the guard ring hits the buried layer. The N^+ predeposition is in all cases 5 $\Omega/\square$; the depths at which the N^+ concentration is reduced to the implanted epi concentration are $\sim$3.5 μm (shallow), $\sim$7 μm (normal), and $\sim$12 μm (extra deep).

The measured β_{eff} versus I_c in the four cases is shown in Fig. 5. (The gate geometry is slightly different from that used for Fig. 3, with a lower ratio of collector to base areas.) It will be seen that a shallow N^+ is only marginally better than none at all. This is because of the thick epi layer underneath the shallow N^+ diffusion which gives rise to a high base current due to hole recombination far away from the base. β_{eff} for normal, deep N^+ is approximately a factor 2 better.

The effect of the extra deep N^+ is dramatic, increasing β_{eff} by a factor 3 above that for the normal N^+ depth. The reasons for this are that the N^+ concentration is high all the way down

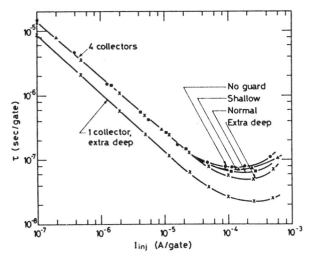

Fig. 6. Delay time versus injector current for four-collector gates, process $D2$, with different depths of the N^+ guard ring. Data for one-collector gates with extra deep N^+ are also included.

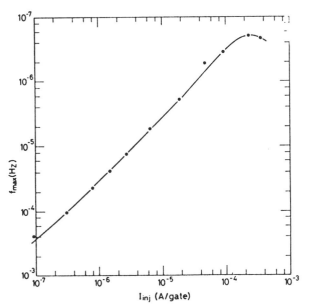

Fig. 7. Highest clock frequency versus injector current, for divide-by-two modules made by process $D2$.

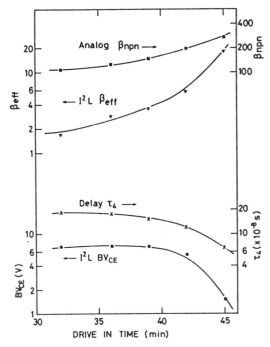

Fig. 8. Plot of basic analog and I^2L properties versus N^+ drive-in time, for process $D2$ with shallow N^+ guard ring. The top curve (scale to the right) shows analog $\beta_{n\text{-}p\text{-}n}$. The curves below show I^2L properties for four-collector gates: β_{eff} (scale to the left), τ (scale to the right), and BV_{CE} (scale to the left).

Finally, we wish to emphasize the sensitivity to variations in process parameters for all the combination processes discussed. As an illustration of this for process $D2$ various I^2L parameters, as well as analog $\beta_{n\text{-}p\text{-}n}$, were measured for various drive-in times for the shallow N^+ diffusion. (We could equally well have chosen to vary the diffusion temperature, or the base diffusion.) Fig. 8 shows the results. As the drive-in time is varied from 35 to 45 min the analog $\beta_{n\text{-}p\text{-}n}$ increases by a factor ~ 2.5. The corresponding change in β_{eff} is a factor 10. The delay time is reduced by a factor ~ 2.5 and, equally significantly, BV_{CE} goes down from 7 to 1.5 V. Thus, process variations which give acceptable spread in analog parameters cause changes in the I^2L which are too big to be tolerated. The reason is that the I^2L active base is considerably thinner than the analog active base, and the *relative* change caused by a process variation is much greater in the I^2L part than in the analog part.

V. CONCLUSIONS

In this paper the I^2L properties of various combination processes have been compared. The processes are all based on the same standard analog process, and one additional step is introduced (or two, giving I^2L with deep N^+ guard ring).

Methods D, based on selective doping of the I^2L epi layer, give much better driving capability than the other methods. The electron recombination component of the base current appears to be smaller, giving a higher β_{up}. Also, the ratio I_{po}/I_{no} is lower due to higher epi doping, making β_{eff} much higher for these processes.

Methods D also give the shortest gate delay at high current levels, due to less hole storage in the more highly doped epi

into the buried layer, and out-diffusion causes the N^+ to touch the base area.

Fig. 6 shows gate delay versus injector current for the same cases of N^+ guard. At low currents there is no difference, but at high currents the delay is shorter for the deeper N^+. The difference in minimum delay for shallow and deep N^+ is ~ 10 percent.

The reason for the reduced delay with deeper N^+ is the reduction of hole charge in the epi underneath the N^+, as well as around the base area due to N^+ out-diffusion.

Fig. 7 shows for process $D2$ the highest clock frequency of D flip-flops in the divide-by-two mode versus injector current. By this process the maximum clock frequency is approximately 6 MHz, at a power of 0.15 mW/gate. This is considerably below the speed of optimized purely digital processes, but for many purposes it is very satisfactory.

layer. However, methods B and C, based on deep I^{2}L collectors and shallow I^{2}L base, respectively, have lower power-delay product than methods D, due to less charge in the emitter-base depletion region.

Comparing methods $D1$ and $D2$, with selective epi doping introduced from below and above, respectively, the electrical data are found to be very similar. One disadvantage of $D1$, however, is that it is sensitive to variations in the epi thickness [5]. The method of epi down-diffusion $D2$ is therefore to be preferred.

For that method it was shown that a deep N$^+$ guard ring gives approximately twice as high β_{eff} as a shallow one. However, the deep N$^+$ only gives a ~10 percent improvement in maximum speed.

Finally, it was demonstrated that the combination processes (represented by $D2$) are considerably more sensitive to variations in processing parameters than the standard analog process.

The "super-gain" transistors produced by the combination processes may also be used for analog circuitry. For processes B and C these have $\beta_{down} \sim 1000$ and $BV_{CE} \sim 8$ V, for processes D $\beta_{down} \sim 500$ and $BV_{CE} \sim 10$ V.

The common geometry used (cf. Fig. 2) is a compromise, and by using different geometries the results for each process can be somewhat improved.

ACKNOWLEDGMENT

We are grateful to ϕ. Engebretsen, D. J. Ruzicka, and P. R. Ulsnaes for growth of epi layers, H. Sandmo for ion-implantation, and H. Skarelven, E. Carlson, and H. Jakobsen for valuable discussions.

REFERENCES

[1] J. L. Saltich, W. L. George, and J. S. Soderberg, "Processing technology and AC/DC characteristics for linear compatible I^{2}L," *IEEE J. Solid-State Circuits*, vol. SC-11, pp. 478–485, Aug. 1975.

[2] F. M. Klaassen, "Device physics of integrated injection logic," *IEEE Trans. Electron. Devices*, vol. ED-22, pp. 145–152, Mar. 1975.

[3] G. Bergmann, "Linear compatible I^{2}L technology with high voltage transistors," *IEEE J. Solid-State Circuits*, vol. SC-12, pp. 566–572, Oct. 1977.

[4] L. Blossfeld, "I^{2}L und standard Bipolartechnik kombiniert: Ein neuer Prozess für digitale und analoge Schaltungen auf einum Chip," *Elektronik*, Heft 4, pp. 57–60, 1977.

[5] T. Watanabe, T. Okabe, and M. Nogaka, "Phosphorous buried emitter I^{2}L for high voltage operating circuits," *Jap. J. Appl. Phys.*, vol. 16, suppl. 16-1, pp. 143–146, 1976.

[6] D. J. Allstot *et al.*, "A new high-voltage analog-compatible I^{2}L process," *IEEE J. Solid-State Circuits*, vol. SC-13, pp. 479–483, Aug. 1978.

[7] R. D. Davies and J. D. Meindl, "Poly I^{2}L–A high-speed linear-compatible structure," *IEEE J. Solid-State Circuits*, vol. SC-12, pp. 367–375, Aug. 1977.

[8] T. Okabe, T. Watanabe, and M. Nagata, "A controller with high speed I^{2}L and high voltage analog circuits," in *1978 ISSCC Dig. Tech. Papers*, pp. 44–45.

[9] A. A. Yiannoulos, "Buried injector logic: Second generation I^{2}L performance," in *1978 ISSCC Dig. Tech. Papers*, pp. 12–13.

[10] H. E. Berger, "The injection model—A structure-oriented model for merged transistor logic (MTL)," *IEEE J. Solid-State Circuits*, vol. SC-9, pp. 218–227, Oct. 1974.

[11] H. E. Wulms, "Base current of I^{2}L transistors," *IEEE Solid-State Circuits*, vol. SC-12, pp. 143–150, Apr. 1977.

[12] W. H. Mattheus, R. P. Mertens, and J. D. Stulting, "Characteristics of I^{2}L at low current levels," *IEEE Trans. Electron. Devices*, vol. ED-24, pp. 1228–1233, Oct. 1977.

[13] E. L. Heasell, "Recombination beneath ohmic contacts and adjacent oxide covered regions," *Solid-State Electron.*, vol. 22, pp. 89–93, Jan. 1979.

[14] A. Scmitz and A. Slob, "The effect of isolation regions on the current gain of inverse npn-transistors used in integrated injection logic (I^{2}L)," in *1974 IEDM Dig. Tech. Papers*, pp. 508–510.

A Monolithic 200-V CMOS Analog Switch

JAMES D. PLUMMER, MEMBER, IEEE, AND JAMES D. MEINDL, FELLOW, IEEE

Abstract—A new high-voltage CMOS technology is described which can increase the operating voltage of these circuits to more than 200 V. This represents approximately an order of magnitude improvement over present-day commercially available CMOS devices. The technology is straightforward to implement and uses n-channel DMOS transistors and high-voltage p-channel devices. As an example of the capability of the technology, a monolithic quad CMOS analog switch has been fabricated which can handle 200-V, 0.3-A analog signals, with a dynamic range in excess of 150 dB.

I. INTRODUCTION

FOR SEVERAL years we have been engaged in the development of medical electronic systems and the application of custom integrated circuits to these systems. The motivation for the work described in this paper came from one such system which is shown in simplified form in Fig. 1 [1]. This particular system uses high-frequency (1–5 MHz) sound waves to provide real-time images of internal organs in the human body. Hence it is called an ultrasonic imaging system. It operates on a principle very similar to sonar or radar systems.

Individual elements in a linear or two-dimensional array of piezoelectric transducers are used to generate the 1–5 MHz sound waves. Each element in the array sequentially transmits a 2 μs sound burst into the body and then "listens" for returning echoes. The echoes which return from internal body structures are then processed to form an image. In order to switch rapidly between the array elements and thus produce real-time images at a frame rate of about 30 Hz, it is very desirable to have an electronic switch to accomplish the multiplexing function illustrated in Fig. 1.

The system requirements placed on any electronic switches used here, however, are quite severe and are described in Table I.

The piezoelectric transducers require peak-to-peak voltages of about 200 V and peak currents of about 0.3 A when they are used to transmit the sound bursts into the body. The echoes which return from deep body structures may be as small as a few microvolts, requiring an analog signal dynamic range in excess of 150 dB. In addition, the multiplexers must have an on resistance less than 50 Ω, a parasitic capacitance C_{DSub} of less than 10 pF to maintain adequate system bandwidth, and a feedthrough capacitance C_{DS} of less than 2 pF to minimize crosstalk in the piezoelectric array. A new high-voltage technology has been devised which is capable of producing devices and monolithic circuits able to operate at the voltage levels indicated in Table I.

Manuscript received June 1, 1976; revised August 6, 1976. This work was supported in part by NIH Grant 1 P01GM1 17940-5 and in part by NSF Grant ENG. 74-18419.

The authors are with the Integrated Circuits Laboratory, Stanford University, Stanford, CA 94305.

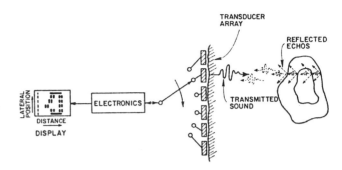

Fig. 1. Basic ultrasonic imaging system showing requirement for high-voltage analog switches.

TABLE I
MULTIPLEXER REQUIREMENTS

1) Analog voltage capability	200 V peak-to-peak
2) Analog current capability	0.3 A peak
3) Analog voltage dynamic range	>150 dB (5 μV to 200 V)
4) On resistance	<50 Ω
5) Parasitic capacitance C_{DSub}	<10 pF
6) Feedthrough capacitance C_{DS}	<2 pF

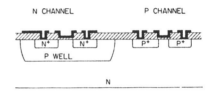

Fig. 2. Conventional low-voltage CMOS structure.

High-voltage integrated circuits in general require either fairly high impedance levels (that is, large resistors) or some sort of complementary structure in order to keep power dissipation at reasonable levels. The approach described in this paper is to devise a complementary MOS (CMOS) structure able to operate at the above voltage levels.

II. VOLTAGE LIMITATIONS OF COMMERCIALLY AVAILABLE CMOS INTEGRATED CIRCUITS

Virtually all commercially available CMOS integrated circuits operate with maximum supply voltages of 15–20 V. These circuits typically use the device structures illustrated in Fig. 2. N-type bulk silicon (typically 5–10 Ω · cm) forms the common substrate for all of the p-channel devices. An ion-implanted or thermally diffused p well is used as the substrate for the n-channel devices. Various local oxidation or channel-stopping techniques [2] are commonly employed; these do not, however, change the basic structure of the n- and p-channel devices.

The p-channel device in these circuits is typically capable of much higher voltage operation than the n-channel device. Enhancement mode p-channel devices can easily be fabricated on substrates doped as lightly as $10^{14}/cm^3$. This light doping

Reprinted from *IEEE J. Solid-State Circuits*, vol. SC-11, pp. 809–817, Dec. 1976.

in the n-substrates makes high junction breakdown voltages possible and a number of authors [3]-[6] have suggested p-channel structures with drain-to-source breakdown voltages (BV_{DSS}) of 50-150 V. These structures have typically been proposed as high-voltage output drivers for standard PMOS integrated circuits but they are also applicable, in general, as high-voltage PMOS components in standard CMOS integrated circuits.

Enhancement mode operation of the n-channel device in Fig. 2 typically requires that the p-well surface be doped to approximately 10^{16}/cm^3. This relatively high doping level implies that junction breakdowns in the n-channel device are much lower than in the p-channel transistor. The combination of higher doping levels and the enhanced fields found under the gate, near the drain, in any standard MOS transistor [7], typically results in these n-channel devices exhibiting breakdown voltages BV_{DSS} of 20-40 V.

III. A High-Voltage n-Channel Transistor

One solution to the voltage limitations of standard n-channel devices is to use a double-diffused (DMOS) n-channel transistor [8]. A cross section of this device is shown in Fig. 3 with the channel region exaggerated in its lateral dimension for clarity, along with the corresponding doping profiles.

The device is fabricated in n-type epitaxial material and isolated with a conventional p$^+$ diffusion. The channel region of the device is formed by sequential boron and phosphorus diffusions through the same oxide cut. The difference in lateral diffusion between the p- and n$^+$-regions forms a controllable 1 to 3 μm channel along the surface much in the same way that base width is controlled in a bipolar transistor. The short channel provides high transconductance and low on resistance.

Unlike conventional MOS transistors, the channel region of the DMOS device is nonuniformly doped. Boron concentration in the channel varies both laterally along the surface and vertically into the substrate. In general, then, calculation of threshold voltage is a complex two-dimensional problem. In the case of the high-voltage devices being described here, however, certain simplifying assumptions may be made.

1) The source n$^+$ diffusion is shorted to the channel p diffusion so source to substrate bias effects are absent.

2) Relatively deep junctions are employed in these structures, as will be seen later, so that the depth of the surface depletion region under the gate is small compared to the junction depth [9]. As a result, we may neglect the variation in impurity concentration vertically.

3) If we further assume that the threshold voltage at any point along the channel is influenced only by the surface doping level at that point, then the threshold voltage of the device will be given simply by

$$V_T \simeq \phi_{ms} + 2\phi_F - \frac{Q_{ss}}{C_{ox}} + \frac{(4\epsilon_s q N_{A_{max}}\phi_F)^{1/2}}{C_{ox}}$$

where

ϕ_{ms} metal semiconductor work function differences;
ϕ_F Fermi potential;

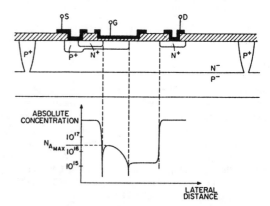

Fig. 3. Cross section of high-voltage n-channel DMOS transistor (channel length exaggerated).

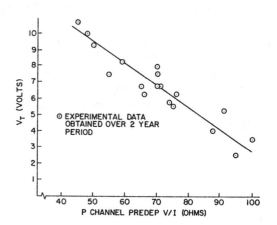

Fig. 4. DMOS threshold voltage versus channel predeposition.

Q_{ss} effective surface state charge density;
C_{ox} gate to channel capacitance;
$N_{A_{max}}$ peak impurity doping level in the channel;
ϵ_s dielectric constant of silicon.

In the technology used to fabricate these devices, the gate oxide is thermally grown after the completion of the channel and source diffusions. As a result, a further complication arises in the prediction of threshold voltage from a given set of impurity profiles. Boron redistribution at the channel surface during gate oxidation can lead to a decrease in $N_{A_{max}}$ of 2 to 5 times below what one would expect from the diffusion processes alone [7].

A reasonably complete treatment of these problems and of the calculation of threshold voltage for the DMOS device may be found in [10]. For the purposes of this paper, it is sufficient to state that for high-voltage DMOS devices with relatively deep junctions (p-channel diffusion depth 4.5 μm) and relatively long channels (2.5 μm) such as the device illustrated in Fig. 3, the threshold voltage is determined largely by the p-channel predeposition step [9].

Fig. 4 presents experimental results obtained over a two-year period of fabricating these devices. The threshold voltage of the device is seen to be a relatively slowly varying function of the channel predeposition V/I. The threshold voltage may be controlled to 5 ± 1 V by controlling the channel predeposition to 80 Ω ± 10 Ω. This is easily achieved with ion implantation techniques; in fact all of the devices we have fabricated have used thermal boron predepositions and we have experienced no difficulty in controlling V_T.

The principal reason for the high-voltage capability of the DMOS device is the presence of an n⁻ drift region between the channel and the drain n⁺ diffusion. The lateral and vertical dimensions of the high-voltage structure are illustrated in Fig. 5. Among the dimensions which are critical to the high-voltage capability of the device are the following.

1) The lateral spacings drain to isolation and source to isolation, and the thickness of the epitaxial layer are necessary to prevent punchthrough breakdown between junctions.

2) The channel length of 2.5 μm is necessary in order to prevent punchthrough breakdown between drain and source. The drain to source depletion region spreads primarily into the lightly doped ($10^{15}/\text{cm}^3$) n⁻ drift region between drain and source. Some depletion region spreading into the channel region (where the peak doping is $\simeq 5 \times 10^{16}/\text{cm}^3$) does occur, however, and the minimum channel length required to prevent punchthrough at 250-V bias has been calculated [9] to be about 2.5 μm.

3) In addition to a minimum channel length, a minimum amount of boron doping must be present in the channel to prevent punchthrough between drain and source. This implies that for any given breakdown voltage BV_{DSS}, the device must have a minimum threshold voltage. A detailed model of the interrelationship between breakdown voltage, threshold voltage, and channel length will be described in a future paper. For the devices described here, a channel length of 2.5 μm and a required $BV_{DSS} > 200$ V sets the minimum device threshold voltage at about 4 V.

4) The gate oxide thickness of 0.4 μm is necessary in order to prevent dielectric breakdown between gate and source. As will be shown later, some circuit applications of this device require high-voltages gate to source. The thick gate dielectric provides the necessary voltage capability while at the same time reducing the maximum transconductance of the device. Sigg *et al.* [8] have shown that at high gate voltages the DMOS device operates with scattering velocity limited transconductance given by

$$g_{m_{\max}} = C_{\text{ox}} Z v_s$$

where

Z channel width;
v_s scattering limited carrier velocity $\simeq 6.5 \times 10^6$ cm/s in silicon.

For a 0.4 μm gate oxide thickness, this implies a maximum transconductance of 5.5 μmhos per micron of channel width, a factor of four lower than what has been achieved with more commonly used 1000 Å gate oxide thicknesses [8].

5) The gate metal extends approximately 5 μ over thin oxide past the channel and then steps up over thick oxide before terminating well short of the drain n⁺ contact. It therefore acts as a field plate, minimizing surface effects, and allows the drain-to-source depletion region to terminate under thick oxide. It is important that the gate metal stop short of

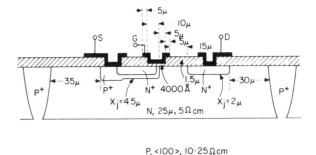

Fig. 5. Detailed dimensions of high-voltage DMOS transistor.

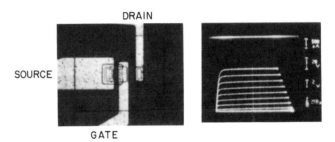

Fig. 6. Photomicrograph and *I–V* characteristics of high-voltage DMOS transistor.

the drain n⁺ contact. If this is not done, avalanching of the surface near the n⁺ contact will severely degrade the voltage capability of the device [11]. The stepped oxide gate structure utilized in these devices is somewhat similar to that suggested by Conti *et al.* [12].

Fig. 6 is a photomicrograph of a high-voltage n channel DMOS device incorporating the features described above. The *I–V* characteristics shown illustrate the 200⁺-V capability of the device. The very high output impedance exhibited by the device is primarily a result of the fact that the drain-to-source depletion region spreads principally into the drain n⁻ region and not into the channel. As a result there is very little channel length modulation.

The thin oxide gate region is 15 × 40 μm giving an indication of the physical size of the device. With a transconductance of 5.5 μmhos per micron of channel width (scattering limited velocity limit) we would expect a g_m of $\simeq 220$ μmhos for the device in Fig. 6, which is close to that observed in the *I–V* characteristics.

Sigg *et al.* [8] have shown that scattering velocity limited transconductance is achieved when

$$\frac{V_{GS} - V_T}{L} \geqslant \frac{v_s}{\mu_n}$$

where

V_{GS} gate-to-source voltage;
μ_n effective mobility of electrons in the channel;
L effective channel length.

With $v_s = 6.5 \times 10^6$ cm/s and $\mu_n = 350$ cm²/V · s, this inequality holds for V_{GS} greater than approximately 10 V for

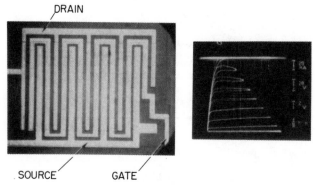

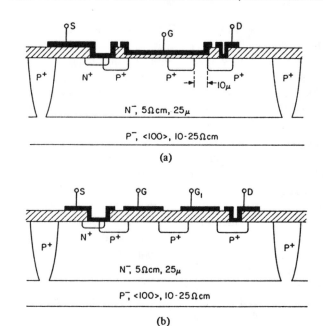

Fig. 7. Photomicrograph and I-V characteristics of large geometry DMOS transistor.

Fig. 8. Two high-voltage p-channel configurations. (a) Thin oxide, floating guard ring structure. (b) Thick oxide, dual transistor structure.

the devices considered here. The constant transconductance, independent of gate voltage, is apparent in the I-V characteristics of Fig. 6.

Higher current capability devices are also possible using the same structure described above. Fig. 7 is a photomicrograph of a larger, interdigitated version of the same basic DMOS device. Source and drain regions alternate and the gate winds back and forth between them to give the device a W/L ratio of about 1500 ($L = 2.5$ μm, $W = 3.75$ mm). The overall size of the device is approximately 0.5 X 0.75 mm (20 X 30 mils). The same basic structure illustrated in Fig. 5 is used for this device.

The I-V characteristics shown on the right of Fig. 7 again illustrate the 200$^+$-V capability of the device. The large W/L ratio in this case gives the transistor a current carrying capability in excess of 0.3 A and an on resistance of about 35 Ω. The measured transconductance of the device is $\simeq$ 20 mmhos which agrees well with the predicted value based on scattering limited velocity operation ($g_m \simeq 5.5$ μmhos/μm X 3.75 mm $\simeq$ 20 mmhos). This device will be used as the analog switch in the integrated circuit to be described later in this paper.

IV. HIGH-VOLTAGE p-CHANNEL TRANSISTORS

In addition to the n-channel DMOS device discussed to this point, a high-voltage CMOS technology requires a high-voltage p-channel component. As already mentioned, considerable previous work [3]-[6] has been done in this area. The structures proposed in these earlier papers have typically been suggested as high-voltage output stages for PMOS integrated circuits. Most of them can be used equally well, however, in CMOS circuits.

Two types of p-channel devices are used in the circuits described here and these are illustrated in Fig. 8. The higher voltage device of the two is the one shown in the bottom portion of the diagram. This device consists essentially of two transistors in series with a floating intermediate drain and thick oxide (1.5 μm) gates. By choosing the voltages on the two gates appropriately, the two transistors effectively divide the applied voltage. This fact along with the use of thick oxide gates which reduce surface fields, allows the device to sustain voltages well in excess of 200 V. In the circuit to be described later, two power supplies are typically used: ±100 V and +15 V. Biasing gate G_1 at +15 V sets the po-

tential of the intermediate p$^+$ region at

$$V_{p^+} \simeq + 15 + |V_T| \simeq + 30 \text{ V}$$

so that an applied voltage of ±100 V between drain and source will be shared by the two transistors. The particular choice of +15 V will become clear later.

The use of thick oxide gates does of course imply a high threshold voltage for this p-channel device. With 1.5-μm gate oxide thickness and a 5-$\Omega \cdot$ cm, $\langle 100 \rangle$ substrate, the device exhibits a threshold voltage of −12 to −15 V. In addition, the field oxide thickness is generally not as well controlled in MOS devices as the thinner gate oxide so that one would expect relatively poor control of V_T for this device. Both of these characteristics make this device unsuitable for use in the input stages of the CMOS circuit to be described since compatibility at the inputs with standard low-voltage logic circuits demands a p-channel device with a low, well-controlled threshold voltage.

The device described above is, however, quite suitable for use in the high voltage output stages of the CMOS analog switch which will be shown later. In the output stages, a full 200 V is available to drive the gate of the device. This makes the high threshold voltage of little importance and also compensates for the low transconductance which the device clearly has.

Fig. 9 is a photomicrograph of one of these p-channel devices. The three p$^+$ regions and the two gates are visible with the source region at the top. The I-V characteristics on the right illustrate the 200$^+$-V capability of the device and, in addition, indicate that it has several milliamps of current capability with the maximum gate voltage of 150 V shown in the figure. One need not pay a severe price in circuit speed because of the low transconductance of this device. This will be demonstrated in a circuit application later in the paper.

The unusual metal pattern shown in the photomicrograph

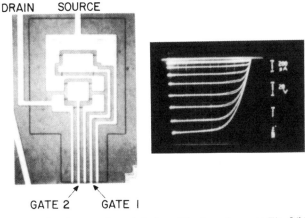

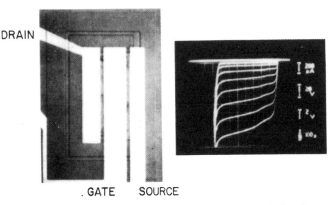

Fig. 9. High-voltage p-channel device of the type shown in Fig. 8(b).

Fig. 10. High-voltage p-channel device of the type shown in Fig. 8(a).

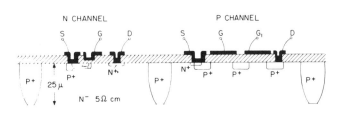

Fig. 11. Cross section of compatible n- and p-channel transistors.

is a result of parasitic p-channel devices which can exist in these structures. Referring again to Fig. 8(b), it is apparent that gates G and G_1 can induce parasitic channels between any of the three p⁺ regions and the p⁺ isolation diffusion if appropriate gate potentials exist in the circuit. These parasitic devices are unavoidable in the straightforward aluminum gate process described here and the metal patterns are used to minimize these effects. Clearly, dielectric isolation, silicon on sapphire, or polysilicon field shields could be used to circumvent these problems, but would do so at the cost of additional processing complexity. The use of n⁺ guard rings to prevent these parasitic channels is not possible here either, since these guard rings reduce the breakdown voltage between drain and substrate to approximately 150 V, too low for operation with ±100-V power supplies.

A second p-channel structure is shown in the top portion of Fig. 8. This device uses a thin (0.4 μm, the same as the n-channel DMOS device) gate oxide to achieve a low, well-controlled -5-V threshold voltage. The low threshold voltage makes the device complementary to the +5-V V_T, n-channel DMOS transistor and, therefore, makes this p-channel device suitable for use in the input stages of our CMOS circuits.

Again a floating intermediate p⁺-drain region is used but in this case there is just one gate electrode. In this device, the p⁺ intermediate drain is located physically close ($\simeq$ 10 μm) to the drain p⁺ region and acts as a guard ring or field limiting ring [13] to increase the device's breakdown voltage. In a typical device, the p⁺ guard ring completely surrounds the drain p⁺ diffusion. In this case, the potential of the guard

ring is determined by the drain depletion region after sufficient voltage is applied for this depletion region to punch through to the intermediate p⁺ region. By proper choice of the spacing between the two diffusions, the field intensity under the gate can be reduced [13] and the breakdown voltage increased as a result. Photolithographic tolerances do not allow precise control of this spacing, but we have found it relatively easy to fabricate devices with $BV_{DSS} > 140$ V using this structure. Since the input stages of our CMOS circuits operate with supply voltages of +15 and -100, this voltage capability is adequate for this application.

Fig. 10 is a photomicrograph of a device of this type. The floating intermediate p⁺ region is visible next to the drain. The I–V characteristics on the right illustrate the 140⁺-V capability of the device. It is also apparent that this device has a much higher transconductance than the thick oxide device in Fig. 9. This also makes the device suitable for the input stages of our CMOS circuits where only the relatively small voltage swings of conventional logic circuits are available to drive it.

V. HIGH-VOLTAGE CMOS TECHNOLOGY

If we now combine the high-voltage n- and p-channel devices described to this point we can realize a CMOS technology. Fig. 11 shows the two devices combined in a monolithic substrate. The thin oxide p channel device described in Figs. 8(a) and 10 is not shown in Fig. 11, but is clearly compatible with the other two devices which are shown.

The fabrication sequence involves seven masking steps through metal definition and is outlined in Table II.

TABLE II
FABRICATION SEQUENCE

1) Epitaxial deposition	n, phosphorus doped, 25 μm, 5 $\Omega \cdot$ cm.
2) Isolation diffusion	boron predeposition and drive-in, $x_j \simeq 30$ μm.
3) p$^+$ diffusion	boron predeposition and drive-in, $x_j \simeq 5$ μm. (This step forms the p-channel source and drain and the n-channel p$^+$ contact.)
4) p$^-$-channel diffusion	boron predeposition and drive-in, $x_j \simeq 4.5$ μm. (This step forms the DMOS channel.)
5) n$^+$ diffusion	phosphorus predeposition and drive-in, $x_j \simeq 2$ μm. (This step forms the DMOS source and drain.)
6) Gate oxidation	
7) Contact opening	
8) Metal definition	
9) Vapox deposition and definition	

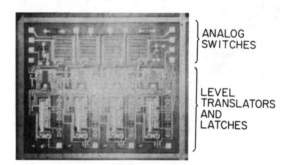

Fig. 12. Photomicrograph of quad analog switch.

VI. A 200-V CMOS QUAD ANALOG SWITCH

Fig. 12 is a photomicrograph of an integrated circuit incorporating the technology described to this point. The particular function performed by this circuit is that of a quad analog switch. It is similar in function, therefore, to commercially available devices such as the CD4066 [14], a widely used CMOS device. The principal distinguishing feature of the integrated circuit shown in Fig. 12 is that it operates at supply voltages up to ±100 V, whereas the CD4066 is rated at ±7.5 V.

The chip is 3 X 3.6 mm. The four analog switches are located at the top of the chip and are similar to the high-voltage, high-current DMOS device shown in Fig. 7. The circuitry on the bottom half of the chip contains both n- and p-channel devices and performs level translating and latching functions. Examples of the n-channel DMOS and the two types of high-voltage p-channel devices which have been described may be seen in the photomicrograph.

This particular circuit operates with supply voltages of ±100 and +15 V, the third supply being used to make the inputs compatible with standard low-voltage CMOS circuits. The analog switches on the chip meet the set of requirements listed in Table I. Several hundred of these integrated circuits have been fabricated and the device is currently in use in the medical ultrasonic imaging system described at the beginning of this paper. Principally because the technology used to im-

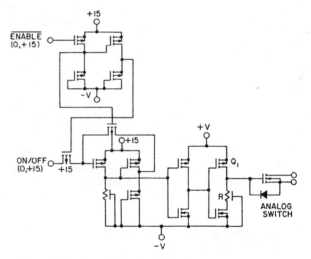

Fig. 13. Circuitry contained in each analog switch section.

plement this circuit is reasonably straightforward, we have observed yields on this device over the past year in excess of 25 percent.

The circuitry contained in each of the four analog switch sections of the chip is shown in Fig. 13. The lower portion of the circuitry is the level translator which shifts the 0-V and +15-V input levels into the ±100 V needed to turn the analog switch on and off. The output stages of this level translator

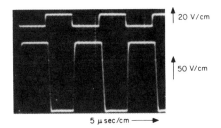

Fig. 14. Switching response of level translating portion of circuit.

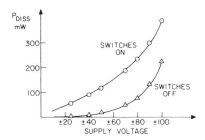

Fig. 15. Power dissipation of quad analog switch chip.

are CMOS and use the high-voltage n- and p-channel devices illustrated in Figs. 6 and 9, respectively. The input stages use p channel devices of the type shown in Fig. 10. Pinched epitaxial resistors are also used as shown in the circuit schematic. The latch circuitry on the chip allows the on or off state of the switch to be stored on the chip. The diode between the gate and the source of the analog switch is included because of the particular requirements of the system in which the circuit is used.

The performance of the level translating portion of the chip is shown in Fig. 14. The input signal on the top (0, +15 V) is translated into ±100-V levels, suitable for turning the analog switch on and off. The switching time is approximately 1 μs in each direction and is limited primarily by Q_1 and R. Both of these devices act essentially as current sources to charge and discharge the gate capacitance of the analog switch. Since both have a current capability of $\simeq 2$ mA, the switching time is given approximately by

$$t \simeq \frac{\Delta V C_{IN}}{I} \simeq \frac{(200)(10^{-11}F)}{2 \times 10^{-3}A} \simeq 1 \ \mu s$$

where C_{IN} is the input capacitance of the DMOS analog switch, in good agreement with the experimentally observed values. Note that even though Q_1 is a thick oxide and hence low transconductance transistor of the type shown in Figs. 8(b) and 9, the circuit switching speed is adequate because of the 200 V available to drive the gate of Q_1.

Power dissipation is, of course, an extremely important consideration in any high-voltage integrated circuit. Current levels must be low in order to keep dissipation within reasonable limits. The need for low currents was pointed out at the start of this paper as one of the main attractions to a complementary technology. Fig. 15 illustrates the power dissipated by the circuit described here. The upper curve applies with all four analog switches on; the lower curve with all four switches off. As the diagram indicates, at ±100 V, the chip consumes

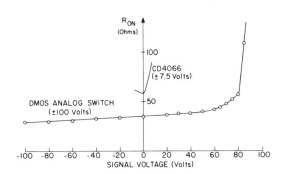

Fig. 16. On resistance of DMOS analog switch.

about 400 mW with the switches on and about 225 mW with the switches off.

Most of the power dissipation occurs in the input stages of the level translators and in the latches. Complementary circuitry is not used in these locations and as a result dc dissipation occurs. Approximately one quarter of the chip dissipation occurs in parasitic devices of the type described in connection with Fig. 9. This could be eliminated through the use of dielectric isolation or silicon on sapphire techniques.

One of the important parameters of an analog switch is its on resistance. Fig. 16 illustrates this parameter for the DMOS analog switches used in this device. The CD4066 is a standard commercially available CMOS quad analog switch, limited to an operating voltage range of ±7.5 V. Within this voltage range, the CD4066 analog switches typically have an on resistance between 60 and 90 Ω. The DMOS analog switches used in the circuit described here have more than an order of magnitude greater operating voltage range and have an on resistance well under 50 Ω over most of this range. At high positive voltages where the switch begins to turn off, the on resistance rises.

The high-voltage and -current capability of the DMOS switch do give rise to one important difference in the device model, in comparison to a standard MOS device. The device

151

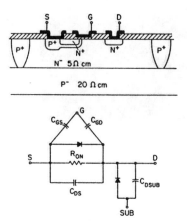

Fig. 17. Equivalent circuit of DMOS analog switch.

TABLE III
ANALOG SWITCH PARAMETERS

1) $BV_{DSS} > 200$ V
2) $I_{max} > 300$ mA
3) $R_{ON} < 50 \ \Omega$
4) $C_{DSub} \simeq 7$ pF at 50 V reverse bias[a]
5) $C_{DS} \simeq 1$ pF at 50 V reverse bias[a]
6) $C_{IN} \simeq 10$ pF

[a]The device is typically operated with at least 50 V between drain and substrate and with at least 50 V drain-to-source when the switch is off.

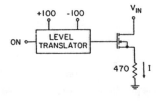

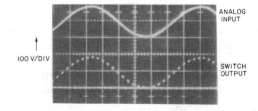

Fig. 19. 200-V analog signal being switched by DMOS analog switch.

Peak-to-peak voltage and current are 150 V and 0.3 A, respectively. Fig. 19 shows a 200-V analog signal being switched on and off to a load through the analog switch.

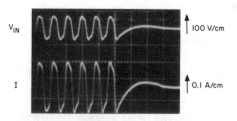

Fig. 18. Current and voltage capability of DMOS analog switch.

model illustrated in Fig. 17 shows a diode between the drain and source of the device. This diode is not present in standard low-voltage MOS devices and must be taken into account in any application of the DMOS device. Furthermore, C_{DS} will typically be larger in this structure than in a conventional MOS transistor, again because of the presence of diode between drain and source. One can, of course, place two DMOS devices in series, with the diodes back to back, in specific applications where the diode is unacceptable.

The specific parameters associated with the analog switches used in this circuit (Fig. 7) are listed in Table III.

The final two figures illustrate the current and voltage capability of the DMOS analog switches. Fig. 18 shows a 2-MHz analog signal passing through the switch to a resistive load.

VII. CONCLUSION

This paper has presented a new high-voltage CMOS technology which can be used to implement virtually any function commonly performed by low voltage CMOS circuits. High-voltage n-channel DMOS devices and high-voltage p-channel transistors have been described, both of which operate at more than 200 V. A quad analog switch has been fabricated using this technology, which can switch 200-V 0.3-A analog signals with a dynamic range in excess of 150 dB. Circuits built using this technology may have wide application in driving transducers and high-voltage displays, and in realizing crosspoint switches as well.

REFERENCES

[1] J. D. Plummer, J. D. Meindl, and M. G. Maginness, "A new ultrasonic imaging system for real time cardiac imaging," *ISSCC Digest Tech. Papers*, pp. 162–163, Feb. 1974.
[2] E. C. Douglas and A. G. F. Dingwall, "Surface doping using ion

implantation for optimum guard layer design in COS/MOS structures," *IEEE Trans. Electron Devices*, vol. ED-22, pp. 849–857, Oct. 1975.

[3] H. G. Dill, "A new insulated gate tetrode with high drain breakdown potential and low Miller feedback capacitance," *IEEE Trans. Electron Devices*, pp. 717–728, Oct. 1968.

[4] J. D. Plummer, J. Berger, and J. D. Meindl, "High voltage monolithic MOS driver arrays," *IEDM Conf. Digest*, p. 102, Oct. 1971.

[5] K. Saraswat, J. D. Meindl, and J. Berger, "A high voltage MOS switch," *IEEE J. Solid-State Circuits*, vol. SC-10, pp. 136–142, June 1975.

[6] G. A. May, T. R. Gheewala, M. Shimizu, and R. D. Melen, "A 120-V micropower CMOS tactile display driver," *ISSCC Digest Tech. Papers*, pp. 210–211, Feb. 1976.

[7] A. S. Grover, *Physics and Technology of Semiconductor Devices*. New York: Wiley, 1967.

[8] H. J. Sigg, G. D. Vendelin, T. P. Cauge, and J. Kocsis, "D-MOS transistor for microwave applications," *IEEE Trans. Electron Devices*, vol. ED-19, pp. 45–53, Jan. 1972.

[9] M. D. Pochá, "High voltage double diffused MOS transistors for integrated circuits," Tech. Rep. 4956-1, Stanford Electronics Laboratories, Stanford Univ., Stanford, CA, Mar. 1976.

[10] M. D. Pocha, A. G. Gonzalez, and R. W. Dutton, "Threshold voltage controllability in double-diffused-MOS transistors," *IEEE Trans. Electron Devices*, vol. ED-21, pp. 778–784, Dec. 1974.

[11] M. J. Declercq and J. D. Plummer, "Avalanche breakdown in high-voltage D-MOS devices," *IEEE Trans. Electron Devices*, vol. ED-23, pp. 1–4, Jan. 1976.

[12] F. Conti and M. Conti, "Surface breakdown in silicon planar diodes equipped with field plate," *Solid State Electronics*, vol. 15, pp. 93–105, 1972.

[13] V. C. Kao and E. D. Wolley, "High-voltage planar P-N junctions," *Proc. IEEE*, pp. 1409–1414, Aug. 1967.

[14] Manufactured commercially by RCA, National Semiconductor, Motorola, Harris and other semiconductor companies.

Enhanced CMOS for Analog–Digital Power IC Applications

GARY M. DOLNY, MEMBER, IEEE, OTTO H. SCHADE, JR., BARRY GOLDSMITH,
AND LAWRENCE A. GOODMAN, MEMBER, IEEE

Abstract—Elementary process additions to 2–3-μm polygate CMOS provide enhanced high-voltage MOSFET's and broadband complimentary bipolars. This allows monolithic integration of a modern logic family and quality analog function with high-voltage high-current buffers and drivers. The technology is suitable for data conversion, telecommunication, analog switch, and industrial IC applications where low-voltage digital and analog control circuitry must be interfaced to high-voltage high-current outputs.

I. INTRODUCTION

THE NEED to interface low-voltage logic-level control signals with medium-to-high power output devices has led to great interest in the development of high-voltage high-power IC technology. Integrated circuits that combine high-voltage output buffers and drivers with high-performance logic are therefore becoming increasingly important to system designers as a means of obtaining reduced size, enhanced performance, and improved reliability, all at lower systems cost.

Numerous approaches for combining logic with high-voltage or power devices have been proposed and implemented. These include all bipolar [1], [2], all N-MOS, [3], [4], high-voltage CMOS, [5]–[7], and combination bipolar and MOS (BIMOS) [9], [10].

Of these approaches BIMOS offers significant advantages in that many applications can be most effectively addressed with a technology providing both FET and bipolar devices. Logic and switching functions are inherently simple and efficiently implemented in CMOS, while analog gain/bandwidth is readily achieved with high bipolar transconductance. Additionally, many system elements such as voltage references, analog-sensing functions, and signal amplifiers benefit from a mixture of both.

In this paper we describe an enhanced CMOS technology that allows high-voltage CMOS structures and broadband vertical bipolars to be integrated with low-voltage CMOS devices. The bipolar and high-voltage CMOS structures were realized through elementary additions to a 3-μm polysilicon gate CMOS process. The high-voltage CMOS devices were designed for and achieved 60-V operation. This technology is well suited for applications that require the combination of low-voltage analog and digital signal processing with high-voltage buffers and drivers.

II. DEVICE STRUCTURE AND FABRICATION

The objective of the present investigation is to enhance the performance of a standard 3-μm polygate CMOS technology, known as QMOS, with analog capability and increased MOS breakdown voltage. Fig. 1 shows the silicon cross sections of the *enhanced QMOS* (EQMOS) process. The performance of 3-μm polysilicon gate devices is enhanced by offsetting the heavily doped n^+ and p^+ drain contacts from the gate edge and through the addition of n^- and p^- drain extensions that self-align to the polysilicon gate. These drain extensions serve to increase the avalanche breakdown voltage of the drain junction by allowing the depletion region to penetrate back into the lightly doped extension regions as well as into the channel. Unlike the classical lightly doped drain (LDD) approaches, EQMOS provides the low-concentration self-aligning extensions only at the drain, thereby avoiding source transconductance degradation. In addition, the drain extensions are deeper than and completely surround the heavily doped contact regions thus reducing drain capacitance, improving the dynamic output resistance and enhancing logic speed. Moreover, these extensions serve as the bases of vertical bipolar transistors and provide well-matched high-value resistors.

Extension length and doping concentration controls the maximum electric field at the drain, which in turn determines the avalanche breakdown voltage. However, the series resistance of the regions is known to degrade device performance [11], [12]. Therefore, the extension regions must be carefully designed in order to achieve the desired blocking voltage without paying a severe performance penalty. In order to investigate these effects, a series of test structures consisting of n- and p-channel MOS devices with varying channel and extension lengths was designed and fabricated. In addition the test chips contained n-p-n and p-n-p transistor structures in order to facilitate investigation of bipolar properties.

The test devices used in this study were fabricated from a standard 3-μm polysilicon gate process using 0.6–0.9-Ω · cm (100) silicon wafers. The junction depths of the heavily doped source and drain contact regions were nominally 0.5 μm with extension depths of 1.1 μm. The resulting bipolar base width is 0.6 μm. The detailed impurity profiles are shown in Fig. 2.

Manuscript received May 13, 1986; revised July 25, 1986.

G. M. Dolny and L. A. Goodman are with RCA Laboratories, David Sarnoff Research Center, Princeton, NJ 08543-0432.

O. H. Schade, Jr. is with RCA Solid State Division, Somerville, NJ 08876.

B. Goldsmith is with RCA Solid State Division, Findlay, OH 45840.

IEEE Log Number 8610704.

Reprinted from *IEEE Trans. Electron Devices*, vol. ED-33, pp. 1985–1991, Dec. 1986.

154

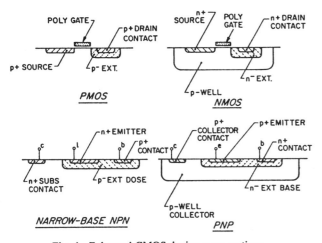

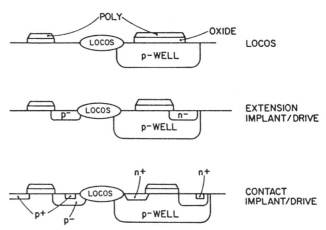

Fig. 1. Enhanced CMOS device cross sections.

Fig. 3. Enhanced CMOS process sequence.

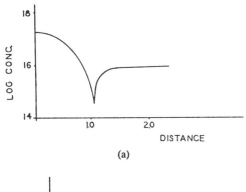

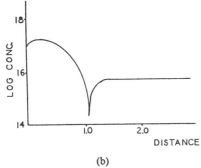

Fig. 2. Drain extension impurity profiles: (a) n-extension and (b) p-extension.

mask against the implantation. A total of eleven mask steps are required for this process.

III. MOS DEVICE CHARACTERIZATION

The MOS devices fabricated for this study were characterized through measurements of the forward I–V curves, threshold voltages, subthreshold characteristics, and avalanche breakdown voltage. The bipolar devices were studied in terms of I–V characteristics, forward current gain, frequency response, and breakdown voltage.

A. I–V Characteristics

Fig. 4 shows the I–V characteristics for both standard and drain-extended n-channel devices with a 2.2-μm effective channel length and 100-μm effective channel width. The sheet resistance of the n$^-$ extension was nominally 1.2 kΩ/$\square$. Fig. 5 presents similar data for p-channel devices. In each case, the drain-extended devices exhibit essentially no transconductance degradation at typical "analog" current levels of 100 μA due to series resistance of the extension regions. Degradation of the triode/saturation knee is minimized at higher "digital-level" currents of several milliamperes since the extension implant is excluded from the source regions by a photoresist mask.

The transconductance-output resistance product $g_m \cdot R_{out}$ is the maximum voltage gain a simple (noncascoded) amplifier stage can achieve and may be used as a figure of merit. Table I compares standard CMOS devices having 3- and 4-μm drawn channel lengths to drain extended devices. In addition to having enhanced breakdown, the drain extended devices exhibit improved g_m-output resistance product, providing better stage voltage gains in both analog and logic devices. The improvement in R_{out} is not independent of current level; the enhancement is less at higher values of drain current as can be seen in Fig. 5. In addition, Table I shows that R_{out} improves with increases in extension resistance at the expense of transconductance. However, the percentage increase in R_{out} is greater than the degradation in transconductance thus the net g_m-R_{out} product improves.

Fig. 3 shows the fabrication sequence for the EQMOS devices. An initial oxide is grown and patterned for the p-well. Boron is implanted and driven to a depth of approximately 5 μm. Following a conventional field oxidation process, a blanket implant is used to set the threshold voltages and a 500-Å gate oxide is grown. The polysilicon gate is then deposited, doped, patterned, and etched. Following poly oxidation, drain extensions are formed by implanting boron for the p$^-$ extensions and phosphorus for the n$^-$ extensions. These two implants self-align to the gate edge to form the extended drains of the FET's and also act as the bases of the bipolar transistors. After a drive in step, the heavily doped n$^+$ and p$^+$ contact regions are implanted. These regions act as the sources and drain contacts for the MOS devices and form the emitters of the bipolar structures. In the FET's, these contact regions are offset from the gate edge using photoresist as a

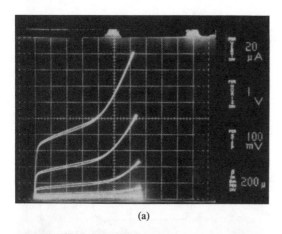

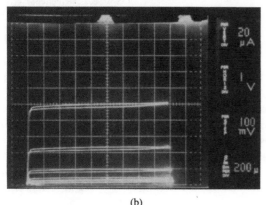

Fig. 4. n-channel MOSFET *I–V* characteristics (a) with no drain extension and (b) with n⁻ drain extension.

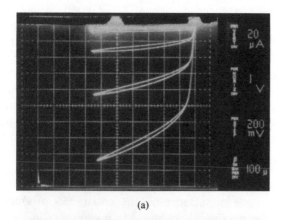

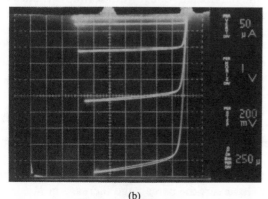

Fig. 5. p-channel MOSFET *I–V* characteristics (a) with no drain extension and (b) with p⁻ drain extension.

B. Avalanche Breakdown

Various theoretical models have been developed to analyze the effect of drain extensions on MOSFET performance. The two-dimensional numerical analysis of Koyangi *et al.* [13] has shown the effectiveness of drain extensions in reducing the channel electric field and thus increasing MOSFET drain to source breakdown voltage. In addition, Lee *et al.* [14] have developed analytical techniques to study the tradeoff between electric field and channel resistance in drain offset LDD MOSFET's. Their work as well as that of others [15], [16] provides insight into the mechanism by which drain extensions modify the channel electric field to improve BV_{DSS} and illustrates the various tradeoffs between on-state resistance and drain-to-source breakdown voltage. In the present work, experimental techniques are used to determine the influence of channel length, extension length, and extension resistivity on the MOSFET drain-to-source breakdown voltage and on-state resistance.

Figs. 6 and 7 illustrate the effectiveness of drain extensions in improving MOSFET avalanche breakdown voltage. The increase in breakdown voltage for these devices comes about because the lightly doped extension regions allow the depletion layer to penetrate into the drain as well as into the channel, thus reducing the maximum electric field at the junction. However, the high resistivity of the extension regions leads to increased drain series resistance and degraded performance in the on-state. Thus, tradeoffs between avalanche breakdown voltage, extension length, and channel length must be carefully studied in order to enable device performance to be optimized. The choice at 2-μm, 1-kΩ/s$\square$ extensions, for example, typically increase the 5-V R_{on} of 3-μm logic devices by 10 percent.

Fig. 6 plots the breakdown voltage as a function of extension length. For the voltage range of interest in this study breakdown is not significantly influenced by extension length. Since series resistance is directly proportional to extension length, improved performance can be obtained by choosing the minimum extension length consistent with the desired blocking voltage.

MOSFET breakdown voltage as a function of effective channel length is shown in Fig. 7. As the channel length is reduced increases in the electric field lead to reduced breakdown voltage. This data indicates that even with long high-resistivity extensions, micrometer or submicrometer channel length MOSFET's will not support the 50–60-V operating potentials required in many applications.

The tradeoff between on-state resistance and drain-to-source breakdown voltage is illustrated in Table II, for n- and p-channel devices with varying extension lengths and sheet resistivities. In each case, the channel width is 400 μm. The specific on-state resistance of the 60-V device is 7.5 mΩ $\cdot$ cm², which compares favorably with other high-voltage CMOS processes [5]–[7], [13].

The data of Table II indicate that for a given channel length and extension length, increasing the extension resistivity dramatically increases the drain-to-source break-

TABLE I
DRAIN-EXTENDED QMOS COMPARISON

	$L(\mu)$	$ext(\mu)$	$Leff(\mu)$	Sheet resistance	50μA gm	50μA Rout	gmRout product	BV_{dss}
n-channel	3	0	2.2	--	360×10^{-6}	.33M	120	8-9
	4	3	2.4	1.2K/sq	320×10^{-6}	1.0M	320	25-30
	4	3	2.4	2.4K/sq	230×10^{-6}	2.0M	460	55-60
p-channel	3	0	2.2	--	210×10^{-6}	.24M	70	22-25
	4	3	2.4	1.0K/sq	290×10^{-6}	.60M	170	30-34
	4	3	2.4	2.6K/sq	240×10^{-6}	2.0M	480	50-55

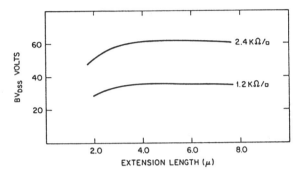

Fig. 6. Effect of extension length on drain breakdown voltage for n-channel MOSFET's.

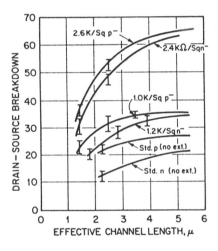

Fig. 7. Effect of channel length on drain breakdown voltage.

TABLE II
EFFECT OF DRAIN EXTENSION LENGTH ON BREAKDOWN VOLTAGE AND ON-STATE RESISTANCE

$L_{ch}(\mu)$	$ext(\mu)$	$R_{on}(\Omega)$	BV_{DSS}(volts)
N channel 1.2 K /sq extension			
3	0	35	10
4	2	50	25
4	3	65	33
4	4	70	33
4	8	110	33
N channel 2.4K /sq extension			
3	0	30	12
4	2	55	48
4	3	70	55
4	4	73	56
4	8	118	61
P channel 1.0K /sq extension			
3	0	85	20
4	2	150	28
4	3	185	33
4	4	205	33

C. Subthreshold Conduction

The subthreshold current, consisting of weak surface inversion, junction leakage, and bulk punchthrough components, provides a good indication of device quality. Fig. 8 compares the subthreshold characteristics of both n- and p-channel devices with and without drain extensions. The figures show no significant degradation of the subthreshold slope or leakage current brought about by the drain extensions.

IV. BIPOLAR CHARACTERISTICS

I–V traces for n-p-n and p-n-p bipolar transistors fabricated from the EQMOS process are presented in Figs. 9 and 10. The high sheet resistance and narrow base width result in a relatively high bipolar gain.

Table III compares the electrical characteristics of the n-p-n and p-n-p bipolar transistors. The most important parameters for these devices are the current gain β, collector-to-emitter breakdown BV_{CEO}, and gain bandwidth product f_t.

The dependence of current gain and BV_{CEO} on the base implantation can be determined from Table III. The n-p-n devices exhibit a relatively high gain that increases as the base implant dose is reduced. However, these devices

down voltage. However, the corresponding increase in on-state resistance is small. This indicates that the overall contribution of the series resistance in the drain extension is small compared to the channel resistance and contact resistance for the devices under study. Analytic models for the on-state resistance verify this observation. The channel resistance may be calculated using $R_{on}W = L_{ch}/\mu_{ch}C_{ox}(V_g - V_t)$ while the series resistance of the extension region may be calculated by using $R_{on}W = L_{ext}/q\mu_{ext}N_dX_j$ where the subscripts ch and ext refer to the channel region and extension region, respectively. Further increases in BV_{DSS} could be achieved using more lightly doped extensions; however, analog performance would be compromised since the extension diffusion also forms the bipolar base.

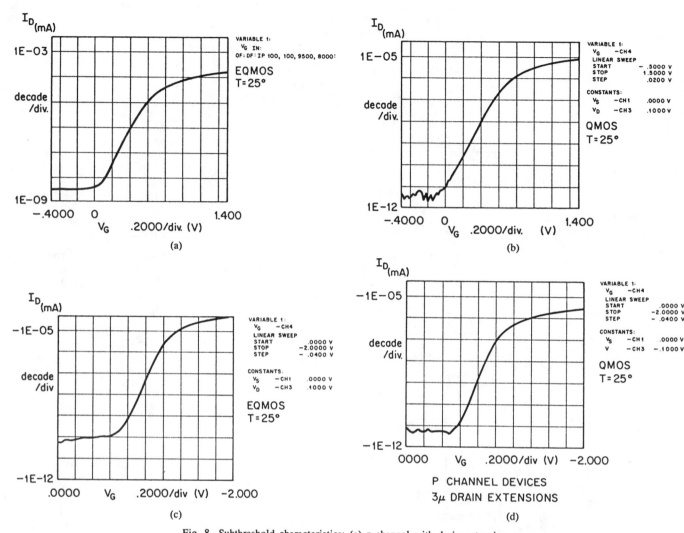

Fig. 8. Subthreshold characteristics: (a) n-channel with drain extension, (b) n-channel with no extension, (c) p-channel with extension, (d) p-channel with no extension.

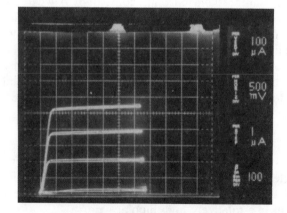

Fig. 9. n-p-n bipolar *I–V* characteristics.

Fig. 10. p-n-p bipolar *I–V* characteristics.

are limited in BV_{CEO} because of punchthrough effect. The p-n-p transistors exhibit more moderate current gain but with a corresponding increase in BV_{CEO}.

Figs. 11 and 12 show the dependence of current gain β on collector current for both n- and p-channel devices. From these the maximum emitter loading, which has been defined as the current density at which beta falls to 70

percent of its peak value, is determined. Emitter loadings of 30 $\mu A/\mu m^2$ and 3 $\mu A/\mu m^2$ were measured for the n-p-n and p-n-p transistors, respectively.

The gain bandwidth product (f_t) is estimated to be 700 MHz for the n-p-n transitors and approximately 350 MHz for the p-n-p. These estimates are based on the high-frequency performance of operational amplifiers fabricated

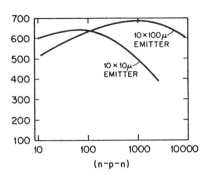

Fig. 11. Dependence of current gain on collector current for n-p-n bipolar.

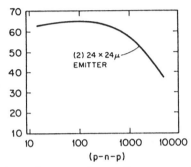

Fig. 12. Dependence of current gain on collector current for p-n-p bipolar.

TABLE III
BIPOLAR DEVICE CHARACTERISTICS

	NPN		PNP	
Emitter sheet resistance	25Ω/sq		70Ω/sq	
Base width	0.6 (ext)	0.6 (ext) 5u (well)	0.6 (ext)	
Base sheet resistance	2.6K/sq 1.0K/sq	5.0K/sq	1.2K/sq	
Beta	700 170	200	60	
BV$_{ceo}$	14v 22v	40v	30v	
70% Beta emitter density	15-30 uA/u^2		3 uA/u^2	

using the EQMOS process [18]. Both devices lack the low-resistance pocket needed to reduce collector series resistance. Reduction in collector resistance due to the addition of deep heavily doped buried layers would correspondingly increase f_t.

V. CONCLUSIONS

Elementary additions to a 3-μm polysilicon gate CMOS process have provided enhanced voltage capability CMOS as well as bipolar components. Sixty-volt CMOS devices were designed for and achieved with improved output resistance and stage gain and without severe transconductance degradation or increases in on-state resistance. The bipolar components provide broad-band analog function, good current drive capability, and high-performance merged bipolar/CMOS circuitry. This technology is suitable for data conversion, telecommunications, analog switches, and industrial applications as well as in integrated circuits requiring the combination of low-voltage control circuitry and high-voltage high-current buffers, drivers, and output stages.

ACKNOWLEDGMENT

The authors wish to express their appreciation to J. Olmstead at RCA, Somerville, NJ, who was among the earliest investigators of drain extensions, for helpful guidance during the formative stages of EQMOS. Further, T. Deegan, RCA, Somerville, reduced the self-alignment principles to practice, set up and evaluated process design rules and developed computer artwork critiques. A. Frim, RCA, Somerville, generated layout designs for numerous test devices and consolidated procedures for subsequent commercial IC layout.

REFERENCES

[1] A. Y. Tang, R. Johnston, and P. J. Mexa, "A dual buried layer technology for the fabrication of high voltage NPN devices compatible with 1.5 micron epitaxial bipolar process," in *IEDM Tech. Dig.*, pp. 298–301, 1985.

[2] Y. Sugawara, T. Kamii, Y. Hosokowa, and M. Okamura, "Practical size limits of high voltage IC's," in *IEDM Tech. Dig.*, pp. 412–415, 1983.

[3] S. A. Buhler, D. L. Heald, R. R. Ronan, T. Gannon, and P. Elkins, "Integrated high voltage/low voltage MOS devices, in *IEDM Tech. Dig.*, pp. 259–262, 1981.

[4] T. Yamaguchi and S. Morimoto, "Process and device design of a 1000-V MOS IC," *IEEE Trans. Electron Devices*, vol. ED-29, no. 8, p. 1171, 1984.

[5] T. Kuriyami, H. Sakuma, and K. Hirata, "A monolithic high voltage SOS/CMOS operational amplifier," in *IEDM Tech. Dig.*, pp. 432–435, 1983.

[6] R. Blanchard, "Power control with integrated CMOS logic and DMOS output," in *Electro 84 Professional Program Session Rec.*, pp. 25/1, 1984.

[7] E. Habekotti, B. Hoefflinger, W. Renker, and G. Zimmer, "A coplanar CMOS power switch, *IEEE J. Solid-State Circuits*, vol. SC-16, no. 3, pp. 212–225, 1981.

[8] R. S. Wrathall, D. Tom, L. Terry, and S. P. Robb, "Integrated circuits for the control of high power," in *IEDM Tech. Dig.*, pp. 408–411, 1981.

[9] E. J. Wildi, T. P. Chow, and M. E. Cornell, "A 500V junction isolated BiMOS high voltage IC," in *Electro 84 Professional Program Session Rec.*, p. 25/1, 1984.

[10] A. Alvarez, R. M. Roop, K. I. Ray, and G. R. Gettemeyer, "Latered DMOS transistor optimized for high voltage BiMOS applications," in *IEDM Tech. Dig.*, pp. 420–423, 1983.

[11] F. Lai, J. Sun, and S. D. Long, "Design and characteristics of lightly doped drain (LDD) devices fabricated with self-aligned titanium disilicide," *IEEE Trans. Electron Devices*, vol. ED-33, pp. 345–353, 1986.

[12] F. S. Lai, and Y. C. Sun, "An analytic one-dimensional model for lightly doped drain MOSFET (LDD) devices," *IEEE Trans. Electron Devices*, vol. ED-32, pp. 2803–2811, 1985.

[13] M. Koyanyi, H. Koneko, and S. Shimuza, "Optimim design of n$^+$-n$^-$ double-diffused drain MOSFET to reduce hot-carrier emission," *IEEE Trans. Electron Devices*, vol. Ed 32, no. 3, pp. 562–570, Mar. 1985.

[14] J. Lee, K. Mayaram, and C. Hu, "A theoretical study of gate/drain offset in LDD MOSFET's," *IEEE Electron Device Lett.*, vol. EDL-7, no. 3, pp. 152–154, Mar 1986.

[15] P. J. Tsang, S. Ogura, W. Walker, D. L. Chritchlow, and J. F. Sheppard, "Fabrication of high-performance LDDFET's with oxide sidewall spacer technology," *IEEE Trans. Electron Devices*, vol. ED-29, no. 4 pp. 590–596, Apr. 1982.

[16] K. W. Terill, C. Hu, and P. K. Ko, "An analytical model for the channel electric field in MOSFET's with graded drain structure," *IEEE Electron Device Lett.*, vol. EDL-S, no. 11 pp. 440–442, Nov. 1984.

[17] W. G. Meyer, G. W. Dick, K. H. Olsen, K. H. Lee, and J. A. Shiner, "Integrable high voltage CMOS: Devices, process, applications," in *IEDM Tech. Dig.*, pp. 732–735, 1985.

[18] O. Schade, Jr. and R. Isham, "EQMOS, COS based mixed analog-digital technology," *RCA Rev.*, vol. 47, no. 3, Sept. 1986.

An <u>A</u>nalog Technology Integrates <u>B</u>ipolar, <u>C</u>MOS, and High-Voltage <u>D</u>MOS Transistors

SURINDER KRISHNA, SENIOR MEMBER, IEEE, JAMES KUO, AND ISAURA SERV́IN GAETA, MEMBER, IEEE

Abstract—This paper describes the development of an analog technology that integrates bipolar, CMOS, and DMOS transistors on a single chip. The architecture of the process was chosen for its simplicity and versatility. The influence of the process variables and trade-offs in the performance of the devices have been outlined. Some key elements of DMOS and bipolar transistor behavior are discussed. The successful application of the technology to a plasma display driver has been demonstrated.

I. INTRODUCTION

ONE WAY to obtain a high degree of integration in LSI circuits is to use a technology that combines bipolar (BJT), CMOS, and DMOS devices on a single chip. Bipolar technology is often used in analog circuit design because the transistors have a high transconductance, low $1/f$ noise, and the V_{be} can be matched with precision. CMOS cannot match bipolar transistor parameters, but does provide superior chip density, high noise threshold, and a low power dissipation that is well suited to the demands of logic and memory circuits. DMOS transistors are attractive where both high-voltage and high-speed switching are required. This work describes the development of an analog technology that incorporates BJT, CMOS, and DMOS transistors. This technology has been successfully applied to fabricate a circuit to drive plasma display panels. A viable technology that includes all these features is made possible by a judicious choice of the process architecture. The core fabrication sequence is a relatively straightforward metal gate CMOS process. Detailed experiments and device performance analysis were used to select additional process steps to integrate the BJT and DMOS structures with minimal perturbation of the core process sequence.

This paper is comprised of 7 sections. Section II provides details on the process architecture; Section III covers the process parameters and characterization of the DMOS transistors; Sections IV and V cover BJT and CMOS structures in a similar fashion. Section VI addresses some reliability aspects of DMOS transistors and compares then with BJT's in power switching applications. The technology was applied to develop a plasma display driver whose performance is outlined in Section VII. The conclusion contains comments on the versatility and relevance of the present technology, and directions for future work in this area.

Manuscript received March 28, 1983; revised August 29, 1983.
The authors are with Fairchild Semiconductor, Linear Division, Mountain View, CA 94039.

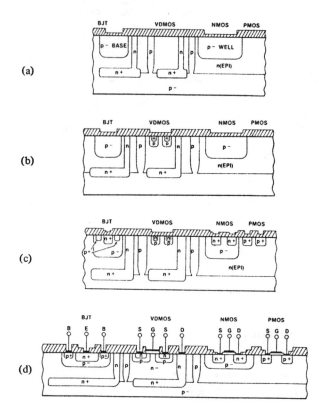

Fig. 1. Key steps in the process architecture for the integration of BJT, CMOS, and DMOS structures. Body contacts for the MOS transistors are not shown.

II. PROCESS ARCHITECTURE

As mentioned earlier, the core of the fabrication sequence is a metal gate CMOS process with 8 mask levels. Two mask levels are introduced to incorporate the bipolar transistors (vertical n-p-n and lateral p-n-p), and another mask step is included for the DMOS structures. The starting material is a 11–18-$\Omega \cdot$ cm p-type $\langle 100 \rangle$ Czochralski pulled silicon crystal. The process sequence is as follows:

a) n^+ buried layer is diffused, $R_s = 20 \, \Omega/\square$.
b) Epitaxial growth of an n-layer 5-$\Omega \cdot$ cm, 20 μm thick, and epi-reoxidation.
c) p^+ isolation mask and p^+ diffusion.
d) Standard bipolar n^+ sinker diffusion.
e) Open p^- well for n-channel CMOS and base of BJT.
f) Implant boron B^{11}, $Q = 3.2 \times 10^{13}$ cm^{-2} at 60 keV followed by diffusion (Fig. 1(a) shows a cross section of the VDMOS, CMOS, and BJT devices at this step).
g) Open source region for DMOS structures.

Reprinted from *IEEE Trans. Electron Devices*, vol. ED-31, pp. 89–95, Jan. 1984.

h) Implant sequentially arsenic $Q = 3 \times 10^{14}$ cm^{-2} at 100 keV and boron $Q = 8 \times 10^{13}$ to 3×10^{14} cm^{-2} at 60 keV. (The reasons for this range of implant dose are discussed in Section III.) (This implant step is followed by a diffusion cycle, Fig. 1(b).)

i) Open source and drain for p-channel CMOS, extrinsic base for vertical n-p-n and emitter and collector for lateral p-n-p transistors.

j) Implant boron B^{11}, $Q = 5 \times 10^{15}$ cm^{-2} at 100 keV and diffuse. $R_s = 45$ $\Omega/\square$.

k) Open source and drain for n-channel CMOS, drain of LDMOS and emitter for vertical BJT.

l) Phosphorus deposition and diffusion $R_s = 20$ $\Omega/\square$, junction depth of 2 μm, Fig. 1(c).

m) Open gates for VDMOS, LDMOS, and CMOS structures.

n) Gate oxidation $t_{ox} = 900$ Å.

o) Implant for p-channel threshold adjustment $Q = 2.6 \times 10^{11}$ cm^{-2} at 45 keV.

p) Getter, anneal, contact opening, metal evap/etch/alloy, Fig. 1(d). The wafers are passivated with a low temperature CVD oxide and the metal pads are defined for assembly.

III. DMOS TRANSISTORS

In an effort to raise the power-speed performance and to increase the density in integrated circuits, Masuda et al. [1] proposed the lateral double diffused MOS (LDMOS) transistor. The source and channel are diffused n and p regions, respectively. The channel length is determined by the difference in the lateral diffusion dopants, and can be well controlled down to about 1 μm. The applied voltage is supported almost entirely by the drain, which consists of a lightly doped n region in series with an n$^+$ contact. The channel length gives the LDMOS transistor its speed and transconductance, and the n$^-$ drain results in a high blocking voltage capability. In such a structure, the maximum electric field intensity occurs at or near the silicon–silicon dioxide interface. As a consequence, the avalanche breakdown voltage is lower than the breakdown voltage set by the bulk. To overcome this problem, Krishna[2] proposed the vertical diffused MOS (VDMOS) transistor. The source and channel are identical to the LDMOS. The drain current, however, flows in bulk rather than the surface. The maximum electric field also occurs in bulk. These changes give the VDMOS superior voltage capability over the LDMOS, while retaining the speed and gain performance of the latter.

A. Lateral DMOS

Obtaining good channel length control requires a self-aligned structure. In this process, the self alignment between source and body is accomplished by sequentially implanting arsenic and boron through the source opening. The channel length is controlled by the implant dose, the relative diffusivities of the species, and the diffusion time and temperature.

In these experiments, the arsenic implant dose was maintained at 3×10^{14} cm^{-2}. The boron was implanted at various doses ranging from 8×10^{13} cm^{-2} to 3×10^{14} cm^{-2}. At implant levels below 8×10^{13} cm^{-2}, the LDMOS transistor is a deple-

TABLE I
LDMOS

P DOSE ions/cm^2	V_T (V) ($I_{DS} = 0$)	BV$_{DSS}$ (V) @ 1 mA (I_{DSS})	g_m (mmho) @ 20 mA	R_{ON} (Ω) @ $V_G = 10$V
8.0×10^{13}	0.70	86 (270 μA @ 50V)	10	100
1.0×10^{14}	0.72	73 (380 μA @ 50V)	9.5	89
1.5×10^{14}	1.01	110 (130 μA @ 50V)	9.2	88
2.0×10^{14}	1.45	148 (5 μA @ 50V)	8.5	91
2.5×10^{14}	1.78	158	8.2	98
3.0×10^{14}	1.92	164	7.2	105

tion mode device which will conduct with zero gate bias. The influence of the channel implant dose on the key electrical parameters can be seen in Table I. When the channel is lightly doped, the depletion layer reaches through the channel. This lowers the potential barrier and leads to the injection of electrons from the source.

Further increase in voltage results in space-charge limited current flow between source and drain. To avoid punchthrough breakdown, a boron implant of greater than 2×10^{14} cm^{-2} is needed. Increasing implant dose levels are accompanied by a reduction in transconductance, which significantly degrades the switching performance of the transistor. The increase in channel length with increasing boron concentration is a result of the increased lateral diffusion.

The measured value of on-state resistance R_{on} is 100 Ω, and is in close agreement with the analytical values given in the Appendix. The observed insensitivity of the resistance to implant dose (and therefore to channel length) may be understood from this analysis. It is shown that the contribution of channel resistance to the total device resistance is less than 20 percent.

Table I and Fig. 2 show that the threshold voltage and its temperature coefficient increase with implant dose. The increase in the temperature coefficient with increasing doping level in the channel poses a potential reliability problem for the device. This subject is discussed in some detail in a later section. From the LDMOS transistor dc characteristics, it was concluded that a boron implant dose of 2.5×10^{14} cm^{-2} was optimum. Below this voltage level, punchthrough breakdown occurs; and above this level, a reduction in gain and speed occur. The dynamic performance of the LDMOS transistors is further discussed in Section VI.

B. Vertical DMOS

As mentioned earlier, in the vertical DMOS structure, the voltage is supported in the bulk of the semiconductor. Bringing the drain contact to the surface requires a buried n$^+$ layer and a sinker diffusion. These steps are often present in bipolar IC technology. The source and channel regions are formed by a process identical to that of the self-aligned LDMOS. A cross section of the VDMOS structure is shown in Fig. 1(d). The influence of the boron implant levels on the electrical param-

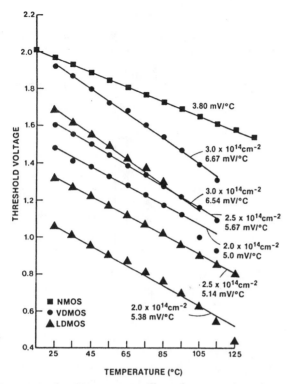

Fig. 2. Threshold voltage as a function of temperature and channel implant dose for DMOS transistors. The NMOS threshold voltage is established by the surface concentration of the p-well.

TABLE II
VDMOS

P DOSE ions/cm^2	V_T (V) (I_{DS} = 0)	BV_{DSS} (V) @ 1 mA	g_m (mmho) @ 20 mA	R_{ON} (Ω) @ V_G = 10V
8.0 x 10^{13}	0.85	188	10.7	150
1.0 x 10^{14}	0.93	170	9.2	170
1.5 x 10^{14}	1.32	164	9.0	180
2.0 x 10^{14}	1.66	195	7.5	213
2.5 x 10^{14}	1.85	165	7.0	228
3.0 x 10^{14}	1.93	196	6.0	250

eters of this device are given in Table II. A comparison with Table I clearly identifies some similarities, but also significant differences between the VDMOS and the LDMOS transistors. The variations in transconductance and threshold voltage as functions of implant dose are similar, as is the temperature coefficient of threshold voltage (see Fig. 2).

While the source to drain breakdown voltage BV_{dss} of the LDMOS transistor depends, however, on implant level, the breakdown voltage of the VDMOS transistor depends only on the bulk resistivity of the drain and the curvature of the p-n junction. It was also seen that the breakdown voltage of the device is independent of gate oxide thickness in the range of 900–1500 Å. This insensitivity is further evidence that the surface field does not determine BV_{dss}. The thinner (900 Å) gate oxide was chosen for its higher g_m and superior subthreshold current characteristics.

The on-state resistance R_{on} of the VDMOS transistors is seen to be strongly influenced by the implant dose. The reason for this dependence becomes evident from the calculations and

Fig. 5 in the Appendix. A channel implant of 8×10^{14} cm^{-2} produces an on-state resistance of 130 Ω. This reduces the width of the vertical n$^-$ channel of the JFET, and increases the resistance of the JFET component to 91 Ω, and the total R_{on} to 214 Ω. An obvious solution is to increase the surface area of the n$^-$ region and to trade-off device size for R_{on}. Unfortunately, increasing the active surface area of the VDMOS transistor exacerbates a phenomena that has been identified as the injection of holes into the gate dielectric. This injection increases the charge on the gate, thereby altering the apparent gate threshold voltage. The implications of this phenomenon are discussed later.

The studies of various channel implant dose levels demonstrated that an optimized LDMOS structure requires an implant dose of 2×10^{14} cm^{-3}. Superior vertical DMOS transistor performance requires an implant level of 8×10^{13} cm^{-2}. Optimization of the characteristics of both transistors would therefore require an additional mask layer and implant step.

IV. BIPOLAR TRANSISTORS

A significant strength of this technology is that it provides the designer with a variety of bipolar transistors without sacrificing process simplicity. The lateral p-n-p transistors are formed by the diffusion of boron simultaneously into the emitter and collector regions during the formation of the source and drain of the p-channel MOS transistors. The epi-resistivity and junction spacing determine the current gain and voltage capability of this transistor. A variety of vertical n-p-n transistors are possible. Test structures were designed having the bases formed by implanting boron during any one of the following steps: p$^-$ well of the NMOS, p-channel of DMOS or the p$^+$ source and drain of the PMOS transistors. These variations produce transistors with a range of electrical parameters such as current gain, breakdown voltage, early voltage and speed. The BJT formed with the p$^-$ well shows the highest gain values. By reducing the p$^-$ well doping to 1.4×10^{13} cm^{-3}, the current gain increases to 800 as shown in Table III. The lighter doping also enhances the NMOS transistor speed, but makes it susceptible to latchup. The CMOS transistors formed with all the implant levels given in Table III function very well. The emitters of all n-p-n transistors were formed during the source/drain diffusion of the NMOS devices. These emitters are more lightly doped (20 Ω/□) then a "conventional" emitter. The shrinkage in the bandgap of the emitter ΔE_g was experimentally determined and found to be about 40 meV. The contributions come from the combined effects of degeneracy [3]–[5] and post emitter processing [6]. As a consequence of the small value of ΔE_g, the current gain of the transistors were less temperature sensitive, increasing 30 percent from 0 to 90°C. At these reduced levels of emitter doping, the CMOS transistors are less susceptible to latch up, and the bipolar transistors should have little burst noise [7].

Several structures were included to reduce the extrinsic base resistance by using an additional p$^+$ doped region (introduced in the PMOS source/drain step) at the emitter perimeter. It was found that the introduction of the p$^+$ collar around the emitter perimeter increased the current gain by as much as 20 percent. There are two possible reasons for this increase: a) The

TABLE III
Bipolar Transistors

VERTICAL NPN				
BASE P DOSE (ions/cm^2)	BETA	LV$_{CEO}$ (VOLTS)	BV$_{CBO}$ (VOLTS)	BV$_{EBO}$ (VOLTS)
3.2 x 10^{13}	300	68	93	7.2
2.8 x 10^{13}	500	64	98	7.5
2.4 x 10^{13}	600	60	92	7.6
2.2 x 10^{13}	600	58	92	7.5
1.8 x 10^{13}	600	56	91	7.6
1.4 x 10^{13}	800	54	92	7.5

LATERAL PNP			
BETA	LV$_{CEO}$ (VOLTS)	BV$_{CBO}$ (VOLTS)	BV$_{EBO}$ (VOLTS)
23	40	42	7.2

TABLE IV
CMOS

N CHANNEL			
V$_T$ (VOLTS)	V$_{TF}$ (VOLTS)	BV$_{DSS}$ (VOLTS)	g$_m$ (mmho)
0.8	9.6	28.0	0.30

Z = 27 μm, L = 8 μm, T$_{ox}$ = 900 Å

P CHANNEL			
V$_T$ (VOLTS)	V$_{TF}$ (VOLTS)	BV$_{DSS}$ (VOLTS)	g$_m$ (mmho)
0.83	11.2	45.0	0.180

Z = 27 μm, L = 8 μm, T$_{ox}$ = 900 Å

heavy doping in the extrinsic base increases the electron injection from the side walls due to the reduction in the bandgap. This provides an additional component of emitter current; b) The electron injection is reduced at the side wall of the emitter, thereby reducing the recombination current in the extrinsic base. We found no reduction in the bandgap caused by the p$^+$ doping of the extrinsic base and therefore conclude that the reduced electron injection into the side-wall produces the enhancement in the current gain.

V. CMOS

As mentioned earlier, the process architecture was built around an 8-μm metal gate CMOS process. The choice of this technology as the building block was made since the process is relatively straightforward, and there are a minimum number of additional steps needed to incorporate the DMOS and bipolar transistors.

The electrical parameters of the CMOS devices are given in Table IV. It should be pointed out that parametric values of the CMOS transistors in this technology are identical to those achieved with a conventional metal gate process.

The only variations in the CMOS process arise from the gain requirements of the vertical BJT. As seen in Table III, the p-well implant may be between 1.4×10^{13} and 3.2×10^{13} cm^{-2} depending on the design need. At the higher dose, an n-channel threshold voltage of about 0.8 V is obtained without any im-

plant adjustment. For lower values of p-well surface concentration, a blanket implant dose of 3×10^{11} cm^{-2} may be used to adjust both the n- and p-channel thresholds to approximately 0.8 V. This step eliminates a masking level, further simplifying the process.

VI. DMOS Versus BJT for Power Switching Application

The advantages of DMOS transistors over BJT's have been attributed to two factors: a) the negative temperature coefficient for carrier mobility which insures against the formation of hot spots; b) freedom from storage time effects of the majority-carrier DMOS transistor, and hence, a faster turn off. While these statements are indeed correct, they are not complete. The differences between these two types of devices goes even further.

The decrease in mobility with temperature provides a mechanism for quenching a hot spot, which may arise due to an uneven temperature distribution over the active device area. If we ignore an obvious source of nonuniformity in temperature (equally applicable to the DMOS and BJT) that comes from a poor die attach operation, we may ask if there is any intrinsic mechanism that would generate hot spots. It has been suggested that in the case of the BJT, localized variations in the bandgap of an emitter may give rise to hot spots [6]. For a hot spot to occur, a degenerately doped emitter must be forward biased. The DMOS transistor does not have an injecting junction and is therefore inherently immune to hot spot formation. There is however, the possibility of a thermal instability in the DMOS transistor. In a lightly doped channel, the mobility is determined by lattice scattering and decreases with a rise in temperature. As the doping in the channel is increased, a necessity in the case of the LDMOS, the mobility becomes relatively insensitive to temperature. However, the threshold voltage decreases more rapidly with temperature at these higher doping levels. These two factors result in an increase of the drain current with rising temperatures. The crossover point occurs at a doping concentration of about 10^{17} cm^{-3} in the channel. Beyond this doping level, the situation may lead to excessive power dissipation and result in the failure of the device.

The dynamic performance of the DMOS transistor is significantly superior to the BJT. The BJT is a minority-carrier device with its turn off time delay comprised of two components, a storage delay and a fall time. The storage delay comes from the recombination time of minority carriers in the base and collector of the device. The fall time results from the discharging of the junction capacitors. If the rate of voltage rise is rapid, there is an additional component to the fall time. This component occurs as the charge injected into the base from the discharging collector/base capacitor turns the emitter back on. An analysis of this effect [8] has shown that fall times can increase by an order of magnitude if the slew rate is sufficiently high. The DMOS transistors in this circuit are switching at a rate of 1000 V/μs (see Table VI). In a BJT with a current gain of 100, this switching rate produces an additional emitter current density of 1200 A/cm^2 which almost certainly prevents the device from turning off.

As mentioned in Section II, the DMOS transistors are susceptible to turn on without an external gate drive. This behavior occurs when the gate terminal is connected to an electrometer and the source-to-drain voltage is increased to avalanche breakdown. The gate charges up to a positive potential which turns the MOS transistor on. As the source-to-drain current rises, it in turn further increases the multiplication of carriers and charges the gate to a higher potential. This sets up a regenerative process. Without an adequate load resistor, this would lead to thermal runaway and catastrophic failure of the device. The hypothesis that the gate is being charged by the injection of hot holes into the oxide is supported by two facts; the polarity of the gate potential was positive, and the current density through the oxide was estimated at 10^{-8} to 10^{-9} A/cm^2 at $E = 3 \times 10^6$ V/cm, which is in good agreement with earlier published results [9]–[11]. Although the investigations into hot carrier effects is not complete, our experiments have revealed the following: a) The PMOS transistors did in all cases exhibit hot electron injection into the oxide. The typical time for the gate dielectric to charge to 1 V was about 1 s. b) There was no evidence of hot carrier effects in the NMOS transistor for bias times up to 10^4 s. c) The time constants for the DMOS transistors to charge up to 1 V was in the range of 1–10 s. Moreover, the injection phenomena was not observed in every DMOS transistor. The differences in behavior between the DMOS and the n-channel transistors are not completely understood. The factors influencing hot hole injection and trapping are: the magnitude of the electric field intensity normal to silicon–silicon dioxide surface; and the surface area of gate electrode in this high field region (which in the case of the DMOS is 1.5×10^4 μm and is only 30 μm^2 for the NMOS). The nature of the oxide also plays an important role. Even though that gate oxide is grown simultaneously for the DMOS and CMOS transistors, the heavier channel doping of the former results in gate oxides that are different. It is clear from these preliminary findings that the injection of hot holes is a potential reliability problem for DMOS transistor in both discrete and integrated form. Further investigation is required in this area.

VII. CIRCUIT PERFORMANCE

There were several factors that determined the choice of the ABCD technology for a plasma display driver. A primary requirement is an output transistor capable of switching 100 V across a 25-pF capacitive load in less than 200 ns. The DMOS transistor was chosen for reasons discussed in the preceding section. The logic was designed in CMOS to provide a high packing density minimal power dissipation, and an immunity in the noise environment produced by the high-speed switch. The linear function could have been designed using either CMOS or bipolar transistors. With bipolar transistors, precision gain control was achieved using simple compensation techniques.

The driver shown schematically in Fig. 3 consists of four parts: an input stage, a quiescent current generator, a voltage spike generator, and an output stage. The DMOS transistors, DM1 and DM2, are connected in a totempole output. A lateral p-n-p transistor Q1 provides the gate voltage drive for DM1. DM3 and M3 are used to switch current for the base of Q1. Because the lateral transistor has a poor frequency response, its base is overdriven to achieve a fast turn on. The base cur-

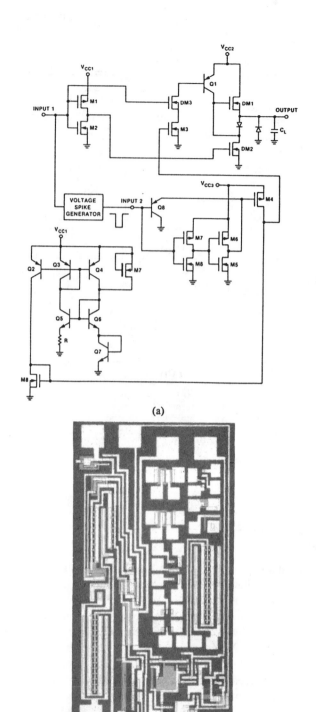

(a)

(b)

Fig. 3. (a) Schematic diagram for a display driver. (b) Photomicrograph of the plasma display driver circuit.

rent of Q1 is controlled by the drain current of M3 and is approximately 10 μA in its quiescent state. A current spike is generated during the rising edge of the input voltage, thereby enhancing the turn on speed of Q1. The output transistor DM1 is connected in a source follower configuration. Its voltage rises to the V_{cc2} rail in about 50 ns giving a slew rate of 1000 V/μs.

The quiescent current generator sets up a current I_R from the value of the resistor R. Since both Q2 and Q3 have common base-emitter voltage and equal emitter areas, the drain current of M8 is identical to I_R. Similarly, the current in M3 is equal to that of M8. The positive input voltage step passes

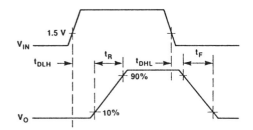

Fig. 4. Switching waveforms for the DMOS transistors.

TABLE V

RESPONSE TIME IN NS	TYPE OF DMOS	V_{CC3}				
		3 V	4 V	5 V	6 V	7 V
t_{DLH}	VERTICAL	160	145	135	130	130
	LATERAL	125	115	110	110	110
t_R	VERTICAL	225	180	165	155	150
	LATERAL	135	125	120	115	115

$V_{CC1} = 7$ V, $V_{CC2} = 50$ V

TABLE VI

RESPONSE TIME IN NS	TYPE OF DMOS	V_{CC1}					
		4 V	5 V	6 V	7 V	8 V	9 V
t_{DHL}	VERTICAL	125	85	60	40	30	25
	LATERAL	160	160	90	65	48	35
t_F	VERTICAL	145	140	110	95	85	85
	LATERAL	400	395	220	145	110	85

$V_{CC3} = 7$ V, $V_{CC2} = 50$ V

through a current spike generator and produces a negative voltage spike V_{IN2}. This negative pulse turns on Q8 first and one gate delay later turns on M5. M4 is turned on by Q8 and M5 which produces a large current spike I_{DM3} for transistor M3. The current spike helps reduce the response time of the lateral p-n-p transistor Q1, and drives the gate of DM1 from ground level up to V_{cc2}.

Source follower transistor DM1 charges load capacitor C_1 and rises towards V_{cc2} in the same way as its counterpart, the bipolar emitter follower transistor. When the voltage spike V_{IN2} terminates, Q8 and M5 turn off and M6 turns on. The p-channel transistor M6 pulls the gate of M4 to V_{cc1} and turns off M4. The current of M3 drops to its quiescent level but is enough to keep Q1 in saturation. The output remains at a level of $V_{cc2} - V_{sat}(Q1) - V_t(DM1)$.

When the positive input step voltage drops to zero, M2 turns off and M1 turns on. As soon as the gate voltage of DMOS transistor DM2 rises above its gate threshold DM2 begins to turn on and pulls DM1 gate voltage to ground. Following the turn off of DM1, the output load capacitor is discharged to ground by DM2.

From Fig. 4, it can be seen that V_{cc3} influences the delay times during both the turn on (t_{DLH}) and turn off (t_{DHL}) intervals. The increase in voltage of V_{cc3} not only reduces the turn on delay of M3, but also increases the spike base current for Q1. The overdriven base of Q1 turns on its collector current which pulls the gate and therefore the source of DM1 toward V_{cc2}. This reduces the rise time (t_R). The rise time of the lateral DMOS transistor is seen to be less than that of the vertical DMOS transistor. The reason for this is not clearly understood and is presently under investigation.

V_{cc1} influences both the fall (t_F) and delay times (t_{DHL}). The delay time during turn off is less than the turn on delay because in the former there is only one gate delay from M2. The higher V_{cc1} will also help to turn on the gate of DM2 faster (i.e., smaller t_{DHL}) and provide a larger drain current. This will enable the capacitor C_L to be discharged faster, hence a smaller fall time. The higher transconductance of the vertical over the lateral DMOS gives the former a superior fall time response. Tables V and VI summarize the dynamic performance of the LDMOS and VDMOS transistors as a function of V_{cc1}, V_{cc2} and V_{cc3}.

CONCLUSIONS

This paper has described the development of an analog technology that integrates bipolar, CMOS, and DMOS transistors, and was applied to fabricate a circuit to drive a plasma display panel. The process architecture is centered around an 8-μm metal gate CMOS technology and can be exercised in several ways. In those cases where the high performance bipolar transistor is dispensable, an LSI technology consisting only of CMOS and LDMOS can be put in it's place. This will eliminate two masking operations. The process can be further refined by incorporating twin tubs for the n- and p-channel transistors. Besides providing greater immunity from latchup and the concomitant higher density, it allows the design of higher voltage DMOS transistors without compromising CMOS performance. The VDMOS structure is easy to implement when bipolar performance is required. In those cases where the BJT is dispensable, the cost effective process uses the LDMOS transistor for the power switching requirements.

APPENDIX

From Sun and Plummer [12], the on-state resistance of the VDMOS (see Fig. 5) is given by:

$$R_{on} = R_E + R_D + R_{JFET} + R_4$$

where

R_E is the enhancement mode resistance

R_D is the JFET on-resistance

R_{JFET} is the JFET on-resistance

R_4 is the bulk epi-layer resistance.

For case a) $Q = 8 \times 10^{13}$ cm^{-2}

$X_{jp} = 4.66$ μm

case b) $Q = 3 \times 10^{14}$ cm^{-2}

$X_{jp} = 7.5$ μm

From SRP measurements.

Lateral diffusion $\simeq 0.85$ X_{jp}.

Epi-resistivity = 4.5 $\Omega \cdot$ cm.

Gate capacitance = 3.84×10^{-8} F/cm^2.

Channel width = 900 μm.

Electron mobility in inversion layer = 560 cm^2/V $\cdot$ s for $N_{MAX} = 5 \times 10^{16}$ cm^{-3}.

Electron mobility in accumulation = 1050 cm^2/V $\cdot$ s for $\langle 100 \rangle$ surface, $V_G = 0$.

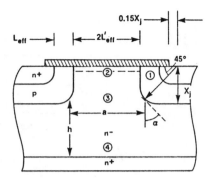

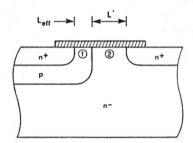

Fig. 5. Model for VDMOS used to calculate on-resistance. Regions 1), 2), 3), 4) correspond to resistors R_E, R_D, R_{JFET}, and R_4 respectively.

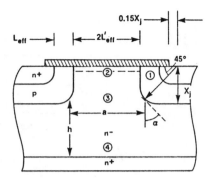

Fig. 6. Model for LDMOS used to calculate on-resistance.

Threshold voltages $V_{TE} = V_{TD} = 0.85$ V   Case (a)
$\qquad\qquad\qquad\qquad = 1.93$ V   Case (b).

Applied gate voltage $V_G = 10$ V.

Case a)	Case b)
$Q = 8 \times 10^{13}$ cm^{-2}	$Q = 3 \times 10^{14}$ cm^{-2}
$R_E = 16.8$ Ω	$R_E = 35$ Ω
$R_D = 4.3$ Ω	$R_D = 6.4$ Ω
$R_{JFET} = 45.0$ Ω	$R_{JFET} = 91$ Ω
$R_4 = 64.6$ Ω	$R_4 = 81$ Ω
$R_{on} = \underline{130.7 \text{ Ω}}$	$R_{on} = \underline{213.6 \text{ Ω}}$

R_{on} (Table II) = 150 Ω. R_{on} (Table II) = 250 Ω.

For the LDMOS referring to Fig. 6

$$R_{on} = R_E + R_2$$

where R_E is the enhancement mode channel resistance and R_2 is the bulk resistance between the channel and the drain n$^+$ contact.

For $Q = 8 \times 10^{13}$ cm^{-2} substituting values for W, L_{eff}, C_0, μ_E, V_G, and V_T

$$R_E = 16.77 \text{ Ω}$$

and

$$R_2 = 73.53 \text{ Ω}.$$

Hence

$$R_{on} = 90.30 \text{ Ω}.$$

Measured value (Table I) $R_{on} = 100$ Ω.

REFERENCES

[1] H. Masuda, T. Masuhara, M. Nagata, and N. Hashimoto, in *Proc. 4th Conf. Solid-State Devices*, Tokyo Japan, 1972.
[2] S. Krishna, *Solid-State Electron.*, vol. 20, p. 875, 1977.
[3] R. J. Van Overstraeten, H. J. De Man, and R. P. Mertens, *IEEE Trans. Electron Devices*, vol. ED-20, p. 290, 1973.
[4] J. W. Slotboom and H. C. de Graff, "Measurements of bandgap narrowing in Si bipolar transistors," *Solid-State Electron.*, vol. 19, p. 857, 1976.
[5] H.P.D. Lanyon and R. A. Tuft, "Bandgap narrowing in heavily doped silicon," presented at IEDM, (Washington, DC), 1978.
[6] S. Krishna, *IEEE Trans. Electron Devices*, vol. ED-29, p. 430, 1982.
[7] P. J. Kannam, *IEEE Trans. Electron Devices*, vol. ED-20, p. 845, 1973.
[8] S. Krishna, *IEEE J. Solid-State Circuits*, vol. SC-14, p. 776, 1979.
[9] E. H. Nicollian, A. Goetzberger, and C. N. Berglund, *Appl. Phys. Lett.*, vol. 15, p. 174, 1969.
[10] E. H. Nicollian and C. N. Berglund, *J. Appl. Phys.*, vol. 41, p. 3052, 1970.
[11] D. Frohman-Bentchkowsky, *Solid-State Electron.*, vol. 17, p. 517, 1974.
[12] S. C. Sun and J. D. Plummer, *IEEE Trans. Electron Devices*, vol. ED-27, p. 356, 1980.

Lateral HVIC with 1200-V Bipolar and Field-Effect Devices

MIKE F. CHANG, MEMBER, IEEE, GEORGE PIFER, HAMZA YILMAZ, MEMBER, IEEE,
ERIC J. WILDI, MEMBER, IEEE, ROBERT G. HODGINS, KING OWYANG,
AND MICHAEL S. ADLER, SENIOR MEMBER, IEEE

Abstract—The 1200-V blocking capability of lateral high-voltage devices has been achieved through theoretical and experimental investigation. The feasibility of a 1200-V lateral n-p-n bipolar junction transistor, p-n diode, and lateral DMOSFET has been demonstrated for the first time. The on-resistance of the 1200-V DMOSFET is 4 times less than its 1200-V n-p-n BJT counterpart. The major contribution to high BJT on-resistance comes from the series JFET pinch resistance.

I. INTRODUCTION

THE TECHNOLOGY advances in VLSI and high-power discrete devices have resulted in the birth of high-voltage integrated circuits (HVIC's). Since 1980, many HVIC approaches have emerged that address different application arenas. They basically fall into three distinct categories [1] that differ in their isolation schemes, namely, self-isolation (SI), dielectric isolation (DI), and junction isolation (JI). Self-isolation typical in CMOS is provided by the reverse biased junction between the source, drain, and body regions. Although SI is the lowest cost approach, it is limited to majority-carrier devices because of its susceptibility to parasitic effects. On the other hand, DI can completely eliminate parasitic effects; it is nonetheless limited to applications where cost is not a critical factor. This paper presents an advanced lateral junction isolated HVIC technology that uses a thin epi layer in conjunction with a modified CMOS fabrication process to provide up to 1200-V blocking capability. It is much less sensitive to parasitics than SI technology, and offers lower cost than the DI approach.

The need for a more efficient interface between low-power logic-level signals and medium- to high-power output devices was the main incentive for developing this advanced HVIC technology. To maintain compatibility with mainstream IC processing techniques, a RESURF [2] based technology was chosen to satisfy this need. This approach, as opposed to that employed in conventional high-voltage discrete devices, does not require the growth of thick epitaxial layers. A large group of basic semiconductor devices such as diode, CMOS, n-p-n bipolar tran-

sistor, lateral p-n-p transistor, JFET, and DMOSFET, have been investigated theoretically and experimentally.

The device structures and process are presented in Section II, followed by device physics study and experimental data analysis in Section III. A simple application example of this technology is described in Section IV.

II. DEVICE STRUCTURES AND PROCESS

Appel *et al.* [2] proposed the innovative drift region concept to reduce the surface field, thus allowing high-voltage devices to be made in a thin epi layer instead of the conventionally used thick epi approach. A great deal of work has been done around this concept [3], [5]. It was demonstrated [6] later that the uniformity of impurity distribution in this epi layer was not essential. As a matter of fact, HVIC's up to 500 V were made with ion implantation to control the charge. Using a similar approach, the blocking capability has been extended beyond 1200 V. This section will describe the various low- and high-voltage device structures and the process steps used to make these HVIC's.

The high-voltage blocking capability is mainly dominated by 1) drift region length, 2) total charge per unit area in the drift region, 3) impurity concentration of the substrate, and 4) the curvature of the anode junction [2]. An array of 85 high-voltage test devices and test circuits has been designed. Basically, there are five types of devices: high-voltage diode, high-voltage n-p-n bipolar transistor, high-voltage DMOS transistor, high-voltage metal line crossover, and low-voltage BIMOS logic. The length of drift region for each type of device is varied from 40 to 170 μm and the anode curvature also is varied in some device groups. There are other parametric variations in this mask set; their effects on device performance will be discussed in a later section. The detailed mechanism of device function as well as the sensitivity of parameter-related performance also will be analyzed and discussed then. Fig. 1 shows a simplified cross section of five major devices. A combination of bipolar IC process and modified CMOS process was used to fabricate these devices. Fig. 2 shows the major process steps of the 14-mask HVIC process. The starting material is high-resistivity ⟨100⟩ p-type bulk silicon. The resistivity ranges from 100 to 300 $\Omega \cdot$ cm. The first step is to grow thick oxide and pattern it for antimony buried island implantation as illustrated in

Manuscript received April 15, 1986; revised July 25, 1986.
M. F. Chang, H. Yilmaz, E. J. Wildi, R. G. Hodgins, and K. Owyang are with the General Electric Company, Research Triangle Park, NC 27709.
G. Pifer is with the General Electric Company, Syracuse, NY.
M. S. Adler is with the General Electric Company, Corporate Research and Development Center, Schenectady, NY 12301.
IEEE Log Number 8610705.

Reprinted from *IEEE Trans. Electron Devices*, vol. ED-33, pp. 1992–2001, Dec. 1986.

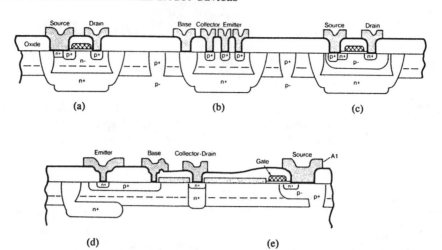

Fig. 1. Schematic drawings of five major device structures. From upper left, they are (a) p-channel MOSFET, (b) lateral p-n-p transistor, (c) n-channel MOSFET, (d) high-voltage n-p-n bipolar transistor, and (e) high-voltage DMOSFET.

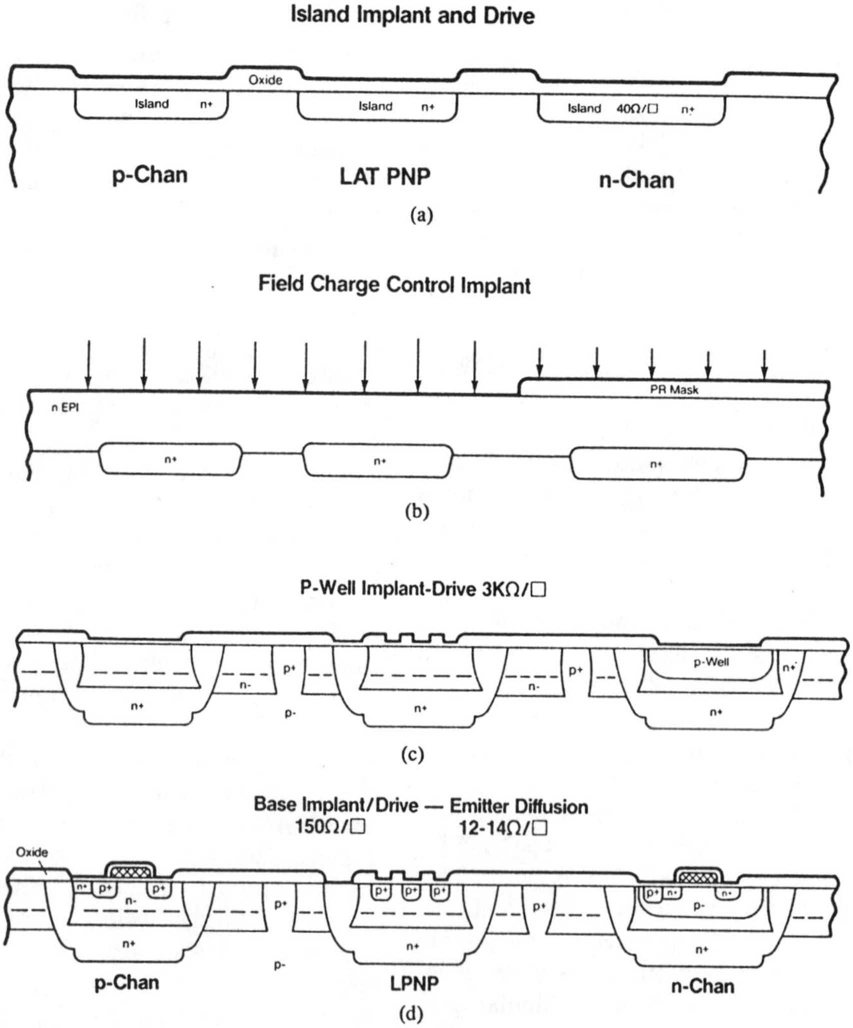

Island Implant and Drive

(a)

Field Charge Control Implant

(b)

P-Well Implant-Drive 3KΩ/□

(c)

Base Implant/Drive — Emitter Diffusion
150Ω/□   12-14Ω/□

(d)

Fig. 2. The major wafer fabrication steps: (a) Buried islands. (b) Epi growth and field implantation. (c) p-well implantation. (d) Source–drain formation.

Fig. 2(a). A high-resistivity (40 Ω · cm) n-type epi layer ~7 μm thick is grown atop the silicon wafer following oxide removal. Then a predetermined phosphorus dose is selectively implanted into the high-voltage drift region. The phosphorous dose in this study ranged from 1E11 to 1E12 cm^{-2}. The isolation diffusion was done with BN solid source and the sinker diffusion was achieved with POCL$_3$ diffusion. In Fig. 2(c), a high-energy (380 keV) boron implantation was introduced into the n-channel MOSFET area through both p-well photoresist windows and the earlier active area oxide mask so as to also provide channel stop function. Phosphorus-doped polysilicon gates were used for both CMOS and DMOSFET devices following the growth of a 1000-Å gate oxide. To simplify the process, the p$^+$ boron implantation serves for p-channel source–drain as well as for the base of n-p-n transistor and the emitter/collector of the lateral p-n-p transistor as shown in Fig. 2(d). The n$^+$ diffusion was used as the source–drain for n-channel MOSFET, the emitter of the n-p-n transistor and the source of the high-voltage DMOS transistor. The p-well implantation for the n-channel MOSFET also was used to make the high-voltage DMOS-FET. A proper passivation material is applied over the high-voltage drift region to provide high-voltage blocking capability and device stability. For the high-voltage metal crossover, sufficient dielectric layer thickness such as low-temperature oxide or plasma oxide on top of the field shield layer is needed to reduce vertical and fringing electric fields; this avoids interference among the devices. This process offers low-voltage bipolar and MOS complimentary devices rated to 25 V and nonlatching CMOS logic capability. It also allows low-voltage devices and circuits to be referenced up to 1200 V above substrate.

III. DEVICE ANALYSIS AND EXPERIMENTAL RESULTS

This section will be divided into two parts. The first part will examine the low-voltage devices while the second part will illustrate the high voltage devices.

A. Low-Voltage Devices

All active devices such as diodes, n-p-n bipolar transistor, lateral p-n-p transistor, and CMOS devices are well isolated by p$^+$ isolation, n$^+$ sinker, and n$^+$ buried island. Therefore, they are safely protected from high-voltage operation. This arrangement also completely avoids the CMOS latching problem and other parasitic interference since each device can be located in an isolation tub.

The lateral p-n-p transistor is a byproduct of p-channel MOSFET diffusion and provides a useful tool for level shifting, bias string, temperature sensing, and comparator design. This device is also wrapped around by n$^+$ sinker and n$^+$ buried island. The required high gain for the lateral p-n-p transistor is achieved by n$^+$ buried layer. The built-in potential difference between the n$^-$ epi layer and the n$^+$ buried island reflects injected holes to enhance the lateral p-n-p transistor common emitter current gain and kills the vertical substrate p-n-p gain. However, as the emitter–base forward bias is increased, high-level injection [8] causes the common emitter current gain to decrease as shown in Fig. 3.

The low-voltage n-channel MOSFET in this study consistently provides 25 V of dc blocking. At high current level, or as the device is stressed beyond breakdown, it snaps back to 15–18 V—a phenomenon commonly referred to as BV_{CEX}. While the nature of this BV_{CEX} snap-back is a hard to control, complicated bipolar characteristic [9], there are ways to avoid this problem. Fig. 4(a) shows the cross section of an n-channel MOSFET and Fig. 4(b) shows its equivalent circuit diagram. A parasitic n-p-n [10] transistor is in parallel with the n-channel

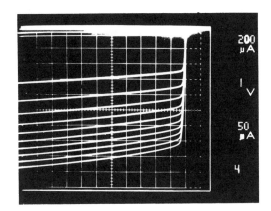

Fig. 3. Lateral p-n-p transistor I–V characteristics show the drastic decline of current gain at higher current level.

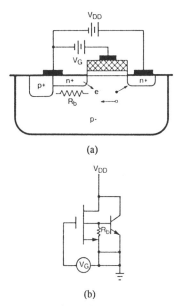

Fig. 4. Schematic drawings of (a) a low-voltage n-channel MOSFET and (b) its equivalent circuit.

MOSFET. There is a pinch resistor R_b under the source diffusion junction. As drain bias increases beyond junction breakdown, avalanche injection starts to generate electron–hole pairs. The holes are swept by the electric field towards the p$^+$ short through the pinch resistor R_b and develop a voltage drop V_b across R_b. The source junction near the channel portion will inject electrons into the p-well (including channel area) as V_b approaches a critical value. From this analysis, it is clear that the device performance can be greatly enhanced through optimized device design to minimize the effect of leakage current (I_L) at the dc breakdown voltage before it triggers BV_{CEX}. As shown in Fig. 5(a), a properly designed n-channel MOSFET can easily withstand 700 µA of leakage current at 25 V, but the other device can barely sustain 120 µA (Fig. 5(b)).

One key attribute of this technology is the ability to reference any of the above-mentioned low-voltage devices up to 1200 V with respect to the p-type substrate potential. To illustrate this point, Fig. 6 shows a low-voltage p-n diode (anode to cathode breakdown voltage

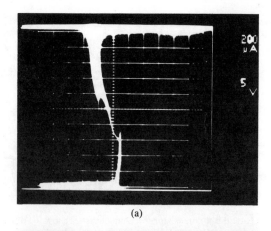

(a)

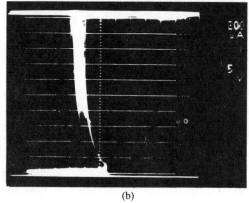

(b)

Fig. 5. Pictures of *I–V* characteristics for two different n-channel MOS-FET devices where device (a) has a much higher sustaining current capability than device (b).

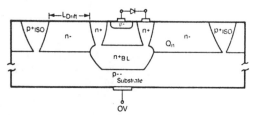

Fig. 6. Low-voltage p-n diode referenced at high voltage with respect to substrate ground.

of 60 V) contained in an n$^+$ tub and separated from the isolation region by an appropriate distance L_{DRIFT}. It can be referenced several hundred volts above the substrate potential, provided that its internal breakdown limitations are not exceeded. In a similar way, all low-voltage components may be referenced at arbitrarily high voltages with respect to chip substrate. A summary of key parametric data for low-voltage devices is listed in Table I.

B. High-Voltage Devices

The RESURF-based concept was implemented to construct high-voltage n-p-n BJT, DMOSFET, and diodes for 1200-V HVIC's. Even though the principle of RESURF is valid for 1200-V device designs, the two- and three-dimensional effect becomes more significant for such high-voltage device structures. A basic diode structure is used to simulate and optimize the blocking and on-resistance characteristics of the high-voltage devices as shown in

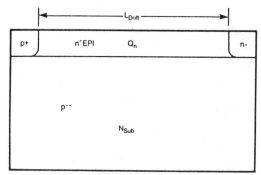

Fig. 7. A simple high-voltage diode to illustrate the device blocking characteristics.

TABLE I
LOW-VOLTAGE DEVICE PARAMETERS

N-Channel	P-Channel	npn BJT	Lateral pnp (Base width =4.8um)
$V_T = 1.8V$	$V_T = -1.8V$	$\beta = 20\text{-}40$	$\beta = 15$
$BV_{SD} = 25V$	$BV_{SD} = 60V$	$BV_{CEO} = 35V$	$BV_{CBS} = 60V$
		$BV_{CBS} = 60V$	

Fig. 7. The lateral device simulations were done by using a computer program called BVCALC [11]. The aim of this device optimization is to achieve the required 1200-V blocking capability with the largest possible charge and the shortest possible length in the n$^-$ drift region to minimize device on-resistance and chip area. The n$^-$ drift region total charge Q_N can be increased by increasing the impurity concentration of the p$^-$ substrate. As illustrated in Fig. 8(a), if the substrate is lightly doped with a large Q_N in the drift region, the peak electric field occurs at the p$^+$-n$^-$ junction. For the case of a substrate with high impurity concentration, the electric field is reduced at the p$^+$-n$^-$ junction, and the overall electric field becomes higher but still less than the breakdown value as shown in Fig. 8(b). This reduction in the peak electric field at the p$^+$-n$^-$ junction is helped by charge sharing effect. With yet higher doped p$^-$ substrates, the effective n$^-$ drift region charge Q_N is reduced at the blocking voltage since the increased charge in the p$^-$ substrate forces a larger depletion into the n$^-$ drift region as shown in Fig. 9. Therefore, the net charge in the n$^-$ drift region is reduced for the lateral p$^+$-n$^-$ junction blocking, and thus lowers the maximum electric field at this junction. This n$^-$ region will deplete at relatively low voltages and the rest of the voltage will be distributed across the drift region length. Since the n$^-$ drift region is completely depleted, the n$^+$ cathode diffusion will stop the lateral as well as the vertical depletion, and result in an increase of electric field at the n$^-$-n$^+$ boundary. As the impurity concentration in the p$^-$ substrate is further increased, the electric field starts to peak up at the n$^-$-n$^+$ boundary and may increase beyond the breakdown point.

The computer simulated field distribution for these three

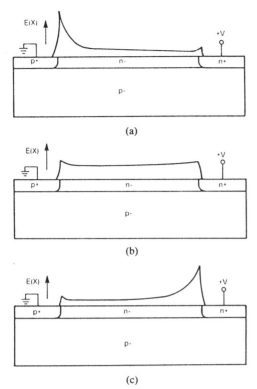

Fig. 8. Schematic drawings of surface field strength in response to substrate doping concentration. The substrate doping concentration gradually increases from case (a) to case (b) and the case (c).

cases is shown in Fig. 9(a), (b), and (c), respectively. The measured results as shown in Figs. 10 and 11 follow the theoretical trends. However, the measured results are lower than the theoretical estimated breakdown voltage values. Since RESURF concept is sensitive to total charge in the n^- drift region, the difference between the theory and the experiment, to a degree, is due to the surface passivation and/or mechanical stress induced surface charges in real devices. Another important factor which accounts for the discrepancy is the three-dimensional junction curvature effect which becomes more critical for 1200-V blocking devices. Due to the three-dimensional effects of the n^--n^+ and/or n^+-p^- junction, more lightly doped p^- substrate is necessary for 1200-V blocking, otherwise, breakdown of the n^+-p^- junction will dominate the device blocking capability instead of the charge and the length of the n^- drift region. In this case, the increase of the n^- drift region length does not affect the breakdown voltage as illustrated in the curve marked by ×'s of Fig. 11. On the other hand, when the breakdown is limited by the n^+-n^- boundary rather than by the p^+-n^- or n^+-p^- junctions, the breakdown voltage increases significantly with increasing drift length as shown in the curve marked by Δ's of Fig. 11. The optimum substrate resistivity is 200–300 $\Omega \cdot$ cm for 1200-V blocking. The n^- drift region charge has been varied to minimize on-resistance of devices without sacrificing the blocking capability. As shown in Fig. 10, the net charge of 7E11 cm^{-2} is the optimum dose for 1200-V blocking. The minimum drift region length (L_{DRIFT}) required to support 1200 V of blocking is 120 μm.

The optimized diode blocking structure is used in lateral BJT and DMOSFET designs. The cross-sectional structures of a lateral BJT and a DMOSFET are shown in Fig. 12(a) and (b), respectively.

The lateral high-voltage n-p-n BJT device is a composited device consisting of a low-voltage n-p-n in a cascode connection with a lateral high-voltage JFET. As shown in Fig. 12(a), this JFET device is part of the base diffusion and is a normally "on" device. In the off (blocking) state, the JFET pinches off and isolates the n-p-n BJT emitter area from the high collector voltage. The high voltage is supported by the drift region as in the case of the simple high-voltage diode. The extended part of the base diffusion beyond the buried island is the effective JFET channel. The effective JFET channel length (L_d) is one of the critical factors in determining the n-p-n BJT blocking capability as illustrated in Fig. 13, where the measured BJT blocking voltage is plotted as a function of JFET length. It is clear from this picture that a channel length greater than 25 μm is required for 1200-V application. The buried n^+ layer increased the current gain of the lateral n-p-n BJT, but it results in devices with poor SOA capability. An n-p-n BJT without the n^+ buried layer has lower gain but larger SOA. The high-current and high-voltage (I–V) characteristics of the n-p-n BJT's with and without the n^+ buried layer are shown in Fig. 14(a) and (b), respectively. The narrow SOA performance of n-p-n BJT's is due to their current gain. It takes only a small avalanche current density to cause localized secondary breakdown in BJT's (or devices with current gain). An I–V characteristic of the lateral DMOSFET with square SOA capability is shown in Fig. 15. A 1200-V DMOSFET is not only more rugged than the BJT, it also has lower on-resistance per unit area (3–4 times) than the BJT structures. The base drive and the JFET pinching in the BJT structures result in its higher on-resistance. Fig. 12 shows a simplified schematic cross section for (a) an n-p-n BJT and (b) a DMOSFET with related parameters for on-resistance analysis. For higher voltage DMOSFET, the channel resistance R_C is negligible in comparison to the drift resistance R_D.

Therefore

$$R_{\mathrm{DMOS}} = R_C + R_D \cong R_D. \qquad (1)$$

In the case of an n-p-n BJT, the JFET pinch resistance R_J is a significant part of on-resistance. With the assumption of low conductivity modulation, the on-resistance of a BJT can be expressed as

$$R_{\mathrm{BJT}} = R_J + R_D \qquad (2)$$

$$R_D = \frac{L_{\mathrm{DRIFT}}}{Z \cdot Q_N \cdot u_n} \qquad (3)$$

$$R_J = \frac{L_{\mathrm{JFET}}}{Zu_n \displaystyle\int_{\mathrm{JFET}} Q_{dx}} \qquad (4)$$

where Q_n is the total charge density in the drift region and

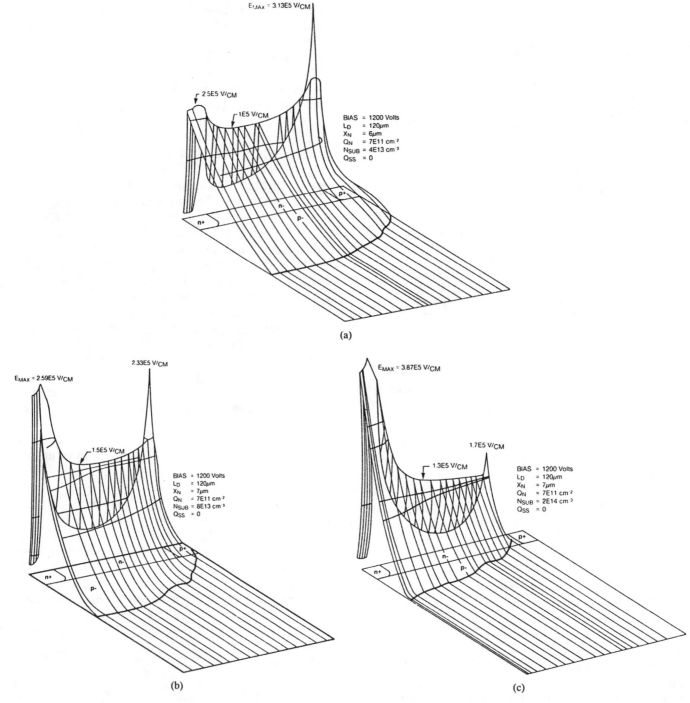

Fig. 9. Computer simulated electric field distributions for substrates with three different doping concentrations.

$\int_{JFET} Q_{dx}$ is the effective net charge contributing for conduction in the JFET channel region. The ratio of on-resistance between BJT and DMOSFET is

$$\frac{R_{BJT}}{R_{DMOS}} \cong \frac{R_D + R_J}{R_D} = 1 + \frac{R_J}{R_D}. \qquad (5)$$

A simplified model based on an uniformly doped epi layer was used to illustrate the JFET pinching effect on this resistance ratio.

The predicted and measured ratios are plotted on Fig.

16. The devices for this plot had a 30 μm of JFET channel, 7 μm of epi thickness, and 2 μm of base junction depth with 7E11 cm^{-2} of phosphorous charge in the drift region. Even though the simple model predicted curve is smaller than the measured ratio, it did explain the effect of JFET pinching on the BJT on-resistance. The total charge in the drift region was introduced by phosphorous ion implantation instead of uniform epi doping. The amount of charge in the JFET channel region was much less and resulted in a higher resistance ratio as shown in Fig. 16.

172

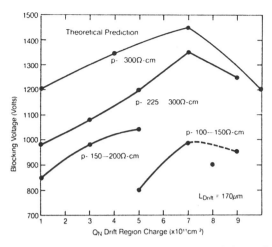

Fig. 10. A plot of blocking voltage as a function of total charge Q_N in the the drift region.

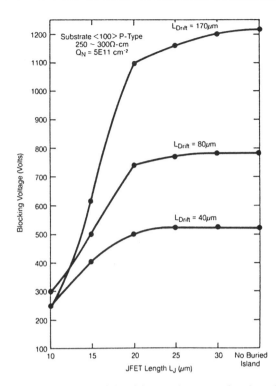

Fig. 13. A plot of n-p-n BJT breakdown voltage as a function of JFET channel length (L_J).

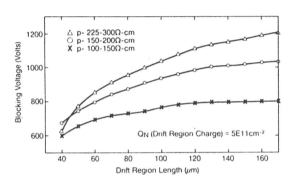

Fig. 11. A plot of breakdown voltage as a function of drift region length (L_{DRIFT}).

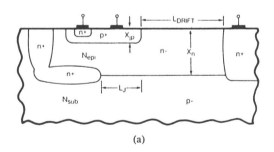

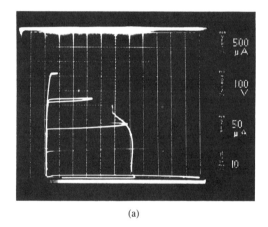

(a)

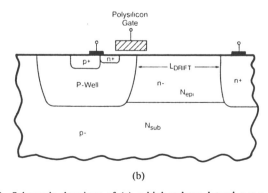

(a)

(b)

Fig. 12. Schematic drawings of (a) a high-voltage lateral n-p-n bipolar transistor and (b) a high-voltage DMOSFET.

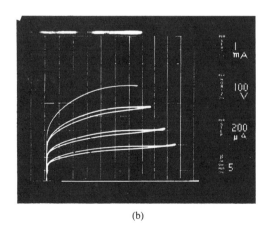

(b)

Fig. 14. High-voltage and high-current I–V characteristics of (a) an n-p-n BJT with buried island and (b) an n-p-n BJT without buried island.

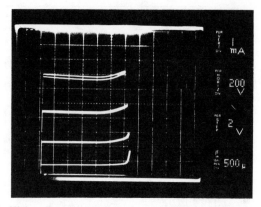

Fig. 15. High-voltage and high-current *I–V* characteristics of a DMOS-FET shows the hard SOA performance.

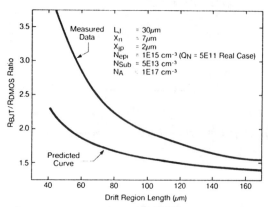

Fig. 16. A plot of predicted and measured ratios of on-resistance of a high-voltage n-p-n BJT over an equivalent DMOSFET.

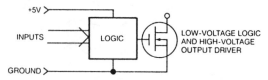

Fig. 17. A schematic block diagram of an HVIC that takes 5-V input and drives high-voltage output devices.

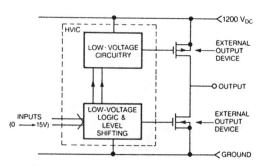

Fig. 18. A schematic block diagram of a half-bridge curcuit made with this HVIC process.

IV. APPLICATION

There are a great deal of applications that do not necessitate high-voltage capability, but do require a mix of analog and digital circuitry. High-level integration of such systems has been lagging because of the unavailability of a mainstream rugged analog–digital IC technology. The availability of CMOS logic tailored for operation from 5 to 20 V, coupled with 20-V MOS and bipolar devices, gives substantial latitude in selecting voltage bias levels or adapting this technology to an existing one. As an added feature, the ruggedness of this process guarantees latch-proof operation of CMOS logic circuitry. Actuators, relay drivers, and servo loops are a few examples of where the low-voltage features of this process can be applied.

A standard class of applications that this technology can easily handle is illustrated in Fig. 17. In this example, we show a 5-V low-voltage logic block receiving an arbitrary number of inputs and controlling the state of an output high-voltage transistor. Because our technology allows multiple high-voltage devices to reside on the same chip, the example could just as well have shown the logic core controlling the states of an array of high-voltage DMOS-FET and/or n-p-n devices. Such a configurations would be typical of plasma and electro luminescent display functions. The ability to reference low-voltage devices up to 1200 V in our technology opens up 300–500 VAC industrial applications.

The half-bridge circuit function is generic to power circuits and is used across the board in applications such as motor controls, power supplies, ballasts, etc. Fig. 18 shows how HVIC technology can impact this circuit function. In this example, the HVIC decodes logic level inputs and translates these latter to an effective gate drive to the output power devices. As such, this technology provides what we call the "missing link" between signal electronics and power devices. In this application, every feature of our process is utilized. For example, logic decoding of inputs must be performed to establish whether upper P-MOS or lower N-MOS output devices are to be on or off. Naturally, the logic on the HVIC should not allow for both devices to be on simultaneously, since this would short out the dc power source and lead to device failure. Proper time sequencing is needed to insure complete output device turn-off prior to turning on the alternate output device. This requires some form of analog timing capability, which again is within the grasp of this HVIC process. A low-voltage gate drive circuit referenced to the dc link (up to 1200 V) makes use of the ability to reference low-voltage devices at high voltages with respect to substrate (ground). And finally, high-voltage N-MOS or n-p-n devices allow the information generated by the logic and timing circuits to be level shifted up to the output power MOS gate drive circuitry.

V. CONCLUSION

High-voltage diodes, n-p-n BJT's, and DMOSFET's in conjunction with 20-V analog–digital BiMOS circuitry have been integrated on the same chip using a RESURF-based technology. Through device simulation and process development, optimum parameter tradeoffs have been obtained among these device types. As stated, the required JFET channel to form the novel high-voltage n-p-n BJT structure contributes significantly to the total device on-resistance. Also, due to its current gain versus temperature dependence, the n-p-n BJT is not as rugged as the high-voltage DMOSFET. However, with both types of device available, more circuit design freedom is possible. By scaling L_{DRIFT} upward and without modifying the process, the transistor ratings can be scaled from 25 to 1200 V. This feature is attractive since L_{DRIFT} is controlled by lithography exclusively and thus allows devices with different ratings to reside on the same integrated circuit. The versatility of this junction isolated 1200-V BiMOS technology enables several low- and high-voltage functions to benefit from a high-level integration. The ability to operate both logic and analog circuitry safely with bias voltage as high as 25 V, makes this technology ideal for power circuit environments where noise and temperature can be significant and high noise margins are necessary.

REFERENCES

[1] H. W. Becke, "Approaches to isolation in high-voltage integrated circuits," in *IEDM Tech. Dig.*, paper 30.1, pp. 724–727, 1985.
[2] J. A. Appels and H. M. J. Vaes, "High-voltage thin-layer devices (RESURF devices)," in *IEDM Tech. Dig.*, paper 10.1, pp. 238–241, 1979.
[3] S. Colak, B. Singer, and E. Stupp, "Design of high-density power lateral DMOS transistors," in *Proc. Power Electron. Specialists Conf.*, pp. 164–167, 1980.
[4] S. Colak, "Effects of drift region parameters on the static properties of power LDMOST," *IEEE Trans. Electron Devices*, vol. ED-28, no. 12, pp. 1455–1466, Dec. 1981.
[5] T. Yamaguchi and S. Morimoto, "Process and device design of a 1000-V MOS IC," *IEEE Trans. Electron Devices*, vol. ED-29, no. 8, pp. 1171–1178, 1982.
[6] E. Wildi, T. Chow, M. Adler, M. Cornell, and G. Pifer, "New high-voltage IC technology," in *IEDM Tech. Dig.*, paper 10.2, pp. 262–265, 1984.
[7] S. M. Sze and G. Gibbons, "Effect of junction curvature on breakdown voltages in semiconductors," *Solid-State Electron.*, vol. 10, p. 1105, 1967.
[8] S. Chou, "An investigation of lateral transistors—DC characteristics," *Solid-State Electron.*, vol. 14, pp. 811–826, 1971.
[9] S. M. Sze, *Physics of Semiconductor Devices*. New York: Wiley-Interscience, 1969.
[10] E. Sun, J. Moll, J. Berger, and B. Alders, "Breakdown mechanism in short-channel MOS transistors," in *IEDM Tech. Dig.*, paper 19.5, pp. 478–482, 1978.
[11] M. Adler, V. Temple, and A. Ferro, "Theoretical bases for field calculation in multidimensional reverse biased semiconductor devices," *Solid-State Electron.*, 25, pp. 1179–1186, 1982.
[12] S. K. Ghandi, *Semiconductor Power Devices*. New York: Wiley-Interscience, 1977.

A *DI/JI*-Compatible Monolithic High-Voltage Multiplexer

RICHARD K. WILLIAMS, MEMBER, IEEE, LARRY T. SEVILLA, MEMBER, IEEE, ERIC RUETZ, MEMBER, IEEE, AND JAMES D. PLUMMER, FELLOW, IEEE

Abstract—A high-voltage multiplexer fabricated with both junction-isolated (*JI*) and dielectrically isolated (*DI*) D/CMOS process technologies is described in this paper. This eight-channel multiplexer is capable of switching a ±50-V analog-signal range from a ±60-V power supply. The switches exhibit less than 50 Ω of on-resistance and are capable of peak currents in excess of 0.5 A. An off-switch current model incorporating junction area and lifetime-dependent lateral DMOS drain-to-body and drain-to-substrate leakages is described. Elimination of the drain-to-substrate diode with dielectric isolation results in a factor of 15 reduction in leakage at 25°C and a factor of 10 improvement at 125°C, which agrees well with the model developed. Results show that the generation current from the space-charge region dominates device leakage at room temperature, while diffusion current from the neutral regions is predominant at elevated temperatures. In high-voltage testers, dielectrically isolated multiplexers offer the low leakage and high accuracy required by critical channels where less costly junction-isolated devices will not suffice.

I. INTRODUCTION

HIGH-VOLTAGE monolithic multiplexers provide significant performance improvements in test and measurement systems [1] requiring analog-signal handling capability greater than ±15 V. To meet a variety of system needs, a high-voltage multiplexer must drive low impedances with minimal deviations in on-resistance over the entire analog-signal range. For most applications, peak currents of 0.5 A and on-switch resistances of less than 50 Ω optimize the output device size without introducing unacceptable levels of distortion and insertion loss. Low interdevice capacitances are necessary to provide good off-isolation and minimize crosstalk for signals ranging from dc to greater than 10 MHz. Moreover, minimal off-switch leakage currents are highly desirable to minimize system measurement errors. To test common 24- to 30-V industrial and military electrical systems, an analog-signal range of ±50 V is desirable. The use of ±60-V power supplies minimizes the increase·in on-switch resistance for +50-V analog signals.

Other circuit characteristics are also desirable. Standby power dissipation should be less than 2 mW to allow battery operation. Furthermore, the logic inputs should be either TTL or CMOS compatible and interface easily with

Manuscript received May 6, 1986; revised August 1, 1986.
R. K. Williams, L. T. Sevilla, and E. Ruetz are with Siliconix Incorporated, Santa Clara, CA 95054.
J. D. Plummer is with the Integrated Circuits Laboratory, Stanford University, Stanford, CA 94305.
IEEE Log Number 8610816.

microprocessor-based controllers. Finally, guaranteed break-before-make switch action prevents channel-to-channel interference, loading, and feedthrough.

Considering these low power dissipation and high-voltage circuit requirements, a D/CMOS process technology was chosen to implement the high-voltage multiplexer.

II. MULTIPLEXER CIRCUIT DESCRIPTION

The circuit block diagram in Fig. 1 shows the functional building blocks needed to implement a 1-of-8 multiplexer. Table I describes the truth table for the address, "write bar," and "reset bar" logic inputs. These logic inputs are CMOS compatible with a series resistor and diode clamps to V_{logic} and ground for protection against electrostatic discharge. CMOS buffers provide complementary address signals to drive the decode circuitry, and CMOS NAND gates implement the 1-of-8 decoder. The decoder outputs, with the "write bar" and "reset bar," control the CMOS transmission gate latch, operating from the 15-V logic supply. The latch outputs control the level shift circuitry.

Fig. 2 shows a schematic of the level shift circuitry that takes low-voltage logic signals and translates them to high-voltage signals. The use of cross-coupled level shift stages is a key factor in achieving ultralow power dissipation. The level shift circuit has a static condition where only leakage current flows in either logic state. The first stage of the level shifter consists of a cross-coupled pair of high-voltage PMOS devices, each connected in series to one of a pair of high-voltage n-channel lateral DMOS devices. These devices are driven out of phase by the latch stage. The n-channel lateral DMOS drains swing between $V+$ and ground, thus providing the first level shift. Since the n-channel devices are driven out of phase, the device that is on is in series with the off PMOS device. Therefore, $V+$ power supply current flows only during the level transitions. Device sizing ensures a limited peak current that is quickly reduced to zero by the positive feedback action of the cross-coupled stage.

The second stage of the level shifter consists of high-voltage PMOS devices driven out of phase by the first stage. Each of these devices is connected in series with one of a pair of cross-coupled high-voltage n-channel lateral DMOS devices. The output of this stage swings between $V+$ and $V-$, driving the output switch section. Low

Reprinted from *IEEE Trans. Electron Devices*, vol. ED-33, pp. 1977–1984, Dec. 1986.

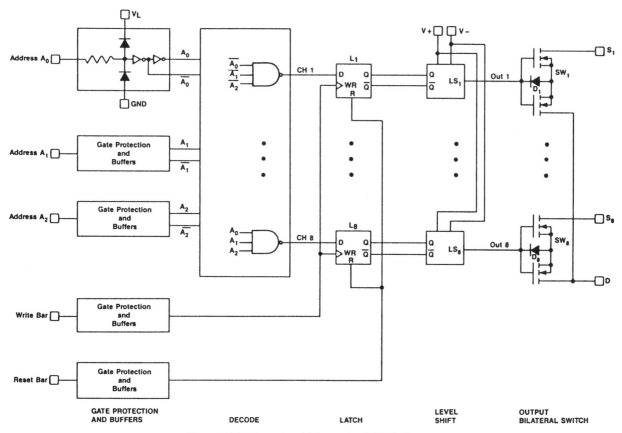

Fig. 1. Eight-channel multiplexer circuit block diagram.

TABLE I
MULTIPLEXER TRUTH TABLE

A_2	A_1	A_0	$\overline{WR}$	$\overline{RS}$	On Switch
x	x	x	⌐	1	Maintains previous switch condition
x	x	x	x	0	None
0	0	0	0	1	1
0	0	1	0	1	2
0	1	0	0	1	3
0	1	1	0	1	4
1	0	0	0	1	5
1	0	1	0	1	6
1	1	0	0	1	7
1	1	1	0	1	8

standby power dissipation is achieved by this method. The n-channel lateral DMOS devices include resistors that are extensions of their drain regions. Device sizing ensures minimum current during transitions and that the "low-to-high" transition (turn-on) time is longer than the "high-to-low" transition (turn-off) time. This behavior is critical in multiplexer applications.

The output switch section consists of two common-gate common-source and body high-voltage n-channel lateral DMOS devices connected in series. This arrangement allows analog signals of both polarities to pass or be blocked. The device thus functions as a bilateral switch. A diode across the switch gate-to-source node improves off-isolation by shunting ac signals to $-V$ when the switch is turned off.

As summarized in Table II, this circuit implementation

requires low-voltage CMOS devices capable of 15-V operation and high-voltage p- and n-channel MOS devices capable of operating between the plus and minus high-voltage power supplies (i.e., 135 V total). This ground-referenced three-supply ($+60$, $+15$, and -60 V) circuit is most conveniently implemented as a monolithic device, using a junction-isolated or dielectrically isolated process. When using junction isolation, the substrate and isolation diffusions are tied to the most negative potential, namely -60 V, to prevent forward biasing of any n-epi island to substrate junctions.

III. *JI* PROCESS IMPLEMENTATION

Junction-isolated D/CMOS is a combination of bipolar and p-well CMOS process technologies capable of implementing high-voltage n-channel lateral DMOS and high-voltage PMOS. The starting material consists of a 3- to 8-$\Omega \cdot$cm p-type $\langle 100 \rangle$ silicon substrate. First, a 25-μm layer of 3- to 8-$\Omega \cdot$cm n-type epitaxial silicon is deposited. The resistivity and thickness of this layer determines the maximum breakdown of the high-voltage devices. Inter-device isolation is achieved by conventional diffused p$^+$ regions having a junction depth exceeding the n-type epitaxial layer thickness. A p-well is next implanted and diffused. The p-well is used to fabricate the body region of low-voltage NMOS transistors. It also serves as a graded drain for high-voltage PMOS transistors. Field areas are next masked to protect them during oxide etch-back of active areas. This oxide also serves as the gate

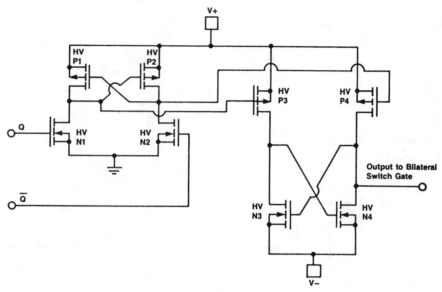

Fig. 2. High-voltage level-shift circuitry.

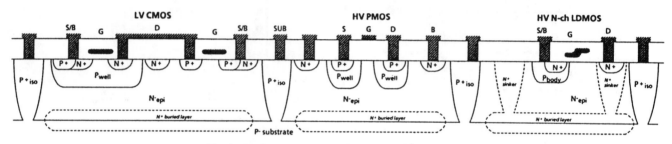

Fig. 3. Device cross sections of *JI* DMOS/CMOS process.

TABLE II
DEVICE REQUIREMENTS OF HIGH-VOLTAGE MULTIPLEXER CIRCUIT

DEVICE	CIRCUIT	CRITERIA			
		V_T (V)	BV_{DSS} (V)	$BV_{epi/sub}$ (V)	BV_{ox} (V)
LV CMOS	control logic	1 to 2	>20	>90	>30
HV PMOS	level shift stages	-7 to -10	>135	>135	>75
HV N-CH LDMOS	level shift stage I	2 to 4	>75	>135	>50
	level shift stage II and output	4 to 6.5	>135	>135	>135

dielectric of high-voltage PMOS devices. Due to the relatively low level of integration and high latchup immunity required by the circuit, heavily doped guard rings, rather than locally oxidized field regions, are employed to prevent field inversion. A 100-nm gate oxide is grown and n^+ doped polysilicon gates and interconnects are defined. All subsequent implants are self-aligned to these gate regions. Using a boron implant and subsequent drive-in, the DMOS body regions and PMOS source–drain areas are formed. An arsenic implant and anneal are used to fabricate the shallow n^+ source–drain regions, followed by a PSG deposition and flow. Finally, the wafers are contact-etched, metallized, and passivated.

The junction-isolated D/CMOS process described thus far is appropriate for a large variety of devices, including high- and low-voltage MOS and bipolar transistors [2]. In

particular, it is used to fabricate the DG568 high-voltage multiplexer, combining low-voltage CMOS, high-voltage PMOS, and high-voltage n-channel lateral DMOS (see Fig. 3). To achieve proper operation of the high-voltage n-channel lateral DMOS device, an optional n^+ buried layer can be employed to suppress parasitic lateral and vertical p-n-p betas. The n^+ buried layer also improves the punchthrough voltage of the high-voltage PMOS devices. High-voltage structures employing this buried layer are generally incompatible with thin-epitaxial RESURF techniques [3]. Therefore, a thick-epitaxial non-RESURF process sequence, which maintains dielectrically isolated process compatibility, was chosen.

IV. *DI* PROCESS IMPLEMENTATION

Numerous DI process technologies have been described in the literature. Among these, one technique has been successfully applied to many power integrated circuits [4]. Starting with a 3- to 8-$\Omega \cdot$ cm n^- substrate, the process (shown in Fig. 4) utilizes a deep V-groove or moat etch followed by a thermal oxidation. This oxide isolates devices in separate n-type silicon tubs. Next, 500 μm of polysilicon are deposited on the wafer for mechanical support during subsequent processing. Finally, the single crystal silicon is ground and polished to a thickness of 25 μm. After a 700-nm oxidation, the wafer process is identical to the junction-isolated D/CMOS process flow. Con-

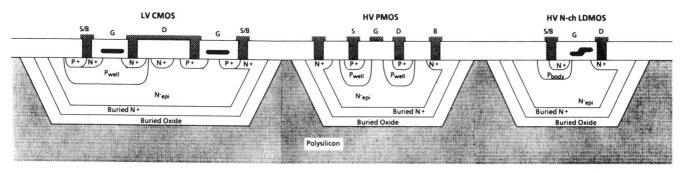

Fig. 4. Device cross sections of *DI* DMOS/CMOS process.

sequently, the devices fabricated with the *DI* D/CMOS process are identical to the junction-isolated devices with the exception of reduced parasitics. To reduce $R_{DS(on)}$ of the high-voltage n-channel lateral DMOS and prevent high-voltage field effects at the silicon–buried oxide interface, an optional n$^+$ buried layer and sinker are employed.

Due to the expense of the thick poly deposition and the mechanical loss due to breakage during grinding and uniformity control of the silicon tub thickness, dielectrically isolated wafers are more costly than their junction-isolated counterparts. This cost difference is offset by performance advantages from improved isolation, which is required for many high-voltage integrated circuits.

V. Layout Considerations

Since dielectric isolation does not require heavily doped guard rings to prevent field inversion, it can produce higher device-packing density than junction isolation, particularly at high voltages. However, to maintain mask set compatibility, the DG568 high-voltage multiplexer uses the same layout and die size for both *JI* and *DI* versions (see die photo in Fig. 5). Even so, some mask changes are necessary to convert a *JI*-based product into a *DI*-compatible layout. In particular, because the wafer is inverted during *DI* processing, the *DI* isolation (moat etch) mask is a mirror image of its *JI* equivalent. Furthermore, the corners are compensated to prevent rounding during the V-groove etch. Contacts to the isolation regions are also eliminated to prevent etching of the field oxide between tubs. It is undesirable to implement epitaxial resistors with tight absolute tolerances of resistance since the silicon thickness and uniformity in a dielectrically isolated process depends on the mechanical grinding and polishing operations.

VI. Results and Discussions

Both junction-isolated [5] and dielectrically isolated high-voltage multiplexers were successfully fabricated and characterized. Table III compares basic device and circuit electrical parameter targets with measured values. High-voltage PMOS and n-channel lateral DMOS exceeded the target values of breakdown for both *JI* and *DI* versions. Signal handling capability is demonstrated in Fig. 6 where a 100-V peak-to-peak sine wave on channel

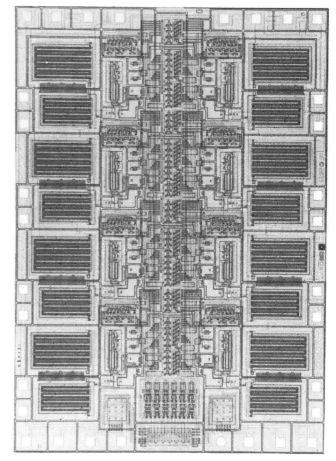

Fig. 5. Die photo of *DI* high-voltage multiplexer.

TABLE III
ELECTRICAL CHARACTERISTICS OF HIGH-VOLTAGE MULTIPLEXER

Component	Parameter	Condition	Circuit Requirement		Measured Value	
			Spec	Target	JI	DI
HV PMOS	BV_{DSS}	I = 10μA	128V	135V	170V	170V
HV N-ch LDMOS	BV_{DSS}	I = 10μA	128V	135V	140V	140V
entire circuit	I_{HV} supply	+ V = 60V;-V = -60V	20μA	5μA	1μA	0.5μA
	t_{on}	V_{logic} = 15V	1.5μs	0.5μs	0.6μs	0.8μs
	t_{off}	V_{logic} = 15V	0.5μs	0.25μs	0.1μs	0.1μs
	I_{HV} latchup	+ V = 60V;-V = -60V	100mA	200mA	500mA	N/A
HV bilateral switch	R_{DS}	V_S = + 50V	150Ω	50Ω	55Ω	55Ω
	I_{Dsat}	V_S = + 30V	300mA	500mA	750mA	750mA
parasitic PNP	B	I = 10mA	0.5	0.1	w/o BL 6 w/BL .15	0

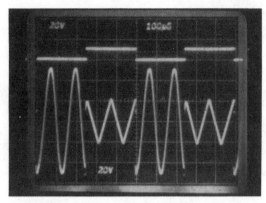

Fig. 6. Multiplexing 100-V p⁺-p sine wave with 40-V p⁺-p triangle wave.

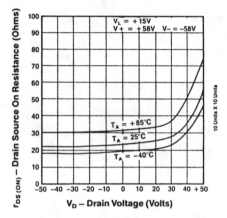

Fig. 7. Measured values of bilateral switch on-resistance.

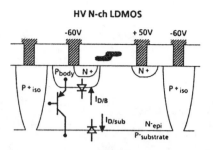

Fig. 8. Parasitic elements of *JI* high-voltage n-channel lateral DMOS.

one is multiplexed with a 40-V peak-to-peak triangle wave on channel eight. Likewise, target values were met for high-voltage supply current and switching speed over voltage and over temperature. The multiplexer on-resistance is comprised of two unequally sized n-channel lateral DMOS devices in series. Fig. 7 illustrates the multiplexer on-resistance versus the applied signal voltage. For analog signals from −50 to +30 V, the resistance is a relatively constant 25 Ω. For signals above +30 V, the on-resistance increases resulting from a decrease in gate-to-source drive voltage as the signal becomes more positive. For a +60-V supply, a maximum signal of +50 V results in a 55-Ω resistance at room temperature, closely matching the design target. In junction isolation, analog signals greater than the negative high-voltage supply forward bias the high-voltage n-channel drain(epi)-to-substrate diode, resulting in either signal distortion or CMOS latchup. With dielectric isolation, this diode is eliminated. Furthermore, eliminating the drain-to-substrate junction prevents p-n-p bipolar action parasitic to junction-isolated high-voltage n-channel lateral DMOS (see Fig. 8). The elimination of the epi-to-substrate diode has direct implications on the leakage specifications of the multiplexer outputs. To determine the degree that leakage can be reduced, the various leakage components must first be identified.

As shown in Fig. 8, junction-isolated high-voltage n-channel devices in the off-state contain two reverse biased diodes, the lateral DMOS drain-to-body diode and the drain-to-substrate diode. Of the two, the latter contributes the majority of the leakage current due (in part) to its larger junction area. At first glance, one expects that eliminating the drain-to-substrate diode using dielectric isolation would result in a reduction in leakage commensurate with the fraction of junction area eliminated. Instead, an improvement in leakage exceeding that predicted by simple junction area arguments is observed. To understand this improvement, the leakage mechanisms responsible must be analyzed.

At room temperature, junction leakage is generally dominated by carrier generation in the space-charge region [6]. Using Shockley–Hall–Read (or SHR) generation–recombination, we can estimate the generation leakage per unit area J_{GEN} as

$$J_{\text{GEN}} = q \int_0^w G \, dx = \frac{q n_i X_i}{2\tau} \tag{1}$$

by assuming the recombination centers are at midgap and are physically located within the space-charge width X_i. At room temperature, the ratio of the drain-to-substrate diode leakage current $I_{D\text{sub}}$ to the drain-to-body leakage I_{DB} is given by

$$\frac{I_{D\text{sub}}}{I_{DB}} = \frac{A_{D\text{sub}}}{A_{DB}} \frac{\tau_{DB}}{\tau_{D\text{sub}}} \equiv \frac{A_{D\text{sub}}}{A_{DB}} m \tag{2}$$

where $A_{D\text{sub}}$ and A_{DB} are junction areas and $\tau_{D\text{sub}}$ and τ_{DB} are the carrier lifetimes in these regions. Equation (2) illustrates that the ratio of drain-to-substrate and drain-to-body leakage depends on material lifetime as well as junction area. Material lifetime can be reduced by crystallographic defects, dislocations, and heavy metal precipitates associated with the strain field surrounding heavily doped junctions. Consequently, the drain-to-substrate junction region, with its heavily doped buried-layer, isolation, and sinker diffusions, may exhibit a lower material lifetime and higher leakage per unit area than the lightly doped drain-to-body diode. (This assumes the drain-to-body depletion region does not extend into the buried layer strain field.) Letting $m \equiv \tau_{DB}/\tau_{D\text{sub}}$, it was empirically determined from a 400-piece sample that m typically ranges from 2 to 5 with a median value of 3.7. The exact value depends on both material quality and processing conditions. Well-known chemical, intrinsic, and extrinsic

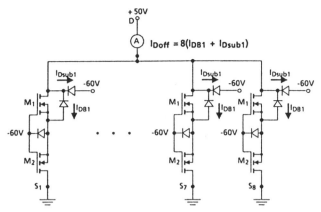

Fig. 9. Equivalent circuit of I_{Doff} leakage.

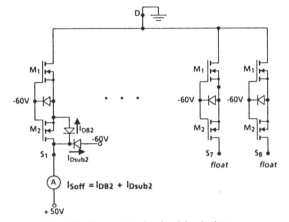

Fig. 10. Equivalent circuit of I_{Soff} leakage.

gettering techniques prevent order-of-magnitude variations in lifetime and leakages.

Each bilateral switch is composed of a series combination of two dissimilar sized lateral DMOS devices $M1$ and $M2$. Provided the drain/body and drain/substrate diodes are reverse biased at the same voltage, the total leakage I_t for each device can be expressed as

$$I_{t1} = I_{DB1} + I_{Dsub1} = J_{DB}(A_{DB1} + m A_{Dsub1}) \quad (3)$$

$$I_{t2} = I_{D21} + I_{Dsub2} = J_{DB}(A_{DB1} + m A_{Dsub2}) \quad (4)$$

where J_{DB} is the leakage/unit area of the drain-to-body diode and where the junction areas including sidewalls are $A_{DB1} = 114 \times 10^3 \ \mu m^2$, $A_{DB2} = 165.4 \times 10^3 \ \mu m^2$, $A_{Dsub1} = 447.6 \times 10^3 \ \mu m^2$, and $A_{Dsub2} = 574.1 \times 10^3 \ \mu m^2$.

Since the DG568 multiplexer consists of an array of eight bilateral switches, the total multiplexer leakage may be specified in a variety of ways. One such technique measures the leakage of the common side (labeled "drain" using conventional multiplexer nomenclature) of the bilateral switch array. As shown in Fig. 9, I_{Doff} is the total off-state leakage of all eight $M1$ transistors, namely

$$I_{Doff}(JI) = 8(I_{DB1} + I_{Dsub1}) = 8J_{DB}(A_{DB1} + m A_{Dsub1}). \quad (5)$$

A complementary test, shown in Fig. 10, measures I_{Soff}, the off-state leakage of transistor $M2$ on any individual

channel (labeled "source" using conventional multiplexer nomenclature), so that

$$I_{Soff}(JI) = (I_{DB2} + I_{Dsub2}) = J_{DB}(A_{DB2} + m A_{Dsub2}). \quad (6)$$

Given the aforementioned junction areas for junction isolation, the ratio

$$\frac{I_{Doff}(JI)}{I_{Soff}(JI)} = \frac{8(A_{DB1} + m A_{Dsub1})}{A_{DB2} + m A_{Dsub2}} \quad (7)$$

remains a constant value of 6.2 regardless of the value of m. For dielectric isolation, the leakage $I_{Dsub} = 0$, so the ratio

$$\frac{I_{Doff}(DI)}{I_{Soff}(DI)} = \frac{8(A_{DB1})}{A_{DB2}} \quad (8)$$

equals 5.5 regardless of the value of m.

By eliminating I_{Dsub} using dielectric isolation, the reduction in leakage at room temperature is determined by the ratios

$$\frac{I_{Doff}(JI)}{I_{Doff}(DI)} = \frac{A_{DB1} + m A_{Dsub1}}{A_{DB1}} \quad (9)$$

$$\frac{I_{Soff}(JI)}{I_{Soff}(DI)} = \frac{A_{DB2} + m A_{Dsub2}}{A_{DB2}}. \quad (10)$$

Equations (9) and (10) assume that material lifetime is unaffected by DI processing, i.e., $\tau_{DB}(JI) = \tau_{DB}(DI)$. With DI, the expected reduction in room temperature leakage when $2 \leq m \leq 5$ ranges from a factor of 8 to 17 (see Fig. 11(a)).

At elevated temperatures, leakage due to diffusion current from the neutral regions becomes significant [7]. Referring to the basic wide-base diode equation, the saturated leakage per unit area J_{sat} can be expressed as

$$J_{sat} = \frac{qn_i^2}{N_{epi}} \sqrt{\frac{D}{\tau}} \quad (11)$$

where N_{epi} is the concentration of the epi and D is the hole diffusivity in the n-type epi. Contrasted with the linear dependence of J_{GEN} on n_i, J_{sat} is proportional to n_i^2, becoming dominant at high temperatures despite its low magnitude at room temperature. At elevated temperatures, the ratio of the drain-to-substrate diode leakage current I_{Dsub} to the drain-to-body leakage I_{DB} is given by

$$\frac{I_{Dsub}}{I_{DB}} = \frac{A_{Dsub}}{A_{DB}} \sqrt{\frac{\tau_{DB}}{\tau_{Dsub}}} = \frac{A_{Dsub}}{A_{DB}} \sqrt{m}. \quad (12)$$

Because of this square root dependence on lifetime, the difference in leakage/unit area between the drain-to-substrate and drain-to-body diodes is not as great as at room temperature. Consequently, at elevated temperatures, less improvement can be expected by eliminating the drain-to-substrate diode with dielectric isolation.

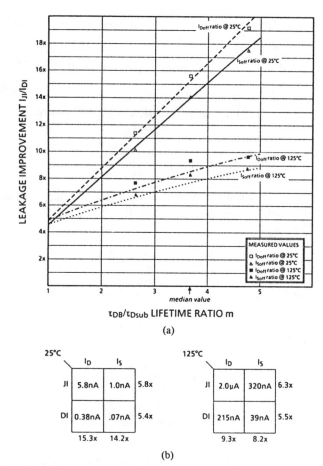

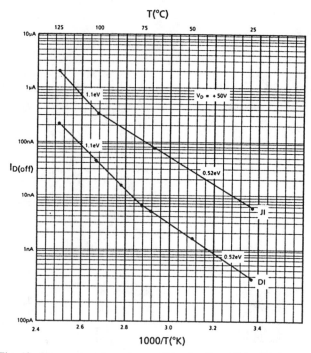

Fig. 12. Temperature dependence of I_{Doff} for *JI* and *DI* multiplexers.

Fig. 11. Multiplexer I_{Doff} and I_{Soff} at 25 and 125°C. (a) Measured versus theoretical values of I_{JI}/I_{DI} ratios. (b) Median values of sampled data, I_D/I_{Soff} and I_{JI}/I_{DI} ratios.

Provided both diodes are reverse biased at the same voltage, the total leakage I_t for devices $M1$ and $M2$ is now expressed as

$$I_{t1} = I_{DB1} + I_{Dsub1} = J_{DB}(A_{DB1} + \sqrt{m} \, A_{Dsub1}) \quad (13)$$

$$I_{t2} = I_{D21} + I_{Dsub2} = J_{DB}(A_{DB1} + \sqrt{m} \, A_{Dsub2}) \quad (14)$$

Though the ratio of I_{Doff} to I_{Soff} remains the same as before for both *JI* and *DI* cases, the *JI/DI* leakage ratios become

$$\frac{I_{Doff}(JI)}{I_{Doff}(DI)} = \frac{A_{DB1} + \sqrt{m} \, A_{Dsub1}}{A_{DB1}} \quad (15)$$

$$\frac{I_{Soff}(JI)}{I_{Soff}(DI)} = \frac{A_{DB2} + \sqrt{m} \, A_{Dsub2}}{A_{DB2}}. \quad (16)$$

For values of m between 2 and 5, the expected reduction in leakage at elevated temperatures using *DI* ranges from a factor of 4.5 to 9 (see Fig. 11(a)).

Median values of I_{Doff} and I_{Soff} measured on the test runs at 25 and 125°C are also shown in Fig. 11(b) for both *JI* and *DI* versions of the high-voltage multiplexer. At both temperatures, the ratio of I_{Doff} to I_{Soff}, shown at the right of each square, closely corresponds to the aforementioned value of 6.2 for junction isolation and of 5.3 for dielectric isolation. At room temperature, the measured *JI/DI* improvement ratios are in reasonable agreement with the

predicted values of 16.7 for I_{Doff} and 14.3 for I_{Soff} when $m \cong 3.7$. Likewise, the improvement with dielectric isolation at 125°C agrees closely with the theoretical values of 8.9 for I_{Doff} and 8.0 for I_{Soff}. The close agreement between theoretical and measured values of leakage confirms the assumption that $\tau_{DB}(JI) = \tau_{DB}(DI)$, suggesting *DI* processing does not necessarily degrade material lifetime.

A plot of I_{Doff} leakage versus reciprocal absolute temperature (see Fig. 12) clearly indicates a change in slope from 0.52 eV at room temperature to a slope of 1.1 eV at elevated temperatures. The slope of this curve represents the activation energy associated with a particular leakage mechanism [8]. The change in slope from an activation energy equal to half the bandgap of silicon $E_g/2$ at room temperature to a slope of E_g at elevated temperatures indicates a corresponding transition from space-charge-region-dominated device leakage to a regime where diffusion current from the neutral region dominates.

Perhaps the most important conclusion from these measurements is that *DI* structures can be significantly better in leakage current than *JI* devices. In addition, a significant reduction in the range (variability) of leakage currents was observed.

VII. Conclusion

The successful implementation of an 8-channel monolithic high-voltage multiplexer compatible with junction-isolated and dielectrically isolated process technologies has been demonstrated. A model predicting an order of magnitude reduction in multiplexer leakage currents using dielectric isolation has been developed and experimentally verified over temperature. In high-voltage testers, dielectrically isolated multiplexers offer low leakage and high accuracy required by critical channels where less costly junction-isolated devices will not suffice.

ACKNOWLEDGMENT

The authors wish to express their gratitude to R. Blanchard for his technical guidance in the multiplexer development and to P. Shackle for his valuable review of this paper. The authors would also like to thank T. Tran for her extensive characterization of both *JI* and *DI* multiplexers and S. Diehl for her valuable assistance in the preparation of this paper.

REFERENCES

[1] L. T. Sevilla, J. D. Plummer, P. F. McCarthy, and J. Sherman, "A high-voltage monolithic multiplexer for use in vehicle tester applications," *GOMAC Dig. Papers*, pp. 405–408, Nov. 1985.

[2] R. A. Blanchard, "Power control with integrated CMOS logic and DMOS output," *Siliconix MOSPOWER Applications Handbook*, pp. 2-43–2-48, 1984.

[3] J. A. Appels and H. M. J. Vaes, "High voltage thin layer devices (RESURF devices)," in *IEDM Tech. Dig.*, pp. 238–241, 1979.

[4] H. W. Becke, "Approaches to isolation in high voltage integrated circuits," in *IEDM Tech. Dig.*, pp. 724–727, 1985.

[5] "Data for DG568," in *Siliconix Integrated Circuits Data Book*, pp. 2-240-2-248.

[6] R. S. Muller and T. I. Kamins, *Device Electronics for Integrated Circuits*. New York: Wiley, 1977, pp. 174–177.

[7] A. Bar-Lev, *Semiconductors and Electronic Devices*. London: Prentice Hall, 1979, pp. 115–119.

[8] K. L. Wang, A. H. Shah, H. Shichijo, C. Gosmeyer, and P. K. Chatterjee, "A subthreshold load element for high density static RAM," in *IEDM Tech. Dig.*, pp. 628–631, 1982.

Part IV
Smart Power Devices

THE term "smart power devices" has been coined to describe the integration of analog and/or digital circuitry with a discrete device. The discrete device can be either a bipolar device or an MOS controlled device such as a MOSFET or MOS-IGT. In some cases, multiple high voltage devices may be included on the same chip.

Early examples of this type of integration effort were aimed at simplifying the ability to control the power device. A prime case in point is the monolithic Darlington transistor, where several stages of bipolar transistors are connected in a cascade configuration in order to increase the current gain and reduce the input gate drive current. These types of bipolar transistors are available with breakdown voltages over 500 volts and current ratings of several hundred amperes.

With the advent of power MOS technology, it was apparent that an even higher input impedance was achievable. However, the large on-resistance of high voltage power MOSFETs was found to severely limit their power handling capability. An obvious solution to this problem was to use a Darlington configuration with the power MOSFET driving a bipolar transistor. In this circuit, the bipolar transistor was used to carry the output current while the MOSFET provided the desired high input impedance. The problem with this approach is the complex process technology and the inefficient silicon area utilized by the MOSFET section on the chip. Further, all the problems previously encountered with the bipolar transistor with regard to paralleling and second breakdown continue to occur. Despite these shortcomings, this approach is still being advocated by several companies. It is believed that this technology will be superseded by the development of the power MOS-IGT which has a high input impedance and much greater power handling capability.

In recent years, the term smart power has been directed at discrete devices that contain analog and logic circuitry. The low voltage circuitry is used to perform over-voltage, over-temperature, and over-current sensing. In addition, the circuitry is used to shut down the operation of the device if any of the above parameters exceed a specified limit. The ability to perform the sensing and feedback locally on the chip greatly improves the response time. This creates the opportunity to make the devices virtually indestructible and immune from inadvertant misuse in power circuits.

An important new category of smart power devices are those being developed for use in automotive electronics. With the recognition that a large cost and productivity improvement can be obtained by reducing the wiring harness in cars, multiplexed power control systems have become attractive. The implementation of such systems requires the availability of smart switches that can be distributed throughout the automobile to actuate loads such as lamps, and to run motors when commanded by the central computer. The smart switch must not only protect itself against adverse circuit conditions but has to be capable of communicating with the central computer. The smart power chip must perform encode and decode functions. It must recognize incoming actuation signals from the central computer and be able to send back information on the status of the load. This ability automatically provides a powerful diagnostic capability which is of value to the consumer.

This part on smart power devices contains five papers. The first paper describes the monolithic integration of a bipolar transistor with two power MOSFETs. The bipolar transistor is used as the output stage to obtain a high current handling capability. One of the MOSFETs is used to provide the base drive current, while the other MOSFET is used across the emitter-base junction to speed up the device turn-off. A composite device capable of operating at 500 volts and 10 amperes has been fabricated. Although this device provides a high input impedance MOS gate and better current handling capability than the MOSFET, its performance lies between that of the bipolar transistor and the power MOSFET. Its performance has been superseded by the insulated gate transistor described in the following paper. By merging the MOS gate structure with an internal bipolar current conduction path, the IGT exhibits the high input impedance of the MOSFET and five times the current handling capability of the bipolar transistor. Devices capable of handling up to 1800 volts and 50 amperes have been developed with this structure.

The next three papers deal with chips that combine logic and analog circuitry with a vertical power device. The first of these papers, by Wrathall, describes a solid state switch for automotive applications. This type of device has also been called the high side switch because it is connected to the high voltage rail in the system. The on-board circuit must perform many important functions. It allows for thermal shutdown, current limiting, and the encode/decode interface with the multiplexing network. The power device is a 50 volt vertical DMOSFET. A similar technology called multipower BCD is the topic of the paper by Andreini et al. In this case a buried layer technology is used with a lightly doped substrate to allow the integration of multiple power DMOSFETs on a single chip. A 60 volt H-bridge circuit has been fabricated. The final paper in this part describes a chip in which control circuitry is combined with an MOS gated thyristor. The on-board circuitry is used to perform over-voltage and over-temperature sensing. Under these adverse conditions, a signal is applied to the MOS gate of the thyristor to trigger it into the latched state. This allows the detection of a fault condition and the removal of power from the load before damage can occur.

REPRINT PAPERS

[1] T. Tanaka, Y. Yasuda, and M. Ohayashi, "A New MOS-Gate Bipolar Transistor for Power Switches," *IEEE Trans. Electron Devices,* vol. ED-33, pp. 2041–2045, 1986.

[2] B. J. Baliga, M. S. Adler, R. P. Love, P. V. Gray, and N. D. Zommer,

"The Insulated Gate Transistor: A New Three Terminal MOS Controlled Bipolar Power Device," *IEEE Trans. Electron Devices,* vol. ED-31, pp. 821–828, 1984.

[3] R. S. Wrathall, "The Design of a High Power Solid State Automotive Switch in CMOS-VDMOS Technology," *IEEE Power Electronics Specialists Conference Digest,* pp. 229–233, 1985.

[4] A. Andreini, C. Contiero, and P. Galbiati, "A New Integrated Silicon Gate Technology Combining Bipolar Linear, CMOS Logic, and DMOS Power Parts," *IEEE Trans. Electron Devices,* vol. ED-33, pp. 2025–2030, 1986.

[5] D. Zaremba and J. Mansmann, "Power Integrated Circuit Makes Board Level Overvoltage and Overtemperature Protection Simple and Inexpensive," *Power Conversion International Magazine,* pp. 14–20, 1985.

A New MOS-Gate Bipolar Transistor for Power Switches

TOMOYUKI TANAKA, YASUMICHI YASUDA, AND MASAYUKI OHAYASHI

Abstract—A new monolithic integrated power device, the MOS-gate transistor (MGT), which consists of a bipolar transistor for an output stage and two MOSFET's for a driver stage, has been investigated. The purpose of the study was to obtain a power switch having characteristics of an easy drive, a short turn-off time, and a high current density. The developed device structure featured the integration of three elements into a small cell from a large number of which the MGT chip was constructed. This device had no parasitic thyristor, making it free from the latchup phenomenon. Unit MGT devices with a blocking voltage of 400–500 V were fabricated. A high current density of 90 A/cm^2 at a collector–emitter voltage of 2 V and a short turn-off time of less than 1 μs were obtained. The MGT devices, which contained 36 cells, were fabricated with chip sizes of 5 × 5 mm. They exhibited a blocking voltage of 500 V, on-state voltage of 2.3 V at a current of 10 A, and turn-off time of 0.5 μs at 150°C.

I. INTRODUCTION

IDEAL POWER switching devices should have characteristics of a low on-state voltage, a fast switching speed, and a small gate input power to be supplied by a trigger circuit. In spite of much work to realize such switches, present conventional devices, such as bipolar transistors (BJT's), gate turn-off thyristors (GTO's), and power MOSFET's, do not satisfy the requirements completely. The drawbacks of these devices are a low switching speed and a large input power for the bipolar devices (BJT's, GTO's), and a high on-state voltage for the MOSFET's. Recently, research efforts have turned to combining the bipolar transistor with the MOSFET. Examples include Bi-MOS Darlington [1] and BiMOS parallel [2] configurations, MOS-gate thyristor [3], and insulated gate transistor IGT [4] (or COMFET [5] or bipolar-mode MOSFET [6]). Particular emphasis has been placed on the IGT, which is a functionally integrated device consisting of an n MOSFET and a p-n-p transistor. Its structure is similar to that of the vertical MOSFET, except for an additional emitter that brings about a low on-state voltage. The overcurrent capability of the IGT is limited, however, by the loss of gate control after the turn-on of a parasitic thyristor, although emitter shorting brings about high latchup current capability.

A new bipolar-MOS integrated device MGT that is free of the latchup phenomenon has been proposed in [8]. In this paper, the device structure and operation, its fabri-

Manuscript received April 28, 1986; revised July 31, 1986.
The authors are with the Hitachi Research Laboratory, Hitachi Ltd., 4026 Kujimachi Hitachi Ibaraki 319-12, Japan.
IEEE Log Number 8610817.

cation process, and the resulting electrical characteristics are described.

II. DEVICE STRUCTURE

The MGT (MOS-gated transistor) is not merely a hybrid device [9] that contains one bipolar transistor block and two separate MOSFET blocks, but an integrated device that contains a large number of unit MGT cells, each of which consists of one bipolar transistor and two MOSFET's. The equivalent circuit of the unit MGT is shown in Fig. 1(a). The output stage is the BJT Q_0. The MOSFET's Q_1 and Q_2 serve as the driver of the BJT Q_0. They turn on alternately, according to their gate voltage signals as shown in Fig. 1(b). The MOSFET Q_1 supplies the base current for Q_0 in order to turn on and then maintain on-state.

On the other hand, the MOSFET Q_2 provides a low resistance by-pass between the emitter and the base of Q_0 during the turn-off period T_2. By turning on Q_2, the turning off action of Q_0 is accelerated as a result of shunting a part of the output current through the by-pass Q_2. In addition, the blocking voltage of the MGT becomes equal to the collector–base breakdown voltage BV_{CBO} of Q_0, not to the collector–emitter breakdown voltage BV_{CEO}. This allows a thinner base width than that of the conventional BJT for the same blocking voltage. Consequently, the MGT can be expected to have characteristics of a low on-state voltage, a faster switching speed than the BJT, and a high input impedance equal to the MOSFET.

The basic device structure of the unit MGT is shown in Fig. 2. The BJT Q_0 is formed as an n$^+$-p-n$^-$-n$^+$ vertical transistor having a long emitter stripe. The MOSFET Q_1 has the same structure as a conventional vertical DSA MOSFET in order to withstand high applied voltage. The p-well and n$^+$ source are formed by the same diffusion processes as for the base and the emitter of the Q_0, respectively. The MOSFET Q_2 is formed in the p-base of Q_0 and laid out along the periphery of the emitter stripe of Q_0 in order to avoid current localization during the turn-off period. In the case of the hybrid device, this current localization, which leads the device to destructive failure, occurs at low current. The n$^+$ emitter of Q_0 also serves as a source of Q_2, so that the chip area and resistance of the by-pass between the emitter and the base of Q_0 are minimized. As can be seen in Fig. 2, the MGT contains no parasitic thyristor. The actual device consists of as many

Reprinted from *IEEE Trans. Electron Devices*, vol. ED-33, pp. 2041–2045, Dec. 1986.

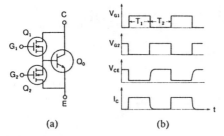

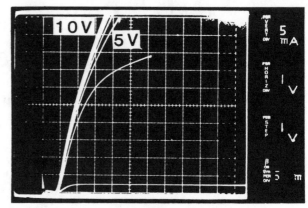

Fig. 1. Equivalent circuit and operational time sequence of the MGT: (a) equivalent circuit; (b) time sequence. The quantities V_{G1}, V_{G2}, V_{CE}, and I_C are gate applied voltages for G_1 and G_2, collector–emitter voltage, and collector current, respectively.

Fig. 3. Static output characteristics of the MGT.

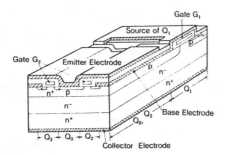

Fig. 2. Cross-sectional view of the unit MGT.

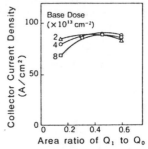

Fig. 4. Conduction current density as a function of the area ratio of Q_1 to Q_0. Gate voltage of Q_1 was 10 V.

units as required from current specifications and termination area.

III. EXPERIMENTS AND DISCUSSION

Samples of the unit MGT were prepared by using fabrication processes similar to those of an n-channel polysilicon gate vertical DSA MOSFET. An n-on-n$^+$ epitaxial silicon wafer having a 15–20-$\Omega \cdot$ cm, 40–45-μm-thick epitaxial layer was used. The wafer was oxidized and polysilicon gate film for Q_1 was deposited. Boron was diffused to form the base layer. The wafer was oxidized again and implanted with boron to adjust the gate threshold voltage of Q_2 to that of Q_1. Polysilicon gate film was deposited again, and phosphorus was diffused to form the emitter layer. After aluminum deposition the device was subsequently overcoated with a CVD layer and the emitter and collector regions were metallized. The thickness of the gate SiO$_2$ films was 150 nm for Q_1 and 45 nm for Q_2. The active area of the devices was 0.038 mm^2, not including the edge termination area. A guard ring structure was used for junction termination in order to realize a high blocking voltage of up to 500 V. In order to determine the best range of device factors, samples of unit MGT's with various area ratios of Q_1 to Q_0 and base acceptor dopings were fabricated.

Fig. 3 shows typical output characteristics of the samples. The gate threshold voltage in this case was about 2 V, for both the MOSFET's Q_1 and Q_2. The MOSFET Q_2 maintained an off-state by shorting the gate G_2 with an emitter. The collector output current increased as the collector–emitter on-state voltage increased when the collector–emitter voltage was larger than about 0.7 V. This offset of collector–emitter voltage was brought about by implementing a Darlington configuration for Q_1 and Q_0. A

gate voltage of 5–10 V was required to attain high conduction.

Fig. 4 shows the relation between the Q_1/Q_0 area ratio and the current density of those samples measured at a collector–emitter voltage of 2 V. The current density increased with increases of the Q_1/Q_0 area ratio and decreased with increases of the base dose at Q_1/Q_0 area ratios less than about 0.4. These facts were interpreted as follows: The current density of the MGT was determined by the base current supplied by Q_1 and the current amplification factor h_{FE} of the BJT Q_0. The drivability of Q_1 depended on the area ratio of Q_1 to Q_0, while the h_{FE} could be controlled by the doping level of the base layer of Q_0.

It can also be seen in Fig. 4 that the current density reached a maximum for a Q_1/Q_0 area ratio of about 0.4, regardless of the base dose, and decreased slowly with increases of the Q_1/Q_0 area ratio for values above that. This decrease of current density was thought to be limited by a reduction of the Q_0 area. The base dose should be determined by considering the effects of turn-off time and gate threshold voltage of Q_1 rather than current density because the maximum value of current density had only a weak dependence on it.

Fig. 5 shows the forward conduction characteristics of the MGT. For comparison, the forward conduction characteristics of a 400-V power MOSFET are also plotted. At room temperature, the current density of the MGT was 90 A/cm^2 for a forward voltage drop of 2 V. This current density was about three times higher than that of the MOSFET and comparable to that of a BJT designed for the same blocking voltage.

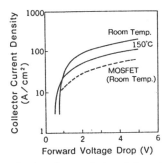

Fig. 5. Forward conduction characteristics of the unit MGT and conventional MOSFET with a blocking voltage of 400 V. Gate voltage of Q_1 was 10 V.

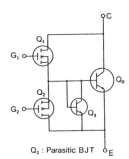

Fig. 6. Equivalent circuit of the unit MGT including the parasitic effect of the MOSFET Q_2.

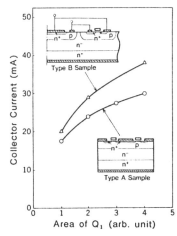

Fig. 7. Collector currents of two unit MGT's as a function of the area of the MOSFET Q_1. Type A corresponded to the standard MGT shown in Fig. 2, while in type B, Q_0 and Q_2 were isolated from each other.

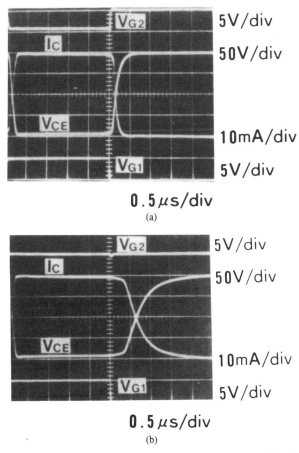

Fig. 8. Turn-off waveforms of the unit MGT: (a) with driving of the MOSFET Q_2; (b) without driving of the MOSFET Q_2. The quantities V_{G1}, V_{G2}, V_{CE}, and I_C are gate voltages for G_1 and G_2, collector–emitter voltage, and collector current, respectively.

It was apparent from Fig. 2 that the BJT Q_0 and the MOSFET Q_2 were not isolated from each other. In this structure, the drain electrode of the MOSFET Q_2 was fabricated in contact with both the well (or base) and drain layers, so that the base and the collector of a parasitic transistor were shorted to each other. Considering the parasitic bipolar effect of the MOSFET Q_2, an equivalent circuit of the MGT is drawn in Fig. 6. The parasitic device Q_3 was a lateral bipolar transistor in which the collector, base, and emitter corresponded to the drain of Q_2, and the base and emitter of Q_0, respectively. The BJT Q_3 turned on when the base current of Q_0 was supplied from Q_1. Then, a part of the base current supplied from Q_1 flowed through Q_3 and did not contribute to the collector current of Q_0. This resulted in degradation of the collector current density. In order to clarify this effect, another type of MGT, type B, in which Q_0 and Q_2 were isolated from each other, were fabricated.

Fig. 7 compares the collector currents of the type A and B samples. The former was the standard MGT shown in Fig. 2. Both samples were formed on the same wafer and possessed same areas for Q_1 and Q_0. Then, the difference between the two curves showed the reduction of collector current by the parasitic effect. The rate of current reduction was about 10–20 percent in Fig. 7, and was thought to become smaller by lengthening the gate of Q_2. By the way, the current density of the type B sample was smaller than that of type A because the isolated structure required extra chip area.

Switching characteristics of the sample MGT's were measured with a resistive load and 200-V dc collector voltage. The collector current was selected so that the cur-rent density became 95 A/cm². The turn-on time t_{on} of the sample was less than 0.3 μs for temperatures from 25 to 150°C. Fig. 8 shows typical waveforms of the sample MGT with and without driving of the Q_2. The turn-off time t_{off} of the MGT with Q_2 driving was 0.3 μs, whereas that without Q_2 driving was 1.5 μs. This showed clearly that Q_2 was effective in speeding up device turn-off ac-

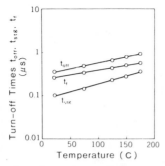

Fig. 9. Temperature dependence of turn-off time t_{off}, storage time t_{stg} and fall time t_f of the MGT with blocking voltage of 400 V. Gate voltage was 5 V for both G_1 and G_2. Collector current density during the on-state was 95 A/cm^2.

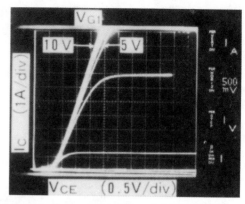

Fig. 11. Static output characteristics of an MGT.

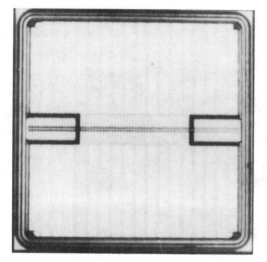

Fig. 10. Photograph of the MGT with chip sizes of 5 × 5 mm.

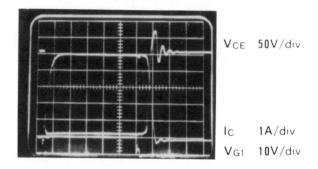

0.5 μs/div

Fig. 12. Switching waveforms of the MGT with blocking voltage of 500 V at 150°C.

tion. The temperature dependence of turn-off times of the MGT is shown in Fig. 9. Turn-off time t_{off} of the MGT was less than 0.8 μs even at 150°C.

IV. 500-V 10-A DEVICE

The MGT devices were designed with chip sizes of 5 × 5 mm and fabricated by using the techniques described earlier. The active area of the device was 19 mm^2. Fig. 10 shows a photograph of it. It contained 36 unit cells, as seen in the photograph of Fig. 10, and exhibited blocking voltages ranging up to 500 V.

Fig. 11 shows the static output characteristics of the device. The gate threshold voltage was about 2 V both for the MOSFET Q_1 and Q_2. With a gate voltage of 10 V, the collector current of the MGT device was 10 A at the collector–emitter voltage of 2.3 V. The collector current density of this device corresponded, however, to about half of that obtained for the unit MGT. The reason for the poor current density was thought to be due to not optimizing the ratio of Q_1 to Q_0.

Fig. 12 shows the switching waveforms of the device measured with a resistive load. The MGT device could turn off within about 0.5 μs even at 150°C.

Fig. 13 shows the relation between turn-off time and

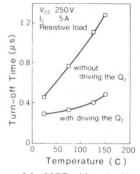

Fig. 13. Turn-off time of the MGT with and without driving of the MOSFET Q_2 as a function of temperature.

TABLE I
ELECTRICAL CHARACTERISTICS OF THE MGT

Item	Value
Blocking Voltage	500 V (25 C)
Current Capability	7.5 A (25 C, V_{CE} = 2 V)
Gate Threshold Voltage	2 V (25 C)
Turn-on Time	0.2 μs (125 C)
Turn-off Time	0.5 μs (125 C)
Device Active Area	19 mm^2

temperature of the MGT with and without driving of the Q_2. The higher the temperature rose, the larger the difference between turn-off times in the two cases shown. These device characteristics are summarized in Table I.

V. CONCLUSION

A new MOS-gate transistor (MGT) that integrates one bipolar transistor for the output stage and two MOSFET's for the driver on a silicon wafer was proposed. Basic characteristics of the MGT were revealed through experimental studies using the unit MGT with a blocking voltage of 400 V. It was confirmed that the MGT had a high current density equal to a BJT and a shorter turn-off time than a BJT designed for the same blocking voltage. These characteristics were brought about by turning on the MOSFET Q_2 connected between the emitter and the base of the BJT Q_0 during the turn-off period. 500-V 10-A MGT devices were fabricated and found to exhibit excellent characteristics. The MGT can be used for an output stage in power IC's as well as for discrete power switches.

ACKNOWLEDGMENT

The authors wish to thank S. Sakamoto, K. Nagata, K. Miyata, and T. Yatsuo for their useful discussions. They also wish to thank Dr. T. Sasaki, Dr. T. Takasuna, Dr. Y. Kawamoto, and Dr. M. Okamura for their encouragement through this work.

REFERENCES

[1] G. R. David et al., "A new VMOS/bipolar Darlington transistor for power applications," in *IEDM Tech. Dig.*, pp. 83–86, 1980.
[2] N. Zommer, "The monolithic HV BIPMOS," in *IEDM Tech. Dig.*, pp. 263–266, 1981.
[3] J. D. Plummer and B. W. Scharf, "Insulated-gate planar thyristor: I—Structure and basic operation," *IEEE Trans. Electron Devices*, vol. ED-27, pp. 380–387, 1980.
[4] M. F. Chang and G. C. Pifer, "25 amp, 500 volt insulated gate transistors," in *IEDM Tech. Dig.*, pp. 83–86, 1983.
[5] A. M. Goodman et al., "Improved COMFET's with fast switching speed and high-current capability," in *IEDM Tech. Dig.*, pp. 79–82, 1983.
[6] A. Nakagawa et al., "High voltage bipolar-mode MOSFET with high current capability," in *Extended Abstracts 16th Conf. Solid State Devices and Materials* (Kobe, Japan), pp. 309–312, 1984.
[7] H. Yilmaz et al., "Insulated gate transistor modeling and optimization," in *IEDM Tech. Dig.*, pp. 274–277, 1984.
[8] T. Tanaka et al., "A new MOS-gate bipolar transistor with fast switching speed and high current capability," in *Extended Abstracts 17th Conf. Solid State Devices and Materials* (Tokyo), pp. 389–392, 1985.
[9] M. S. Adler et al., "The evolution of power device technology," *IEEE Trans. Electron Devices*, vol. ED-31, no. 11, pp. 1570–1590, Nov. 1984.

The Insulated Gate Transistor: A New Three-Terminal MOS-Controlled Bipolar Power Device

B. JAYANT BALIGA, FELLOW, IEEE, MICHAEL S. ADLER, SENIOR MEMBER, IEEE, ROBERT P. LOVE, MEMBER, IEEE, PETER V. GRAY, MEMBER, IEEE, AND NATHAN D. ZOMMER, MEMBER, IEEE

Abstract—A new three-terminal power device, called the insulated gate transistor (IGT), with voltage-controlled output characteristics is described. In this device, the best features of the existing families of bipolar devices and power MOSFET's are combined to achieve optimal device characteristics for low-frequency power-control applications. Devices with 600-V blocking capability fabricated using a vertical DMOS process exhibit 20 times the conduction current density of an equivalent power MOSFET and five times that of an equivalent bipolar transistor operating at a current gain of 10. Typical gate turn-off times have been measured to range from 10 to 50 μs.

INTRODUCTION

THE IDEAL semiconductor device for power switching applications should exhibit a low forward voltage drop in order to keep the forward conduction losses small and a high turn-on/turn-off speed in order to keep the switching losses small. In addition, the device should operate at high current density in order to minimize the size of the chip (and hence the cost required) for any desired current handling capability. The gate drive power requirements for the ideal devices should also be low. For applications that do not require gate turn-off capability, the thyristor has been extensively used because of its high current density of operation even when designed for handling high operating voltages. However, these devices require reversal in the collector potential to achieve turn off. Consequently, for gate turn-off applications, the power bipolar transistor has been extensively used. These devices are capable of high switching speeds but have the disadvantage of requiring high base drive current both during the on state and during turn off. Other competitive devices that have been developed for gate turn-off applications are the gate turn-off thyristor (GTO), the field-controlled thyristor (FCT), the power MOSFET, and the power JFET. The physics of the operation of these devices has been recently reviewed [1]. The GTO and the FCT have the advantage of operating at higher current densities than the bipolar transistor but operate at lower switching speeds and require very high gate turn-off currents. In contrast, the power MOSFET and JFET are capable of very high switching speeds and require low gate drive currents. However, these devices operate at much lower current densities than the

Manuscript received August 16, 1983; revised February 3, 1984.
B. J. Baliga, M. S. Adler, R. P. Love, and P. V. Gray are with the General Electric Co., Corporate Research and Development Center, Schenectady, NY 12345.
N. D. Zommer was with Intersil, Inc., Cupertino, CA.

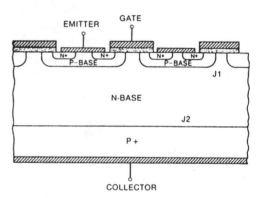

Fig. 1. Cross section of basic IGT structure.

bipolar transistor. A more detailed comparison of the electrical characteristics of these devices has been recently published [2]. Thus it can be seen that all of the power devices developed in the past have had some deficiencies when compared with the ideal device requirements. The insulated gate transistor (IGT) is a new power semiconductor device whose electrical characteristics approach those desired in an ideal switch. This paper discusses the device structure and operation, its fabrication process and the resulting electrical characteristics. Similar devices have been previously discussed in [7] and [8].

IGT STRUCTURE

The basic structure of the IGT is shown in cross section in Fig. 1. In this structure, current flow will be blocked when negative biases are applied to the collector with respect to the emitter because the lower junction, J2, will become reverse biased. This provides the device with its reverse blocking capability. When positive voltages are applied to the collector with the gate shorted to the emitter, the upper junction, J1, becomes reverse biased and the device operates in its forward blocking mode. However, if a positive gate bias is applied of sufficient magnitude to invert the surface of the p-base region under the gate, the device switches to its forward conducting state because electrons can now flow from the emitter n+ region to the n-base region. In this forward conducting state, the junction J2 is forward biased and the collector p+ region injects holes into the n-base region. As the collector forward bias is increased, the injected hole concentration increases until it exceeds the background doping level of the n-base. In this regime of operation, the device operates like a forward-

Reprinted from *IEEE Trans. Electron Devices*, vol. ED-31, pp. 821–828, June 1984.

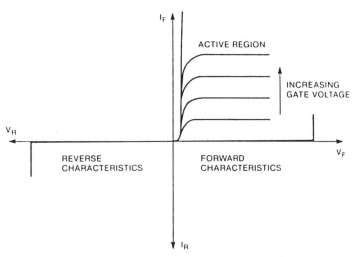

Fig. 2. Electrical output characteristics of the IGT.

biased p-i-n diode with heavy conductivity modulation of the n-base region. This results in the operation of these devices at high current densities even when designed for operation at high blocking voltages. As long as the gate bias is sufficiently large to produce enough inversion layer charge for providing electrons to the n-base region, the IGT forward conduction characteristics will thus look like those of a p-i-n diode. However, if the inversion layer conductivity is low, a significant voltage drop will begin to appear across this region like that observed in conventional MOSFET's. At this point, the forward current will saturate and the device will be operating in its active region. The composite electrical characteristics predicted on the basis of the above operating mechanisms are shown in Fig. 2.

In order to switch the IGT from its on state to the off state, it is necessary to switch the gate bias off by shorting the gate to the emitter. This operation will remove the inversion region at the surface of the p-base under the gate and thus shut off the supply of electrons to the n-base. This initiates the turn-off process. The electron concentration in the n-base at junction J2 is large at the beginning of the turn-off process. As a result of this, significant electron injection into the p+ collector region will occur while a corresponding hole current will flow into the p-base. As the electron concentration drops, the electron injection into the p+ collector will also decrease, leaving a plasma of electrons and holes in the n-base which must decay by recombination. The turn-off process is, therefore, expected to contain two phases: the first phase in which the collector current will fall rapidly and a second phase in which the current will decay exponentially with time forming a tail in the collector current waveform.

From the above description of IGT operation, it can be seen that this device will operate at high current densities in the forward conduction mode and also exhibit gate turn-off capability. In addition, the device requires very low gate drive power since only small gate capacitance charging and discharging currents are required. This device thus exhibits electrical characteristics that approach those of the ideal switch.

It is worth pointing out that the IGT structure shown in Fig. 1 contains a parasitic p-n-p-n thyristor structure between the collector and the emitter terminals. If this thyristor latches

on, the current can no longer be controlled by the MOS gate. Consequently, it is important to design the device in such a manner that this thyristor action will be suppressed. This can be achieved by preventing the injection of electrons from the n+ emitter region into the p-base during device operation. Since the n+ emitter region will begin to inject electrons into the p-base if the n+-p junction becomes forward biased by more than 0.7 V due to any lateral current flow in the p-base, the injection can be suppressed by designing narrow n+ emitter regions and by keeping the p-base sheet resistance low.

DEVICE MODELING

Exact numerical modeling can be a valuable tool when analyzing new device types such as the IGT. It provides insights as to the basic physics of device operation, which for a new device type as complex as the IGT is extremely helpful. It can also be used to anticipate problems which one might encounter during development as well as providing an accurate quantitative prediction of the device characteristics. In the case of the IGT, this was important since the size of the reduction of the on-resistance was the major factor motivating the device development. In addition to doing this, the exact numerical model greatly helped in the initial device design by pointing out a potential problem associated with latchup of the parasitic thyristor structure.

Fig. 3 shows the result of a calculation on the structure shown in the inset. The gate voltage used is 15 V and the collector-to-emitter voltage is 1.25 V. In this figure the electron concentration is shown as a function of the x and y space coordinates. One can see the high electron concentration in the n+ emitter region with the considerably lower concentration in the p-channel directly below the n+ region (in the +y direction). One can also see the high electron concentration in the inverted surface channel as well as the accumulated surface under the gate where the n-region comes to the surface. In the bulk of the device, the electron concentration drops off slowly and abruptly drops to a very low value in the p+ collector region. Fig. 4 shows the results of a calculation performed on the same device structure with the collector voltage increased to 1.5 V. One can see dramatic differences in the modulation level in the n-region between the two and the cur-

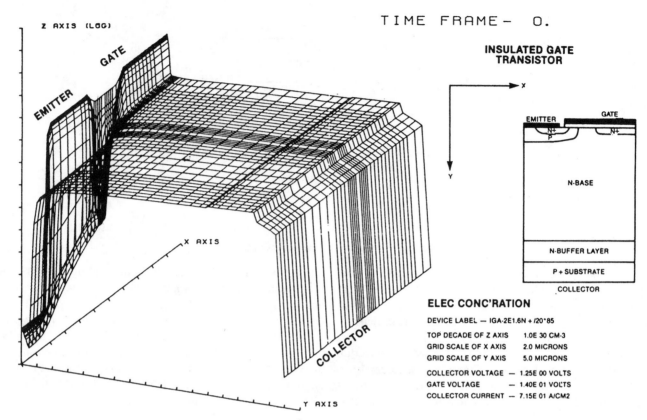

Fig. 3. Distribution of the electron concentration in the IGT structure at a forward drop of 1.25 V.

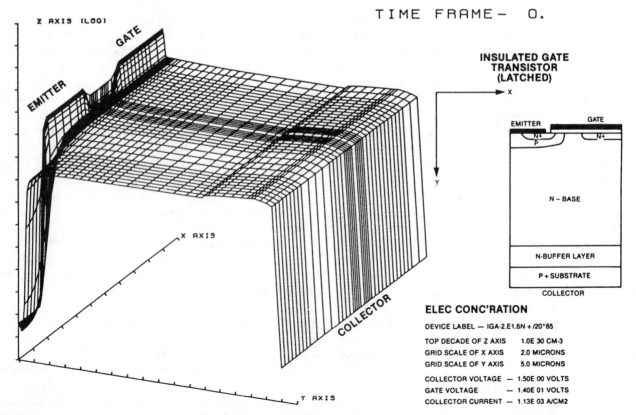

Fig. 4. Distribution of the electron concentration in the IGT structure at a forward drop of 1.5 V.

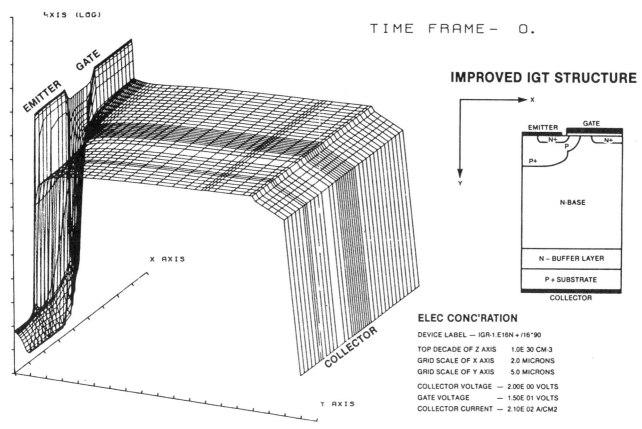

Fig. 5. Distribution of the electron concentration in the improved IGT structure (containing a p+ region in the p-base) at a forward drop of 2.0 V.

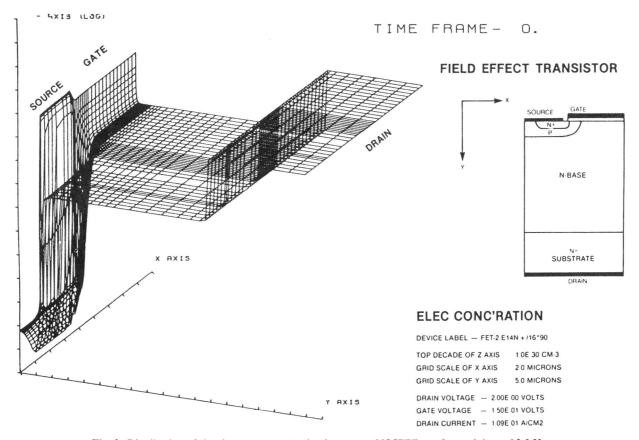

Fig. 6. Distribution of the electron concentration in a power MOSFET at a forward drop of 2.0 V.

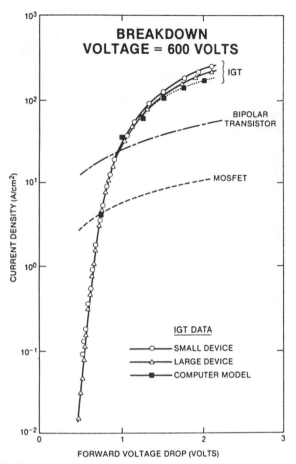

Fig. 7. Comparison of the forward current density of the IGT with the bipolar transistor and the power MOSFET.

The solution to this is either to reduce the length of the path from the edge of the outer p-region to the short or to increase the conductivity of this region, with the goal of both techniques being to reduce the lateral voltage drop below 0.5 V. One solution to increase the p-base conductivity without increasing the gate turn-on threshold voltage is by the addition of a deep p+ region as shown in Fig. 5. When this structure is modeled, Fig. 5 shows that even when the collector voltage is 2 V, the electron concentration in the channel region is well below that in Fig. 3. The modeling has shown that the presence of the deep p+ region allows device operation at collector current densities in excess of 200 A/cm² without latchup.

The modeling can also be used to obtain a comparison between the IGT and a 600-V MOSFET. The results of modeling the MOSFET are shown in Fig. 6. In this case, the p+ collector region is replaced with an n+ drain region, and it can be seen that there is no modulation of the n– region compared to that found in Fig. 5. As a result of this, the MOSFET operates at a current density which is 19 times lower than the IGT at a forward voltage drop of 2 V. A detailed comparison of the forward conduction *I–V* characteristics is provided in Fig. 7 which shows the forward conduction characteristics for the IGT, MOSFET and bipolar transistor devices. As can be seen, the IGT has considerably higher current handling capabilities than these devices for forward voltage drops greater than 1 V.

DEVICE DESIGN AND FABRICATION

Insulated gate transistor dies were designed with die sizes of 60 × 60 mils and 130 × 130 mils. Both devices were included on the same mask set to allow simultaneous fabrication. The devices had a three-guard-ring termination design intended to produce 600-V blocking capability.

The fabrication techniques necessary to produce IGT devices must satisfy the combined requirements of bipolar and MOSFET device processing. The minority carrier lifetime must be high enough to ensure good conductivity modulation of the lightly doped n-region during conduction and high-quality MOS gate oxide must be grown and preserved throughout the fabrication cycles. The device fabrication started with the growth of a two-step n-type phosphorus-doped epitaxial layer on p+ boron-doped (0.01 Ω · cm) (111) orientated substrates. The epitaxial layers were grown using silicon tetrachloride in a carefully calibrated induction-heated chemical vapor deposition system. The doping levels in the epitaxial layers were controlled to within ± 10 percent and thickness variations of less than ± 10 percent were obtained. The lightly doped n-type layer is the central region of the IGT and is fully depleted when the device is supporting voltage. The n-buffer layer prevents punch through of the depletion region to the p+ substrate. The doping level in this buffer layer can not be allowed to become too high because the injection efficiency of the p+-n junction during conduction will be badly degraded. For epitaxial growth the temperature was slowly ramped in the epitaxial growth process to prevent the formation of slip lines and to ensure that high-quality flat surfaces were produced with a total focal plane deviation of less than 8 µm. To

rent density is 1130 A/cm² at 1.5 V compared to 71.5 A/cm² at 1.25 V. One can also see that the electron modulation level no longer drops off quickly in the p-channel region adjacent to the n+ emitter as it did in Fig. 3. This indicates that with the increased forward applied voltage the device has become latched into a thyristor-like conducting state. This is caused by the high level of lateral hole current from the edge of the p-base to the short between the n+ region and p-base. The p-base collects all of the hole current injected from the collector that reaches the emitter side of the device, and, because of the extreme current densities (>1000 A/cm³) involved in this lateral current flow, a 0.7-V drop is developed between the outer and the inner edge of the p-base adjacent to the n+ emitter region. This is sufficient to cause electron injection from the n+ emitter region with the result that the structure became latched in spite of the fact that the n+ and p-regions were shorted at one edge of the n+ region. Under these latched conditions, relatively little of the electron current is flowing through the channel region and gate control of the current flow has been lost. The IGT can now be turned off by either reducing the collector current below the holding current of the thyristor section or by reversing the collector potential and commutating the IGT as if it were a thyristor. In this mode, the device is operating like the MOS gated thyristor [4]–[6].

fabricate the IGT devices, a standard polysilicon gate power DMOS process was then utilized.

DEVICE CHARACTERISTICS

The IGT devices were found to exhibit forward blocking voltages ranging up to 650 V. The threshold voltage for turning on the devices was typically +5 V. It was found that a gate bias voltage of +25 V was necessary in order for the devices to conduct higher currents without going into the active region of the output characteristics. A typical set of device output characteristics as observed on a curve tracer are shown in Fig. 8. It can be seen that these characteristics are similar to those anticipated in Fig. 2 based upon the physics of the operation of these devices.

The forward conduction characteristics of the IGT are compared to the modeling data in Fig. 7, where the forward current density has been plotted as a function of the forward voltage drop. To obtain these characteristics, a gate bias voltage of +25 V was used to ensure that the inversion channel drop was minimized. From these data, it can be seen that the IGT devices are operating at a current density of 20 times that of MOSFET's and five times that of bipolar transistors designed for the same operating voltage. This is in excellent agreement with the device analysis.

These devices were also tested for gate turn-off capability. To perform this measurement the device was turned on and off by using a 1–2-μs-wide (25 V) gate pulse while a dc power supply of 50–400 V was connected between the collector and emitter with a series load resistance which determined the collector current prior to gate turn-off. The collector current was indeed observed to be completely controlled by the gate voltage and forced gate turn-off was observed at the maximum rated current of 1 A for the small (60 mil) device and 10 A for the large (130 mils) device for collector voltages ranging from 50 to 400 V. In all cases, the collector current was found to undergo turn-off in two stages as expected based upon the device physics. A typical collector turn-off waveform is shown in Fig. 9. The collector current can be observed to initially fall very rapidly to about half its original value followed by a slow current decay. This tailing in the collector current is due to recombination of the stored charge in the n-base as discussed earlier. Typical gate turn-off times were in the range of 10–40 μs. The dependence of the gate turn-off time upon the collector current and collector voltage was measured and is shown in Figs. 10 and 11, respectively. As illustrated in these figures, the gate turn-off time has been defined as the time taken for the collector current to drop to 10 percent of its forward conduction value from the time at which the gate voltage is reduced from 25 V to zero. This gate turn-off time includes both the storage time and the fall time as usually defined for gate turn-off devices. The storage time of the IGT devices was found to be very short (less than 100 ns) and the turn-off time was determined primarily by the current tailing. It can be seen from Fig. 10 that the turn-off time decreases when the collector current is increased. This is an unusual feature for the IGT's

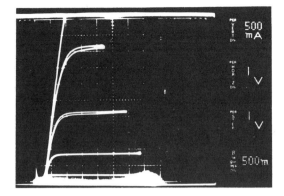

Fig. 8. Typical output characteristics of an IGT device.

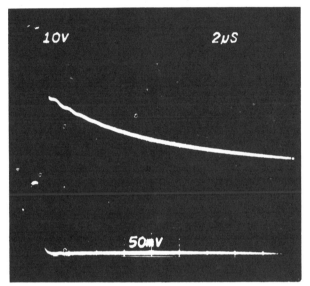

Fig. 9. Gate turn-off waveforms for the 130-mil IGT device. The collector current being turned-off is 10 A (2 A per division) and the collector voltage after turn-off is 400 V.

since other bipolar devices show an increase in turn-off time when the current increases because of the larger concentration of stored charge. In the case of the IGT's, it was found that increasing the collector current results in an increase in the initial drop in the collector current (indicated as ΔI_c in Fig. 10) without significantly increasing the tail in the collector current decay. As explained in an earlier section, the initial drop in the collector current is due to electron injection into the p+ collector region when the electron concentration in the n-base is high. Consequently, when the collector current being turned-off is raised, more electrons are removed during the initial drop in collector current leaving the same amount of trapped charge in the n-base irrespective of the magnitude of the collector current being turned-off. The collector current tailing is thus the same for all collector currents. Since the current tailing determines the turn-off time, raising the collector current being turned-off results in reducing the gate turn-off time in the IGT. In the case of Fig. 11, it can be seen that raising the collector voltage that must be blocked after turn-off causes a slight increase in the gate turn-off time. This is similar to the behavior of other bipolar devices. It is due to the need to

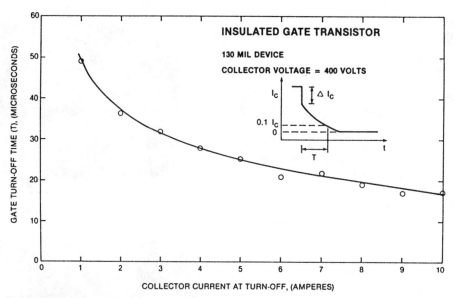

Fig. 10. Dependence of the gate turn-off time upon the collector current at turn-off for the 130-mil device. The collector voltage that must be blocked after turn-off is maintained at 400 V for all the collector currents.

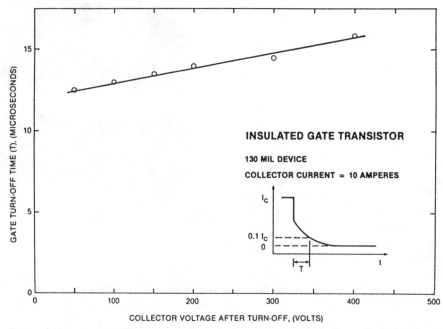

Fig. 11. Dependence of the gate turn-off time upon the collector voltage blocked after turn-off for the 130-mil device. The collector current being turned-off is maintained at 10 A for all the collector voltages.

establish a wider depletion region at higher collector blocking voltages. This requires the removal of more charge from the n-base causing an increase in the turn-off time.

Conclusions

A new power semiconductor switching device called the insulated gate transistor (IGT) has been developed. In this device, the advantages of the high current density of bipolar operation have been combined with the advantages of the high input impedance of MOS gated devices. Devices capable of blocking 600 V have been fabricated using a polysilicon gate DMOS process similar to that used at present to manufacture power MOSFET's. The devices were found to operate at

forward current densities that are 20 times higher than that of the power MOSFET and five times higher than that of the bipolar transistor. In spite of these high operating current densities, the gate turn-off capability is retained. Typical gate turn-off times were found to range between 10 and 50 μs. This slow switching speed will limit the devices to lower frequency applications. However, the devices have the following unique features:

1) forward *and* reverse blocking capability,
2) high forward conduction current density,
3) high impedance MOS gate,
4) low input gate capacitance,

198

5) gate-controlled active region with no negative resistance region,

6) high breakdown voltage devices feasible,

7) normally off device characteristics.

These features make the IGT especially attractive for phase control circuits operating at low frequencies where gate turn-off capability is required.

ACKNOWLEDGMENT

The authors wish to thank Dr. V. A. K. Temple for assistance with device termination design, and N. Waldron and J. Badalucco for manuscript preparation.

REFERENCES

[1] B. J. Baliga, "Silicon power field controlled devices and integrated circuits," in *Silicon Integrated Circuits*, D. Kahng, Ed., Applied Solid State Science Series, Supplement 2B. New York: Academic Press, 1981.

[2] ——, "Switching lots of watts at high speeds," *IEEE Spectrum*, vol. 18, pp. 42-48, 1981.

[3] M. S. Adler and V.A.K. Temple, "The dynamics of the thyristor turn-on process," *IEEE Trans. Electron Devices*, vol. ED-27, pp. 483-494, 1980.

[4] B. J. Baliga, "Enhancement and depletion mode vertical channel MOS gated thyristors," *Electron. Lett.*, vol. 15, pp. 645-647, 1979.

[5] J. Tihaji, "Functional integration of power MOS and bipolar devices," presented at the Int. Electron Devices Meeting, 1980, paper 4.2, pp. 75-78.

[6] J. Plummer and B. W. Scharf, "Insulated gate planar thyristors," *IEEE Trans. Electron Devices*, vol. ED-27, pp. 380-394, 1980.

[7] B. J. Baliga, M. S. Adler, P. V. Gray, R. P. Love, and N. Zommer, "The insulated gate rectifier (IGR): A new power switching device," *IEDM Tech. Dig.* pp. 264-267, 1982.

[8] J. P. Russell, A. M. Goodman, L. A. Goodman, and J. M. Neilson, "The COMFET—A new high conductance MOS-gated device," *IEEE Electron Device Lett.*, vol. EDL-4, pp. 63-65. 1983.

THE DESIGN OF A HIGH POWER SOLID STATE AUTOMOTIVE SWITCH
IN CMOS-VDMOS TECHNOLOGY

Robert S. Wrathall

Motorola, Inc., Semiconductor Research and Development Laboratories
Phoenix, AZ 85008

This paper presents the design of a solid state automotive switch. The design criteria for choosing a VDMOS power device and a charge pump drive circuit are discussed. The performance of the fabricated device is discussed.

OUTLINE OF PROBLEM

This paper details the design of a monolithic solid state automotive power switch. In the first section, the basic electrical and environmental conditions which determine the switch design are outlined. In the second section the specific responses to these requirements are discussed in terms of circuits and technology. Results of the technology and design are also discussed in the second section.

REQUIREMENTS FOR A SOLID STATE AUTOMOTIVE SWITCH

The major electrical constraint on the automotive switch is requirement of a high side switch. This is required for the sake of safety and for increased corrosion resistance. Since the ON/OFF signal is referenced to ground, this demands a level shift between the logic signal and the control electrode on the power device. The level shift imposes several constraints on the switch design.

The under-hood automotive evironment is among the harshest for semicondcutor devices. The temperature range is from -40°C to +125°C. The high end of this temperature range requires low power dissipation in the switch to keep the junction temperature below 150°C. The power limiting function may take the form of a thermal limit or a duty cycle mode. Both can be effective in keeping the junction temperature below the nominal maximum.

Special techniques are required to drive an automotive lamp load. The tungsten filament has a very temperature dependent conduction characteristic. At ambient temperatures its resistivity is a small fraction of the resistivity at operating temperatures. The low resistance allows high currents to flow during turn-on. Typical inrush currents vs. time are shown in Figure 1. Because currents of this magnitude and duration can destroy a semiconductor switch, an integrated current limit is required. This circuit allows the filament to heat slowly until operational temperatures are reached without damaging the semiconductor device or causing premature failure. The current limit also protects the switching device against inadvertent short circuits.

A substantial requirement of the switch is the need to drive an inductive load. In the absence of a freewheeling diode inductive clamp, the switch must be able to dissipate a substantial fraction of the inductive stored energy without destroying the device. A switch which does not require a clamp diode is greatly desired for many applications.

There are several requirements which are unique to the automotive environment. The first are large bipolar transients which exist on the automotive power system. Some of these transients are due to switching noise and other inductive load transients. The condition of "load dump" is a result of disconnecting the battery from the alternator while the alternator is charging the battery. This induces a substantial and long spike on the power buss. A second requirement is the survival of a reversed battery due to inadvertent wrong battery connection.

Last, but not least, the normal operational voltage range is rather large. The switch must operate when the battery voltage is low during cold starts, and it must operate under rapid charging conditions. This range is nominally from 9 to 24 volts. The switch must not lose its state memory over a somewhat broader range.

A SOLID STATE ADAPTATION TO THE
AUTOMOTIVE ENVIRONMENT

During normal operation, the switch must have a low pass voltage and low power dissipation. The forward drop of bipolar devices such as thyristors, Darlington transistors and the newer thyristor-related GEMFET (Gain Enhanced MOS FET) transistors are too large. A single bipolar device will have sufficiently small forward drop, but the power dissipated in the base drive circuit is usually too high. The power dissipation curves of the three devices are shown in Figure 2. Because of power dissipation and forward drop, the obvious choice

Reprinted from *IEEE 16th Power Electronics Specialists Conf.*, pp. 229–233, 1985.

for the power switching device is the vertical DMOS device.

A process can be devised for manufacturing a control circuit in conjunction with a high quality vertical DMOS device (1). The process cross section is shown in Figure 3. This process combines high voltage CMOS with the n channel VDMOS within a single process flow. In fact, within the process, high quality bipolar transistors can also be fabricated. It can be called the universal power BIFET technology. At Motorola it is known as "SMART-power™ II."

The high side switch would be conceptually easiest to implement in a p-channel power FET technology. Two considerations rule out the p-channel device. First, the hole mobility is such that a 3:1 area penalty must be paid to use a p-channel device.

Also, typically, the surface concentration for reasonable thresholds of n-channel devices is substantially higher than the equivalent p-channel device, the n-channel is easier to fabricate. In the planar device technology the surface concentration requirement can be met with a threshold adjust implant. This cannot be readily accomplished with the p-channel DMOS process without severely impacting the epi requirements. Thus, a p-channel process is not forthcoming even if the hole mobility did not dictate an n-channel power DMOS device.

Because of these considerations, the application is forced to use an n-channel switch in a common drain configuration. Since these devices have a low transconductance compared to an equivalent bipolar device, the gate voltage must be raised substantially higher than the Vdd power supply rail to reduce the R_{don} to an acceptable level. This can only be accomplished by the use of a charge pump to supply upwards of 30 volts on chip. This subcircuit diagram is shown in Figure 4.

The current limit circuit is shown in Figure 5. The current limit is accomplished by the insertion of a small resistor in the source of a single cell in the power transistor. If the voltage drop across the resistor is kept small compared to the gate-source and drain-source voltage, it will only slightly perturb the current through the device. The voltage drop across the sense resistor is monitored and kept below a certain predetermined value. This, then, becomes the current limit.

The current limit is implemented with two comparitors with built-in offsets. The schematic of one of the comparitors is seen in Figure 6. Two comparitors are necessary to obtain rail-to-rail operation. The outputs of the comparitors are switched at some mid-range point so that the current limit operates in a continuous fashion as the load voltage changes. The current limit acts on the charge pump in a bang-bang servo loop to limit the current flow in the load device.

A block diagram of the entire circuit is shown in Figure 7. A duty cycle mode is incorporated along with a thermal limit on chip to limit power dissipation. An on-board oscillator is used to power the charge pump and also to facilitate a duty-cycle power reduction scheme. An override inductive protect circuit is included to keep the device out of avalanche. Because of the high voltage on the gate of the power device, a direct short can cause extreme currents to flow, upward of 100 amperes. A fast gate discharge circuit is used to keep the device from immediate destruction under these conditions.

A complete die photograph is seen in Figure 8. Figure 9 shows some of the typical wave forms seen in turning on a tungsten filament. Figure 9a is the wave form of the gate potential during turn-on. The small steps are the result of the operation of the charge pump yielding an overall exponential shape to the curve. Figure 9b shows the action of the fast protection circuit when the load is shorted during normal operation. The current peaks quickly and is discharged into the operation of the normal current limit. Figure 9c shows the action of the current limit into a hard short over a longer period of time. Again, duty cycling reduces power dissipation. Figure 9d shows the operation of the circuit in normal turn-on. The current peaks and the device begins cycling to reduce total power dissipation as the current starts to fall as the filament heats up.

REFERENCES

(1) Proceedings of the IEDM, 1983, "Integrated Circuits for the Control of High Power," R. Wrathall, D. Tam, L. Terry and S. Robb.

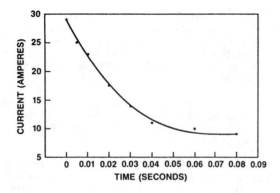

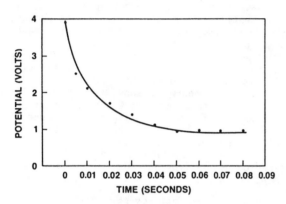

Figure 1.   Plots of the typical in-rush current and the voltage across a typical VDMOS switching device during turn-on of an automotive head lamp load.

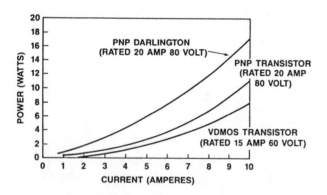

Figure 2.   Total power dissipation of various switching devices during steady state on conditions with a twelve volt power supply. Considered here are an n-channel VDMOS, a PNP and a PNP Darlington transistor.

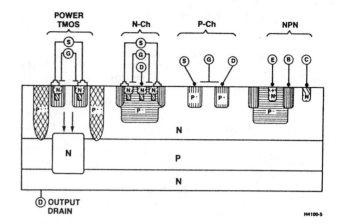

Figure 3.   A schematic process cross section showing the structure of the control CMOS and the power VDMOS devices.

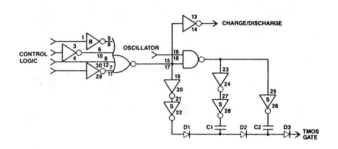

Figure 4.   The schematic representation of the charge pump circuit used to drive the gate of the VDMOS device.

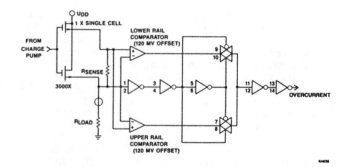

Figure 5.   The schematic representation of the current limit circuit used to sense the current in the main power device.

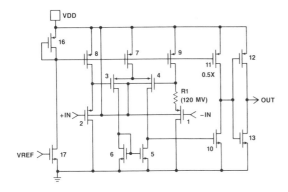

Figure 6. The schematic representation of one of the comparitors used in the current limit circuit.

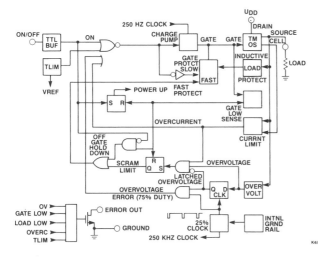

Figure 7. The block diagram of the complete switch circuit showing the major function blocks and protection loops.

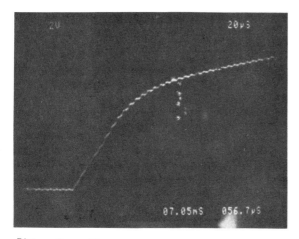

Figure 9a. The voltage wave form on the VDMOS gate during turn on.

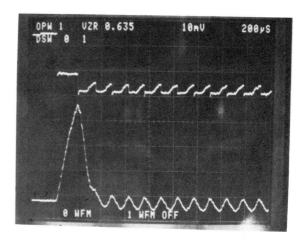

Figure 9b. Current response to a hard short during normal switch operation. The top trace is the diagnostic feedback and the bottom trace is the device current at 5 amperes per division.

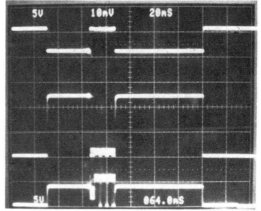

Figure 9c. Extended time response of the switch on a hard short circuit. Notice the start of duty cycling. The upper trace is the diagnostic feedback, the center trace is the load voltage and the lower trace is proportional to current.

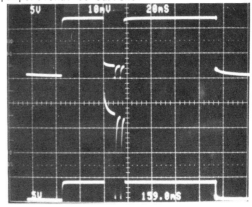

Figure 9d. The wave form of the initial turn-on into an incandescent lamp load. The upper trace is diagnostic feedback and the lower trace is current in 5 amperes per division.

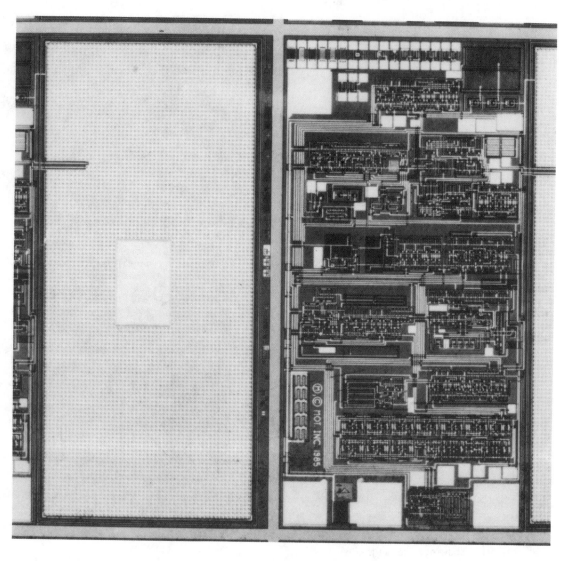

Figure 8. A die photograph of the fabricated chip.

A New Integrated Silicon Gate Technology Combining Bipolar Linear, CMOS Logic, and DMOS Power Parts

ANTONIO ANDREINI, CLAUDIO CONTIERO, AND PAOLA GALBIATI

Abstract—This paper describes a new mixed technology, called Multipower BCD, that, starting from the merging of the VDMOS silicon gate process with the conventional junction isolation process, allows the integration on a single chip of bipolar linear, CMOS logic, and DMOS power functions. The architecture of the process was chosen to optimize the power part, which generally occupies the most chip area. With the DMOS device, many other signal components have been obtained whose electrical and structural characteristics are discussed in relation to some process variables. Many test vehicles have been processed to evaluate the different structures and a first electrical application of the technology is indicated.

I. INTRODUCTION

RAPID ADVANCES in integrated circuit and power technology have created new opportunities to develop integrated circuit families where power and control functions are integrated on the same chip [1]–[5]. To integrate complex systems and subsystems without compromising performance [6]–[8], CMOS devices are the best choice as logic parts because of their high layout density and low power consumption. They also can be utilized for analog functions where very high input impedance is required. Nevertheless, for analog functions bipolar transistors are more suitable because they offer better performances in high gain stages (high transconductance, high output current, and low noise) and in high-precision linear parts (low offset voltage due to high matching in V_{be}).

To put the power in a monolithic system the best way is to use power DMOS devices in place of bipolar power transistors; in fact they exhibit technological compatibility with CMOS silicon gate devices [9], very fast switching speed, no driving power in dc condition, and no secondary breakdown limitation. Thanks to the very high efficiency of power DMOS devices, it is possible to realize chips that deliver very high output powers without high dissipation overcoming the heating effects of high current densities that are the main obstacle to the miniaturization of power switching.

Following these guidelines a new technology called Multipower BCD has been developed. This technology allows the mixing on the same chip of two or more power

MOS devices, isolated from each other, which exhibit high-voltage and high-current capability, together with low-level signal and high-voltage components. The first example of this technology mixing bipolar, CMOS, and DMOS devices has been realized in the range of 60 V as the maximum supply voltage for the power part, obtaining at the same time a broad range of breakdown voltages (from 15 to 90 V) for the different signal components.

To evaluate process feasibility, a test chip has been realized that incorporates four integrated n-channel enhancement power DMOS transistors connected in an H-bridge configuration (the power section) and n-p-n, p-n-p bipolar transistors, CMOS, high-voltage p-channel MOS, Zener diodes, junction and polysilicon resistors, and junction and MOS capacitors as signal and passive components. Finally, this technology has been successfully applied to a commercial product, a switch-mode motor driver.

This work describes the development of this new technology. Section II deals with the process architecture and its main key features. In Section III the signal components structure and electrical characteristics are provided. Section IV gives an insight into the design parameters and the electrical features of the DMOS transistors. Finally, Section V covers the applications of this technology, giving some details about the switch-mode motor driver developed by SGS.

II. DEVICE TECHNOLOGY—PROCESS ARCHITECTURE

The architecture of the Multipower BCD structure is the result of the merging of two well-known technologies: the vertical DMOS silicon gate process and the standard junction isolation technique. The former is the final and winning evolution of the development of a process to obtain power MOS devices; the latter is a well-controlled technique that has been extensively used in integrated bipolar devices and that is less costly to produce compared to the dielectric isolation technique.

The simplest version of this process consists of 10 masking steps: seven from the DMOS process and three from the standard junction isolation technique. With the introduction of some additional masking steps (2 or 3), it is possible to integrate many different structures with minimal disturbance to the basic process.

Manuscript received April 28, 1986; revised July 14, 1986.

The authors are with SGS Microelettronica SpA, Monolithic Microsystem Division, 20019 Settimo Milanese, Milan, Italy.

IEEE Log Number 8610538.

Reprinted from *IEEE Trans. Electron Devices*, vol. ED-33, pp. 2025–2030, Dec. 1986.

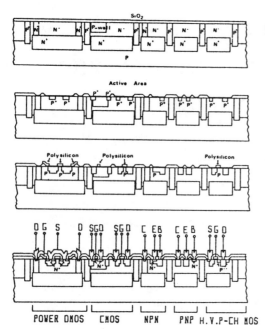

Fig. 1. Cross section illustrating some key processing steps of the 12-mask Multipower BCD process.

The key processing steps, illustrated in Fig. 1, starting from a p-type ⟨100⟩ substrate 2–4 $\Omega \cdot$ cm, are:

a) n^+ buried layer antimony implant and diffusion, R_s = 20 Ω/sq.

b) Epitaxial growth of an n-layer 10 μm thick and 1.3 $\Omega \cdot$ cm.

c) p-well implant to form the body of the CMOS n-channel FET and the base of a first kind of n-p-n transistor (n-p-n-1), R_s = 5 kΩ/sq.

d) Standard bipolar p^+ isolation and n^+ sinker high-temperature diffusion; after this treatment the p-well junction reaches a depth equal to 4.5 μm (Fig. 1(a)).

e) High-doped p^+ implant to form contact regions, lateral p-n-p emitter and collector, and channel stops in the CMOS n-channel FET.

f) Opening of active areas with tapered oxide steps to improve the performances of the high-voltage devices and step coverage.

g) Gate oxidation (t_{ox} = 850 Å) and boron threshold voltage adjustment implant in CMOS structure without any extra mask.

h) Polycrystalline silicon layer deposition and phosphorus doping.

i) Gates, field plates, and interconnections definition.

j) Boron implant and diffusion (600 Ω/sq) to form the DMOS body, the CMOS p-channel FET source and drain, and the base of other two kinds of n-p-n transistor (a standard n-p-n-2 and an optional n-p-n-3).

k) Drain extension boron implant in high-voltage p-channel MOS transistor without any extra mask (Fig. 1(c)).

l) Heavy arsenic ion implant (R_s = 20 Ω/sq) to form contacts, n-p-n-1 and n-p-n-2 emitters, DMOS source, and CMOS n-channel FET source and drain.

m) After a phosphorus-doped silicon-oxide layer de-

position and a gettering step, the whole structure is provided with the conventional next contact opening step, metal deposition, and passivation (Fig. 1(d)).

Adding as an option an extra mask before the gettering step and without modifying the process thermal condition a phosphorus-doped emitter is obtained for the optional n-p-n-3 transistor.

III. SIGNAL COMPONENTS STRUCTURE AND ELECTRICAL CHARACTERISTICS

The proposed 12-masking-step mixed technology (13 masks to form optional n-p-n-3) is centered around the vertical DMOS silicon gate process. Using the dopant profiles introduced in the process it is possible to obtain at the same time many different structures with different electrical characteristics.

A. Bipolar Transistors

The electrical characteristics of the lateral p-n-p transistors are connected to the epitaxial layer resistivity and to the spacing between the p^+ junctions of the emitter and collector. In Fig. 2 and in Table I are given the gain behaviors and the more considerable electrical characteristics with regard to four different window spacings of the p^+ diffusions.

In regards to the n-p-n transistors, three kinds of structures are available. The first one (n-p-n-1) is obtained by using as a base the p-well doping profile involved in the CMOS and as an emitter the n^+-As source doping. Its features are: high gain (h_{FE} = 250) and high-voltage capability (BV_{CBO} = 90 V, BV_{CEO} = 40 V, BV_{EBO} = 16 V), but, owing to the high base width (=4 μm), the cut-off frequency is low (=140 MHz).

The second one (n-p-n-2) is obtained by using as a base and as an emitter the same dopant profiles involved in the DMOS transistor to respectively form the body and the source. In this case the gain is low (h_{FE} = 30) but very constant (over more than two decades of I_c current) and very reproducible (spread less than 5 percent) thanks to the controlled characteristics of the process that is essentially a VLSI MOS process. The breakdown voltage capabilities are: BV_{CBO} = 60 V, BV_{CEO} = 35 V, BV_{EBO} = 7.5 V, and the cut-off frequency is about 300 MHz.

With the same base-doping profile of the n-p-n-2 transistor, but with a phosphorus-doped emitter obtained with an extra masking step, it is possible to realize, as an option, the third kind of n-p-n transistor (n-p-n-3). In this case the gain is high (h_{FE} = 200–350) and also the cut-off frequency (f_t = 1 GHz). The n-p-n exhibits BV_{CBO} = 60 V, BV_{CEO} = 25 V, and BV_{EBO} = 7.5 V.

Table II reports the electrical characteristics of the different n-p-n's.

B. CMOS Structures

By adding the p-well diffusion to the DMOS process it is possible to realize self-isolated CMOS structures. The main characteristics of the p- and n-channel MOS in the CMOS structure can be observed in Table III.

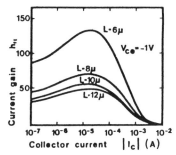

Fig. 2. Current gain versus collector current of p-n-p transistors with regard to four different window spacings L between emitter and collector p^+.

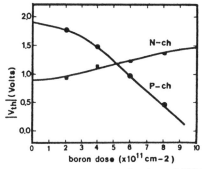

Fig. 3. Threshold voltage of n-channel and p-channel MOS as a function of boron adjustment implant.

TABLE I
ELECTRICAL CHARACTERISTICS OF LATERAL p-n-p TRANSISTORS WITH
DIFFERENT BASE WIDTHS

L (μ)	6	8	10	12
h_{fe}	134	72	57	49
LV_{ceo}(V)	18	45	50	54
BV_{cbo}(V)	62	62	62	62
BV_{ces}(V)	12	62	62	62
BV_{ebo}(V)	75	75	75	75
f_t (MHz)	–	10	–	–

TABLE II
ELECTRICAL CHARACTERISTICS OF THE THREE DIFFERENT KINDS OF n-p-n
TRANSISTORS

	NPN1	NPN2	NPN3
h_{fe}	250	27	250
LV_{ceo}(V)	40	40	25
BV_{cbo}(V)	90	64	60
BV_{ebo}(V)	16	7.5	7.5
f_t (MHz)	140	300	1000

TABLE III
MAIN ELECTRICAL CHARACTERISTICS AND GEOMETRICAL PARAMETERS OF
DMOS HIGH-VOLTAGE p-CHANNEL MOS AND CMOS

		V_{th}(V)	BV_{dss}(V)	g_m/Z(S/cm) $V_{gs}=10V, V_{ds}=5V$	$R_{on} \cdot Z$ ($\Omega \cdot$cm) $V_{gs}=10V, V_{ds}=0.1V$	$L_{ch}(\mu)$ (1)	t_{ox}(Å) (2)
CMOS	N-ch	0.9	16	0.161	1.9	3.0	850
	P-ch	1.9	35	0.073	11.3	2.6	850
	P-ch H.V.	1.9	80	0.053	18.0	3.3	850
DMOS		2.7	70	0.25	3.5	1.5	850

$(R_{on} \cdot A)_{Dmos} = (R_{on} \cdot A)_{Si} + (R_{on} \cdot A)_{metal\ layout} \cdot (6+3) \cdot 10^{-3}\ \Omega \cdot cm^2$

(1) mos electrical channel length ; (2) gate oxide thickness

TABLE IV
HIGH-VOLTAGE p-CHANNEL MOS BV_{dss} AND $R_{on} \times Z$ VALUES VERSUS
DRAIN EXTENSION IMPLANT DOSE

Dose $(\times 10^{12} cm^{-2})$	BV_{dss} (V)	$R_{on} \times Z$ ($\Omega \times$cm)
2.5	75	32.2
3.0	72	29.8
4.0	91	23.6
5.0	89	17.6
6.0	60	16.0
7.5	46	13.3
9.0	38	11.9
10.0	35	11.2

structures, the combination of an epitaxial layer grown on a low shunt resistance n^+ buried layer and a p^+ ring around the p-well regions gives an improved reliability against this problem up to a maximum operating voltage of 15 V. The current process design rules allow integration of up to 900 MOS transistors per square millimeter.

C. High-Voltage p-MOS Transistor

To satisfy the driving requirements of the high-voltage DMOS device, it is necessary to have a component of inverse polarity sustaining a supply voltage exceeding the DMOS maximum voltage by a value equal to its driving voltage. Adding a boron implant without any extra mask to the 60-V DMOS process it is possible to introduce drain extension regions in a p-channel MOS device increasing its voltage capability up to 80 V. Several process and layout trials have been carried out to optimize the structure. The results are reported in Tables III and IV.

IV. DMOS TRANSISTORS

The power DMOS device consists of a number of transistors with parallel source and gate electrodes integrated on a single isolated area with a common drain. The integration of this component requires bringing the drain contact to the surface via an n^+ buried layer and an n^+ sinker diffusion. The DMOS channel length is very short and does not depend on lithographic accuracy because it is obtained by the difference in lateral diffusion lengths of two different impurity distributions introduced through the same opening in the polysilicon mask. The body lateral

The threshold voltage of the CMOS p-channel FET device is set by the epitaxial layer resistivity whose value is fixed by the breakdown requirement of the high-voltage DMOS device. Its value can be adjusted by an implant of boron ions. The tradeoff between the doping levels of the p-well and the p-channel threshold voltage adjustment gives complementary threshold voltages without inserting any extra masking steps (see Fig. 3). The adjustment is so light that it does not cause any perturbations to the other integrated structures.

As regards the typical latchup susceptibility in CMOS

207

diffusion peak concentration in the channel region sets the threshold voltage of the DMOS device. A heavy-doped p^+ region is formed inside the DMOS body, but outside the channel region, to reduce the value of the pinched resistance under the source that is the base resistance of the parasitic intrinsic bipolar n-p-n transistor. As a consequence the parasitic bipolar latch-back limit increases. In the design of power DMOS components the key parameters are the breakdown voltage, the device ON resistance (R_{on}) for a given area, and the threshold voltage.

A. Breakdown Voltage

To obtain the best tradeoff between maximum (close to ideal) breakdown voltage and minimum epitaxial bulk resistance, design considerations and investigations concentrate on the structure of the edge termination of the p-body/n-epitaxy junctions. In our case an efficient and reliable solution consists in a polysilicon field plate overlaying silicon dioxide of two different increasing thicknesses connected with a very low angle ($\sim 20°-30°$), forming a biplanar structure [10]. This edge termination exhibits an efficiency (experimental BV value divided by ideal bulk BV value) of 0.85.

Knowing the edge termination efficiency, the epitaxial layer specification for the Multipower process (60 V) has been established according to minimization of epitaxial layer contribution to the DMOS R_{on}. As a consequence the body–drain junction depletion layer reaches the n^+ buried layer through the epitaxy. The epitaxial layer characteristics are so fixed as follows: $\rho = 1.3\ \Omega \cdot$ cm; $W_{epi} = 7.5\ \mu$m.

B. ON Resistance

The R_{on} parameter is strictly dependent on the topological layout that is the shape and size (packing density) of the unit DMOS cell. Besides, the drain electrode positioning on the top adds, with respect to the discrete device, an extra contribution to the R_{on} that depends on the n^+ buried layer drift region, the n^+ sinker contact region, and the layout choice for drain and source interdigitation.

Our goal was to minimize the product $R_{on} \times$ Area, that provides a measure of the efficiency of DMOS design, according to a mathematical model.

Studying the structure (DMOS cells) $-$ (n^+ buried layer) $-$ (n^+ sinker) (see Fig. 4), we can give the product $R_{on} \times$ Area as a function of the physical and layout parameters of the component. Using the symbols shown in Fig. 4, we have for the given structure the following expression:

$$R_{on} \cdot \text{Area} = \left\{ \frac{R_c}{N} + \frac{1}{12} \cdot R_{bl} \cdot N + \frac{1}{12} \cdot R_{bl} \right.$$
$$\left. \cdot \frac{2Y}{l} + \frac{R_{sink}}{l \cdot X_{sink}} \right\}$$
$$\cdot l \cdot (N \cdot l + X_{sink} + 2Y)$$

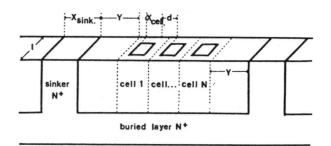

Fig. 4. Model of the integrated power VDMOS for the $R_{on} \times A$ calculation.

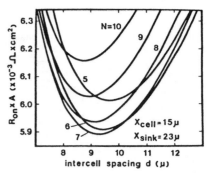

Fig. 5. Theoretical $R_{on} \times A$ as a function of DMOS intercell spacing (d) and number of cells (N) between two drain sinker fingers.

where

R_c is the ON resistance of the DMOS cell and consists of four distinguishable components,

R_{ch} is the channel resistance,

R_{acc} is the accumulation layer resistance,

R_{JFET} is the parasitic JFET on resistance,

R_{epi} is the epitaxial layer resistance.

The expression used for R_c relates to the well-known model of the DMOS structure [11], [12].

R_{bl} is the n^+ buried layer sheet resistance;

R_{sink} is the n^+ sinker resistance per unit area;

l is the cell pitch $= X_{cell} + d$, where X_{cell} is the DMOS cell window and d is the spacing between two DMOS cells;

X_{sink} is the n^+ sinker window width;

N is the number of cells between two sinker fingers; and

Y is the distance between the edge of sinker window and half spacing of the last cell (this value includes the extension of the junction edge termination).

According to this model we have written a FORTRAN program that calculates the minimum value for $R_{on} \times$ Area varying the parameters X_{cell}, d, N, and X_{sink}.

As a result of this theoretical calculation, in Fig. 5 the $R_{on} \times$ Area functional dependence on the intercell spacing d, with regard to the different values of the number of cells between the two drain fingers, can be observed. The other two design parameters (X_{cell} and X_{sink}) are considered to be equal to constant values set by additional requirements: $X_{cell} = 15\ \mu$m—as a present technological

Fig. 6. Photomicrograph of the integrated DMOS H-bridge with the control section.

standard. $X_{sink} = 23$ μm—as imposed by the drain metal strip width needed to lower its contribution to R_{on}.

The minimum value of $R_{on} \times$ Area is found at a value of d in the range from 9 to 10 μm, at $N = 7$ and is equal to 5.92×10^{-3} $\Omega \cdot$ cm², in good agreement, within 5 percent, with the experimental value (see Table III).

C. Threshold Voltage

The value of the threshold voltage is mainly related to the thickness of the gate oxide and to the peak impurity concentration of the laterally diffused body in the region included between source and drain. The doping profile of the body region is multifunctional in an integrated circuit and consequently many tradeoffs must be satisfied. In fact it is related to the DMOS channel length and to avoid channel punchthrough that could occur under strong reverse bias [13]. Besides, in the Multipower process the body region forms the n-p-n-2 transistor's base, also setting the value of its h_{FE}.

According to these guidelines the tradeoff in Multipower process is:

1) DMOS — channel length = 1.5 μm, $BV_{dss} = 70$ V, $V_{th} = 2.7$ V;

2) n-p-n — $h_{FE} = 25$–30.

Table III summarizes the electrical characteristics of the integrated DMOS transistors.

V. Technology Application

The first product developed with Multipower BCD technology is a full integrated H-bridge control system for dc and stepping motors that can be driven at the input by logic-level TTL or CMOS compatible signals (a chip photo is shown in Fig. 6). This device provides the driving in the switching mode of motors or inductive loads with supply voltages up to 60 V and dc load currents up to 1.5 A and is suitable for operation at high-switching frequencies (300 kHz) and high efficiency [14]. The complete integration of the power stage becomes possible thanks to the free-wheeling diode intrinsic to the DMOS structure that is necessary in applications on inductive loads. In transient conditions the circuit can drive the load with currents up to 5 A for a time limited only by the thermal constant of the package. The level of dissipated power is low (1.5 W at 1.5 A of load current); this feature makes possible the insertion of the die in a cheap DIP package with no need for a heatsink.

VI. Conclusions

It has been shown in this paper that combining the well-known DMOS silicon gate and junction isolation processes it is possible to obtain at the same time a lot of different structures (bipolar, CMOS, DMOS) whose type and characteristics depend on the complexity of the process. The technological approach followed was to center the process around the DMOS silicon gate structure, obtaining the other components adding only two masking steps and two ion implants without any thermal perturbation to the 10-masking-step base process. Our goal was to optimize the power part that generally occupies the most chip area in the main application fields of this technology. The first example of this mixed technology, called Multipower BCD, has been developed in the range of 60 V as maximum rating for the DMOS power part and it was successfully implemented to realize an integrated switched-mode motor driver.

Today the minimum lithographic width employed is 4 μm, but future developments will employ reduced lithographic dimensions and multithickness top metallization, permitting a thin patterned metal over the complex part of the circuit to achieve high packing density and a thick metal over the power section of the monolithic system where there is a need to minimize internal voltage drop.

Future developments will include the realization of processes based on the same concepts but with much higher breakdown voltages (250, 450 V) for off-line applications.

References

[1] M. S. Adler, K. W. Owyang, B. J. Baliga, and R. A. Kokosa, "The evolution of power device technology," *IEEE Trans. Electron Devices*, vol. ED-31, no. 11, Nov. 1984.

[2] Texas Instr., *Electronic Design*, pp. 105–111, July 7, 1983.

[3] Siliconix, *Electronic Design*, pp. 37–38, Feb. 9, 1983.

[4] R. S. Wrathall, D. Tam, L. Terry, and S. P. Rob, "Integrated circuits for the control of high power," in *IEDM Tech. Dig.*, pp. 408–411, Dec. 1983.

[5] S. Krishna, J. Kuo, and I. S. Gaeta, "An analog technology integrates bipolar, CMOS and high-voltage DMOS transistors," *IEEE Trans. Electron Devices*, vol. ED-31, no. 1, Jan. 1984.

[6] E. J. Wildi, J. P. Walden, and M. S. Adler, "A 500-V/25-A half-bridge IC with on-chip control logic," in *ISSCC Tech. Dig.*, pp. 266–267, Feb. 1985.

[7] P. G. Blanken and P. van der Zee, "An integrated 8-MHz video output amplifier," *IEEE Trans. Consumer Electron.*, vol. CE-31, no. 3, pp. 109–118, 1985.

[8] R. S. Wrathall, "The design of a high-power solid-state automotive switch in CMOS–VDMOS technology," in *16th PESC Tech. Dig.*, pp. 229–233, June 1985.

[9] J. D. Plummer, "Monolithic high-voltage integrated circuits," in *IEDM Tech. Dig.*, pp. 6–10, 1980.

[10] F. Conti and M. Conti, "Surface breakdown in silicon planar diodes equipped with field plate," *Solid-State Electron.*, vol. 15, pp. 93–105, 1972.

[11] S. C. Sun and J. D. Plummer, "Modeling of the ON-resistance of LDMOS, VDMOS, and VMOS power transistor," *IEEE Trans. Electron Devices*, vol. ED-27, no. 2, Feb. 1980.

[12] C. Contiero, P. Galbiati, and L. Gandolfi, "Layout analysis of a power MOS unitary cell to properly design the value of the ON-resistance," in *Proc. 11th MIEL* (Zagreb), Apr. 1983.

[13] C. T. Wang and D. H. Navon, "Threshold and punch-through behavior of laterally nonuniformly doped short-channel MOSFET's," *IEEE Trans. Electron Devices*, vol. ED-30, no. 7, July 1983.

[14] C. Cini, C. Diazzi, and D. Rossi, "A high-efficiency mixed technology motor driver IC," presented at Powercon 1985, Chicago.

Power Integrated Circuit Makes Board Level Overvoltage and Overtemperature Protection Simple and Inexpensive

by
D. Zaremba and
J. Mansmann
Motorola Inc.

Today's sophisticated electronic systems often represent an investment of hundreds or even thousands of dollars worth of logic and memory components. Considering this, prudent thinking dictates protecting sensitive circuit components against overvoltage and overtemperature conditions. However, some designers forego protection measures citing the extra cost outweighs the risk of damage. Yet overvoltage and overtemperature dangers exist in most circuit environments. For example, a short-circuited series pass element in a voltage regulator or a break in the feedback loop of a switching power

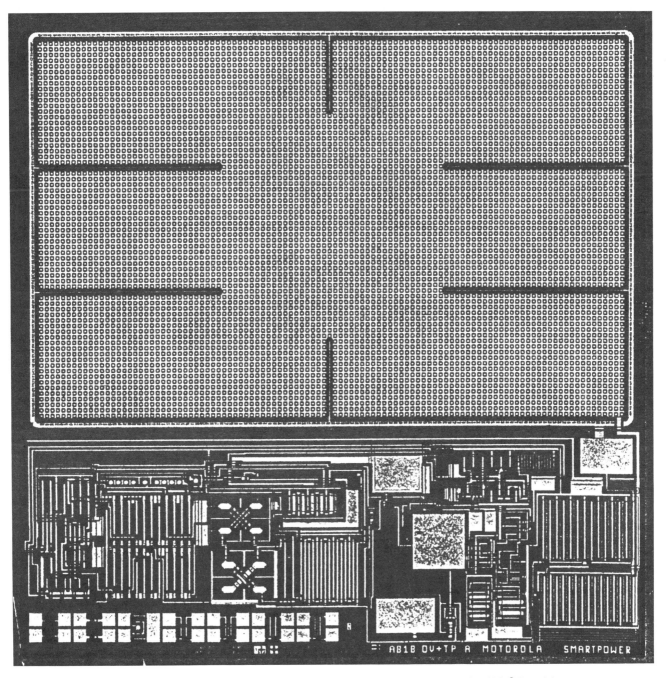

temperatures above the maximum limit. Such high voltages and extreme temperatures can quickly destroy sensitive components. As an example, the curve illustrated in *figure 2* shows the supply voltage limitations of TTL logic. Experiments show that five volt NMOS 64K RAMs exhibit a 13.5 volt Vcc limit independent of pulse duration. Momentary excursion above these limits can result in device destruction. Also, operating semiconductor devices above maximum operating temperatures can result in catastrophic failures, especially when output power transistors and rectifiers fail short-circuited.

Figure 1a: A SMARTpower™ OV + OTP die. See figure 4 for a complete circuit schematic.

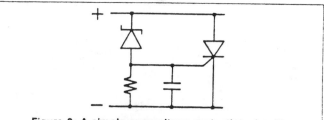

Figure 2: Typical TTL SOA curve: pulsed supply voltage vs. pulse width (taken from Motorola application note AN-789)

Protecting against such occurences often requires weighing cost against performance. For example, the simple overvoltage protection design of *figure 3* includes a zener diode, a resistor, a capacitor, and a SCR (silicon controlled rectifier). The design

Model	Trip voltage (V)	Continuous clamp current (A)	Case type
MPC2004		7.5	TO-220AB
MPC2005	6.2 ± 0.3	15.0	TO-220AB
MPC2006		35.0	TO-204AA
MPC2011		7.5	
MPC2012	13.7 ± 0.7	15.0	
MPC2014	17.1 ± 0.9	7.5	TO-220AB
MPC2015		15.0	

Figure 1b: The SMARTpower™ OV + OTP product family

Figure 3: A simple overvoltage protection circuit

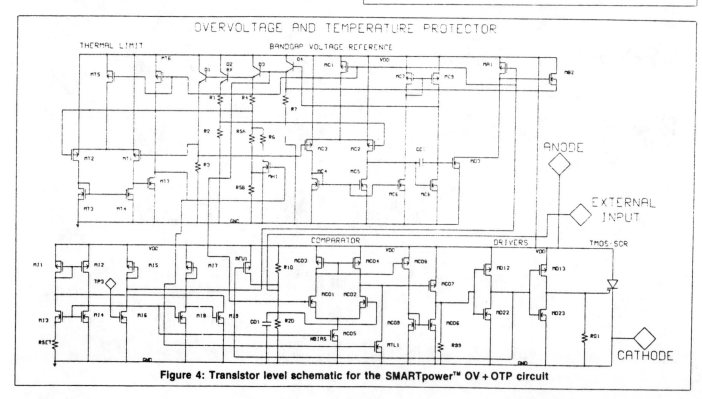

Figure 4: Transistor level schematic for the SMARTpower™ OV + OTP circuit

Power Integrated Circuit

boasts low component count and cost but exhibits relatively poor performance. Circuit operation is simple. The SCR latches when

TO-220 SCRs used in discrete overvoltage crowbar designs. Hence, some customers can reduce their protection circuits to a single package without retooling or refabricating printed circuit boards.

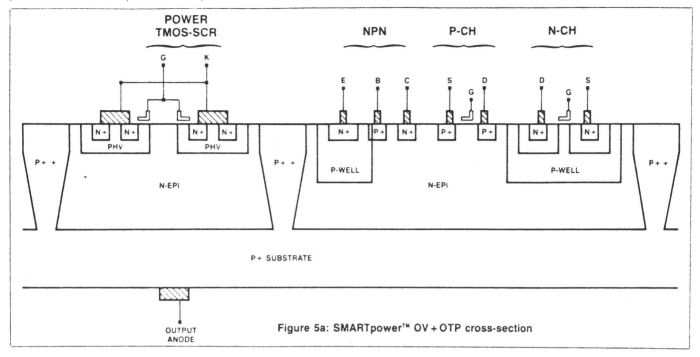

Figure 5a: SMARTpower™ OV + OTP cross-section

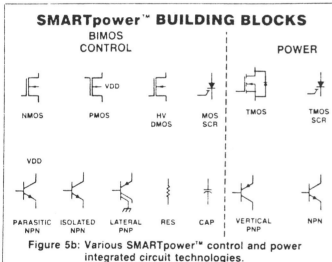

SMARTpower™ BUILDING BLOCKS

Figure 5b: Various SMARTpower™ control and power integrated circuit technologies.

SMARTpower™: Versatile Power Integrated Circuit Technology

The SMARTpower™ cross-section shown below illustrates three different integrated circuit technologies on the same chip. In addition to CMOS, bipolar, and power MOS-SCR, the accompanying figure displays other technologies suitable to the SMARTpower™ process. Although a complicated process, the use of vertical output power technologies yields greater current per unit silicon area, which results in lower overall die cost. Low cost and availability of nearly every type of control and power combination makes possible numerous and cost-effective products. Other SMARTpower™ products include logic driven high and low side switches, DC motor controllers, and high power PWM circuits. Most important, the SMARTpower™ OV + OTP design overcomes discrete design shortcomings at costs approaching that of the least expensive discrete designs.

One can understand the SMARTpower™ OV + OTP operation by studying the block diagram illustrated in figure 6. The resistor-divided rail voltage is compared to a 2.4V bandgap voltage reference. If the rail voltage exceeds the designed trip limit ($V_{trip} = 2.4 \cdot (R_2 + R_1)/R_2$) the voltage at the comparator's

the rail voltage reaches the zener voltage plus approximately one diode voltage drop. The zener voltage, however, varies with temperature and fluctuates along its current-voltage "knee". Thus, the circuit's trip voltage varies considerably about the designed voltage trip point. Furthermore, the SCR starves itself for gate drive thereby decreasing SCR di/dt and noise immunity. Hence, to insure sufficient latching current and protection against SCR degradation, a designer must use a SCR with higher ratings (and greater cost) than bus voltage and current conditions require. This design also prohibits adjustable trip voltages except by zener replacement.

More sophisticated designs improve circuit performance but exhibit increased cost, component count, and size. Increased design time and added printed circuit board area also add to the circuit's cost. SMARTpower™'s (see insert) unique monolithic technology reduces these costs by providing a reliable, single package overvoltage and overtemperature protection (OV + OTP) device. This TO-220 or TO-204 (formerly TO-3) standard package device simply connects between the voltage rails of the circuit or circuits to be protected. Design time is eliminated. Also, SMARTpower™ OV + OTP TO-220 devices replace pin for pin

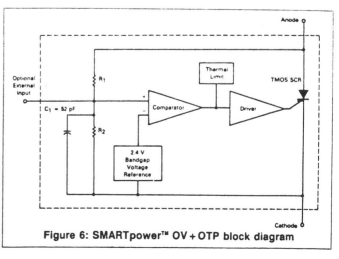

Figure 6: SMARTpower™ OV + OTP block diagram

213

Power Integrated Circuit

non-inverting input raises above 2.4 volts. The comparator then switches and drives two CMOS inverters which supply the necessary gate drive to latch the MOS-SCR. In the on-state, the MOS-SCR acts as a short circuit and shunts bus current from the load. The MOS-SCR remains latched unless reset by momentarily removing the anode voltage or implementing some method to reduce current below the MOS-SCR holding current value. In the off state, the CMOS inverter driver actively pulls down the MOS-SCR's gate to ground insuring maximum dv/dt immunity. The internal fifty-two picofarad capacitor rolls off noise sensitivity (see figure 7) to the comparator's input, thereby reducing nuisance triggering of the CMOS integrated circuit in noisy and switching circuit environments. As photographed in figure 8, the entire circuit sinks only 500μA of quiescent current. Yet within 5μs of detecting an overvoltage or overtemperature fault, this same circuit can withstand up to 350 amperes peak of capacitive discharge current and shunt up to 35 amperes of continuous bus current. Considering the device is only 182 thousandths of an inch on a side, the power and versatility of SMARTpower™ monolithic technology is apparent.

SMARTpower™ technology also eliminates the device's temperature dependence. The ratio of monolithically manufactured resistors tracks evenly with temperature. The bandgap voltage reference range, having a temperature coefficient of only .00625%/°C. A user can then expect a stable, well-defined voltage trip point throughout varying environment conditions.

If environment or circuit conditions raise operating temperatures to dangerous levels, the SMARTpower™ OV + OTP circuit can detect overtemperature, latch the SCR and thus remove power from the overheated load. At the expense of very little additional silicon real estate, the thermal limit circuitry compares the differences in the bandgap's delta Vbe voltages. When the designed temperature limit is reached, the thermal limit circuitry flips the inverter driver thereby latching the MOS-SCR. Since the circuit dissipates very little quiescent power, the junction temperature remains nearly the same as the case temperature. This means a user can monitor the case or heatsink temperatures of other devices or ambient temperatures. This feature proves especially useful in switchmode power supplies since the OV + OTP can mount directly to the case of the output rectifier(s). Since the outboard rectifier's case (cathode) is at supply potential, and dissipates the most power, the OV + OTP can monitor both overvoltage and overtemperature.

The monolithic nature of SMARTpower™ technology itself affords "built-in" circuit reliability. As mentioned previously, monolithic construction insures stable operation over the entire temperature operating range. Single die circuits also allow use of inexpensive, standard TO-220 and TO-204 device packaging. Unlike discrete circuits, single package designs allow fast, automated testing to guarantee operation within data sheet

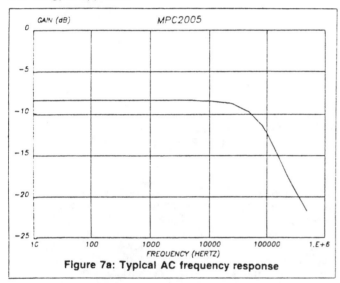

Figure 7a: Typical AC frequency response

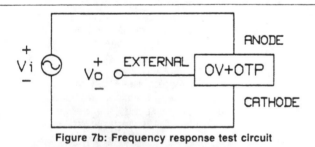

Figure 7b: Frequency response test circuit

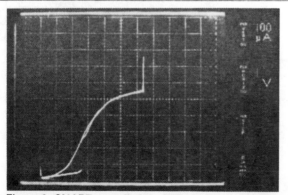

Figure 8: SMARTpower™ OV + OTP I-V characteristics showing quiescent current and onset of latch

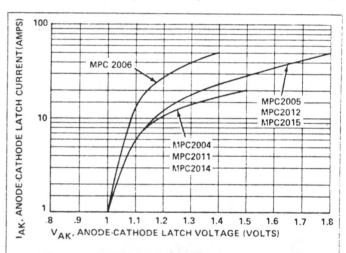

Figure 9: SMARTpower™ OV + OTP Anode-Cathode latched characteristics (pulsed ≈ 300μsec)

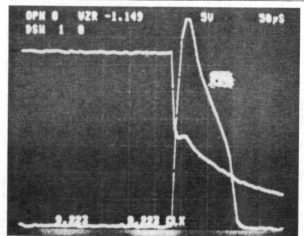

Figure 10: Photograph showing peak capacitive discharge current and anode voltage

Power Integrated Circuit

parameters Using a single package device that does the "whole job" reliably, an engineer saves design and debugging time. However, a designer must consider elements such as heatsinking and peak capacitive discharge currents to insure total system reliability. *Figure 9* shows typical on-voltages for SMARTpower™ OV + OTP devices when latched during free air, 300μs pulsed conditions. By knowing the maximum crowbar current (IAK), the expected on-voltage (VAK), and the negative temperature coefficient of VAK (≈ -1mV/°C), one can calculate the device power dissipation. A designer can then determine the necessary heatsink required. Of course, if the system utilizes circuitry to

industry. Although a two-terminal device, the OV + OTP design utilizes the third pin inherit to TO-220 and TO-204 packaging. Adding two outboard resistors as shown in *figure 12* allows user programmable trip voltages. Any external circuitry designed to raise the third pin voltage above 2.4 volts allows remote SCR triggering. An alarm signal from a separate part of the system, a controlling computer, external monitoring equipment, or a human operator can quickly remove primary DC power to the system. A single OV + OTP device can then be wired to receive a remote alarm signal as well as simultaneously monitor supply voltage and temperature. In extremely noisy environments where nuisance triggering of the CMOS integrated circuit proves troublesome, an external capacitor may be added as shown in *figure 13* to further roll off noise sensitivity. Operation with extremely noisy switching converters and power supplies becomes possible.

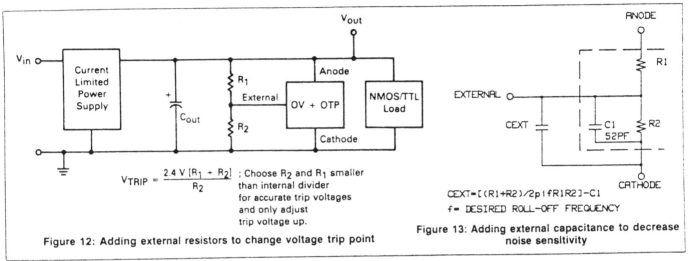

$$V_{TRIP} = \frac{2.4 \ V \ [R_1 + R_2]}{R_2} \quad ;$$ Choose R_2 and R_1 smaller than internal divider for accurate trip voltages and only adjust trip voltage up.

Figure 12: Adding external resistors to change voltage trip point

$CEXT = [(R1+R2)/2p1fR1R2] - C1$

$f =$ DESIRED ROLL-OFF FREQUENCY

Figure 13: Adding external capacitance to decrease noise sensitivity

remove anode voltage after latch, (by resetting a PWM controller or a circuit breaker in a linear supply, for example) a heatsink may not be required. Moreover, heatsinking may not be required in fused systems, provided that the fuse blows before the OV + OTP device degrades or destructs. SMARTpower™ OV + OTP data sheets list I²t data for fusing considerations. [1] When crowbarring the output of large power supplies, OV + OTP devices must withstand large peak capacitive discharge currents as the photograph in *figure 10* illustrates. The curve in *figure 11* gives an example of the number of reliable capacitive discharges a designer can expect for a given capacitor value. Proper selection of output capacitors can increase reliability in systems that may suffer frequent crowbars.

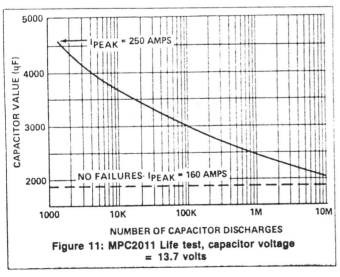

Figure 11: MPC2011 Life test, capacitor voltage = 13.7 volts

SMARTpower™ packaging also improves a system's reliability and versatility. Mounting and heatsinking techniques for TO-220 and TO-204 packages are well documented throughout the

The biggest advantage of SMARTpower™'s single package design, however, is board level protection. Many systems contain dozens of circuit boards stuffed with hundreds of logic and memory integrated circuits powered from several different power supplies. Long lead length inductance from power supplies to circuit boards can induce large voltage spikes at the input power terminals of the circuit boards. If long enough in duration, these spikes can produce disastrous results. Sometimes, improper power supply connections may cause damage to circuit boards during assembly, final test, or field servicing. A TO-220 or TO-204 OV + OTP device placed across each board's power terminals eliminates such problems. Lead-formed and tab-clipped TO-220 surface mount devices usually can be implemented in even the tightest of circuit board layouts. Long lead length inductance from power supply to circuit board also reduces any peak capacitive discharge currents, thus reducing the risk of SCR degradation.

Board level protection also affords unique use of the overtemperature function. Mounted in free air, the device can monitor ambient temperature in a card cage or cabinet. If a cooling fan fails for example, the OV + OTP device can shut down power to the circuit cards. Care must be taken, however, not to exceed the OV + OTP device's power limitations when latching it in free air. Of course, the OV + OTP device can be mounted to the case or heatsink of other power semiconductor devices to prevent thermal runaway and overheating.

Obviously every application of protection circuitry has an ultimate purpose: to sense a fault condition and remove power to the protected load before damage can occur. Engineering doctrine dictates this should be done with the least cost and components count and greatest performance and reliability. SMARTpower™ technology now offers designers a highly reliable, inexpensive, single package, overvoltage and overtemperature protector with enough versatility to accommodate most any application. In fact, only the designer's imagination limits its application.

[1] See Motorola application note AN-789 for information on SCR's and fusing considerations.
η

215

Part V
High Voltage Display Drives

IN this part of the book, papers dealing with high voltage display drives are collected. These papers discuss technology that can not only be used for the control of plasma display panels and electroluminescent displays, but also for driving piezoelectric crystal transducer arrays and electrostatic printers. These applications share a common feature in that the load that is being controlled can be represented as a capacitor. A totem pole configuration is commonly used to connect the load either to the high voltage rail or to ground. This requires the integration of two high voltage devices which are connected in series between the high voltage rail and ground. It is preferable that the upper device be a p-channel transistor and the lower device be an n-channel device. This avoids the need to generate a gate drive voltage above the rail potential. In addition to the high voltage transistors, the chip must contain the low voltage interface logic circuits that perform the decode function.

In the case of the chips designed for display drive applications, the high voltage output devices are configured such that their drain terminals can be bonded off the chip. This avoids the need to perform high voltage interconnections on the chip. Due to this feature, the display drive chips were among the first high voltage integrated circuits to be developed. Chips containing up to 16 output drivers integrated together have been reported. In some cases the output transistors have the ability to operate at voltages up to 850 volts.

This part contains five papers dealing with the display drive technology. The first of these papers, by Wakaumi *et al.*, describes a chip containing an array of 16 high voltage output transistors. In order to keep the power dissipation low, CMOS is used for the logic section. To achieve process compatibility, the high voltage output devices are formed as extended drain NMOS transistors. These devices contain a parasitic bipolar transistor which can degrade the safe operating area. To overcome this problem a shielded source structure is used. This approach is also useful for the low voltage NMOS transistors to suppress any latch-up in the CMOS circuit. The following paper, by Martin *et al.*, describes a display driver with 16 channels achieved using NMOS technology. How-

ever, in this case both pull-up and pull-down high voltage devices are integrated on the same chip with the CMOS logic circuitry. The output stage works as a high voltage inverter.

The next paper in this part describes a chip containing both high voltage pull-up and pull-down devices. In this case the pull-down devices are n-channel DMOSFETs while the pull-up devices are lateral p-channel transistors. Details of the doping profiles required to obtain high breakdown voltages are provided. This circuit is able to operate at 1 MHz with switching times of 100 nanoseconds for the case of an output voltage swing of 300 volts and load capacitance of 200 picofarads.

A BIMOS technology suitable for application to display drives is described in the paper by Heisig. In this case high voltage bipolar output transistors are combined with CMOS shift-registers, latches, and decoders on the same chip. This technology is useful for applications requiring operating voltages of 60 to 100 volts and up to 600 milliamperes of current.

The last paper in this part describes a display driver achieved by using SOS (silicon-on-sapphire) technology. The process used is based upon standard CMOS technology developed for SOS. The lateral high voltage transistors are formed by using an extended drain configuration. These devices are able to handle analog signals of up to 100 volts.

REPRINT PAPERS

[1] H. Wakaumi, T. Suzuki, M. Saito, and H. Sakuma, "A Highly Reliable 16 Output High Voltage NMOS/CMOS Logic IC with Shielded Source Structure," *IEEE Int. Electron Devices Meeting Digest,* Abst. 16.3, pp. 416–419, 1983.
[2] R. A. Martin, S. A. Buhler, and G. Lao, "850-V NMOS Driver with Active Outputs," *IEEE Int. Electron Devices Meeting Digest,* Abst. 10.3, pp. 266–269, 1984.
[3] E. Habekotte, B. Hoefflinger, W. Renker, and G. Zimmer, "A Coplanar Power Switch," *IEEE J. Solid State Circuits,* vol. SC-16, pp. 212–226, 1981.
[4] M. Heisig, "BIMOS—A New Way to Simplify High-Power Custom Interface," *IEEE Custom Integrated Circuits Conference Digest,* pp. 8–12, 1981.
[5] D. Sharma, J. Gautier, and G. Merckel, "A High-Voltage Circuit for Driving Liquid Crystal Displays," *IEEE J. Solid State Circuits,* vol. SC-13, pp. 375–378, 1978.

A HIGHLY RELIABLE 16 OUTPUT HIGH VOLTAGE NMOS/CMOS LOGIC IC WITH SHIELDED SOURCE STRUCTURE

H. Wakaumi, T. Suzuki, M. Saito and H. Sakuma

Microelectronics Research Laboratories, NEC Corporation
4-1-1 Miyazaki, Miyamae-ku, Kawasaki 213, Japan

ABSTRACT

A high voltage MOS IC, which consists of 16 high voltage NMOS transistor array having 400 V, 0.5 A output characteristic and its control CMOS logic, was newly developed. High and low voltage NMOS transistors of the IC are equipped with shielded source structure to realize completely parasitic bipolar effect-free high voltage MOS ICs.

Practically, this IC successfully drove a plasma display panel at 200 V, 2 MHz without any parasitic effect and its high operation reliability was verified.

To examine high integration density possibility, parasitic bipolar effects due to the interferences between high and high voltage transistors, low and low voltage transistors, and high and low voltage transistors, were experimentally investigated. As a result, it was confirmed that the "shielded source structure" realizes high density high voltage MOS ICs.

INTRODUCTION

Recently, the cost and size reduction, and display area enlargement of flat display panels, such as PDP, ELD and dot matrix VFD, have been strongly demanded. Driver circuits for these display panels, necessarily have a lot of high voltage circuit outputs. Therefore, the monolithic IC equipped with high voltage transistors and their control logic circuits on the same chip, is essential to meet the above requirement. High voltage planar MOS ICs are thought to be most suited for such an IC, because of its isolation ease and high speed operation.[1]~[3]

However, negative resistance breakdown due to parasitic bipolar effect, is known to be observed in a high voltage planar NMOS transistor, a key device for high voltage MOS ICs.[4] Therefore, the high voltage transistor has a narrow ASO (Area of Safe Operation). To solve this problem, a high voltage MOS transistor with parasitic effect-free characteristic, was realized using the proposed "shielded source structure".[5][6]

The low voltage logic, for controlling the high voltage transistors, should be CMOS with low power dissipation and large noise immunity characteristic. However, since high resistivity substrate is used to realize high breakdown voltage for the high voltage MOS transistor, latch up phenomena in CMOS logic become easily to occur. Since the latch up is one of parasitic bipolar effect, the shielded source structure will be effective to suppress the latch up.

This paper describes, a newly developed, 16 output high voltage NMOS/CMOS logic IC without any parasitic effect. This is achieved by adopting shielded source structure. The possibility of realizing even higher integration density IC by using the shielded source structure is also discussed, based on experimental results.

DEVICE STRUCTURE

In the new IC, the shielded source structure, in which the high impurity density p^+ ground layer entirely covers n^+ source layer except for the MOS channel plane, is adopted in high voltage NMOS transistors and in low voltage NMOS transistors for CMOS logic, as shown in Fig. 1. Since p^+ ground layer potential is equal to that for the source (n^+), even if voltage drop at the substrate due to substrate current occurs, the source junction is not forward-biased. In consequence, the parasitic bipolar effect doesn't occur. These n^+ source layer and underlying p^+ ground layer are simply fabricated by As^+ and B^+ ion implantations through the same source mask windows in a self-aligned manner.

The IC is made up of 8 input-output buffer circuits, 16 blocks of serial-in/parallel-out shift register, latch, gate and buffer circuit and 16 output high voltage NMOS transistors (Fig. 2). The buffer circuit consisting of 4 stage inverters is designed to have 5 MHz driving capability for the high voltage transistor gate. The high voltage transistors are controlled by Output Enable (OE), Toggle (To) and Data (D in1 or D in2) input signals. The CMOS logic includes about 700 low voltage MOS transistors.

EXPERIMENTAL RESULTS

A photomicrograph of the IC is shown in Fig. 3. IC chip size is 6 mm x 6 mm. The IC electrical characteristics are shown in Table 1. High voltage NMOS transistors having 4 μm long, 10.2 mm wide MOS channel and 40 μm long offset gate, can flow 0.5 A drain current at 10 V gate bias, which is a high enough current level to drive a large display area dot matrix AC refresh PDP. The high voltage transistor shows about 400 V drain breakdown voltage in the 0 V to 15 V wide gate bias range without any negative resistance, according to pulse current-voltage measurement. This characteristic is still superior to that for 100-150 μm long offset gate conventional NMOS transistors. The conventional transistors have larger on-resistance and larger chip

Reprinted from *IEEE 29th Int. Electron Devices Meeting*, pp. 416–419, 1983.

occupation area compared to that for the shielded source transistor. Therefore, this structure enables easily realizing high integration density MOS ICs. Drain current-voltage characteristics for the high voltage shielded source transistor are shown in Fig. 4.

CMOS logic with shielded source structure (about 4 μm gate length) operates at 2-30 V power supply voltage range and follows 9 MHz clock frequency at 10 V (Fig. 5) (5-6 MHz clock frequency will be large enough for about 2000 character AC refresh PDP to be driven). CMOS logic power consumption is 21 mW at 10 V, 5 MHz clock frequency, which is much less than the power consumption for an E/D MOS logic (over 100 mW).

If integration density increases further, there is a possibility that logic error operation due to a capacitive coupling noise pulse would occur. By using CMOS configuration in logic, stable logic operation is expected to be obtained due to its large noise margin. The other possibility is that the interferences between high and high voltage transistors, high and low voltage transistors, and low and low voltage transistors due to a substrate current, would occur. The substrate current will be caused by low and high voltage transistor's avalanche phenomena, p-n junction's (for example, drain junction for CMOS logic) forward-biasing resulting from capacitive coupling noise pulse and surge voltage.

For example, a large quantity of electrons injected into the substrate diffuse to a certain high voltage transistor and are likely to lead this transistor to negative resistance breakdown by causing the parasitic bipolar transistor to turn on. To investigate such a parasitic bipolar effect, the following experiment was made. In a high voltage transistor biased at a lower voltage than its breakdown voltage, electrons are injected from an adjacent high voltage transistor's drain junction into the substrate, by forward-biasing. These electrons enter into the transistor drain depletion layer and cause avalanche breakdown. As a result, a large quantity of holes are injected into the substrate and cause voltage drop at the substrate. According to the experiment, a conventional transistor showed parasitic bipolar action in low injection current in spite of at lower electric field than that of breakdown, whereas the shielded source transistor didn't show negative resistance breakdown, even at experimentally observable 450 mA injection current level.

Also, there is a possibility that latch up might occur in CMOS logic due to the substrate current. Since high voltage MOS IC uses high resistivity substrate, parasitic lateral npn transistor's base resistance, or the substrate resistance, is high, as mentioned previously. Therefore, when the substrate current causes enough voltage drop at the substrate resistance to make n-channel transistor source junction forward-bias, latch up occurs. In order to investigate such a parasitic bipolar effect, CMOS ability to withstand latch up was experimented upon. The conventional CMOS with 20 μm parasitic lateral npn transistor base (p⁻ substrate: $N_A = 6 \times 10^{14}$ cm⁻³) width L_M, results in latch up phenomena, as shown in Fig. 6, at 6 mA parasitic vertical pnp transistor base (n-well region) injection current level, 10 V collector-emitter bias voltage. As compared with this characteristic, the CMOS with shielded source structure doesn't show latch up, even at 300-350 mA base injection current level. The reason is

that current gain α_n for the parasitic npn transistor in the shielded source structure is less than 3×10^{-7}. These experimental investigations show that higher integration density IC will be realized.

The fabricated ICs in 28 pin ceramic packages were applied in a plasma display scan driver. The ICs successfully drove the panel at 200 V, 2 MHz without any parasitic effect and any logic operation error due to a capacitive coupling noise pulse (Fig. 7). As a result, in a practically usable high voltage IC, since parasitic bipolar action was effectively suppressed by using the shielded source structure, the high IC reliability was confirmed.

CONCLUSION

A 16 output high voltage NMOS/CMOS logic IC, designed for driving an AC refresh PDP, was developed using shielded source structure for its NMOS tansistors, to realize completely parasitic effect-free high voltage MOS ICs.

Practically, the IC succeeded in driving an AC refresh PDP and its high reliability was verified.

Parasitic effects due to the interferences between high and high voltage transistors, low and high voltage transistors, and low and low voltage transistors in this IC, were experimentally investigated.

These results indicate that much higher packing density, but still a parasitic effect-free high voltage NMOS/CMOS logic IC, will be realized using shielded source structure.

ACKNOWLEDGEMENT

The authors wish to thank Drs. K. Ayaki and H. Kato for their continuous encouragement and T. Aizawa and K. Hirata for their technical assistance.

REFERENCES

[1] K. Fujii et al., "400 V MOS IC for EL Display," ISSCC Digest of Technical Papers, p.46, Feb., 1981.
[2] S.A. Buhler et al., "Integrated High-Voltage/Low-Voltage MOS Devices," IEDM Technical Digest, p.259, Dec., 1981.
[3] B. Weir, "Integrated High-Votlage Driver Circuits in Gate Array Form," SID 1982 Digest, p.268.
[4] I. Yoshida et al., "Thermal Stability and Secondary Breakdown in Planar Power MOSFET's," IE³ ED, Vol. ED-27, No.2, p.395, Feb., 1980.
[5] H. Sakuma et al., "Parasitic Effect-Free, High Voltage MOS ICs with Shielded Source Structure," IEDM Technical Digest, p.254, Dec., 1982.
[6] H. Sakuma et al., "Parasitic Effect Free, High Voltage NMOS/CMOS Logic ICs with Shielded Source Structure," Technical Report of IECE, ED 83-8, Apr., 1983.

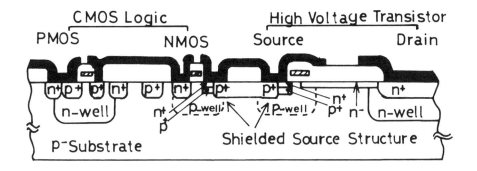

Fig.1 Cross sectional view of high voltage MOS IC with low voltage CMOS logic circuit. Both high and low voltage NMOS transistors have shielded source structure consisting of an upper n⁺ source layer entirely shielded by a lower p⁺ ground layer.

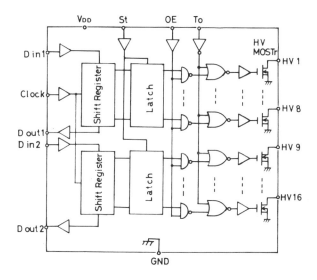

Fig.2 16 output high voltage MOS IC blockdiagram. Logic circuit is composed of serial-in and parallel-out shift registers, latches, gates and buffers.

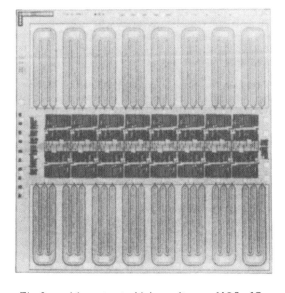

Fig.3 16 output high voltage MOS IC photomicrograph. Chip size is 6 mm x 6 mm.

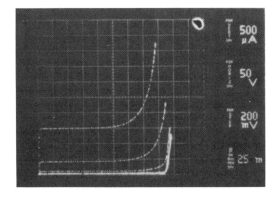

Fig.4 I-V characteristic for high voltage NMOS transistor with shielded source structure, which shows about 400 V drain breakdown voltage.

High Voltage MOS Tr	
B V$_{DSS}$ (at I$_D$<100 μA)	400 V
Ron (at V$_G$=10 V)	30 Ω
I$_{DS}$ (at V$_G$=10 V)	0.5 A
Low Voltage Logic Circuit	
f$_{clock}$ max (at V$_{DD}$=10 V)	9 MHz
V$_{DD}$	2V ∼ 30 V
P$_o$ (at V$_{DD}$=10V, f$_{clock}$=5MHz, C$_L$=15pF)	21 mw

Table 1 Typical 16 output high voltage MOS IC characteristics. CMOS logic circuit can operate in wide power supply voltage range. High voltage NMOS transistor doesn't show any parasitic bipolar effect for wide gate bias range from 0 V to 15 V.

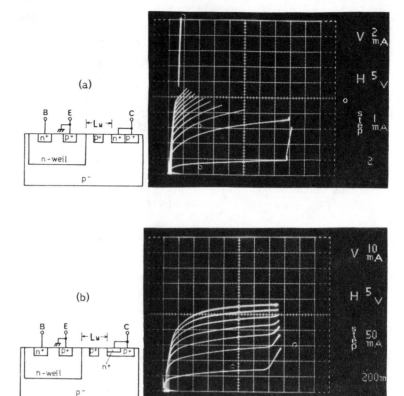

Fig.6 Base noise current at latch up. (a) For conventional CMOS. (b) For CMOS with shielded source structure. Conventional CMOS shows latch up at 6 mA base injection current level, 10 V collector-emitter bias voltage, whereas CMOS with shielded source structure doesn't show latch up phenomena, even at 350-400 mA.

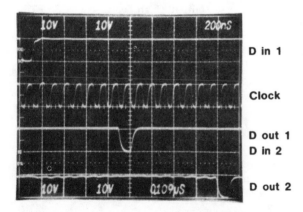

Fig.5 16 stage shift register's input and output waveforms at 9 MHz clock frequency, 10 V. Shift registers operate up to 12 MHz, at 20 V.

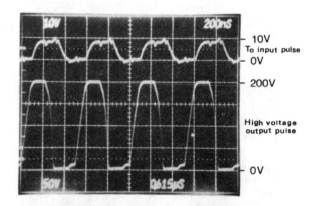

Fig.7 High voltage output waveform, when plasma display panel is driven by the 16 output high voltage MOS IC at 200 V, 2 MHz.

850V NMOS Driver with Active Outputs

Russel A. Martin*, Steven A. Buhler, and Guillermo Lao
Xerox Microelectronics Center
El Segundo, CA 90245

ABSTRACT

This paper describes a unique second generation fully integrated NMOS device operating at up to 850V. The 5.46x5.26 mm^2 chip consists of 16 pull-up/pull-down high voltage output drivers, a 16 bit shift register, and gating logic. The HV output drivers are comprised of two high voltage transistors and a polysilicon pull-up resistor, fabricated on a 70Ω-cm substrate, without dielectric isolation or epitaxial material. The high voltage transistors have closed geometry with a two layer polysilicon field plate. One layer of the field plate has high sheet resistance to set the surface potential above the n- drift region. The low voltage logic is standard TTL compatible NMOS, isolated from the high voltage by a grounded barrier. An analysis of the high voltage transistors, based on a solution of Poisson's Equation[1], is presented which emphasizes the effect of the overlaying metal line on the transistor's performance.

INTRODUCTION

MOS Integrated circuits for high voltage display driving are desirable because of their low cost. A number of ICs, combining a medium scale of low voltage integration and high voltage open drain transistors have appeared in the literature[2-4]. These require external components to provide high voltage to each output. The pull-up can be provided by a resistor or by a combination of active and passive components. In previous work we reported an IC which incorporated on chip pull-up and pull-down capability[5].

To be reliable high voltage MOS transistors must be operated well below their breakdown voltage, they must be able to withstand momentary overvoltages, and they should be uneffected by charge on the top surface of the chip. In order to obtain a chip operating at higher voltages and with greater reliability a study of the limitations to device operation has been performed and a new design has been completed.

OVERVIEW OF DEVICE

This IC provides 16 high voltage outputs which actively switch high or low and are controlled by on-chip low voltage logic. The low voltage logic consists of a 16 bit shift register connecting to latches and control gates for each output. The shift register has an output to allow similar chips to be cascaded for larger systems. It is compatible with normal MOS and TTL logic voltage levels. The four power supply connections are Ground, nominal 5V (for the low voltage logic), nominal 15V (for driving the input to the high voltage output stage), and the high voltage supply.

The chip is laid out with the high voltage stage around the outside on three sides, Fig. 1, separated from the low voltage logic by a barrier of grounded n+, metal, and polysilicon, the only gaps are for the polysilicon crossovers. Contact and pad cuts open the barrier to all layers, preventing charge spreading. The high voltage supply feeds the 16 outputs from a metal line about the outside of the chip. Each high voltage output stage consists of a pull up and a pull down high voltage transistor, an output protection transistor and a pull up resistor. See Fig. 2. The circuit operates as an inverter. To switch the circuit from output low to output high the input is dropped to 0V turning off the pull down transistor. The value of the pull up resistor, the parasitic capacitance, and the transconductance of the pull up transistor determine the rise time of the output.

Figure 3 shows the cross section of the present high voltage pull down transistors and the previous design[5], respectively. The devices have closed geometry. The channel consists of two parts, a conventional thin oxide gate and a thick oxide region. On top of the field oxide is a resistive polysilicon field plate and beneath it is a lightly doped phosphorus channel. Under the metal interconnection gaps must be placed in the field plate because the metal line will modulate the conductivity of the polysilicon and distort the potential distribution in the field plate. These gaps prevent current from flowing in a path under the metal line, instead the field plate potential is determined by the flow of current away from the metal line. In the new design a second layer of polysilicon has been added to shield the substrate from the potential on the metal line. Further, the new design has been modified to have the p+ region wrap around the source in the fashion of a DMOS device. This raises the threshold voltage to 3.5V, however the gate is driven with 15V so this causes no significant performance degradation.

The fabrication of these devices differs somewhat from conventional NMOS processing, both in the definition of field oxide regions and in the polysilicon layer. These devices are fabricated on standard p-type substrates of 70Ωcm resistivity. The p+ regions are the first defined, by ion implantation through the initial oxide. Nitride is then deposited over the oxide. The n-pinched channel region is defined by a nitride etch and phosphorus implant. Another nitride etch defines the other field regions. After field oxidation and gate oxidation polysilicon is deposited. Ion implantation defines the resistivity of the polysilicon for the field plates and the pull up resistors. The polysilicon is patterned and a poly oxide is grown. The poly oxide is removed except in the

Reprinted from *IEEE 30th Int. Electron Devices Meeting*, pp. 266–269, 1984.

regions which are to remain resistive polysilicon. Phosphosilicate glass is deposited and densified. This provides the doping for the source and drain regions and for the polysilicon used in interconnections. The process is completed with contacts, metal, passivation glass, and pad etch.

ANALYSIS AND MODELING

Analysis of the previous design and computer modeling were both integral to the design of the new IC.

A discrepancy in the breakdown voltage between the pull-up transistor, 550V, and the pull-down transistor, up to 900V, showed the direction to pursue. The devices are quite different, the pull-down has the drain on the inside while the pull-up has the drain surrounding the source and an n- region surrounding the drain. This was investigated further by raising the voltage on the drain, with the gate and source grounded, until the devices failed catastrophically and then etching to bare silicon and Secco etching. The location of the damage on the pull-up transistors was consistently under the metal line. On the pull-down transistor the metal line was high during this test while on the pull-up transistor the metal line was low during the test. These results led us to investigate the behavior further using computer simulation.

To model these devices the GEMINI program[1] was used to solve for the electrical potential. This provides a useful tool for the comparison of different designs through examination of the electric field maximum. The program used is our modification of GEMINI. It allows the top surface potential to be fixed in up to 31 regions for definition of the resistive field plate. Further, our version allows the placement of an n- channel so that it is only under the thick oxide.

To simulate the device, the source, substrate and thin oxide gate regions were held at 0V and the drain was fixed at 700V. The field plate was represented as a number of regions of fixed potential across the top of the thick oxide. For the device without the metal lines the space between these regions was left with its potential undefined, the boundary conditions were therefore Neuman. For the case with a metal overpass the space between the field plate rings was taken to be at voltage which was the average of the two adjacent ring voltages and the metal line's voltage. Although this is inaccurate near the rings it should be a good approximation in the silicon.

Figures 4 and 5 show respectively the simulations with the metal high and with the metal low. It is clear that in the case of the metal line being low that the electric field is higher. This is due to the enhancement of the already existing field peak by the presence of the region of low potential from the metal line. The n- region peak concentration was optimized using this method. Figure 6 shows that for all values above $4E15cm^{-3}$ the field is higher when the metal line is low. The minimum, in the curves occurs when the field peak at the n+ drain junction equals the peak under the first gap in the field plate. With the metal line low and the n- dose optimized the effect of the length of extension of the conductive portion of the field plate was examined. Again in this case there are two peaks in the electric field intensity. At long field plate extensions the resistive portion of the field plate is severely shortened and the voltage is drop in a shorter distance. This causes a high peak in the field under the first gap in the field plate, as shown in Fig. 7.

DEVICE PERFORMANCE

The original design had a breakdown voltage of 550V. With the improvements outlined above, excluding the second layer of polysilicon in the field plate, the breakdown voltage is raised to 660V. When the second layer of polysilicon is added the breakdown voltage exceeds 850V. Figure 8 shows the output of a driver with high voltage supply equal to 850V. For reliable operation the device should be used at supply voltages well below its breakdown voltage. Figure 9 shows the rising waveform with high voltage supply equal to 700V, the rise time is $7.5\mu s$, the fall time is under $1\mu s$. The quiescent power with all outputs low is 0.75W. The ability to tolerate substrate current has also been enhanced. The original design could not operate with more than $100\mu a$ of substrate current, do to the tendency of holes to build up in the substrate and forward bias the source, destroying the device. In the new design the field barrier implant surrounds the source of pull down transistors and is shorted to it through metal. With this arrangement the device can tolerate 1ma of avalanche current. With the output low the device can sink 5ma at 600V if sufficient heat sinking is provided.

SUMMARY

To provide an active high voltage output from an Integrated Circuit, high voltage transistors which can be interconnected are needed. At high operating voltages the interconnects can effect the operation of the transistor. For proper modeling, interconnections must be included. When they are included, computer simulation allows optimization of design parameters and gives insight into the nature of limitations of device performance. Through simulation the maximum operating voltage of these devices has been extended to 850V.

ACKNOWLEDGEMENTS

We would like to thank Dale Sumida, Joan Hack, and Larry Shilkoff for their assistance on this work and the Versatec Corporation for their support.

*Present Address, Xerox PARC, 3333 Coyote Hill Rd., Palo Alto, CA 94304

1. J.A. Greenfield and R.W. Dutton, "Nonplaner VLSI Device analysis using the solution of Poisson's equation," IEEE Trans. Electron Devices, vol. ED-27, pp. 1520-1532, Aug. 1980.
2. K. Fujii, Y. Torimaru, K. Nakagawa, T. Fujimoto, Y. Aoki, "400V MOS IC for EL Display", ISSCC Tech. Digest, p.46-7 Feb. 1981.
3. H. Wakaumi, T. Suzuki, M. Saito, and H. Sakuma, "A Highly Reliable 16 Output High Voltage NMOS/CMOS Logic IC with Shielded Source Structrue", IEDM Tech. Digest, p.416-9 Dec. 1983.
4. S. Buhler, D. Heald, R. Ronen, T. Gannon, P. Elkins "Integrated High-Voltage/Low-Voltage MOS Devices", IEDM Tech. Digest, p.259 Dec. 1981.
5. S.A. Buhler, R.A. Martin, D.L. Heald, R.S. Ronen, "High voltage NMOS switching array with active pull-ups and low voltage addressing logic", IEDM Tech. Digest, p.76 Dec. 1982.

Fig. 1   Photograph of Chip.

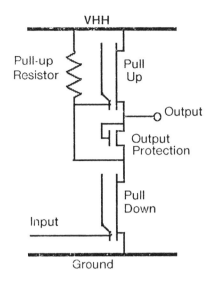

Fig. 2 Schematic representation of high voltage output circuit.

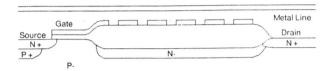

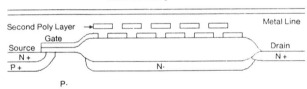

Fig. 3   Cross Section of high voltage pull down transistors from original design, Ref. 5, and the current design. Transistors are axially symmetric about the drain.

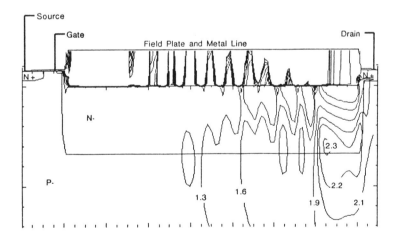

Fig. 4 Cross section of a pull-up transistor with contours of the electric field (units are 10^5V/cm). The metal line over the transistor is at 700V as is the drain.

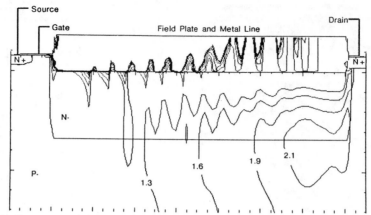

Fig. 5 Cross section of a pull-up transistor with contours of the electric field (units are 10^5V/cm). The metal line over the transistor is at 0V and the drain is at 700V.

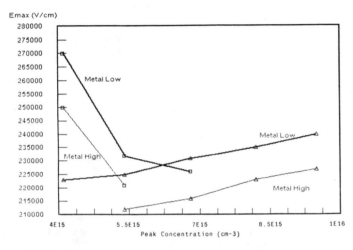

Fig. 6 Electric field peak value vs. peak concentration in the n- region for the conditions where the metal line is at 700V or 0V and the drain is at 700V. Squares are the peak by the drain and triangles are the peak under the first gap in the field plate.

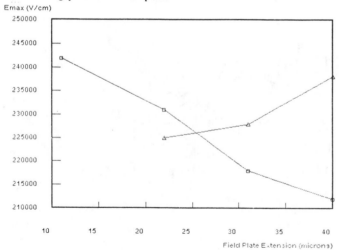

Fig. 7 Electric field peak value vs. extension of the conductive polysilicon of the field plate at the drain end for the condition where the metal line is at 0V and the drain is at 700V. Squares are the peak by the drain and triangles are the peak under the first gap in the field plate.

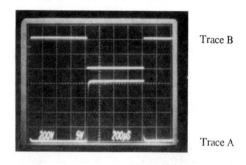

Trace B

Trace A

Fig. 8 Output of high voltage driver with supply voltage equal to 850V, trace A, and oscilloscope trigger, trace B.

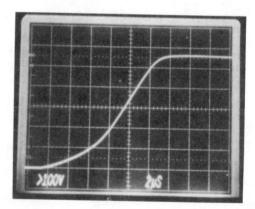

Fig. 9 Rising waveform of high voltage driver with high voltage supply equal to 700V, the rise time is equal to 7.5µs

A Coplanar CMOS Power Switch

ERNST HABEKOTTÉ, MEMBER, IEEE, BERND HOEFFLINGER, MEMBER, IEEE,
WOLFGANG RENKER, AND GÜNTER ZIMMER

Abstract—A 300 V power switch in a high-voltage CMOS technology compatible with a low-voltage MOS/bipolar technology [1] will be presented. This circuit can switch positive and negative 150 V pulses with rise and fall times of 100 ns for a 200 pF capacitive load. The switch has a low-voltage input control (±15 V). Using earth-symmetrical non-overlapping high-voltage pulses as dynamic supply voltages, it is possible to reduce the power dissipation during the switching time considerably in comparison with the power dissipation of power switches, which use static (i.e., constant) supply voltages under the same conditions. Thus, the integration of several switches on a chip has been made possible without exceeding the maximum allowable power dissipation for the commonly used package. The high-voltage n-channel transistor is a DMOS transistor with extended drift region and gate electrodes as field plates. It has a 3 μm effective channel length and 200 nm gate–oxide thickness. The high-voltage p-channel transistor has a pinched resistance between active channel and drain contact. This pinched resistance acts as a drift region. Here the gate–oxide thickness is also 200 nm and the gate electrode has been extended for field plate purposes as well.

I. INTRODUCTION

TO control plasma display panels, electroluminescence displays, piezoelectric crystal transducer arrays, and electrostatic printers, high-voltage (100–300 V) and high-frequency (100 kHz–1 MHz) driver circuits are necessary. The elements used in the arrays present mainly a capacitive load for the output stages. In order to integrate such high-voltage driver circuits with some low-voltage input logic like decoders and flip-flops, as Fig. 1 shows, a few problems have to be solved:

1) a high-voltage MOS technology compatible with a low-voltage process has to be developed, and

2) the on-chip power dissipation and mainly the power dissipation in the output stages have to be kept as small as possible and necessarily smaller than the maximum allowable power dissipation for the commonly used packages (3 W for a twenty-four pin ceramic dual-in-line package [2]).

There are two forms of power dissipation:

1) static power dissipation due to a current flowing directly to ground, and

2) dynamic power dissipation due to charging and discharging capacitors.

The static power dissipation is proportional to the product of the current flowing to ground and the supply voltage. This dissipation can be eliminated if there is no direct current path to ground. Therefore, a CMOS technology has been chosen.

Manuscript received October 22, 1980; revised January 7, 1981. This work was supported by Bundesministerium für Forschung und Technologie, Bonn, West Germany, and Nixdorf Computers, Paderborn, West Germany.

The authors are with the Lehrstuhl Bauelemente der Elektrotechnik, University of Dortmund, Dortmund, West Germany.

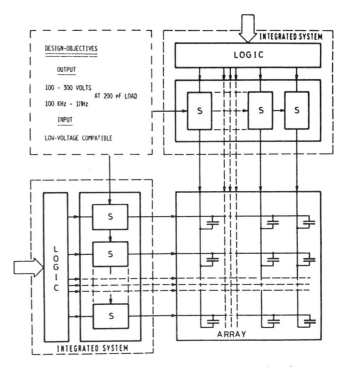

Fig. 1. System diagram with low- to high-voltage interface.

The dynamic power dissipation is proportional to the capacitance, the square of the supply voltage, and the frequency. It cannot be reduced, in principle, except for limiting the on-chip circuitry, which requires a high supply voltage. So a low-voltage input control for the output driver switch is necessary. That means a high-voltage technology, which is compatible with a low-voltage process. This technology is discussed in Section II.

Because of the high output voltage swing and the high output frequency, the dynamic power dissipation in one output driver usually exceeds the maximum allowable dissipation. By shifting the dissipation from the chip to the power supply, it is possible to reduce the on-chip dissipation considerably; the power supply does not produce a constant high supply voltage, which on-chip has to be transferred into a pulsed output signal, but it produces directly the pulses in the form, as they are required at the output with the necessary frequency, duty cycle, rise and fall time, etc. These pulses will be switched to the output controlled by a low-voltage input signal.

The theoretical reduction of the on-chip power dissipation is described in Section III.

The circuit design follows in Section IV. Section V describes circuit simulations and measurements.

Reprinted from *IEEE J. Solid-State Circuits*, vol. SC-16, pp. 212–226, June 1981.

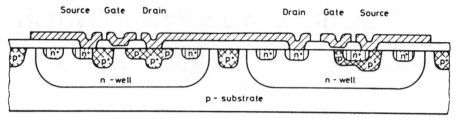

Fig. 2. Cross section of the high-voltage CMOS technology.

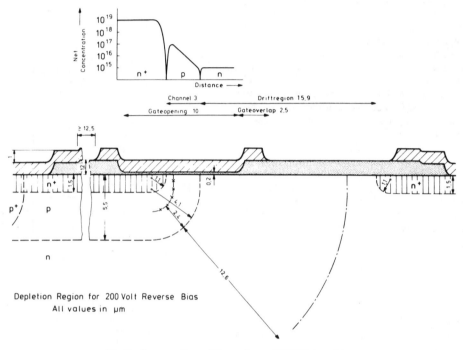

Fig. 3. Cross section of the n-channel DMOS transistor.

II. HIGH-VOLTAGE CMOS TECHNOLOGY

Fig. 2 shows the cross section of both high-voltage CMOS transistors. They are isolated from each other by separate implanted n-wells in a p-substrate. In order to prevent parasitic channels under aluminum interconnections over thick oxide, n⁺-channel stoppers in the n-wells and p⁺-channel stoppers in the p-substrate have been used.

The n-channel transistor is a DMOS transistor. A cross section is given in Fig. 3 showing some important values. The double diffused transistor is capable of withstanding high voltages, mainly because of its drift region [3], [4]. Several parameters which define this high-voltage capability will be discussed here. First, the doping level of the lowest doped region defines the avalanche breakdown voltage. Because the drift region acts as a series resistance for the n-channel transistor, it is necessary to take the n-well doping level as high as possible for a certain breakdown voltage. For example: 200 V is obtainable with a doping level that is not higher than 10^{15} cm⁻³, if the junction is deep enough [5]–[7]. Therefore, an n-well doping concentration of 10^{15} cm⁻³ was chosen. The substrate doping concentration was taken a little bit lower ($3 \cdot 10^{14}$ cm⁻³), so that the depletion region extends farther into the substrate than into the n-well.

This makes it possible to use rather shallow n-wells (diffused to ~26 μm) without a low punchthrough voltage from source

to substrate when source is biased with respect to substrate (Fig. 6). Punchthrough in the channel region depends on the maximum channel doping $N_{A,\max}$, the effective channel length L_{eff}, and the n-well doping concentration N_D. This is described by the following expression [8], [9]:

$$V_P = \frac{q}{\epsilon_{\text{Si}}\epsilon_O} \left(\frac{1}{3} N_{A,\max} + \frac{1}{8} \frac{N_{A,\max}^2}{N_D} \right) (L_{\text{eff}})^2.$$

This simple relationship (Fig. 4) shows that for an effective channel length of 3 μm and a punchthrough voltage V_P higher than 200 V, the maximum doping level in the channel $N_{A,\max}$ has to be higher than $2 \cdot 10^{16}$ cm⁻³. The maximum channel doping and the threshold voltage are correlated as shown in Fig. 5 [9], [10]. In order to prevent gate breakdown (>200 V), the gate–oxide thickness has to be 200 nm and this results in an $N_{A,\max}$ of 10^{17} cm⁻³ for a threshold voltage of ~6 V. The n⁺-contact diffusion has a doping concentration of 10^{19} cm⁻³ and is 1.5 μm deep. The lateral diffusion depth is 1.1 μm. For a channel length of 3 μm, the p-implanted channel area has to be diffused to a total junction depth of 5.5 μm in order to realize a sideways diffusion depth of 4.1 μm. This gives a 3 μm channel length. With the known doping levels and junction depths, it is possible to calculate the depletion widths [11] as shown in Fig. 6.

228

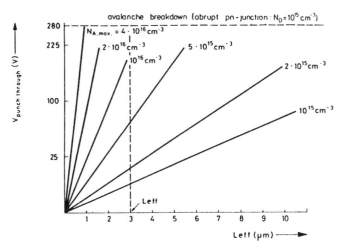

Fig. 4. Punchthrough voltage V_p in DMOS channel as function of effective channel length L_{eff} and maximum channel doping concentration $N_{A,max}$.

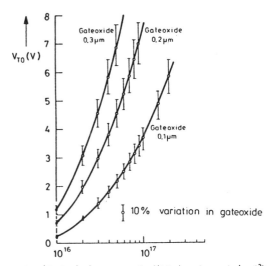

Fig. 5. Threshold voltage as function of $N_{A,max}$.

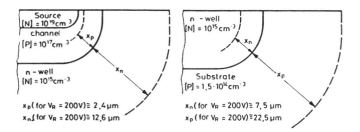

Fig. 6. Depletion widths for the DMOS transistor (200 V).

Simple addition results in a minimum n-well depth of 26 μm in order to prevent early punchthrough in the n-well (5.5 μm + 12.6 μm + 7.5 μm). The n-well will have a sideways diffusion depth of approximately 19 μm and a depletion width in the p-substrate of 22.5 μm. So, the minimum distance between two n-wells should not be smaller than 100 μm using one p^+-channel stopper (10 μm wide).

A computer program [12] is used to calculate the two-dimensional doping level distribution in the DMOS structure

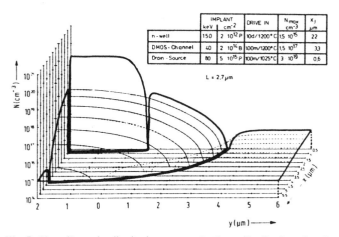

Fig. 7. Two-dimensional doping concentration distribution in the DMOS transistor.

(Fig. 7). Here, the important parameters like channel length, channel and n-well doping concentration, and, last but not least, the junction depth of the channel implant and the source can be determined easily.

For a high breakdown voltage, it is necessary to implement field plates to reduce the effects of rather shallow p-n junctions [13], [14]. This can be made clear with a computer program, which calculates the two-dimensional potential and field distribution from input data describing drain, source, gate, and substrate potentials using the two-dimensional impurity distribution (Fig. 7) in the transistor [15], [16]. Fig. 8 shows the result of two computer simulations of the DMOS transistor with a drain–source voltage of 200 V and a gate–source voltage of 0 V in both cases. It shows the effect of the gate electrode, which has been extended to a field plate. Without field plate, the field strength in Si exceeds the maximum allowable value ($\sim 5 \cdot 10^5$ V/cm) right underneath the end of the gate electrode. This means that avalanche breakdown has already taken place. The field plate reduces the electrical field strength to almost half, which is shown in the lower part of Fig. 8. This extension of the gate electrode over the thick oxide must be done with the necessary care. If it is too close ($<10~\mu$m) to the drain n^+-contact, an early avalanche breakdown will occur because of the high field between gate electrode and drain n^+-contact [17].

The minimum distance of 10 μm between gate electrode and drain contact diffusion was chosen in order to keep the serial resistance introduced by the drift region as small as possible. The total drift region is 15.9 μm long. Fig. 9 shows the output characteristics of the high-voltage n-channel test transistor (500 μm wide) presenting a drain–source breakdown voltage higher than 200 V.

Some measurements and computer calculations are compared in the following figures to check theory with the experiment.

1) The effective channel length can be measured indirectly using the hot electron model of Hoefflinger et al. [18]. First, the parabola, which divides the transistor output characteristics into the saturated and unsaturated region, has been measured [Fig. 10(a)]. The hot electron model gives an analytical relationship for the measured channel current assuming the electrons reach their maximum velocity (E_C is the correspond-

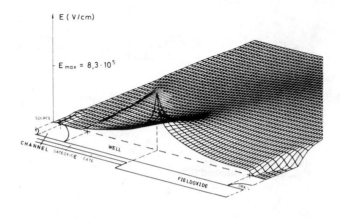

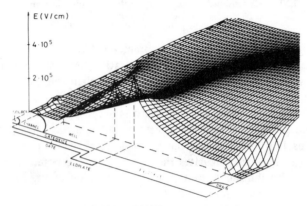

Fig. 8. Simulated field in a DMOS transistor with V_{DS} = 200 V.

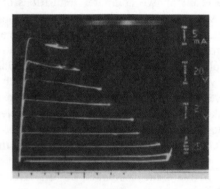

HIGH VOLTAGE P-CHANNEL

Fig. 9. *I–V* characteristics of DMOS transistor (500 μm wide).

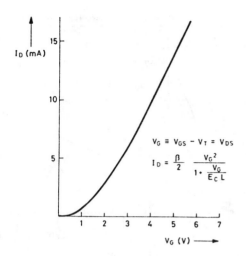

$V_G \equiv V_{GS} - V_T = V_{DS}$

$$I_D = \frac{\beta}{2} \frac{V_G^2}{1 + \frac{V_G}{E_C L}}$$

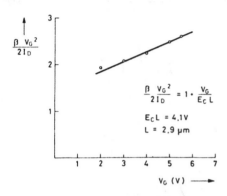

$$\frac{\beta}{2} \frac{V_G^2}{I_D} = 1 + \frac{V_G}{E_C L}$$

$E_C L$ = 4,1 V

L = 2,9 μm

Fig. 10. Determination of the channel length for DMOS transistor.

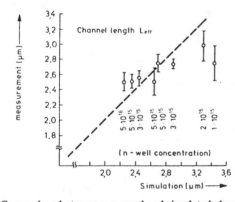

Fig. 11. Comparison between measured and simulated channel lengths.

ing field strength, which in this case is assumed to be equal to the pinchoff field E_g). This relationship is written down in another form, from which the effective channel length L_{eff} can be derived directly. Using this equation, which stands for a straight line with $1/E_c \cdot L_{eff}$ as slope, the measured values are transferred into a new curve shown in Fig. 10(b). Knowing $E_c = 1.4 \cdot 10^4$ V/cm it is possible to calculate L_{eff}. These measured channel lengths are put together in one figure with the channel lengths obtained from the two-dimensional doping level distributions calculated by the computer (Fig. 11). Here it is important to notice that, when the n-well doping concentration gets higher, the measured L_{eff} is getting longer than calculated with the computer. This can be explained qualitatively by the influence of the phosphorus on the diffusion con-

stant of boron. The lower the n-well phosphorus doping concentration, the less its influence on the Si crystal, the smaller the diffusion constant of boron.

2) The n-well depth can be measured rather accurately using the angle lap and staining technique because it is quite deep. Fig. 12 shows the measured and the calculated n-well depths together. The calculated data are obtained with the same simulation program, which is used to calculate the two-dimensional doping concentration distribution of the DMOS transistor. The concentration of phosphorus has an influence on its own diffusion constant [19] and this has been taken into account quantitatively in the simulation program.

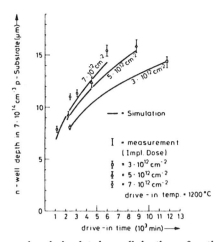

Fig. 12. Measured and simulated n-well depths as function of drive-in time.

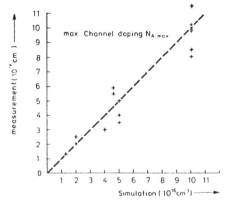

Fig. 13. Comparison between measured and simulated $N_{A,\max}$ in the DMOS channel.

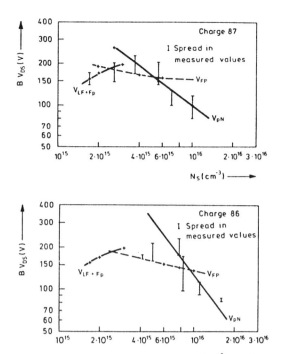

Fig. 14. Drain–source breakdown voltage as function of the background doping concentration.

3) The maximum channel doping $N_{A,\max}$ can be derived from the threshold voltage measurements knowing the gate-oxide thickness [9], [10]. Fig. 13 shows how the calculated $N_{A,\max}$ from the two-dimensional doping level distribution fit the measured ones.

4) It is important how well the breakdown voltage can be foretold. Hence three breakdown phenomena have been considered and related to measured breakdown voltages (Fig. 14):

Curve V_{pn}: Theoretical breakdown voltage of an one-sided abrupt junction, where a lower n-well doping concentration than the one at the SiO_2–Si interface has been taken into account assuming the field plate effect of the gate electrode. The avalanche breakdown is not influenced by the junction curvature.

Curve V_{fP}: The theoretical breakdown voltage, which results from the end of the field plate only. Here "junction" curvature evoked by the end of the field plate and its influence on the maximum field strength has been taken into account [20].

Curve V_{lffp}: Field "laterally" from the p-n junction between channel and n-well coincides with the field "vertically" from the end of the field plate electrode. Both result theoretically in an early avalanche breakdown.

In principle, the same considerations about the high-voltage

capability, as discussed above, can be made for the high-voltage p-channel transistor as well.

The high-voltage p-channel transistor has a p-implanted pinched resistance surrounding the drain contact. It acts as a drift region.

In Fig. 15 some values concerning the high-voltage p-channel transistor are given. As the channel here is defined by a photolithographic step in the process instead of a difference in the lateral diffusion depth, the channel length is longer than for the n-channel DMOS transistor. Therefore, the drift region for the p-channel transistor has been made shorter than for the n-channel transistor. The total drain–source distance for both transistors is equal to 20 μm. The effective channel length of the p-channel transistor is 6-7 μm. So, the implanted drift region has to be 12-13 μm. It is clear, that the relationship for the punchthrough voltage in the channel of the DMOS transistor is not valid here because the channel here has a uniform doping concentration (n-well). Yet, the pinched resistance has to have a lower doping concentration than the channel region as well to prevent an early punchthrough. The output characteristics of the p-channel test transistor indicate an avalanche breakdown voltage higher than 160 V (500 μm wide) (see Fig. 16).

This high-voltage CMOS technology is compatible with a low-voltage CMOS/bipolar technology, which has already been developed in Dortmund [1]. Fig. 17 shows a cross section of the total CMOS technology.

The breakdown voltage of the n-well/p-substrate diode depends on n-well dope and depth. This has been investigated. The measured and the theoretical values are given in Fig. 18. Table I gives the fabrication sequence for the high-voltage CMOS transistors.

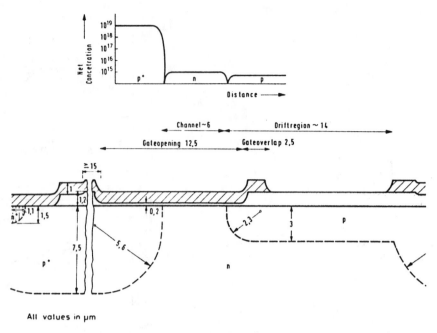

Fig. 15. Cross section of the p-channel transistor with pinched resistance.

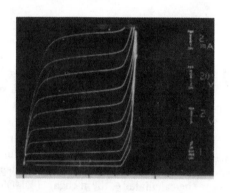

HIGH VOLTAGE   N-CHANNEL

Fig. 16. *I–V* characteristics of the p-channel transistor with pinched
resistance (500 μm wide).

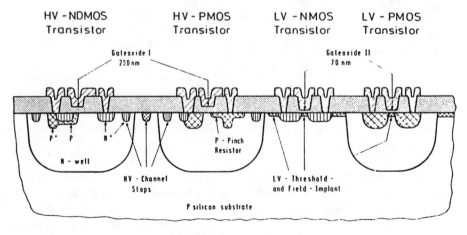

Fig. 17. Compatible high- and low-voltage CMOS process.

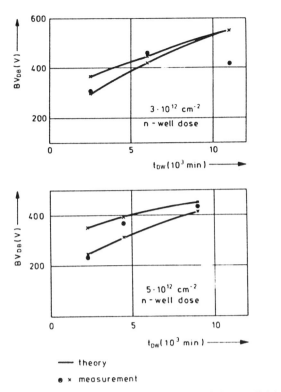

Fig. 18. An n-well breakdown voltage as function of the n-well drive-in time.

TABLE I
HIGH VOLTAGE CMOS FABRICATION SEQUENCE

1) n-well oxide
2) n-well window etch, phosphorus implant
3) oxidation, drive-in
4) 1st masking oxide, p⁺-contact window etch, boron implant
5) 2nd masking oxide, photoresist mask, drift region window etch, boron implant
6) oxidation, n⁺-source window etch, thin oxide, boron implant, drive-in
7) field oxidation, n⁺-drain window etch, phosphorus deposition
8) contact window etch, gate window etch, gate oxide
9) contact window etch, Al-deposition
10) Al-etch

III. REDUCTION OF THE ON-CHIP POWER DISSIPATION

As already mentioned in the Introduction, the trick is the use of a dynamic supply voltage instead of a static supply voltage. Fig. 19 will be used to explain the theoretical reduction of the on-chip power dissipation.

In the static version the output stage is driven by a constant supply voltage V_E. By an activated output transistor, here represented by its average on-resistance R, the output capacitive load C_E is charged to V_E. Assuming a total switching time of Δt and a time constant $\tau = R \cdot C_E$, the average power dissipation during switching is $1/\Delta t \cdot (1/2 \cdot C_E \cdot V_E^2)$ ($\tau \ll \Delta t$). The voltage drop over the activated transistor is indicated by the shaded area. The discharge of C_E is similar, although another transistor has to do the job now.

In the dynamic version the output stage is driven by the voltage pulse Φ_p acting as supply voltage. Φ_p is as required at the output. By the activated output transistor, here also represented by its average on-resistance R, the output follows Φ_p

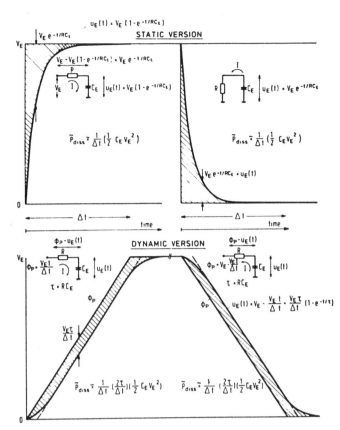

Fig. 19. Comparison of the theoretical power dissipation for the static and the dynamic version of the supply voltage.

both during charging and discharging. So, here only one activated output transistor is necessary instead of two as in the static version. The voltage drop over the activated output transistor indicated by the shaded area is almost constant and equal to $V_E \cdot \tau/\Delta t$ ($\tau = R \cdot C_E$), if the time constant τ is small compared to the total switching time Δt. It is much smaller than the voltage drop in the static version and therefore the power dissipation in the dynamic version is much smaller than in the static version. The reduction factor is $2 \cdot \tau/\Delta t$, as can be easily derived.

Furthermore, the activated transistor in the dynamic version remains always in unsaturated mode, so that the average on-resistance R can be kept small far more easily than in the static version.

IV. CIRCUIT DESIGN

The circuit is built symmetrically using nonoverlapping positive- and negative-pulsed supply voltages Φ_p and Φ_n, as drawn in Fig. 20.

The CMOS driver circuit is controlled by the capacitive voltage divider at the gate of the output transistor. This capacitive voltage divider creates a gate–source voltage difference, which activates the output transistor during the time the high-supply voltage pulse is at the source. The activated output transistor transfers the high-voltage pulse at the source to the drain, which is the output of the CMOS switch. The gate–source voltage difference is assumed to be high enough to activate the output transistor. The capacitors, which form the capacitive voltage divider, are a simplified representation of the intrinsic parasitics of an MOS transistor.

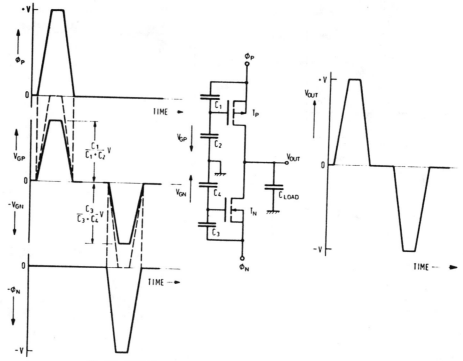

Fig. 20. CMOS switch with pulsed supply voltages in principle.

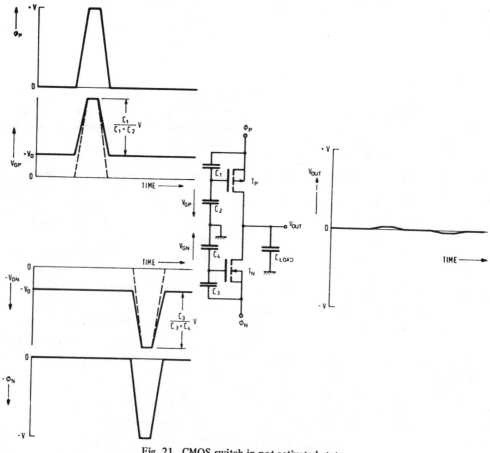

Fig. 21. CMOS switch in not activated state.

Because of symmetry, we will restrict ourselves to the p-channel output transistor T_p. Further, we will assume at first that the threshold voltage is 0 V to make it easier to discuss the circuit.

In Fig. 20 the starting gate potential is 0 V. By raising the gate potential high enough to compensate for the voltage difference created by the capacitive voltage divider C_1, C_2 during Φ_p, it is possible to keep the output transistor T_p inactive. This situation is shown in Fig. 21. It is evident that this precharge voltage V_O has to be transferred before the high-voltage

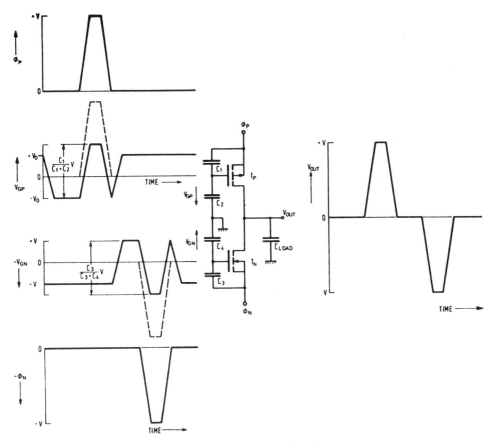

Fig. 22. CMOS switch in activated state.

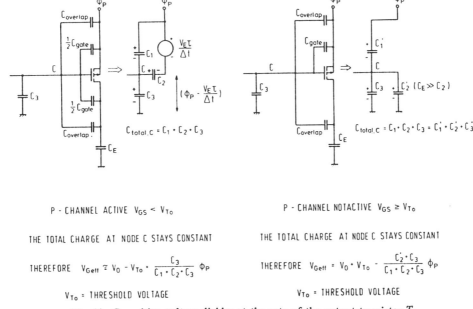

Fig. 23. Capacitive voltage divider at the gate of the output transistor T_p.

pulse Φ_p arrives at the source of T_p. For the n-channel output transistor T_n V_O has to be negative in order to keep it inactive during Φ_n.

Lowering the starting gate potential to a negative level makes the output transistor T_p already active before Φ_p is there and more active during Φ_p (Fig. 22).

Using an earth-symmetrical precharge voltage V_O it is possible to optimize the capacitive voltage divider, so that two times V_O is available to activate the output transistor (Fig. 23). How V_O is realized and transferred to the gate of the output transistor is shown in Fig. 24. A low-voltage CMOS inverter defines the precharge voltage V_O with its polarity. The trans-

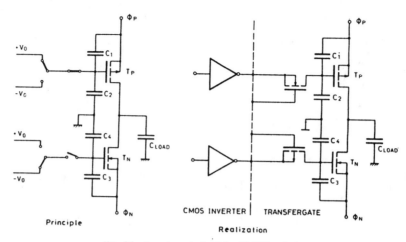

Fig. 24. Input control of the CMOS switch.

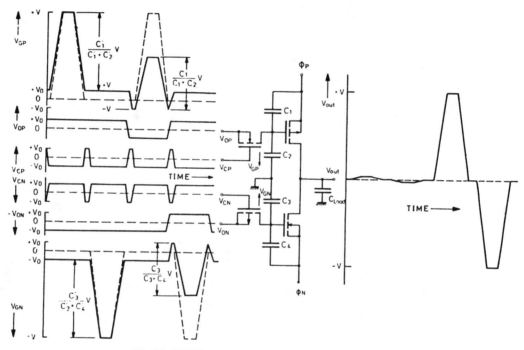

Fig. 25. CMOS power switch with the necessary signals.

fer gate transfers V_O to the gate of the output transistor and makes it possible to isolate this gate (floating gate). Note that a p-channel output transistor has an n-channel transfer gate and vice versa. Fig. 25 shows the complete CMOS output switch with the necessary waveforms.

First the inactive and then the active state has been drawn. Before every high-voltage pulse Φ_p, Φ_n the transfer gates are activated with a clock to precharge the gates of the output transistors. In the case of the inactivity the p-channel output transistor needs a positive V_O. For the n-channel it has to be negative. For the active case only one of the output transistors may be activated at the same time, here first the p-channel and then the n-channel output transistor. When the p-channel output transistor is to be activated, the n-channel has to stay inactive and the other way round.

If one takes a closer look at the high-voltage transistors in the switch (Fig. 26), it will be clear that the drain–source diodes

for both CMOS transistors are not always reversely biased. Under certain conditions these diodes are forward biased.

For the output transistor this happens if they have been activated and the source voltage is returning to ground potential. This is advantageous because the output capacitor is discharged by the activated output transistor and by the forward biased diode as well.

For the transfer gates this can occur between the high-voltage pulses. This happens only if two conditions are fulfilled: First, if the precharge voltage V_O has that polarity which keeps the output transistor inactive, and second, if the output transistor has been activated one period earlier or, otherwise if high leakage currents were involved.

Also again, the diodes are well suited in order to keep the output transistors inactive. The precharge voltage with the right polarity will be transferred by these diodes to the gate of the output transistors. This is, of course, only possible, if the

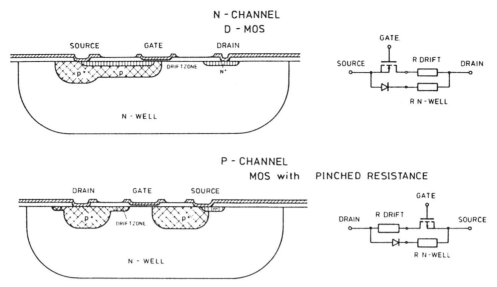

Fig. 26. Drain–source diodes in both CMOS transistors.

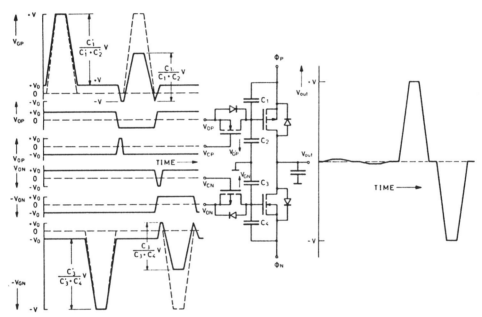

Fig. 27. CMOS power switch with the drain–source diodes.

n-well resistance, which is in series with the drain–source diodes, is small enough compared to the other resistances involved. Fig. 27 shows how the waveforms will look if the diodes have been implemented.

With a ±15 V precharge voltage, the starting effective gate-source voltage difference $V_{Geff,min}$ for the output transistor is 15 V–V_{TO} and the maximum effective gate-source voltage difference $V_{Geff,max}$ is 30 V. So the average V_{Geff} is approximately 20 V. During charging and discharging (Δt), the voltage drop over the activated transistor is almost constant and small compared with the effective gate-source voltage ($\tau \ll \Delta t$, $\tau = R \cdot C_E$). Therefore, the output transistor stays in the unsaturated mode and the on-resistance of the activated channel is much smaller than the serial resistance of the drift region.

For the on-resistance, it is possible to write the following:

$$R_{on} = V_{DS}/I_{DS} = 1/\beta_O \cdot (W/L) \cdot V_{Geff}$$

(unsaturated mode and $V_{DS} \ll V_{Geff}$).

The resistance of the drift region can be approximated with the following expression [21]:

$$R_{drift\ region} = (\rho/(W \cdot \pi)) \cdot (\ln((L' - r_1)/r_1) + \ln((L' - r_2)/r_2)$$

Here, one line source of current and one line sink of current in an infinite homogeneous medium with the resistivity ρ (ohm · cm) have been assumed. The distance between the source and the sink is L'. The total length of both lines is W and r_1 and r_2 are the two radii corresponding to the effective current source and sink surfaces near the diffused regions.

TABLE II
TABLE II
TOTAL ON-RESISTANCE OF DMOS AND PINCHED RESISTANCE TRANSISTOR

	n-Channel DMOS Transistor	p-Channel Pinched-Resistance Transistor
B_0	$10.0 \, \mu A/V^2$	$6.0 \, \mu A/V^2$
L	$3.0 \, \mu m$	$6.0 \, \mu m$
V_{Geff}	20.0 V	20.0 V
resulting in:		
R_{on}	$2/W \, \Omega/cm$	$5/W \, \Omega/cm$
L'	$21.1 \, \mu m$	$17.6 \, \mu m$
r_1	$4.1 \, \mu m$	$2.3 \, \mu m$
r_2	$1.1 \, \mu m$	$2.3 \, \mu m$
ρ	$5.0 \, \Omega/cm$	$10.0 \, \Omega/cm$
resulting in:		
$R_{drift region}$	$7/W \, \Omega/cm$	$12/W \, \Omega/cm$

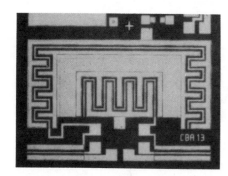

Fig. 28. Microphotograph of the CMOS switch.

Taking the width of T_n equal to 2500 μm and of T_p equal to 5000 μm, both transistors will have a total on-resistance of approximately 34 Ω (see Table II). This results in a total average power dissipation of 1.34 W for an output voltage swing of 300 V at a capacitive load of 200 pF in a repetition rate of 1 MHz and with rise and fall times of 100 ns. For the p-channel output transistor alone this means 0.67 W.

For the transfer gates, the widths have been taken equally because the difference in their capacitive loads will counter-match the difference in their on-resistances. Here, twice the precharge voltage V_O minus the threshold voltage is available as the effective gate–source voltage difference because the clock has the same voltage swing as V_O. The transfer gate is mostly in the unsaturated mode and the capacitive load for the n-channel transfer gate is approximately 20 pF. The width for the transfer gates have been taken equal to 500 μm in order to realize relatively small precharge times of 20–30 ns.

Fig. 28 gives a microphotograph of the test chip with a complete CMOS power switch. Both output transistors have been folded into meander structures. The p-channel output transistor lies halfway around the n-channel output transistor. The two transfer gates lie underneath. The total covered area is 2.6 mm^2.

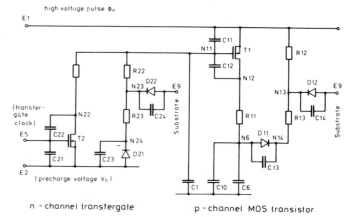

Fig. 29. A p-channel output transistor with n-channel transfer gate for the simulation.

V. SIMULATIONS AND MEASUREMENTS

Because of long CPU times necessary to calculate the total CMOS switch, the p-channel and the n-channel output transistor with transfer gate have been simulated separately. The simulations have been carried out with the simulation program DOMOS [22]. Here, all parasitic elements can be considered as shown in Fig. 29 for a p-channel output transistor with a n-channel transfer gate. Fig. 30 shows the simulated output voltage, the precharge voltage V_O and the transfer gate clock for the p-channel output transistor first in the activated state and then kept inactive (frequency (Φ_p) = 2.2 MHz, rise and fall time equal to 100 ns, a voltage swing of 150 V and 200 pF capacitive load). In Fig. 31, a comparison is made between the power dissipation of the output stage for the p-channel output transistor with static and dynamic supply voltage. The extra power dissipation during the rise time for the static version is caused by the extra inverter necessary to control the gate of the output transistor (Fig. 32). The power consumption in the static version exceeds 90 W and the average value is 8.25 W (for one half CMOS output stage). In the dynamic version, it does not exceed 6 W, and the average lies around 0.7 W. So it is at least 10 times smaller than in the static version.

To measure the output stage, we had problems finding a pulse generator with the right specifications to supply the switch with the dynamic positive and negative pulsed supply voltages with variable rise/fall times and repetition rate. So, we measured a discrete n-channel output transistor with a discrete p-channel transfer gate with 50 V pulses at a 750 kHz rate and rise/fall times of 100 ns. The upper part of Fig. 33 shows the negative pulses Φ_n, the transfer gate clock, and the precharge voltage V_O. The lower part shows the output signal first for an active and after that for an inactive state of the n-channel output transistor. The transfer gate clock and V_O are peak-to-peak 10 V. How V_{out} follows Φ_n in the active state is shown in Fig. 34.

VI. CONCLUSIONS

It has been shown that the CMOS output stage with dynamic nonoverlapping positive- and negative-pulsed supply

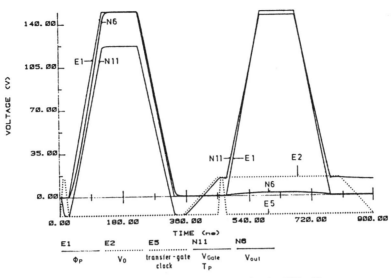

Fig. 30. Simulated waveforms in the circuit of Fig. 29.

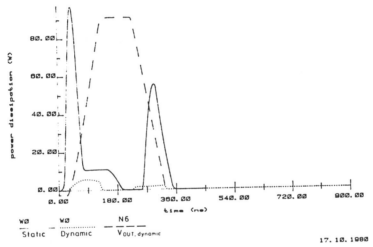

Fig. 31. Comparison between the dynamic (see also Fig. 29 and Fig. 30) and the static power dissipation (see also Fig. 32) under the same conditions.

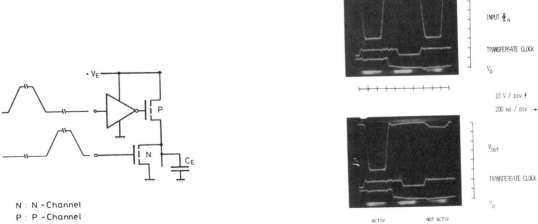

Fig. 32. The p-channel output transistor needs an extra static inverter to control its gate potential.

Fig. 33. Measured waveforms for an n-channel output transistor with a p-channel transfer gate.

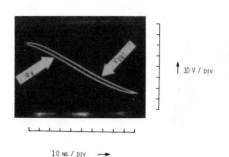

Fig. 34. In the active state from Fig. 33, V_{out} follows ϕ_n with a maximum delay of 7.5 ns.

TABLE III
PERFORMANCE TABLE FOR THE CMOS POWER SWITCH

Total area	2.6 mm^2
for a:	
Frequency	1.0 MHz
Switching time	100.0 ns
Output voltage swing	300.0 V
Capacitive load	200.0 pF
V_{in}	30.0 V
there is a:	
Total power dissipation	1.4 W
$I_{out,max}$	350.0 mA
Maximum delay	12.5 ns

voltages has considerably reduced power consumption compared to the same stage with a static supply voltage under the same conditions. The capacitive voltage divider at the gate of the output transistor is used for a low-voltage input control. The high-voltage CMOS technology permits a low-voltage CMOS process, so that the integration of several high-voltage power switches with a low-voltage input control circuitry has been made feasible [23].

It is important to notice, that the total dynamic power dissipation has not been reduced. With a static supply voltage, it is dissipated mainly in the output stage and with a dynamic supply voltage mainly in the power supply. Table III lists the important features.

ACKNOWLEDGMENT

Discussions with H. G. Graf, R. Schweer, and H. Fiedler are gratefully acknowledged. Particular contributions come from E. Salten, D. Krey, and J. Jesper. The authors wish to thank E. Neubert, M. Obst, P. Staks, and M. Zimmermann for their technology support, K. Schmidbauer and V. Dohmann for the drawings, and C. Menke for typing the manuscript.

REFERENCES

[1] G. Zimmer, B. Hoefflinger, and J. Schneider, "A fully implanted NMOS, CMOS, bipolar technology for VLSI of analog–digital systems," *IEEE J. Solid-State Circuits*, vol. SC-14, pp. 312–318, Apr. 1979.
[2] L. Cergal, "Thermal design considerations in CMOS circuits," *Electron. Eng.*, pp. 56–57, Apr. 1976.
[3] H. J. Sigg, G. D. Vendelin, T. P. Cauge, and J. Kocsis, "DMOS transistor for microwave applications," *IEEE Trans. Electron Devices*, vol. ED-19, pp. 45–53, Jan. 1972.
[4] T. J. Rodgers, S. Asai, M. D. Pocha, R. W. Dutton, and J. D. Meindl, "An experimental and theoretical analysis of double-diffused MOS transistors," *IEEE J. Solid-State Circuits*, vol. SC-10, pp. 322–330, Oct. 1975.
[5] A. S. Grove, *Physics and Technology of Semiconductor Devices*. New York: Wiley, 1967, ch. 5.
[6] S. M. Sze, *Physics of Semiconductor Devices*. New York: Wiley, 1969, ch. 5, pp. 109–126.
[7] A. Blicher, "Thyristor physics," *Applied Physics and Engineering*. New York: Springer-Verlag, 1976.
[8] M. D. Pocha, J. D. Plummer, and J. D. Meindl, "Tradeoff between threshold voltage and breakdown in high voltage double-diffused MOS transistors," *IEEE Trans. Electron Devices*, vol. ED-25, pp. 1325–1327, Nov. 1978.
[9] B. Hoefflinger, *Großintegration Band 2–Technologie, Entwurf, Systeme*. Munich, Germany: Oldenbourg, to be published.
[10] M. D. Pocha, A. G. Gonzalez, and R. W. Dutton, "Threshold voltage controllability in double-diffused MOS transistors," *IEEE Trans. Electron Devices*, vol. ED-21, pp. 773–784, Dec. 1974.
[11] H. Lawrence and R. M. Warner, Jr., "Diffused junction depletion layer calculations," *Bell. Syst. Tech. J.*, vol. 39, pp. 389–404, Mar. 1960.
[12] E. Salten, "Two-dimensional doping level distribution," private communication.
[13] A. Rusu and C. Bulcea, "Deep-depletion breakdown voltage of silicon-dioxide/silicon MOS capacitors," *IEEE Trans. Electron Devices*, vol. ED-26, pp. 201–204, Mar. 1979.
[14] V. P. O'Neil and P. G. Alones, "Relation between oxide thickness and the breakdown voltage of a planar junction with field relief electrode," *IEEE Trans. Electron Devices*, vol. ED-26, pp. 1098–1100, July 1979.
[15] J. Tihany, "Untersuchungen über die isolation in integrierten n-kanal-MOS-schaltungen," Ph.D. dissertation, Universität Erlangen-Nürnberg, Germany, 1978.
[16] D. Krey, "Two-dimensional-MOS-transistor modeling," private communication.
[17] M. J. Declerq and J. D. Plummer, "Avalanche breakdown in high-voltage DMOS devices," *IEEE Trans. Electron Devices*, vol. ED-23, pp. 1–4, Jan. 1976.
[18] B. Hoefflinger, H. Sibbert, and G. Zimmer, "Model and performance of hot-electron MOS-transistors for VLSI," *IEEE Trans. Electron Devices*, vol. ED-26, pp. 513–520, Apr. 1979.
[19] D. J. Hamilton and W. G. Howard, *Basic Integrated Circuitry Engineering*. New York: McGraw-Hill, 1975.
[20] S. M. Sze and G. Gibbons, "Effect of junction curvature on breakdown voltage in semiconductors," *Solid-State Electron.*, vol. 9, pp. 831–845, 1966.
[21] M. D. Pocha and R. W. Dutton, "A computer aided design model for high-voltage double-diffused MOS (DMOS) transistors," *IEEE J. Solid-State Circuits*, vol. SC-11, pp. 718–726, Oct. 1976.
[22] H. Sibbert, "Modellierung und netzwerkanalyseprogramm für MOS-schaltungen mit hoher leistungsfähigkeit," Ph.D. dissertation, Universität Dortmund, Dortmund, Germany, 1977.
[23] B. Hoefflinger and G. Zimmer, "New CMOS technologies," to be published in *Solid-State Devices*, 1980 (J. Carrol, Ed.), The Institute of Physics, London, England.

BIMOS - A NEW WAY TO SIMPLIFY HIGH-POWER CUSTOM INTERFACE

Mark Heisig - Applications Engineer
(Paul Emerald-Manager Applications Engineering)
SPRAGUE ELECTRIC COMPANY
115 Northeast Cutoff
Worcester, MA 01606
617-853-5000

BiMOS combines high-power bipolar output structures with low-power CMOS shift registers, latches and decoders on the same chip to form MSI to LSI power interface devices with intelligence (smart muscle chips). Present BiMOS devices, BiMOS technology limitations, and the suitability of BiMOS (and other technologies) for display applications will be discussed. BiMOS appears to be a very key technology for the future. Its product niche will be for applications requiring 60-100V breakdowns (or more), up to 600mA output drive current, low power logic, wide supply range, and modest speeds.

Expansion of BiMOS into linear as well as digital applications will produce circuits with analog bipolar inputs, digital CMOS logic, and high power bipolar outputs all on the same chip. Chips with linear output structures will also emerge. Such a circuit might be a constant current cathode driver with latches for gas discharge display applications.

INTRODUCTION

Recently, Sprague has emerged as a leader in the design and development of high-voltage, high-power interface IC's associated with driving displays, relays, solenoids, small stepper motors, thermal print heads, and incandescent lamps. One of the newest developments at Sprague, somewhat initiated by the arrival of the μP revolution, is BiMOS. BiMOS combines high-voltage, high-current bipolar ("Bi") output structures with low-power CMOS ("MOS") logic structures on the same chip to form MSI to LSI power interface devices. These devices consist of low-power CMOS shift registers, latches, and decoders which translate data to high-power bipolar outputs.

The intent of BiMOS and Sprague Semiconductor Division (Digital Products) is to provide "nuts & bolts" solutions to customer problems or needs, rather than use the most sophisticated technology. In many instances, BiMOS does provide a "nuts & bolts" approach to simplify high-power custom interface.

Present BiMOS devices include those in Table I.

THE BIMOS TECHNOLOGY

A cross-section of the BiMOS technology is shown in Figure 1 and is basically self-explanatory. This process utilizes 12 mask layers, 5 ion implants, and 3 diffusions. The BiMOS process typically yields bipolar output structures with 50V breakdowns (BV_{cex}) and 35V sustaining voltages BV_{ce} (sus). Breakdowns can be obtained up to 100V (BV_{cex}) and BV_{ce}(sus) = 50V by increasing the epi thickness and resistivity. To accommodate high-power bipolar structures, CMOS gates have channel lengths typically longer than standard CMOS (8-10 um), with a minimum compromise of 25% additional area. A photomicrograph of a standard UCN-4810A device is shown in Figure 2. The UCN-4810A has a chip area of 107 mils x 150 mils (16,050 mils^2) and has 60V, 40 mA sourcing output drivers $\approx$ 13 mils x 15 mils in area ($\approx$ 195 mils^2). This device also makes use of a polysilicon thin-film resistor technology with values ranging from 8KΩ

TABLE I

1. UCN-4401A & 4801A; 4-Bit and 8-Bit Latch/Sink Drivers

2. UCN-4805A & 4806; Latched Decoder/Source Driver (Fluorescent Displays)

3. UCN-4808A; 8-Bit High-Power Addressable Latch/Sink Driver

4. UCN-4810A; 10-Bit Serial In/Parallel Out/Source Driver (Fluorescent Displays)

5. UCN-4815A; 8-Bit Latch/Source Driver (Fluorescent Displays)

6. UCN-4820A; 8-Bit Serial In/Parallel Out/Latched Sink Drivers

Reprinted from *IEEE 3rd Custom Integrated Circuits Conf.*, pp. 8-12, 1981.

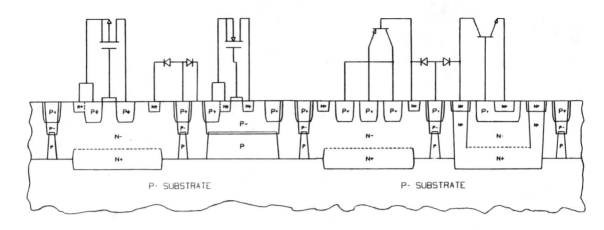

THE BIMOS CROSS-SECTION

FIGURE 1

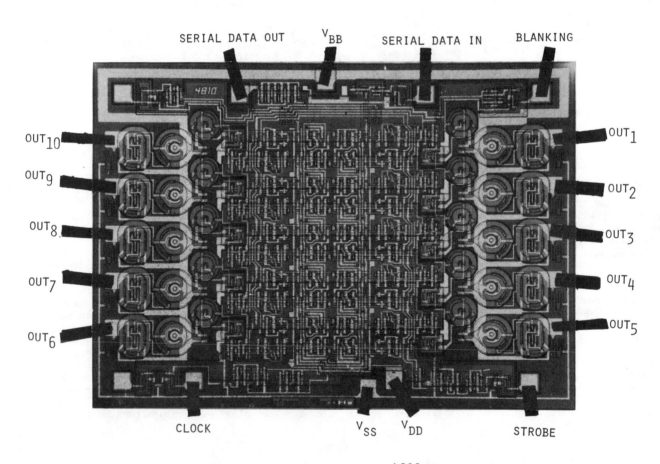

PHOTO-MICROGRAPH OF UCN-4810A DEVICE

FIGURE 2

to 125KΩ. Present BiMOS technology limits are well below the output current-voltage ratings of standard bipolar although BiMOS is definitely headed toward tracking bipolar capabilities. Maximum limits for current devices are shown in Table II.

TABLE II

OUTPUT BREAKDOWN VOLTAGE	to 100V (max)
OUTPUT CURRENT	to 600mA (max)
LOGIC SUPPLY RANGE	5V to 15V ± 5%
LOGIC SWITCHING SPEEDS (S/R)	to 1 MHz @ 12V
CHANNELS/DIP	10 (max)

BiMOS AND OTHER TECHNOLOGIES (DISPLAY INTERFACE)

Shown in Table III is a comparison of various device technologies including BiMOS for suitability in display applications.

STANDARD BIPOLAR:

Standard bipolar is limited basically to relatively simple MSI circuits requiring voltages $\geq$ 100V or high-current outputs $\geq$ 2A. Cost, chip size, and package power dissipation will restrict these circuits largely to versatile, simple buffers.

I^2L:

Present limits of I^2L appear to be limited to applications below 50 to 60V levels. I^2L with its combination of circuit density, low power, reasonable switching speeds, etc. should make a good match for LED or other low voltage display applications. For the higher voltage ($>$ 25-30V) prospects, the penalty of reduced circuit density may diminish its cost effectiveness. Some increase in standoff voltage may be accomplished by cascaded output transistors or process improvements such as double layer epi thus reducing the need to sacrifice logic density. Primary display applications for I^2L are LED and vacuum fluorescent and electromagnetic.

CMOS/DMOS:

This technology consists of DMOS outputs rated at 60 to 100V breakdowns, $\leq$ 25mA output currents, and CMOS logic which operates at speeds to 4 MHz. The major disadvantage of this technology is the limited CMOS supply range specified only at 12V (may be done for max speed) and its limited output current. Larger matrix panels will require 100mA or more drive current.

DIELECTRIC ISOLATION:

This technology affords the highest breakdown capability since there is no collector to substrate PN junction, nor is there a collector to isolation wall junction. Breakdowns from

TABLE III
IC TECHNOLOGY -- DISPLAY INTERFACE

Technology	Breakdown V	Output I	Speed	Complexity (max)	Supply Range	Power	Primary Display Suitability
Linear Process Bipolar	10 to 170V	10mA to 2A	1 MHz	MSI	5V	High	LEDs, GD, VF, ACP, DCEL, EM
I^2L	20 to 60V	10mA to 2A	3-6 MHz	LSI	5V	Low-Modest	LED, VF, EM
BiMOS	50 to 150V	10mA to 500mA	2-5 MHz	LSI	5 to 15V	Low	LED, GD, VF,
CMOS/DMOS	60 to 100V	25mA	2-4 MHz	LSI	12V	Low	GD, VF, ACP, LED
DI	200 to 300V	10mA to 100mA (est)	1 MHz (est)	MSI	5V	High	GD, VF, ACP, DCEL

Code: GD = DC Gas Discharge & Glow Transfer   DCEL = DC Electroluminescent

ACP = AC Plasma   EM = Electromagnetic

VF = Vacuum Fluorescent

100V to 280V are possible with transistor sizes considerably smaller than their PN isolated counterparts. Major disadvantages of DI are process complexity, cost and alternate sourcing. If these can be overcome, DI has great promise with the potential of 300V transistors.

BiMOS:

BiMOS for interface ICs seem to fit a technology niche of higher breakdowns than I^2L, and where logic power and supply voltage range is important. With additional time and greater concentration on increasing BV, it appears that higher voltages ($\geq$ 150V) for output buffers can be obtained. By obtaining breakdowns in the 120V to 160V range, BiMOS becomes a viable IC technology for interfacing higher voltage displays; dc gas discharge ±100V to ±130V; a-c plasma 160V to 170V; and glow transfer or dc electroluminescent (DCEL) 120V-160V.

TYPICAL APPLICATION OF BiMOS: UCN-4810A

The UCN-4810A is specifically targeted for use with vacuum fluorescent displays. This device functionally replaces a 10-bit serial in, parallel out shift register, 10-bits of data latch, and 10 high-voltage sourcing buffers (including output pulldown resistors).

Absolute Max Ratings for this device are shown in Table IV.

TABLE IV

OUTPUT VOLTAGE, V_{OUT}	60V
LOGIC SUPPLY VOLTAGE RANGE, V_{DD}	4.5V to 18V
DISPLAY SUPPLY VOLTAGE RANGE, V_{BB}	5.0V to 60V
CONTINUOUS OUTPUT CURRENT, I_{OUT}	-40mA
INPUT VOLTAGE RANGE, V_{IN}	V_{DD}

The UCN-4810A functional block diagram is shown in Figure 3, and device pinout in Figure 4. Devices may be cascaded; the SERIAL DATA OUT of device #1 connects to SERIAL DATA INPUT on device #2, etc. During serial data entry, the BLANKING input should be held HIGH to prevent data transfer from showing on the display. The BLANKING input is switched low to allow latch control of outputs.

SERIAL DATA present at the input is transferred to the shift register during the low to high ("0" to logic "1") transition of the CLOCK input pulse. Succeeding CLOCK inputs will continue shifting data information toward the SERIAL DATA OUTPUT. SERIAL DATA must be present at input prior to rising edge of CLOCK input (see Timing Condition--Figure 5)

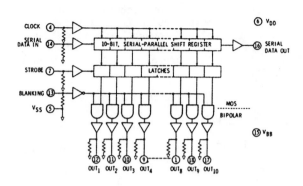

FIGURE 3

Register data is transferred to its respective latch during period when STROBE is held high (converts serial to parallel). Latches will continue to accept new data while the STROBE is high. Any application which bypasses the latches (STROBE connected high) requires that the BLANKING input be held high during data entry. Such applications are generally associated with the use of the device as a grid driver (VF displays).

Figure 6 depicts six UCN-4810A's driving a 20 character 5 x 7 dot matrix VF display. Two devices are cascaded for grid selection and the other 4 are used as dot drivers. With proper control of data, such an interface can be accomplished with 5-6 input lines. Data to the 4 dot drivers is rapid (a burst), and may be loaded in under 80 us with this scheme. The 2 units used as grid drivers need only load a single "1" each scan cycle and this bit would be shifted at the MUX frequency ($\approx$ 2 kHz for a 20 character display). Blanking is required between each character and should be $\geq$20 μs. Failure to provide sufficient blanking may cause display flickering or "ghosting". Minimum ON time for each is $\approx$ 100 μs, although typical values range from $\geq$200 us to $\leq$ 500 μs. A 20 character display scanned at 2 kHz (100 Hz/character) allows 480 μs max on time + 20 μs min blanking = 500 μs for each character.

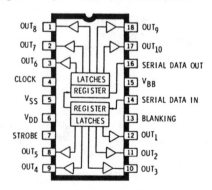

FIGURE 4

244

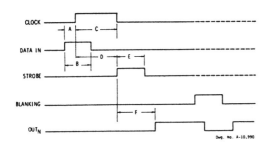

FIGURE 5

		$V_{DD} = 5.0$ V	$V_{DD} = 15$ V
A.	Minimum Data Active Time Before Clock Pulse (Data Set-Up Time)	250 ns	150 ns
B.	Minimum Data Pulse Width	500 ns	300 ns
C.	Minimum Clock Pulse Width	1.0 μs	250 ns
D.	Minimum Time Between Clock Activation and Strobe	1.0 μs	400 ns
E.	Minimum Strobe Pulse Width	500 ns	300 ns
F.	Typical Time Between Strobe Activation and Output Transition	1.0 μs	1.0 μs

A faster technique for loading is possible but requires more I/O lines. By using the approach in Figure 7, it is possible to load the shift registers during the blanking interval (≳ 20 us). The four 4810's used as dot drivers have separate data input lines but common clock, strobe, and blanking lines.

This approach allows loading the dot drivers in ≈ 20 μs, shift rate = 500 kHz, V_{DD} = 5V. A separate clock is used on the grid drivers (≈ 100 Hz per character). Only 10 bits of data are loaded during blanking which requires ≈ 20 μs and the next character data would be loaded ≈ 480 us later (20 character display 2 kHz scan rate).

Although originally intended for VF display interface, the UCN-4810A has been successfully used in a thermal printer assembly. The device (in chip form) was incorporated into a hybrid thermal printer assembly.

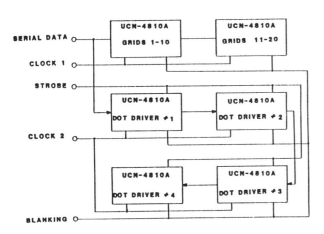

FIGURE 6

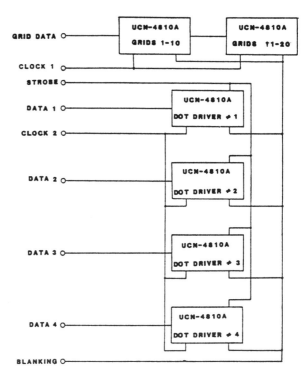

FIGURE 7

FUTURE OF BiMOS

The future trend of BiMOS will be improvement and expansion of existing technology. Chip size will increase from 15K mils^2 to 25-30K mils^2 for added complexity. Output drive lines will increase to 20 and beyond as output voltages exceed 150V. Data rates will improve from 1 MHz to 3-5 MHz and output currents will be limited by package power limitations.

Expansion of BiMOS into linear as well as digital applications will produce circuits with analog bipolar inputs, digital CMOS logic, and high power bipolar outputs all on the same chip. Chips with linear output structures will also emerge. Such a circuit might be a constant current cathode driver with latches for gas discharge display applications.

BiMOS appears to be a very key technology for the near future. Its product niche will be for applications requiring 60-100V (or more) breakdown, low power logic, wide supply range, modest speeds, and MSI to small LSI complexity.

A High-Voltage Circuit for Driving Liquid-Crystal Displays

DINESH SHARMA, JACQUES GAUTIER, AND
GERARD MERCKEL

Abstract—A circuit which can be used as a driver for large multiplexed liquid-crystal displays is described. The electrical requirements from such a circuit are discussed and a technology defined to meet these requirements. The technology is compatible with standard CMOS on SOS processing. The actual performance of this circuit is then described. The drain breakdown voltage of individual transistors exceeds 140 V. The rise and fall times in a 220 pF load are of the order of 2 μs and 1 μs, respectively.

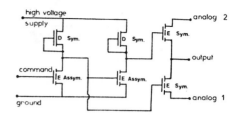

Fig. 1. The circuit.

I. INTRODUCTION

Many applications, such as drivers for large liquid-crystal displays, require circuits which can handle high voltages. A number of high-voltage devices and circuits have been described in literature [1]–[5]. It is of great interest to be able to integrate such a circuit along with standard MOS circuits of MSI to LSI complexity.

We describe a circuit which can be used as a multiplexed LCD driver and which is made with a technology compatible with standard CMOS on SOS processing. Therefore, it is possible to integrate this circuit on the same chip as a normal CMOS on SOS chip without having to change the technology too much.

Several methods exist for driving liquid-crystal matrix displays. These methods fall in two main categories. The "single-frequency" systems vary either the voltage level or the duty cycle of the command signal to write 1's or 0's. The "double-frequency" systems use a low-frequency and a high-frequency signal in order to do the same. The present circuit is intended primarily for "double-frequency" systems, though it can also be used for other systems.

In this paper, we shall first describe the circuit and consider the various electrical requirements from it. We shall then describe the technological solutions to meet these requirements and finally, we shall present the actual performance of various circuit components and the complete circuit itself.

II. DESCRIPTION OF THE CIRCUIT AND ELECTRICAL REQUIREMENTS

The circuit is required to select one out of two high-voltage "analog" signals. These signals actually contain the high and low frequency square-wave signals with appropriate phase relationships. We shall refer to these composite signals as analog signals in this paper. The selection is accomplished by a pair of analog switches, driven in antiphase with the help of an inverter, and a buffer inverter which transforms the normal 0 to -10 V swing available from the low-voltage circuit, to a swing of about 0 to -120 V. The circuit is shown in Fig. 1.

The analog signals have a maximum peak to peak amplitude of about 100 V. This implies that the source as well as drain terminals of analog switches should be able to withstand voltages of this order.

In order to avoid clipping the analog signal, the gate of the "ON" transistor has to be held at least a voltage V_T above the

Manuscript received November 7, 1977; revised January 23, 1978.
D. Sharma is with the Tata Institute of Fundamental Research, Bombay, India.
J. Gautier and G. Merckel are with CENG/LETI/MEA, Grenoble Cedex, France.

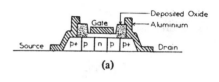

(a)

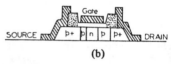

(b)

Fig. 2. Structure of high-voltage transistors (approximate geometrical parameters are given in Table I). (a) Symmetric transistor. (b) Asymmetric transistor.

maximum signal amplitude. Therefore, the gate should be able to stand about 120 V or more.

The buffer should have enough voltage gain to transfer the 0 to -10 V swing at the input to a 0 to -120 V swing at the output with a reasonable transfer characteristic. It should be fast enough to respond to the switching rate of the command signal.

III. SELECTION OF TECHNOLOGY

The voltage levels involved make bulk silicon structures less attractive because of field turn on and body effect problems. Therefore, silicon-on-sapphire technology was selected.

To ensure sufficient gain in the buffer stage, depletion mode devices are used as load transistors. A p-channel technology was chosen in order to avoid carrier multiplication effects encountered in n-channel devices [6], [7].

We have already seen that the analog switches should be symmetric with respect to source–drain interchange. The driver transistors in the buffer and the inverter have their source terminals at ground potential, and so need not be symmetric.

The high breakdown voltages required are achieved by using a modified "extended drain" structure for the transistors [3], [4]. The symmetric and asymmetric devices are shown in Fig. 2. Table I gives approximate geometrical parameters and doping levels.

The technological steps used to get these structures are shown in Fig. 3. It is to be noticed that these steps follow the same sequence as used in standard CMOS-on-sapphire technology with the addition of only one mask and ion-implantation step. One more mask will have to be added if one desires to use the standard gate oxide thickness of $\simeq 1000$ Å in the low voltage MSI part of the circuit. (The high voltage part uses $\simeq 2000$ Å of gate oxide thickness.) The doping levels and ion-implantation doses are compatible for the low-voltage CMOS/SOS and the high-voltage process. The p regions of the high voltage transistors are formed at the time when one is

Reprinted from *IEEE J. Solid-State Circuits*, vol. SC-13, no. 3, pp. 375–378, June 1978.

TABLE I

Approximate impurity concentrations:		
p+ region ≈ 10^{19}; p region ≈ 2 to 3 × 10^{16}; n region ≈ 10^{15} cm^{-3}		
Geometrical parameters:		
gate oxide thickness	=	2000 Å
field oxide thickness	≃	1 μm
gate oxide overlap on p region	=	6 μm
gate metal overlap on p region	=	4 μm
width of drain (extension) p region	=	10 μm
width of source p region (symmetric)	=	10 μm
width of source p region (asymmetric)	=	4 μm
channel length	=	10 μm

TECHNOLOGICAL STEPS

H.V. MOS

1. Definition of Si islands.

2. Oxide deposition, definition of p+ areas, p+ diffusion.

3. Definition of p areas, ion implantation Boron.

4. Oxide stripping, redeposition of field oxide, gate and contact opening, gate oxidation.

5. (Additional step) Masking and ion implant. for depletion devices.

6. Contact opening, Alu. deposition, metal pattern definition.

7. Passivation.

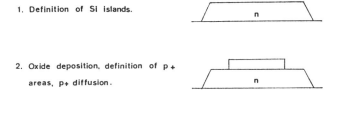

Fig. 3. Description of technology.

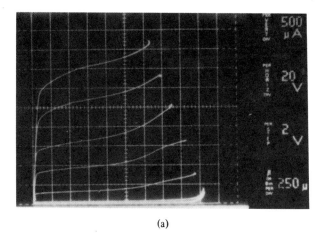

(a)

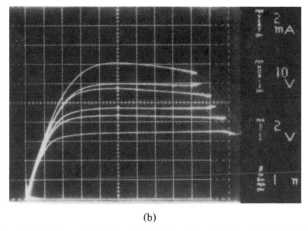

(b)

Fig. 4. I - V characteristics of single transistors ($Z/L \simeq 40$), (a) at low V_G showing V_{BR}, (b) at high V_G showing negative dynamic resistance.

compensating the channel for the n-channel transistors. The p region doping levels are of the order of 2 to 3 × 10^{16}/cm^3 for both these purposes. The substrate (n-type) doping is of the order of 10^{15} cm^{-3}.

IV. CIRCUIT PERFORMANCE

Fig. 4 shows the I - V characteristic of a high-voltage transistor at low- and high-drain currents. It can be seen that the drain breakdown voltage is over 140 V. Higher breakdown voltages can be attained, if required, without much difficulty by using lower doped p regions. This, however, involves a trade-off between breakdown voltage and device "ON" resistance.

Fig. 4(b) shows the transistor under high V_G conditions ($V_G \simeq 20$–30 V). One can see a negative dynamic resistance in the saturation region of the transistor. This effect has been observed before [5], but not fully explained. We believe that this effect is caused by thermal phenomena. Using reasonable

values of junction to ambient thermal resistance (120° C/W), a linear relationship between power dissipated and temperature and taking the mobility proportional to $(T)^{-1.5}$, a computer simulation has been done and it explains this phenomenon well. The simulation also takes into account the nonzero source and drain resistances and mobility reduction due to the gate field. A more detailed analytical treatment of this phenomenon is given in [8].

Fig. 5(a) shows the performance of an "ON" analog switch. The input is a 100 kHz square with a peak to peak amplitude of nearly 90 V. The load capacitance is 220 pF. The performance of an "OFF" switch is shown in Fig. 5(b). It can be seen that the isolation provided in this case is better than 40 dB.

The switching action of the complete circuit is shown in Fig. 6. The oscilloscope traces show the input signal, the command signal, and the output. Here, the command signal is derived from the analog signal by frequency division.

The rise and fall times of the switched waveform after the application of a control signal are shown in Fig. 7. It can be seen that the rise time is 2 μs and the fall time is nearly 1 μs. These times include the delay through the inverter and the buffer in addition to the response time of the switch.

By connecting the analog 1 terminal to the high-voltage supply and the analog 2 terminal to ground, the circuit can be used as a high voltage (push–pull) inverter. In this mode, it can be used as a LCD driver for single-frequency systems using duty cycle variation for writing 1's or 0's.

Finally, Fig. 8 shows a photomicrograph of the circuit.

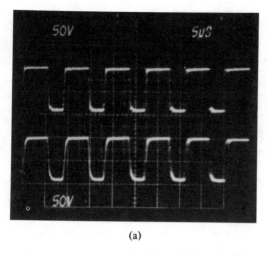

(a)

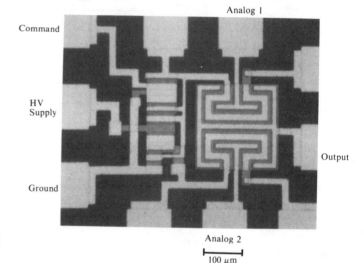

(b)

Fig. 5. Performance of analog switches, (a) in "ON" state, (b) in "OFF"
state (the output is shown at 500 mV/div).

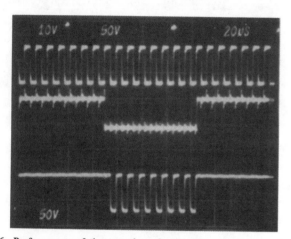

Fig. 6. Performance of the complete circuit. The middle trace shows
the command signal (IO V/div) derived from the analog input (upper
trace) by frequency division.

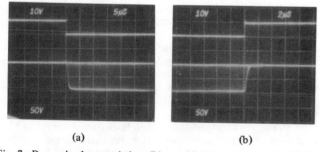

(a)   (b)

Fig. 7. Dynamic characteristics. Rise and fall times of output after the
application of command signal. (a) Rise time = 2 μs. (b) Fall time =
1 μs. Load capacitance = 220 pF.

Fig. 8. Photomicrograph of the circuit; the analog switches are on the
right.

V. CONCLUDING REMARKS

It is to be noted that this circuit is not limited in its application to a liquid-crystal display driver. For example, it can be used as a signal chopper with a large dynamic range.

The figures show signals of nearly 100 V pp being handled. This, however, is a limitation of the signal generator used and not of the circuit itself. As can be seen from the breakdown characteristics, the circuit can handle higher voltages if required.

Some low-voltage test circuits had been put on the same chip as this circuit. These inverters show an acceptable performance.

A circuit combining a low-voltage inverter with two buffers and two analog switches has also been put on the same chip and shows a performance similar to the circuit described here.

ACKNOWLEDGMENT

The authors are thankful to M. Montier for fabrication of these circuits. D. Sharma would like to thank authorities of LETI, CENG, Grenoble, and TIFR, Bombay, for providing the opportunity of working on this project.

REFERENCES

[1] J. D. Plummer and J. D. Meindl, "A monolithic 200-V CMOS analog switch," *IEEE J. Solid-State Circuits*, vol. SC-11, pp. 809-817, Dec. 1976.
[2] W. W. Y. Chu, D. A. Hodges, and G. W. Dick, "High voltage CMOS decoder/driver for plasma displays," presented at the IEEE Int. Solid-State Circuits Conf., 1976.
[3] M. R. Splinter, R. S. Ronen, and R. E. Tremain, "High voltage

SOS/MOS devices and circuit elements," presented at the IEEE Int. Solid-State Circuits Conf., 1976.

[4] R. A. Blanchard et al., "High voltage simultaneous diffusion silicon-gate MOS," IEEE J. Solid-State Circuits, vol. SC-9, pp. 103–110, June 1974.

[5] M. D. Pocha and R. W. Dutton, "A CAD model for high voltage double diffused MOS (DMOS) transistors," IEEE J. Solid-State Circuits, vol. SC-11, pp. 718–726, Oct. 1976.

[6] H. Martinot and P. Rossel, "Multiplication de porteurs dans la zone de pincement des transistors MOS," Electron. Lett., vol. 7, no. 5, pp. 118–120, 1971.

[7] J. Tihanyi and H. Schlotterer, "Properties of ESFI MOS transistors due to the floating substrate and the finite volume," in IEDM Tech. Dig., Washington, DC, Dec. 1974, pp. 39–42.

[8] D. Sharma, J. Gautier, and G. Merckel, "Negative dynamic resistance in MOS devices," this issue, pp. 378–380.

Part VI
Power Amplifiers

IN this part of the book, papers that deal with analog and PWM control are gathered together. These papers discuss circuits developed to address the needs for the creation of operational amplifiers and full bridge circuits for use in motor control. The full bridge circuits can also be used for switch mode power supply applications.

The first paper in this part by Blauschild is reprinted from the JOURNAL OF SOLID STATE CIRCUITS. It describes a monolithic integrated circuit developed for operational amplifiers. The chip contains digital circuitry integrated with high voltage analog components. The op-amp can be operated at 100 volts. The high voltage devices are bipolar transistors. An extended breakdown current source circuit is described to increase the operating voltage.

In the second paper, by Ludikhuize, published in the special issue of the IEEE TRANSACTIONS ON ELECTRON DEVICES ON HIGH VOLTAGE INTEGRATED CIRCUITS, an analog high voltage integrated circuit is realized by using lateral n-MOS and p-MOS transistors capable of operating at 300 volts. The chip also contains 250 volt vertical DMOS transistors and a 20 volt CMOS for the control circuit. Design considerations for each of these elements is provided. This technology has been applied to the fabrication of a video output amplifier operating at 8 MHz. In addition, a full bridge circuit has been built for switching inductive loads as experienced in motor control applications. In this case, the high voltage vertical DMOS-FETs are found to be compact output devices because their inherent integral diode can be utilized. The third paper, by Thomas et al. from the same special issue as the previous paper, also describes a chip suitable for motor control applications. In this case bipolar transistors capable of delivering 1 ampere are utilized.

The last paper, by Kuriyama et al., published in the proceedings of the IEEE International Electron Devices Meeting held in 1983 deals with a monolithic operational amplifier formed using dielectric isolation. This chip has been implemented using SOS (silicon-on-sapphire) technology. The high voltage device is an MOS transistor formed with an offset gate structure. It is capable of operating at plus and minus 100 volts. A gain of 110 db is obtained at 1 kHz using this novel transistor structure.

REPRINT PAPERS

[1] R. A. Blauschild, "High-Voltage Analog Performance with Low-Voltage Digital Devices," *IEEE J. Solid State Circuits,* vol. SC-13, pp. 754–759, 1978.
[2] A. W. Ludikhuize, "A Versatile 250/300-V IC Process for Analog and Switching Applications," *IEEE Trans. Electron Devices,* vol. ED-33, pp. 2008–2015, 1986.
[3] G. Thomas, G. Troussel, and F. Vialettes, "High Voltage Technology Offers New Solutions for Interface Integrated Circuits," *IEEE Trans. Electron Devices,* vol. ED-33, pp. 2016–2024, 1986.
[4] T. Kuriyama, H. Sakuma, and K. Hirata, "A Monolithic High Voltage SOS/CMOS Operational Amplifier," *IEEE Int. Electron Devices Meeting Digest,* Abst. 16.7, pp. 432–435, 1983.

High-Voltage Analog Performance with Low-Voltage Digital Devices

ROBERT A. BLAUSCHILD, MEMBER, IEEE

Abstract—A new circuit technique is described, yielding typical analog system voltage (36 V) operation from a circuit fabricated with low-voltage (LV_{CEO} = 12-15 V) transistors. Such transistors can be fabricated in $\frac{1}{4}$ the area of conventional higher breakdown devices, leading to great reductions in chip size and improved frequency performance due to decreased parasitics. This technique can be used to build complex systems combining high-voltage analog and dense digital circuitry on the same chip, with standard digital processing and without sacrificing analog performance. An extension of the technique uses a typical linear (LV_{CEO} = 40 V) process to build high voltage (80-100 V) circuits. A 100 V op amp was designed and breadboarded with standard linear kit parts.

I. INTRODUCTION

IN MOST analog integrated circuits there are only a few transistors which must withstand large collector-emitter voltage, yet the IC process used is specifically designed for the necessary breakdown characteristics in these few devices. This leads to wasted space and increased parasitics over most of the circuit. A process could be developed to fabricate large high-voltage devices and small low-voltage devices on the same substrate, but this would complicate the fabrication process and probably would not be cost competitive.

These problems can be avoided by optimizing the process for the low-voltage sections of the circuit, and designing the areas that require higher voltages with the dense linear circuit technique described in this paper. This approach has many obvious benefits. Since the process is optimized for the digital circuitry, dense logic compatibility for analog-digital systems is assured. And since decreased isolation spacings give smaller devices, less die area per analog function is used, and reduced parasitics yield improved ac response. Another advantage of the dense linear technique is that it can be applied to extend the operational range of any process. A conventional 40 V process, for example, could be used to build a 100 V circuit.

In this paper, the circuit technique will be presented first, followed by a detailed analysis of the circuit vehicle for the technique—a dense version of the μA 741 [1]. This general purpose operational amplifier was chosen because it is a well-known standard circuit, one on which much characterization data is available.

Manuscript received April 24, 1978; revised June 20, 1978.
The author is with Signetics Corporation, Sunnyvale, CA 94086.

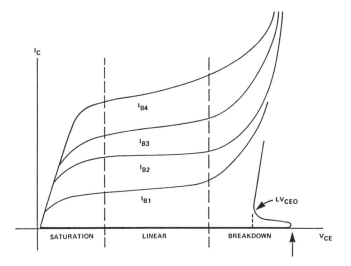

Fig. 1. Transistor operating regions.

II. CIRCUIT BREAKDOWN AND CURRENT SOURCE DESIGN

Fig. 1 shows a typical family of transistor curves of collector current versus collector-emitter voltage for various base currents. Transistor operation can be separated into three regions: saturation for low V_{CE}; forward active (linear) region; and breakdown region for large V_{CE}. Since this paper concerns transistors operating with large V_{CE}, it is important to define mechanisms and terms which are appropriate in the breakdown region.

As V_{CE} increases, the electric field across the collector-base depletion region increases. Eventually, mobile carriers are so accelerated by the field that they bump into other atoms with enough force to break bonds, thereby creating new electron-hole pairs and starting a chain reaction. This process is called avalanche multiplication, and results in a large current flow. For the case when I_B equals zero, the original mobile carriers are provided by collector-base leakage current, and the voltage at which the chain reaction occurs is defined as BV_{CEO}. Once current is flowing through the transistor, the chain reaction can be supported by a lower field produced by a lower V_{CE} known as the latching voltage, or LV_{CEO}. For the case when I_B does not equal zero, the initially high breakdown field is

Reprinted from *IEEE J. Solid-State Circuits*, vol. SC-13, no. 6, pp. 754–759, Dec. 1978.

253

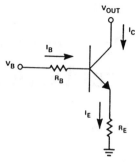

Fig. 2. Single transistor current source.

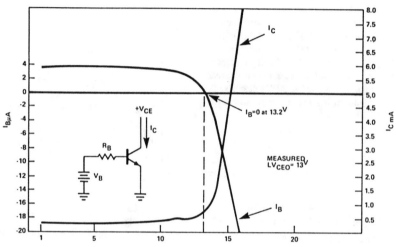

Fig. 3. Transistor characteristics in the breakdown region.

again not necessary and breakdown occurs at a different voltage which depends on the transistor characteristics and external bias conditions.

Consider the useful operating range of the single transistor current source shown in Fig. 2. For the case when the transistor is in cutoff ($V_{BB} \ll 0.6$ V), the calculation is simple and breakdown has been shown to occur when the reverse collector saturation current is avalanche multiplied and causes a large enough voltage drop across R_B to forward bias the base-emitter junction [2]. This happens even if the external base resistor is shorted, since the internal ohmic base resistor of the transistor is always finite.

For the case when V_B is large enough to forward bias the transistor, calculating the useful operating voltage range of the current source is somewhat more complex. As the transistor collector-base reverse bias increases, the common-base current gain (α) increases due to avalanche multiplication as

$$\alpha = \frac{\alpha_0}{1 - (V_{CB}/BV_P)^M},$$

where α_0 is the common-emitter current gain (I_C/I_E) at low

V_{CB}, BV_P is the collector-base plane breakdown, and M is a process constant which is approximately equal to 4 for an n-p-n device. At low values of V_{CB}, $\alpha = \alpha_0$, which is slightly less than one. Collector current I_C is smaller than emitter current I_E, and current I_B flows into the base terminal. As V_{CB} increases, α increases and I_B decreases. When α equals unity, $I_C = I_E$ and base current decreases to zero. For larger values of V_{CB}, α becomes greater than one, and current flows out of the base terminal. Operating in this "negative beta" region, I_B is flowing through R_B in a direction to forward bias the base-emitter junction. This positive feedback mechanism causes a rapid increase in collector current, and the current source becomes useless for circuit operation. Fig. 3 is a plot of measured base current and collector current versus collector-emitter voltage for a typical single transistor current source, showing the sharp increase in collector current in the negative beta region.

Since the magnitude of positive feedback is dependent on the impedance in the base circuit, the actual breakdown voltage of a current source transistor can vary between LV_{CEO} for a high base impedance, and a value close to BV_{CBO} (corner

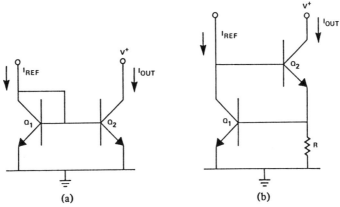

Fig. 4. IC current sources.

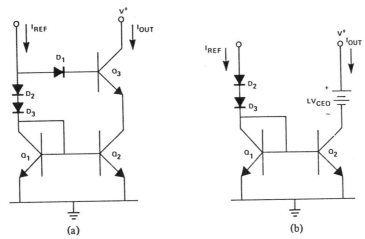

Fig. 5. Extended breakdown current source.

limited collector–base junction breakdown) for a low base impedance. This is illustrated by measurements of the basic IC current sources shown in Fig. 4(a) and (b).

Consider the conventional current mirror of Fig. 4(a) [3]. As $V+$ increases past LV_{CEO}, current flows out of the base of $Q2$ and adds to the reference current flowing into $Q1$. This increase is mirrored in $Q2$, and positive feedback causes an unacceptably large increase in output current. In the process used for this circuit, LV_{CEO} is 12 V, BV_{CBO} is 35 V, and the breakdown of such a current source was measured at 18.6 V for a nominal output current of 50 μA. (Breakdown in this case is measured as the voltage at which the nominal output current doubles, since this is usually undesirable for proper circuit operation.)

An improvement in maximum operating voltage is obtained with the circuit of Fig. 4(b). Although negative base current flows from $Q2$ into $Q1$, it is mirrored logarithmically back to $Q2$ instead of linearly as with the previous circuit. The decreased feedback factor yields a higher breakdown voltage, which was measured to be 24 V.

In order to overcome the limitations described above, a new circuit technique has been developed. The idea of the new technique is to break the loop before the onset of negative base current and therefore prevent positive feedback. This is achieved using a collector–base junction blocking diode, $D1$, and a cascode transistor, $Q3$, shown in Fig. 5(a). As the voltage across $Q3$ increases past LV_{CEO}, current tries to flow out of the base of $Q3$, but is blocked by $D1$. $Q3$ is therefore clamped at LV_{CEO} for further increases in output voltage, $V+$. The current source can now be represented by the equivalent circuit shown in Fig. 5(b). Transistor $Q3$ is replaced by a voltage source with a value of LV_{CEO}, and $D1$ is reverse biased and therefore out of the circuit. The effect of the blocking diode and cascode transistor is to increase the useful operating range of the original source of Fig. 4(a) by LV_{CEO}.

III. APPLICATION OF THE TECHNIQUE TO OP AMP DESIGN

A simplified schematic of the μA 741 is shown in Fig. 6. In this schematic all circled transistors may experience V_{CE} in excess of 35 V during normal operation. The blocking diode technique can be applied to fabricate the circuit with low breakdown voltage transistors. The modification for each trouble spot will be given, followed by an analysis of overall circuit performance.

1) *Input bias current source:* The input bias current source provides a nominal output current of 20 μA with a 40K bias resistor. The current source shown in Fig. 7 operates identically

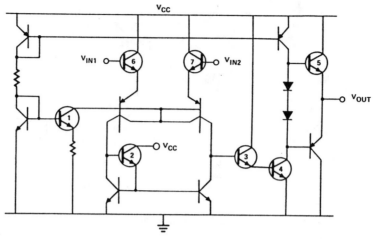

Fig. 6. Simplified μA 741 schematic.

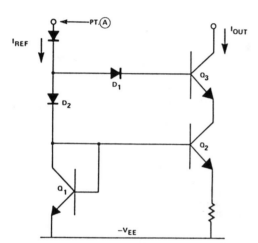

Fig. 7. Input bias current source.

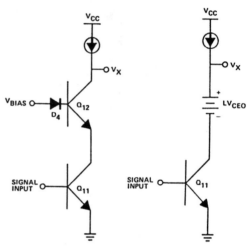

Fig. 8. Common–emitter gain stage.

to the source in Fig. 5(a), with the following exception: since I_{OUT} is much less than I_{ref} (18 μA versus 700 μA), V_{BE2} is smaller than V_{BE1}, and I_{D1} is equal to I_{OUT}/β, a diode ($D3$ in Fig. 5(a)) may be eliminated from the bias string without saturating $Q2$.

2, 3) *Buffer transistors:* Since these devices are used as emitter followers, their collectors may be tied to any common potential, with negligible effect on circuit performance. By returning their collectors to reference point A in the circuit of Fig. 7, the V_{CE} of these devices is clamped at $2\,V_{BE}$, and the high-voltage problem is avoided.

4) *Second gain stage:* In the modified second gain stage of Fig. 8(a), a cascode connection is again used. V_{BIAS} can be obtained from reference point A in the input bias current source, and operation is identical to current source operation. As V_X increases, V_{CB12} increases until $Q12$ clamps, $D4$ reverse biases, and the equivalent circuit of Fig. 8(b) is obtained. For low V_X, V_{C11} is clamped at one V_{BE} above ground, eliminating the need for the extra emitter on the substrate p-n-p buffer which is commonly used to prevent latching.

5) *Output stage:* Since the output stage must supply large

currents, two diodes must be used in the bias string between $D5$ and the base of $Q19$ (Fig. 9(a)). For low output voltages, the equivalent circuit of Fig. 9(b) applies.

6, 7) *Input devices:* Breakdown of the input emitter followers can be avoided by limiting the collector–emitter voltage of these devices as shown in the complete modified 741 schematic in Fig. 10. Current source $Q28C$ provides bias current for the input pair, $Q1$ and $Q2$, and also for the clamp transistors, $Q3$ and $Q4$. The collector base voltages of $Q1$ and $Q2$ are maintained at approximately 0 V, and common-mode input voltage swings appear across $Q28C$. It should be noted here that clamping is not needed to protect the p-n-p current sources and level shifts, since wide basewidths typically yield high LV_{CEO} for p-n-p transistors.

IV. Circuit Performance

Prior op amps have typically been fabricated on 5 Ω · cm, 12–17 μm thick epi. By using the blocking diode technique described here, a 0.75 Ω · cm, 3.8 μm epi can be used to build the 28 × 28 mil op amp shown in the photomicrograph of Fig. 11. Minimum transistor size is greatly reduced, leading to

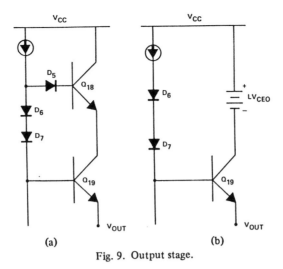

Fig. 9. Output stage.

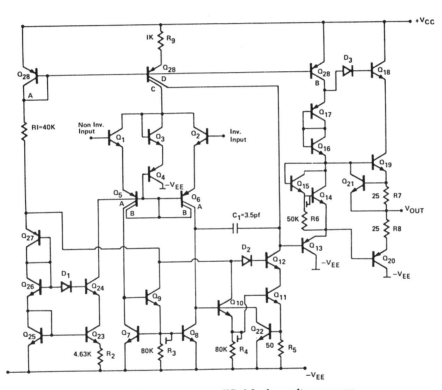

Fig. 10. Dense op amp modified for low-voltage process.

decreased parasitics and improved ac performance as compared with typical 741 specs. The circuit simulator SPICE was used to analyze the ac performance of the dense design and yielded a 4.7 MHz unity gain bandwidth using a 1 pF compensation capacitor. To ensure that the circuit would not oscillate, a conservative compensation capacitor value of 3.5 pF was used, and an actual unity gain frequency of 2.5 MHz was measured on the final circuit. As shown in the measured specifications listed in Table I, this still compares quite favorably with the 1 MHz unity gain bandwidth of the standard 741. Slew rate (2.4 V/µs) is approximately five times greater for this design,

which requires 25 percent less chip area than the smallest previously reported die.

V. Extended Voltage Operation

By starting with a standard linear process ($LV_{CEO} \geq 40$ V), the same circuit (Fig. 10) becomes operational over 100 V. Such a circuit was breadboarded with kit parts from a standard op amp process and performed as expected with ±50 V supplies. Although it was not necessary in the case of the 100 V op amp, several blocking diodes and cascode transistors can be stacked to give even greater voltage capability, limited eventually only

Fig. 11. Photomicrograph of the dense op amp.

TABLE I
TYPICAL OP AMP PERFORMANCE SPECS (±15 V SUPPLIES)

	Dense Redesign	μA 741C
Input offset voltage	1 mV	1 mV
Input voltage range	±13 V	±13 V
Output voltage swing	±13 V	±13 V
Maximum supply voltage	±18 V	±18 V
Voltage gain	120 dB	106 dB
Common-mode rejection ratio	93 dB	90 dB
Power supply rejection ratio	100 dB	100 dB
Slew rate	2.4 V/μs	0.5 V/μs
Unity gain bandwidth	2.5 MHz	1 MHz

and greater density per analog function. The dense 741 described before was useful as a test vehicle, since it required many modifications. But other circuits require fewer high-voltage n-p-n transistors and therefore would require less modification and derive an even greater percentage savings in chip area. For example, calculations show that an LM 124 quad op amp can be done in less than half the present area with the dense technique.

Perhaps the greatest advantage is not in die area savings, however, but in allowing high-performance analog circuits to be directly compatible with dense digital circuitry. This permits single chips to compete directly with multi-chip systems in such areas as A/D conversion for data control and display, automotive electronics, and telecommunications. As an example of this, a complete PCM codec has been built with over 800 I^2L logic gates, 2 op amps, 2 sample holds, a nonlinear DAC, and assorted peripheral circuits on a single 200 mil square die.

VII. CONCLUSION

It has been shown that integrated circuits operating at a given supply voltage need not be built with devices specifically fabricated to withstand such a supply voltage. A technique has been shown whereby low breakdown voltage (smaller geometry) devices can be used in high-voltage integrated circuits with no loss in circuit performance. In particular, it has been shown that this leads to improved ac performance and reduction in die size for many circuits, and increased operational voltage range for others. An additional advantage is the compatibility of high performance analog functions with dense digital circuitry, permitting complex systems to be integrated onto a single chip.

ACKNOWLEDGMENT

The author would like to acknowledge the help of P. R. Gray in circuit analysis and F. Adamic with wafer processing.

REFERENCES

[1] D. Fullagar, "A new high-performance monolithic op amp," *Fairchild Semiconductor Applications Brief*, May 1968.
[2] J. Millman and H. Taub, *Pulse, Digital, and Switching Waveforms*. New York: McGraw-Hill, 1965, pp. 198–204.
[3] P. R. Gray and R. G. Meyer, *Analysis and Design of Analog Integrated Circuits*. New York: Wiley, 1977, pp. 197–210.

by epi-substrate breakdown. Since this breakdown can exceed 200 V for conventional junction isolated structures, it may be possible to apply the dense technique to other high-voltage circuits, such as on-chip 110 V ac line regulators.

VI. SYSTEM ADVANTAGES

An advantage of using a low-voltage process is that smaller geometries lead to lower parasitics, improved ac performance,

A Versatile 250/300-V IC Process for Analog and Switching Applications

ADRIAAN W. LUDIKHUIZE

Abstract—A true analog high-voltage IC process and related devices are described. The process is based on bipolar low-voltage devices to which have been added 300-V lateral n-MOS and p-MOS transistors with source-follower capability. The present process version includes 250-V vertical DMOS transistors for compact switching of moderate power, whereas 5/20-V CMOS is available for control. Application examples are an 8-MHz video output amplifier and a 20-W full-bridge power switch.

I. Process Definition

MONOLITHIC integration of active high-voltage devices is possible in a variety of ways, the one selected being dependent on the intended application and the required low-voltage devices. The present process aims at analog and moderate-power switching applications. Junction isolation has been preferred to the more expensive dielectric isolation; however, inconvenient substrate currents must be avoided and device isolation requires more area. The wish for good-quality analog measurement and control functions involved the choice of bipolar low-voltage devices with the related epitaxial layer, though CMOS is steadily improving in this area. For the high-voltage devices MOS transistors were preferred because of their higher breakdown voltage, better SOAR and lower parasitics in junction isolation; they use self-aligned silicon-gate technology. Low-voltage CMOS is obtained at the same time.

Because of the higher electron mobility, n-MOS and n-p-n transistors are chosen as the principal devices; the n-MOS transistors have a double-diffused (DMOS) structure with good high-frequency and SOAR properties owing to a short channel and a highly doped backgate contacted close to the source. A low backgate resistance is important for high-speed switching and inductive loads; regular high-voltage n-MOS transistors on high-ohmic substrates may require, for this reason, a shielded source [1]. A low-ohmic backgate contact diffusion as known from discrete power DMOST's is a process option. The p-MOS device has a lower transconductance due to a longer channel and lower mobility.

The high-voltage devices can be built in a vertical or lateral way. Vertical devices require a thick epitaxial layer, a deep n^+ diffused contact to the buried layer, and long diffusion times. A source-follower function is easily obtained and the internal DMOS backgate-to-drain diode may be used as in discretes without severe problems. In standard bipolar processes about 80–170 V_{ces} can be obtained. By using buried isolation and collector walls, a 25-μm epitaxial layer can be handled yielding about 250 V for BV_{ds} or BV_{ces} and 140 V for BV_{ceo}; emitter-driven n-p-n transistors can be used to over 200 V in this way [2], [3]. The present process includes a 250-V VDMOS for medium power compact switching and push–pull output stages; the device properties are discussed in Section II-A. Lateral devices allow higher voltages on thinner layers by using pinching and RESURF techniques; breakdown values up to 1000 V have been reported in junction isolation [4], [5]. The device can be considered as a series configuration (cascode) of a short-channel MOST and a JFET. The RESURF pinching condition requires about 1.8×10^{12} cm^{-2} doping in the lateral JFET channel, assuming that this is pinched from at least two sides [6], [7] or in a graded way [8]. The lateral n-channel LDMOS transistor uses the epitaxial layer for the JFET, which at 22-μm thickness should have a specific resistance of 5.5 $\Omega \cdot$ cm. The source-follower function is more complicated for this device, as is explained in Section II-B; the internal backgate-to-drain diode cannot be used as it has a large parasitic injection to the substrate. The process offers source-following LDMOS to over 300 V.

A complementary p-type high-voltage device is very useful for analog circuitry. Since a lateral p-n-p has poor frequency response and is sensitive to parasitic injection, a MOST is preferred. The device uses an implanted offset or extended drain and is called extended-drain PMOST (EPMOST). The incorporation of this EPMOS to over 300 V in a RESURF epitaxial layer requires some care as will be explained in Section II-C. The n-p-n transistors use the DMOS backgate as a base and have a vertical BV_{ceo} of 80 V; a lateral n-p-n has BV_{ceo} over 300 V, but is more sensitive to process tolerances. Up to the vertical 250 V a shielded lateral p-n-p can be used. Details on bipolar devices are discussed in Section II-D. No special processing steps have been included for low-voltage CMOS; this implies moderate performance of the present 5/20-V CMOS (Section II-E). In order to limit the induced fields, the interconnection runs over about 3 μm of oxide; further details are given in Section II-F. The thick oxide is covered with plasma-nitride for stable operation in plastic encapsulations.

Manuscript received April 17, 1986; revised July 10, 1986.
The author is with Philips Research Laboratories, Eindhoven, The Netherlands.
IEEE Log Number 8610537.

Reprinted from *IEEE Trans. Electron Devices*, vol. ED-33, pp. 2008–2015, Dec. 1986.

259

The fabrication steps of the process are based on a bipolar process and have been presented earlier [9] for 17-μm epitaxy; the present version has a 23-μm epitaxial layer, allowing 250-V VDMOS devices. Before epitaxy the isolation and collector-wall patterns are applied as buried layers, thus increasing the total number of masking steps to 13. Processing starts on (100) 30-$\Omega \cdot$ cm p-type silicon, in which buried layers of antimony, phosphorus, and boron are applied by masked implantation. After 23-μm 5.9-$\Omega \cdot$ cm epitaxy, standard collector-wall and isolation are diffused. Next, all oxide is stripped and 0.1-μm gate-oxide is thermally grown. Polysilicon is deposited, doped, and patterned for self-aligned gates, field-plates, and channel stoppers. After this a 9-kΩ/sq boron layer is implanted, which is used for the extended drain of EP-MOS, for junction terminations, and for field corrections at the isolation diffusion edge. Next, boron is implanted and diffused to 285 Ω/sq for DMOS backgate, PMOS source/drain, and for bipolar n-p-n base, followed by 14-Ω/sq phosphorus implantation for DMOS source/drain and n-p-n emitter. The phosphorus is diffused until the DMOS threshold is about 2.8 V; this corresponds to an n-p-n current gain of about 85. Next the slice is covered with 0.7-μm oxide, with a thin nitride layer and with 2-μm oxide. In low-voltage areas and for contact windows, the thick oxide is removed with an oversized window mask, stopping at the nitride layer. Next contact windows are etched and plasma-sputtered AlSi-metallization is applied and patterned. Finally, for scratch, moisture, and dirt protection the slice is covered with plasma-nitride in which bonding-pad windows are etched.

II. DETAILS OF DEVICES AND STRUCTURES

Some aspects of the vertical DMOS, the lateral DMOS, the lateral PMOS, the bipolar devices, the low-voltage MOS devices, and the high-voltage interconnection will be considered in more detail.

A. Vertical DMOS (VDMOS)

The structure is well known from discrete power DMOS devices. The basic structure as adapted for IC (Fig. 1) has an additional n$^+$ buried layer and a deep n$^+$ contact diffusion. The cell uses a hexagonal design and has a double-diffused backgate and source, self-aligned to the polysilicon gate. Breakdown at the inside junction curvature of the backgate is avoided by close, but not too close, neighboring junctions and by the gate as a field plate; breakdown at the outside junction curvature is improved by a p-high-ohmic implanted layer extending 16 μm beyond the main junction. The measured BV_{ds} of 260 V (Fig. 2) agrees with the calculated reachthrough limited breakdown assuming a thickness t-bb between the backgate and updiffused buried layer of about 12 μm after processing. The locus of breakdown has been analyzed using drain and backgate/source as a reverse-biased photodiode; a scanning source of light is applied using a fast CRT and the corresponding photocurrent is monitored (flying-spot scanning). Thus high-field areas attended with multipli-

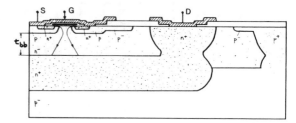

Fig. 1. Cross section of vertical DMOS (VDMOS) transistor.

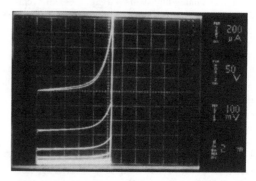

Fig. 2. I_{ds}-V_{ds} characteristics of the VDMOST.

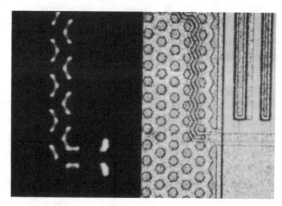

Fig. 3. Photodiode scan of hexagonal VDMOST at 255 V_{ds}. Multiplied photocurrent is visible between gate and source metallization.

cation can be traced. The highest field is seen at the outside edge of the backgate junction, where at 260 V the device breakdown occurs (Fig. 3).

Rather high fields are observed at the hexagon corners, depending on polysilicon-grid width (14 μm), backgate junction depth (4 μm), and epitaxial doping. Considerable multiplication is also found under the whole backgate, indicating operation close to the vertical breakdown limit. The high field close to the channel area is probably responsible for the upward-bended output characteristics (Fig. 2). At high V_{ds} excess electron–hole pairs are generated at a few micrometers below the surface and cause an increased output current. The excess holes will flow through the backgate. Since it is also the base of a parasitic n-p-n its resistance must be low for a good SOAR. A 0.55-mm^2 active area device clamped to 230 V can switch off a 3-mH coil at 0.7 A with a dV/dt of 5 kV/μs. The optional backgate contact diffusion lowers the backgate resistance and shifts the locus of BV_{ds} away from the channel to the vertical part as it penetrates below the

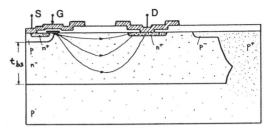

Fig. 4. Cross section of lateral DMOS (LDMOS) transistor.

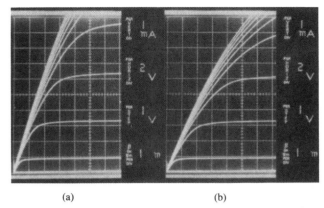

(a)　　　　　　　　　(b)

Fig. 5. Low-voltage I_{ds}–V_{ds} characteristics of source-following epitaxial LDMOST at source-to-substrate voltage of (a) 0 V and (b) 300 V.

backgate. With the same device area, now a 3-mH coil can be switched off unclamped at 1.4 A (avalanching at 265 V). The epitaxial dope required for LDMOS design is close to the optimum value for R_{on} in the VDMOS devices; the specific on-resistance obtained for 250-V VDMOS is 2.3 $\Omega \cdot$ mm^2 to which must be added 0.5 $\Omega \cdot$ mm^2 from the buried layer. At high currents R_{on} increases due to the vertical JFET channel between the backgates, e.g., for a 0.55-mm^2 device typically by 25 percent at 0.8 A. The internal backgate-to-drain diode, if surrounded by the deep n$^+$ contact diffusion, has a maximum parasitic p-n-p current gain of 0.1 at high currents.

B. Lateral DMOS (LDMOS)

The lateral DMOS has a finger layout; a cross-section of the structure (Fig. 4) shows a short-channel DMOST in series with a lateral epitaxial JFET. A longer JFET will increase BV_{ds} but will also increase R_{on}. On thicker lower doped layers R_{on} increases due to spreading effects. Originally this JFET was pinched by substrate and edges using the RESURF technique with a channel dope times thickness product (Q_{ch}) of about 1×10^{12} cm^{-2}. By applying a graded lateral substrate profile a much higher Q_{ch} of 2×10^{12} cm^{-2} was shown to be possible [8]. With these approaches, however, an integrated source-follower as used in analog and push–pull circuits is not possible. For analog operation with constant threshold, the backgate is connected to the related source and so for source-follower use must be separated from the common substrate. At the aimed source voltage the epitaxial bottom depletion must not extend up to the backgate or to the surface. In the first case punchthrough is limiting; this punchthrough voltage, assuming a step junction and a thickness t-bs between backgate and substrate, is written as

$$V_{pt} = (t_{bs})^2 \times \frac{q \cdot N_{epi}}{2\epsilon} \left(1 + \frac{N_{epi}}{N_{sub}}\right) \qquad (1)$$

which gives $V_{pt} = 430$ V as a nominal value ($t_{bs} = 17$ μm). In the second case no conduction at low V_{ds} is possible. This makes the use of local buried n$^+$ shields for prevention of punchthrough [10] less useful for source-followers; in special cases (e.g., for handling supply spikes), their use can make sense. A Q_{ch} of about 2×10^{12} cm^{-2} in combination with pinching from the bottom and top side is a better way [6], [7]. Now at high source voltage the epitaxial bottom depletion does not extend too far. At low source and high drain voltage, additional de-

pletion from the top side is provided by a diffused or field-plated top gate for appropriate pinching together with RE-SURF effects at the edges (double-acting RESURF). Numerical analysis with a 2D Poisson program [7] has been used for fine-tuning the geometry. The pinchoff voltage between field-plate and substrate can be approximated by using [14, eqs. (1)–(3)]; with field-plate and substrate connected to the source and assuming $t_{ox} \cdot \epsilon_{si}/\epsilon_{ox} \ll t_{epi}$ is found

$$V_{po} = \frac{q \cdot N_{epi}}{2\epsilon} \cdot \frac{(t_{epi} + t_{ox} \cdot \epsilon_{si}/\epsilon_{ox})^2}{\left(1 + \sqrt{\dfrac{N_{sub}}{N_{epi} + N_{sub}}}\right)^2} \qquad (2)$$

which reduces for backgate diffusion as a top gate to

$$V_{po} = \frac{q \cdot N_{epi}}{2\epsilon} \cdot \frac{(t_{bs})^2}{\left(1 + \sqrt{\dfrac{N_{sub}}{N_{epi} + N_{sub}}}\right)^2}. \qquad (3)$$

The nominal values of both situations with $t_{ox} = 0.7$ μm are 130 and 65 V. A compromise between a high punchthrough and a low pinchoff voltage is required. As punchthrough is determined by epi-thickness from the backgate to substrate and lateral pinchoff by the epi-thickness between the top gate and substrate, it seems advantageous to use the backgate as a top gate for pinching; then the quotient of V_{pt} and V_{po} is as large as possible. However, the situation is more complex as now at high source voltages close to punchthrough again the channel is pinched off and no current can flow at low V_{ds}; a higher epitaxial dope will be required and the increased channel resistance becomes the limit rather than punchthrough. A diffused top gate gives problems in the LDMOS structure where the current starts from a surface inversion layer; local windows in it or a floating top gate at some distance from the source are practical solutions [7]. The present design uses a stepped field-plate connected to the source or gate. The partial depletion of the epitaxial channel in source-following LDMOS devices by the common substrate has influence on the characteristics at low V_{ds}, as is clearly visible in Fig. 5. The on-resistance at 300-V source-to-substrate is 50 percent higher and the maximum

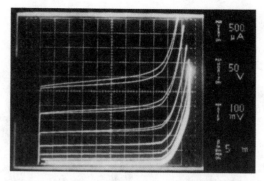

Fig. 6. I_{ds}-V_{ds} characteristics of LDMOST.

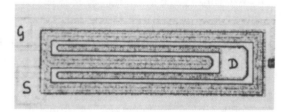

Fig. 7. Photomicrograph of open-drain LDMOST.

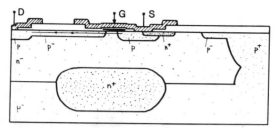

Fig. 8. Cross section of extended-drain PMOS (EPMOS) transistor.

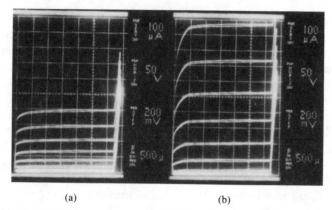

(a)   (b)

Fig. 9. I_{ds}-V_{ds} characteristics of EPMOST with polysilicon gate-length of (a) 16 μm and (b) 10 μm at the same drive condition.

current is lowered, but for many analog applications with saturated MOS operation it is of minor influence. Fig. 6 gives the output characteristics of the 0.2-mm^2 active area open-drain LDMOST shown in Fig. 7. The device has a 38-μm s–d distance on mask (effective distance 33 μm) and shows BV_{ds} of over 500 V with local premature breakdown at the not well-rounded end of the cental source finger. Higher values seem well possible. R_{on} for the active area is 9–10 $\Omega \cdot$ mm^2, whereas for a 300-V design, 6.5 $\Omega \cdot$ mm^2 was found [7]. At high current R_{on} is increased due to JFET action (Fig. 5); at 20 V_{gs} and 50 V_{ds} a maximum current of about 100 mA/mm gate width is found. Switching off a 3-mH coil clamped to 320 V at 1.0 A is quite possible with a 1-mm^2 active area device; as the backgate is alternatingly contacted in the source contact window the backgate resistance is low.

When compared with VDMOS, the LDMOS devices allow higher voltages in IC application, whereas above a crossover voltage their specific on-resistance is better [11]; in IC's this crossover voltage is even lower, as VDMOS requires an area-consuming deep n$^+$ contact diffusion and has additional buried layer resistance. On the other hand, source-following epitaxial LDMOS has higher R_{on} and needs blocking of the internal backgate-to-drain diode for inductive loads. LDMOS devices have a better output impedance and a very low drain-to-gate capacitance above the pinching voltage.

C. Lateral PMOS (EPMOS)

The lateral PMOS also has a finger layout; a cross section of the structure (Fig. 8) shows a short-channel PMOST in series with a lateral implanted p-channel JFET, which is called an extended drain. With good field shaping, BV_{ds} will again be proportional to the drain–source distance. Locally double-sided pinching is used between

a stepped top-side field-plate (connected to gate or source) and the bottom-side epitaxial layer. At high backgate (= epitaxial layer)-to-substrate voltages, the epitaxial layer is depleted from two sides under the p-drain (cf. LDMOS design). This reduces the effectivity of the bottom-side pinching of the p$^-$ extended drain. Therefore a buried n$^+$ layer is applied under the extension; this buried layer is interrupted under the p$^+$ drain because of the limited vertical breakdown voltage between p$^+$ drain (= backgate diffusion) and buried layer. The construction improves the punchthrough voltage between drain and substrate; it also helps to decrease the lateral depletion in the n$^-$ epitaxial backgate, thus permitting shorter channels with higher transconductance and fT. In Fig. 9 the output characteristics of EPMOS transistors with 16- and 10-μm polygate are shown (i.e., 11- and 5-μm n$^-$ length). A p$^-$ dose of 1.8×10^{12} cm^{-2} has been used for a low R_{on}. Both have a BV_{ds} of over 300 V; the 5-μm channel device shows relatively more channel shortening before the drain locally pinches at about 40 V, but has a more than doubled transconductance. The drain is shielded from the common p$^-$ substrate by the backgate (= epitaxial layer), so here source following does not alter the characteristics. For 300-V devices a specific on-resistance of about 29 $\Omega \cdot$ mm^2 is found. At high current, R_{on} increases again; at 20 V_{gs} and 50 V_{ds} a maximum current of 50 mA/ mm gate width is found.

D. Bipolar Devices

The n-p-n transistors use the DMOS backgate as a base; in the chosen processing a DMOS threshold voltage of 2.8 V corresponds to an n-p-n current gain of 85 and a vertical

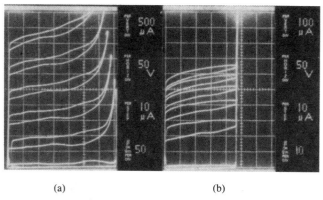

(a)   (b)

Fig. 10. I_c–V_{ce} characteristics of (a) lateral n-p-n transistor and (b) lateral p-n-p transistor.

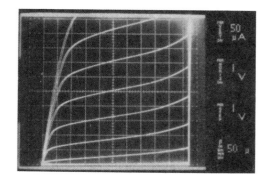

Fig. 11. I_{ds}–V_{ds} characteristics of inverse operated low-voltage LDMOST.

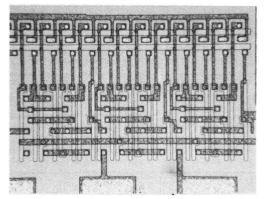

Fig. 12. Divider circuit designed with integrated DMOS logic.

n-p-n BV_{ceo} of 90 V. The rather thick backgate base, designed for good DMOS properties, causes a moderate frequency behavior ($fT = 180$ MHz). Leaving out the buried layer at the collector side results in an n-p-n transistor in series with a lateral epitaxial JFET. This JFET must pinch well before vertical BV_{ceo} is reached instead of BV_{ces}, which is required for LDMOS design, making this device more sensitive to process tolerances. Good transistors have BV_{ceo} of over 300 V (Fig. 10(a)). A drawback in high-voltage lateral p-n-p-transistors is the thick base required for punchthrough. In the present process the pinched p^- implant of the EPMOS is being used in the lateral collector, thus permitting a thinner base. In Fig. 10(b) the characteristics are shown for a device with 16-μm n-base width and 14-μm p-collector extension; due to the low base dope the degradation of current-gain starts at 0.1 mA/mm. With an anti-punchthrough polysilicon field-plate as used in the EPMOS design, a shorter base width can be used. $BV_{ceo} = BV_{cb} = 250$ V is obtained since this voltage is limited by the vertical breakdown of collector to buried n^+ base. The frequency response of the vertical substrate p-n-p is poor due to the thick epitaxial layer; with proper design BV_{ceo} of over 300 V is obtained. Vertical diodes up to 250 V can be integrated; furthermore diodes of 6, 10.5, and 22 V are present for voltage reference and protection.

E. Low-Voltage MOS

The LDMOS and EPMOS structures without intentional drift area have BV_{ds} of 35 and 45 V and can be used for 20-V CMOS. However, the drain of LDMOS is connected to an epitaxial island and has a relatively large size and drain-to-substrate capacitance as no special p-well for n-MOS devices is present. For 5- to 6-V logic the LDMOST can be used inversely where the drain is isolated in the backgate used as a p-well with $BV_{ds} = 10.5$ V; the characteristics are shown in Fig. 11. The devices must operate in common (grounded) source, which is connected to the epitaxial island. A short polysilicon gate allows floating sources in a p-well, obtained by backgate underdiffusion. The process has no field oxide under the

polysilicon and shallow channel stoppers cannot be present under the polysilicon unless this has a width below 3 μm; here a self-aligned polysilicon gate is less convenient than a metal gate. Using 6-μm design rules with these NMOS and PMOS devices a CMOS ring-oscillator has been built with a delay of 26 ns at 6 V. Also current-loaded integrated DMOS logic [12] with a strong resemblance to I^2L is possible; the NMOST gate is loaded by a controllable PMOS current source and is discharged by multiple NMOST drains. The performance is modest with a delay of 200 ns at 10 μA/gate, but the wiring is much simpler than CMOS (Fig. 12). Using 6-μm design rules the density is about 100 (CMOS) to 140 (IDL) gates/mm^2. For driving the power devices the output is converted to 20 V by CMOS on chip.

F. Interconnection

For high-voltage analog circuits the availability of high-voltage interconnection is essential. The minimum thickness for an oxide spacer without shielding techniques is found from the maximum allowed field E_{max} as induced by a metal on the oxide + semiconductor sandwich in deep depletion. The allowed voltage is [15]

$$V_{tot} = \frac{\epsilon_{si} \cdot E_{max}^2}{2q \cdot N_{epi}} + t_{ox} \cdot \frac{\epsilon_{si}}{\epsilon_{ox}} \cdot E_{max} \qquad (4)$$

from which, with the maximum field in silicon and $t_{ox} = 3$ μm, a minimum of 400 V is found at $N_d = 2 \times 10^{16}$. Higher fields occur at abrupt doping gradients under the

TABLE I
SUMMARY OF TYPICAL DEVICE DATA

MOS devices	VDMOST	LDMOST	EPMOST	units
BVds	250	300(500)	300	V
Vthreshold	2.8	2.8	1.5	V
Lchannel	1.5	1.5	5	um
beta-sq	21	21	7	uA/V2
Imax at 20Vgs,50Vds		100	50	mA/mm
Ron.Aact	2.8	6.5(10)	29	Ohm.mm2
fT (i out=i in)	800	1200	200	MHz
Bipolar devices	Vnpn	Lpnp		
BVceo	80	250		V
Current gain	85	150		
fT	180	2		MHz
MOS logic	IDL 5	CMOS 5/20		V
Devices and interconnection to substrate		300		V

oxide. A metal running over a grounded isolation diffusion covered by 2.8 μm of oxide induces a fringing breakdown (attended with walk-out by charge injection) at 180 V. Using a short p$^-$ extension to the isolation diffusion improves this value to over 330 V; with floating p$^-$ rings more than 600 V was obtained. A grounded metal running over an n$^+$ channel stopper connected to an epitaxial island induces a fringing breakdown (without walk-out) of 200 V over a shallow and 320 V over a deep (collector-wall) n$^+$ diffusion and intermediate values over polysilicon on gate oxide. Stable operation in plastic encapsulation requires good performance at intermediate surface potentials; field-plates can shield critical areas. Also important for compact devices and interconnection is a high allowable lateral field. Plasma-nitride for scratch-protection overlay was shown to handle much higher lateral fields than the few volts per micrometer allowed for aluminum with the more common phosphosilicate glass in wet ambient [13].

Table I gives a summary of typical device data.

III. APPLICATION EXAMPLES

The available high-voltage and low-voltage devices can be used for TV applications (video output amplifier, vertical deflection), transducer driving, telephony (e.g., subscriber line interface circuits), and switched mode converters (electronic ballast, motor drive). Two examples have been selected.

A high-quality 200/250-V 8-MHz video output amplifier with a bandwidth of 6 MHz at 100 V_{pp} has been described in detail by Blanken and van der Zee [9]. The circuit diagram (Fig. 13(a)) shows the use of bipolar and low-voltage MOS devices for input-signal amplification, references, and quiescent current generation. High-voltage LDMOS and EPMOS transistors are used for cascode, current mirror load, and complementary output stages. Emphasis for the HV devices lies on low parasitic capacitances and fast response (2 kV/μs) in combination with low static dissipation (0.7 W). Fig. 13(b) shows a 3-mm^2 chip that includes high-voltage protection diodes for CRT flashover discharges up to 10 A.

A 230/250-V full-bridge circuit with simple level-shifting (Fig. 14) has been designed for switching inductive loads; it has VDMOS transistors for compact switching

where the use of the internal anti-parallel diode is not a serious problem. The power switches have about 5-Ω on-resistance at 0.55-mm^2 active area. The level-shifter must handle a 20-V higher V_{ds} and consists of an LDMOST able to sink 80 mA, a 5-kΩ resistor, an HV diode, and an external bootstrap capacitor. When $T1$ and $T4$ are switched on, current will flow into the load consisting of, e.g., an inductor and a series resistor. Next $T1$ and $T4$ are switched off and the inductor will discharge output 01 below zero and charge output 02 above the supply, implying that the internal drain-to-backgate diodes of $T2$ and $T3$ become forward biased. Next $T2$ and $T3$ are switched on parallel to the diodes, the current decreases, reverses, and increases again to complete half the cycle. Never should both power switches in one branch be switched on at the same time. In the circuit this is realized by a delayed switching on using the 5 kΩ series resistor and the input capacitance, and by a fast switching off using a bypass diode or the level-shift transistor. The reverse operation of the switches may lead to problems (Fig. 15). The drain-to-backgate diode of $T3$ injects holes into the substrate causing dissipation and positive substrate biasing; the current is kept low by proper design of the VDMOS transistor, whereas substrate bias can be kept low by a low-ohmic substrate connection. The parasitic drain-to-substrate diode of $T2$ injects electrons into the substrate, which may lead to malfunction in nearby sensing and control circuits. The injection is reduced by putting a series resistor or diode in the substrate connection around this device and forcing all the current through the internal drain-to-backgate diode of $T2$. An n$^+$ ring around the lower transistor connected to the substrate will collect part of the electrons. In principle the situation can latch up, as a parasitic n-p-n and p-n-p are activated in the right direction; however, no proof of this could be found. Both currents partly compensate each other; a negative substrate bias, which could be generated by the chip, prevents parasitic action of $T2$, leaving only the parasitic dissipation of $T3$. The switching characteristics of the full-bridge circuit switching 20 W from a 200-V supply into a load consisting of a 3-mH coil and a 500-Ω resistor are shown in Fig. 16. The output voltage has fast transitions (below 50 ns). The drain current of $T1$ and $T3$ is negative directly after switch reversal and induces a parasitic substrate current which is about 5 percent of the main current. At room temperature the loss in a standard 16-pin dual-in-line package (R_{th} = 50 K/W) is less than 1 W at 33 kHz. With this circuit and an adapted load, mini-fluorescent lamps (5–20 W) up to 230 V dc have been ignited and driven successfully, using external 15-V CMOS logic for control. Fig. 17 shows the 8-mm^2 full-bridge chip including level-shifting and some additional circuitry.

IV. CONCLUSION

A versatile 250/300-V IC process has been described based on LV bipolar and HV lateral DMOS transistors,

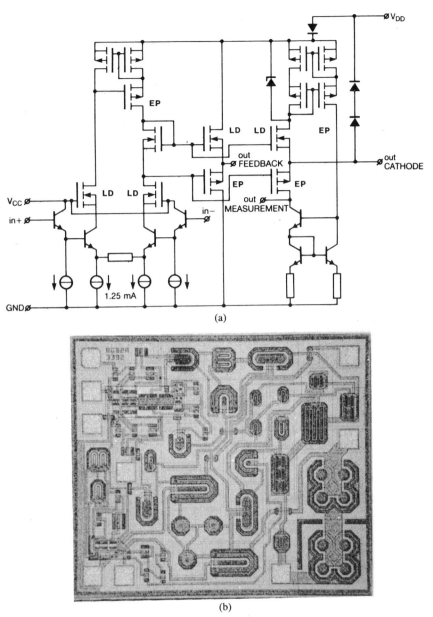

Fig. 13. (a) Schematic diagram and (b) photomicrograph of an 8-MHz video output amplifier.

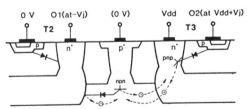

Fig. 15. Substrate currents in full-bridge with inductive load.

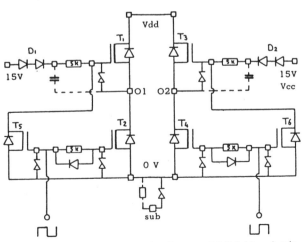

Fig. 14. Schematic diagram of an integrated full-bridge circuit.

which, owing to its special features as source-following LDMOS, complementary HV EPMOS, and high-voltage interconnection, makes true analog HV circuitry possible. The incorporation of high-quality 250-V VDMOS devices is shown to be possible and allows for the compact integration of medium-power switched mode circuits.

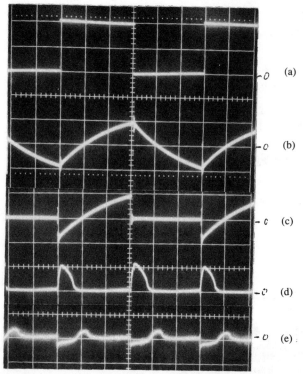

Fig. 16. Waveforms of full-bridge circuit, switching 20 W into 3 mH + 500 Ω at 200 V_{dc}. Horizontal: 5 μs/div. Vertical: curve (a) output voltage 01 at 100 V/div; curve (b) output current 01 at 0.5 A/div; curve (c) drain current $T1$ at 0.5 A/div; curve (d) substrate current at 20 mA/div for V_{sub} = −1.8 V; curve (e) substrate current at 20 mA/div for V_{sub} = 0 V/50 Ω.

ACKNOWLEDGMENT

The author wishes to thank his colleagues for their co-operation and useful discussions. Special contributions to the present work have been made by H. Punter and A. Taskan in the preparation of the samples and by P. Blan-

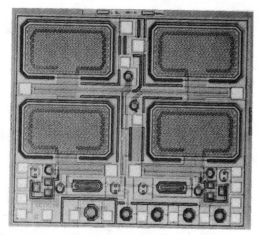

Fig. 17. Photomicrograph of full-bridge with level shifter.

ken and P. van der Zee in designing the video amplifier and the full-bridge layout.

REFERENCES

[1] H. Sakuma *et al.*, in *IEDM Tech. Dig.*, p. 254, 1982.
[2] F. Bertotti *et al.*, *IEEE Trans. Consumer Electron.*, vol. CE-27, p. 295, 1981.
[3] V. Borghese and U. Mastromatteo, in *ESSCIRC Tech. Dig.*, p. 143, 1983.
[4] K. Nakagawa *et al.*, in *IEDM Tech. Dig.*, p. 72, 1982.
[5] T. Yamaguchi and S. Morimoto, *IEEE Trans. Electron Devices*, vol. ED-29, p. 1171, 1982.
[6] H. M. J. Vaes and J. A. Appels, in *IEDM Tech. Dig.*, p. 87, 1980.
[7] A. W. Ludikhuize, in *IEDM Tech. Dig.*, p. 81, 1982.
[8] E. H. Stupp *et al.*, in *IEDM Tech. Dig.*, p. 426, 1981.
[9] P. G. Blanken and P. van der Zee, *IEEE Trans. Consumer Electron.*, vol. CE-31, p. 109, 1985.
[10] A. R. Alvarez *et al.*, in *IEDM Tech. Dig.*, p. 420, 1983.
[11] M. Amato and V. Rumennik, in *IEDM Tech. Dig.*, p. 736, 1985.
[12] K. Wagenaar, private communication.
[13] R. W. Bonne, private communication.
[14] T. Okabe *et al.*, *IEEE Trans. Electron Devices*, vol. ED-27, p. 334, 1980.
[15] A. Rusu and C. Bulucea, in *IEDM Tech. Dig.*, p. 42, 1976.

High-Voltage Technology Offers New Solutions for Interface Integrated Circuits

GILLES THOMAS, GILLES TROUSSEL, AND FRANÇOISE VIALETTES

Abstract—A BIMOS IC technology improving the design of interface circuits that require either high-voltage (up to 120 V) of current (up to a few amperes per output) has been developed. Both bipolar and MOS complementary components are processed together on the same chip for low- and high-voltage applications. Various BIMOS power interface circuits are now in production, e.g., a motor driver, a high-voltage plasma display driver, and a printer head driver. This paper describes the BIMOS technology and the characteristics of its components. As applications, two circuits are presented: the UEB 4732 (plasma display driver) with complementary MOS push–pull output stages (120 V), and the UAA 2081 (stepper motor driver) with power bipolar transistors (1 A per output). Both circuits have a logical part designed with low-voltage CMOS (5–12 V).

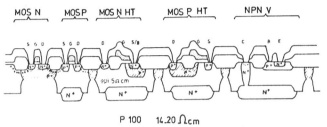

Fig. 1. BIMOS technology.

I. BIMOS TECHNOLOGY

THE NEWLY developed BIMOS technology is a semiconductor fabrication process mixing on the same silicon wafer bipolar components and complementary MOS devices in two voltage ranges, a low voltage of 12 V and a high voltage of 120 V for HVMOS and 80 V for bipolar. Fig. 1 shows a cross section of the process. One can identify the main features of a complementary bipolar process with n-epitaxy on p-substrate $\langle 100 \rangle$ and junction isolation.

To insure availability of a low-power and fair packing density logic, we chose to add to bipolar a CMOS with (1) silicon gate, (2) local oxidation and field implants, and (3) self-aligned source and drain. The "superposition" of both technologies can be used industrially and be profitable only if the number of photolithographic levels does not become too large (13 in our case). This situation leads to multifunction levels:

1) n-p-n base implant common to p-source and drain;
2) n-p-n emitter diffusion common to n-source and drain; and
3) p⁻ well of the NMOS common to isolation, p-channel for the LDMOS [12], and drift region around the HV PMOS drain [12].

Obviously, this situation leads to some compromises:

1) NMOS with drawn gate minimum of 6 μm;
2) PMOS with drawn gate minimum of 8 μm; and
3) HV MOS without self-alignment on the gate.

Manuscript received April 17, 1986; revised July 19, 1986.
The authors are with Thomson Semiconducteurs, Bipolar Division, BP 54, 38130 Saint Egreve, France.
IEEE Log Number 8610707.

We have taken advantage of "up isolation" and buried-layer levels necessary to bipolar to give CMOS an excellent immunity to latch up. More precisely a buried layer lies under PMOS regions in order to reduce resistance R_{N^-} and a p⁻ well parasitic n-p-n is avoided by short circuiting the well to the substrate through the up isolation. Fig. 2 gives some physical and electrical characteristics of process and devices demonstrating their versatility, complexity and performances.

Fig. 3 presents the $I_{DS} = f(V_{DS})$ and $\sqrt{I_{DS}} = f(V_{GS})$ curves for complementary HVMOS devices. The effective length and breakdown voltage of these devices depend, by their construction, on alignment accuracy. Their interest lies in their 120-V blocking capacity and their ability to deliver current in the 250-mA range. However, a more efficient output device is the n-p-n with 0.45 mm² for 1-A output current. The n-p-n has $BV_{CEO} = 80$ V; the Early voltage is in the range of 400 to 500 V and the $F_{tmax} \geq 400$ MHz (Fig. 4).

The high-voltage p-n-p can be of the vertical or the lateral type. L-p-n-p have their base under local oxide and $\beta \geq 80$. To improve further their Early voltage, the collector can be implanted into a p⁻ well acting as a drift region. The space-charge region extends then both in the n-base and p⁻ collector region. The design of L-p-n-p requires use of a polysilicon shield, properly connected to avoid parasitic MOS due to metal connections.

Thanks to the bipolar structure, it is possible to build good high-voltage diodes for use as protection against inductive overvoltages. These diodes (Fig. 5), due to their structure, occupy more space than an ordinary p⁺-n diode with surrounding deep n⁺ plug. But the gain of the parasitic substrate p-n-p associated with these diodes is reduced by a factor of 5 to 10. A low leakage current to the substrate is an interesting characteristic when one considers the deleterious effect of substrate current like parasitic

Reprinted from *IEEE Trans. Electron Devices*, vol. ED-33, pp. 2016–2024, Dec. 1986.

	NPN	L PNP	UNITS
GAIN (β)	> 80	> 60	V
BVCEO	80	80	
$F_{T\,MAX}$	450	3	MHz

	NMOS	PMOS	
THRESHOLD VOLTAGE	+ 1.5	- 1.2	V
K' (μ Co/2)	10 - 11	2.2 - 2.6	μA/V²
BODY EFFECT	1.8 - 2	0.5 - 0.6	$V^{1/2}$
GATE OXIDE THICKNESS	800	800	Å
FIELD OXIDE MOS	> 12	< - 12	V

	VALUES	UNITS
SUBSTRAT P	10 - 20	Ωcm
EPITAXY N	5.5 - 7.5	Ωcm
R□ BASE	120 - 130	Ω□
R□ EMITTER	5 - 7	Ω□
R□ BURIED LAYER	9 - 12	Ω□
R□ POLY	20 - 30	Ω□

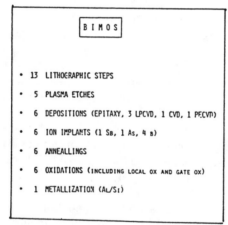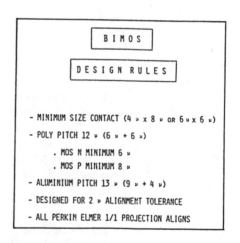

	BIPOLAR			CMOS BT		CMOS HT		
	- NPN	PNP		N	P	N	P	
BV_{EB}	6,5	150 V	V_T	1,2-1,8	1,1-1,6	1,2-1,8	1,1-1,6	V
BV_{CEO}	80 V	80 V	BV_{DS}	24	26	120	120	V
H_{FE}	100 - 200	40 - 80	GM/W MAX	20	6,5	10	5	μA/V.μ
RC/MM²	0,48	Ω/MM²	R_{ON}/MM²	0,24	2,76	13	68	Ω/MM²

BIMOS

- 13 LITHOGRAPHIC STEPS
- 5 PLASMA ETCHES
- 6 DEPOSITIONS (EPITAXY, 3 LPCVD, 1 CVD, 1 PECVD)
- 6 ION IMPLANTS (1 SB, 1 AS, 4 B)
- 6 ANNEALLINGS
- 6 OXIDATIONS (INCLUDING LOCAL OX AND GATE OX)
- 1 METALLIZATION (AL/SI)

BIMOS

DESIGN RULES

- MINIMUM SIZE CONTACT (4 μ x 8 μ OR 6 μ x 6 μ)
- POLY PITCH 12 μ (6 μ + 6 μ)
  - . MOS N MINIMUM 6 μ
  - . MOS P MINIMUM 8 μ
- ALUMINIUM PITCH 13 μ (9 μ + 4 μ)
- DESIGNED FOR 2 μ ALIGNMENT TOLERANCE
- ALL PERKIN ELMER 1/1 PROJECTION ALIGNS

Fig. 2. BIMOS electrical characteristics.

n-p-n action in between adjacent epi islands. For a 1 900-μm² n⁺ cathode the forward voltage at 500 mA is 1.7 V while diode breakdown is 140 V, and 180 V to substrate is allowed.

The logic CMOS part is characterized by: 1) a density of 380 transistors/mm² (n- and p-types mixed); 2) a maximum frequency of 10 MHz (V_{cc} = 12 V) over the military temperature range (up to 125°C), for a static shift register; 3) choice of voltage supply (either 5 V to insure TTL compatibility or 12 V to improve immunity to external interference); 4) no threshold adjustment by implantation; 5) effective lengths and mobilities for minimum size MOS of: LN = 2.8 μm (μN_{max} − 700 cm²/V · s), LP = 3.6 μm (μP_{max} − 225 cm²/V · s); and (6) no latch up. Fig. 6 shows a plot of $I_{DS} = f(V_{DS})$ and $\sqrt{I_D/W} = f(V_{GS})$ for logic CMOS components.

We took advantage of the necessity of two field implants to implement a current limiting device with the p-field implant pinched by an arsenic n⁺ field implant. This device, under the local oxidation, is characterized by V_p = 6 V, R_{ON} = 17.5 kΩ/□, BV = 26 V, I_{DSSO} = 250 μA/□ (Fig. 5).

To ease special analog design (amplifier, voltage reference), the low-voltage CMOS can be completed by low-voltage (12 V) bipolar components. These are deduced from HV bipolar components by adapting the design rules.

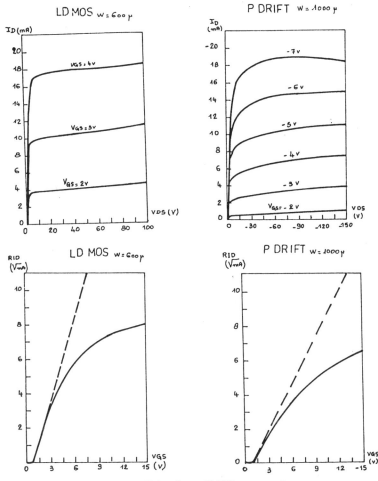

Fig. 3. High-voltage CMOS components.

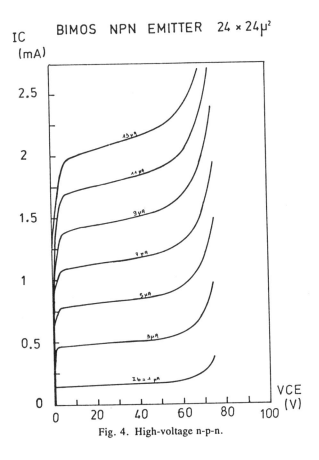

Fig. 4. High-voltage n-p-n.

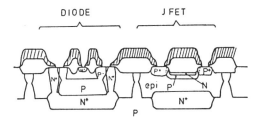

P100   14.20 Ω cm

Fig. 5. Diode and JFET.

For an intermediate complexity process (13 masks), thus at acceptable industrial cost, the technology offers a broad variety of components and therefore flexibility for the designers. This flexibility is exemplified by the presentation of two circuits.

II. A UNIPOLAR STEPPER MOTOR DRIVING CIRCUIT

As an application of BIMOS technology, Thomson Semiconducteurs and Triumph Adler have developed together the UAA 2081, which is a dual unipolar motor driver.

A. The System

A permanent magnet stepper motor consists of a permanent magnet rotor and stator poles with windings (Fig.

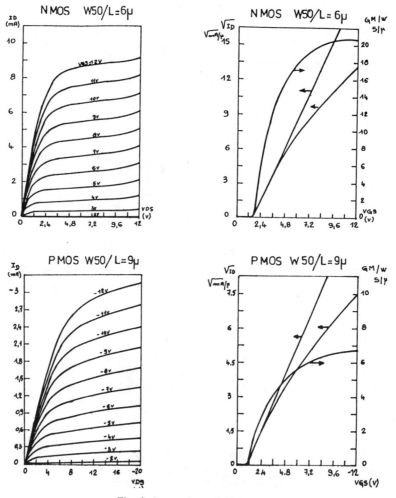

Fig. 6. Low-voltage CMOS.

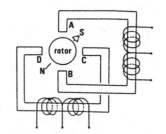

Fig. 7. Stepper motor schematic diagram.

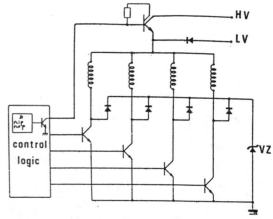

Fig. 8. Bilevel drive diagram.

7). When current flows through 1 or 2 windings, it creates a magnetic field to which the rotor will be aligned. Then, by switching off the current in one winding and by driving the next one, the field turns and the rotor rotates a step [1]. The one-phase-on or ''wave drive'' mode consumes the least power because only one motor phase is energized at one time; sequentially the *A*, *C*, *B*, and *D* winding is driven for 90° steps. The two-phase-on mode or ''overlapping drive'' mode offers less susceptibility to resonance and better single step damping; now *AC*, *BC*, *BD*, or *DA* windings are driven providing again 90° steps. By combining these two modes, the motor can be used in the half-step mode with 45° steps and an *A*, *AC*, *C*, *BC*, *B*, *BD*, *D*, *DA* sequence. This excitation mode produces a

higher acceleration and the smoothest operation. According to these remarks, it is obvious that an extremely versatile integrated circuit solution is required to drive efficiently a stepper motor.

The combination of two basic drive approaches allows to get very short current rise and fall times in order to have good motor efficiency: the bilevel drive and the recirculation diodes (Fig. 8) [2], [3]. To get a short rise

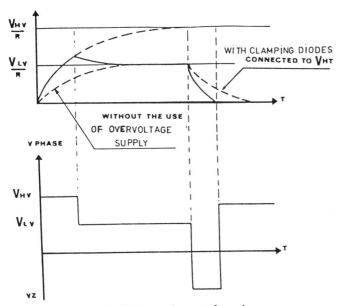

Fig. 9. Voltage and current for a phase.

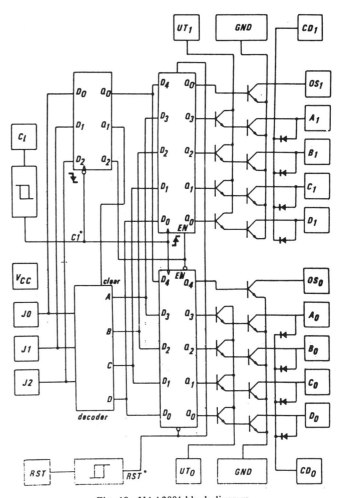

Fig. 10. UAA2081 block diagram.

time, a high voltage supply (20 to 40 V) is used for a rapid current increase at phase turn on. Then a low voltage (5 to 10 V) is used to sustain the current at the rated level. To get a short current fall time, a recirculation diode is used with a high Zener voltage (about 50 V) preventing high-voltage spikes from destroying the switching device, and making the current to decrease rapidly (Fig. 9). So a good circuit must integrate on the same chip both logical elements and power stages with rugged and low dissipation transistors.

B. The Integrated Solution

To get such a good circuit at a low cost, BIMOS technology was the only solution. The present circuit can drive independently two unipolar stepper motors with the bi-level solution [4]. For each motor, four n-p-n transistors deliver 1 A per phase with a low saturation voltage: 900 mV (outputs *A*, *B*, *C*, *D*) (Fig. 10). The transistors can withstand 60 V as BV_{CEO}. The area needed is about 0.45 mm^2 per transistor, but in return the saturation resistance is less than 0.8 Ω at $T_{amb} = 25°$C. The outputs are protected by recirculating clamp diodes (outputs *CD*) characterized by low drop voltage (1.5 V at 1 A) and very low leakage current to the substrate.

An n-p-n transistor (output *OS*) is used as a switch to select the power supply voltage applied on the motors' windings. It has been designed to a current of a few milliamperes (up to 8 mA) with a saturation voltage of 150 mV and drives an external Darlington transistor. As it switches high voltages, it has to withstand 60 V as BV_{CEO}. When transistor *OS* is off, the Darlington is on and the higher supply voltage gives a rapid current increase for improving speed and torque of the motor (Fig. 8). The driver current for switch saturation can be adjusted by external resistances (inputs *UT*) for minimum chip losses. Dissipation for an output of 2 × 0.5 A is 0.55 W, whereas it is 2 W at 2 × 1 A at I_{ut} of 50 mA and 100 mA, respec-

tively, and $V_{cc} = 5$ V. A 24-pin dual in line package is used with an Rth junction ambient of about 55°C/W.

For avoiding lateral n-p-n action between two adjacent epi islands due to current switching in the windings of the motors, we have included an extra n-epi island between them, short-circuited to ground. Thus, the n-p-n parasitic beta is reduced to less than 2×10^{-3} [5].

The logic part consists of 10 flip-flops with a reset signal and a 3- to 4-bit decoder that allows us to define independently all the different driving sequences for bi-level half/full steps. Thanks to the CMOS density, only a small area is necessary: 0.04 mm^2 per flip-flop and less than 0.15 mm^2 for the decoder. All the logic inputs (*J0*, *J1*, *J2*, *RST*, *Cl*) are LS TTL and CMOS compatible. Besides, *RST* and *Cl* inputs have been specially designed for high noise margin (thanks to a 400-mV hysteresis) and high protection against less than 200-ns disturbant signals. The device can operate over a wide range of logical supply voltage (4.5 to 7 V) and because of the use of the CMOS power, the logic current is 2 mA, +2 mA per activated power output.

The main interest is to require few external components to get a performant control device for two unipolar stepper motors (Fig. 11). A microcontroller with two 3-bit words defines acceleration pulse width, forward or re-

271

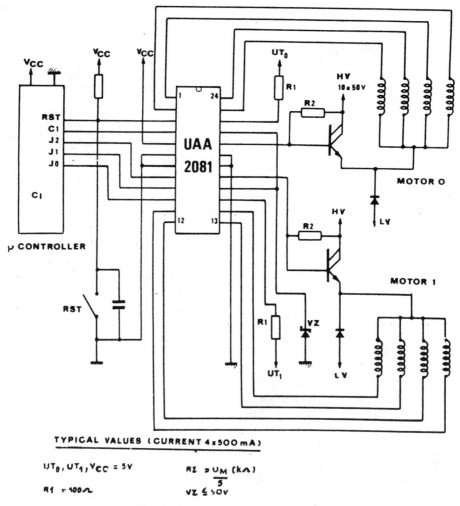

TYPICAL VALUES (CURRENT 4 x 500 mA)

UT$_0$, UT$_1$, V$_{CC}$ = 5V   R2 ≥ U$_M$ (kΩ)
                                                    5
R1 = 100Ω   VZ ≤ 50V

Fig. 11. UAA2081 Application synoptic.

verse rotation (CW or CCW), and half or full step mode. Dissipation is optimized by the choice of the resistance on the UT inputs. The adequacy of the driver transistors avoids the use of a too powerful supply. Fig. 12 shows a photomicrograph of the 14-mm^2 chip.

III. A HIGH-VOLTAGE IC DRIVER FOR AC PLASMA DISPLAY PANEL (UEB 4732)

Thomson Semiconducteurs has designed the UEB 4732 in cooperation with the Thomson-CSF Electron Tube Division and with support from French Direction Générale de l'Armement (DGA) to answer the requirement of integrated drivers for ac plasma panels, and mainly for plasma panels of large dimensions (512 rows × 512 columns, 1024 × 1024, · · ·) [9]. These large display panels are now available from several suppliers in the United States, Japan, and Europe.

A. AC Plasma Display Panel

The ac PDP is an *X–Y* matrix gas discharge display with inherent memory. The pixel defined by the intersection of the line electrode *Y* and the column electrode *X* is driven by the voltage ($V_y - V_x$) created by the difference between the voltages V_y and V_x applied, respectively, to the line *Y*

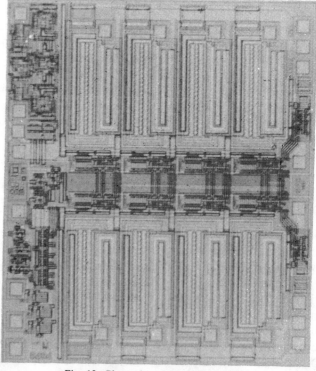

Fig. 12. Photomicrograph of UAA 2081.

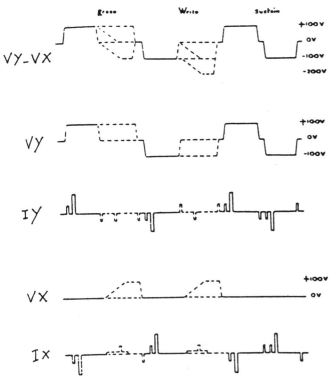

Fig. 13. Command signals for an ac PDP.

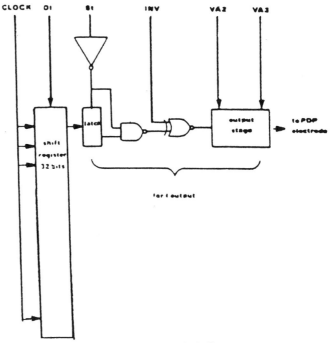

Fig. 14. UEB4732 block diagram.

and the column X. The WRITE, ERASE, and SUSTAIN signals $(V_y - V_x)$ of a pixel are sketched on Fig. 12 with the voltages V_y and V_x of the corresponding electrodes, and with the current flow created by these signals.

Two types of signals are needed by the plasma panel (Fig. 12), [6], [7]: 1) A sustaining voltage, swinging between 0 and $+100$ V, and between 0 and -100 V simultaneously on all the electrodes. The switching time of the sustain waveform is short ($<0.5~\mu s$). The sustain waveform creates the luminous discharge current that can reach 100 mA for an electrode and lasts 0.2 μs. The drive circuit must have a low-voltage drop to maintain the luminous signal of the plasma. 2) Selective writing and erasure address signals [4], bringing the selected electrodes to 100 V above the others. These signals are slow (leading edge $\geqq 1~\mu s$). Their role is to charge the capacitor between a selected electrode and its neighboring electrodes, and to supply the WRITE and ERASE currents of the pixels. These currents appear during the raising slope of the signal and are always below 10 mA. They can be supplied across a high impedance (1 kΩ).

B. The Integrated Solution

The required signals are generated by the UEB 4732 from four CMOS logic inputs and one high-voltage signal [10]. The IC includes a CMOS logic part (decoding, 32-bit shift register with latches) and a low- to high-voltage interface (Fig. 13). The design choosen for the output stages (Figs. 14 and 15) takes advantage of the qualities of diodes and complementary HVMOS of HVBIMOS technology. Diodes with a low forward voltage ($\Delta V < 2$ V for $I_D = 100$ mA), transmit the sustaining signals [11].

During sustain, V_{A2} and V_{ref} are equal and connected to a sustain amplifier, common to all the IC drivers of one axis. The high-voltage stages are disabled during sustain, so the power consumption in the IC is lowered.

The selective signals are created by a complementary (120 V) LDMOSN and p-drift stage. The LDMOSN is directly driven by the logic part of the IC. The MOSP drift uses two reference current sources, common to the 32 output stages. This design presents the following advantages: a small number of high-voltage components per stage (2LDMOSN, 1 MOSPdrift, and 2 diodes), therefore reduced area needed; a low power consumption at a steady level, an easy control from the logic part of the IC (only one logic signal needed per stage).

The 64 diodes (two diodes per stage) are made of p^+-n with a deep n^+ plug. The area covered by the n-island of one diode is 0.038 mm^2. Taking into account the operating conditions of the circuit ($V_{A2} = V_{ref}$ during the peak currents through the diodes), low leakage diodes, demanding a bigger area, were not useful. The forward voltage is typically 1.3 V at $I_D = 100$ mA; BV is $\geqq 130$ V.

The PMOS drift transistor must have an $R_{DSON} < 1$ kΩ with $V_{GS} = -12$ V and $I_{DS} = 10$ mA on the whole military temperature range ($-55°C$, $+125°C$). Taking into account that this component is not self-aligned, and that its R_{DSON} doubles for a 100°C temperature rise, we have designed the MOSP drift with $W = 1000~\mu m$ (area of one MOSP drift island = 0.08 mm^2). We obtained an R_{DSON} typically equal to 0.3 kΩ to ambient.

Two LDMOSN's are needed for each output stage. The biggest one, used with the MOSP drift in the push–pull output, must have $R_{DSON} < 1$ kΩ with $V_{GS} = 12$ V and $I_{DS} = 10$ mA on the whole military temperature range ($-55°C$, $+125°C$). The LDMOSN being favored com-

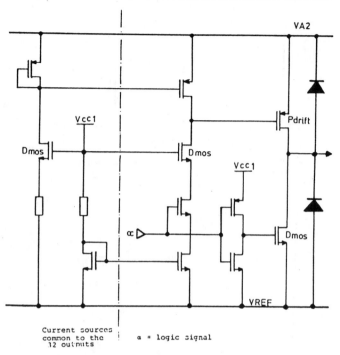

Fig. 15. UEB4732 schematic of one output stage.

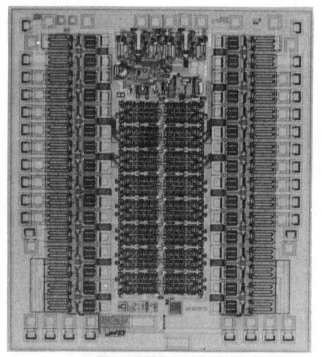

Fig. 16. Photomicrograph of UEB4732.

logic signals. It has a low level direct current and its on resistance is not a main parameter. We designed it with $W = 100\ \mu$m, so it's R_{DSON} is roughly 1 kΩ.

Fig. 16 shows a photomicrograph of the 20 mm^2 chip, with 14 mm^2 for the 32 output stages. It is packaged in a 40-pin DIL, in a version for commercial applications (0, 70°C) and in a version for military applications (-55°C, $+125$°C). A micropackage is on study.

IV. Conclusion

This article has presented the use of various HVBIMOS components in the IC design for two very different interface problems: the driving of two stepper motors (UAA2081) and the driving of an ac plasma display panel (UEB4732). BIMOS is also used in other applications such as thermal printer head driving (UCA4532) or in nonspecific IC (octuple latch UCN4801A). These various interface circuits are at present in full production. Diverse new circuits are on study and design, using BIMOS technology. With a production price only 20 percent higher than a standard high-voltage bipolar technology, HVBIMOS offers high-voltage bipolar components plus high-voltage complementary DMOS and low-voltage CMOS. This diversity allows a great reduction in the number of IC's needed for an application by the integration of logic and power functions on the same IC.

References

[1] H. Bollinger and D. Hirschi, "Le moteur pas à pas, organe d'entraînement du futur," *Tech. moderne*, vol. 3, p. 9, 1985.
[2] D. Jones, J. Anderson, and H. Manson, "The PM step motor, integrated combination, a low cost integrated step motor drive system," in *Proc. Motorcon*, p. 155, Sept. 1982.
[3] D. G. Wilson, "Step motor drivers: An analysis of various approaches," in *Proc. Motorcon*, p. 166, Sept. 1982.
[4] G. Troussel, "L'UAA2081: Une commande intégrée originale de deux moteurs pas à pas unipolaires réalisée en BIMOS," to be published.
[5] F. Van Zanten, "Dispostif de protection contre les courants de fuite dans les circuits intégrés," INPI, vol. 80, p. 10842, May 1980.
[6] J. Deschamps, "L'affichage de données graphiques et alphanumériques par panneau à plasma," *Rev. Technique Thomson-CSF*, vol. 10, no. 2, June 1978.
[7] Texas Instruments, *Display Driver Handbook*, 1984.
[8] T. N. Criscimagna, J. R. Beidl, and J. B. Trushell, "Write and erase waveform for high resolution ac plasma display panels," *IEEE*, 1980. 1980.
[9] F. Vialettes and G. Thomas, "BIMOS technology and its application to plasma panel IC driver," *Opto Dig.*, p. 245, 1985.
[10] L. Delgrange, M. Specty, and F. Vialettes, "Circuit de commande d'un panneau à plasma de type alternatif," INPI, vol. 85.
[11] L. Delgrange, J. Deschamps, and F. Vialettes, "A.C. plasma display panel control circuit," U.S. patent application 431 152.
[12] G. Thomas, "Structure de circuit intégré comportant des transistors CMOS à tenue en tension élevée et son procédé de fabrication," INPI, vol. 84.
[13] L. Degrange, F. Vialettes, J. Deschamps, and G. Thomas, "A high voltage IC driver for large-area A.C. plasma display panels," in *SID Dig.*, p. 103, 1984.

pared to the MOSP, was designed with $W = 600\ \mu$m (the area of one LDMOSN island is 0.045 mm^2). We obtained an R_{DSON} typically below 0.2 kΩ at 25°C ambient. The other LDMOSN, used in the command system of the MOSP drift, is mainly a link between high voltage and

A MONOLITHIC HIGH VOLTAGE SOS/CMOS OPERATIONAL AMPLIFIER

T. Kuriyama, H. Sakuma and K. Hirata

Microelectronics Research Laboratories, NEC Corporation
4-1-1 Miyazaki, Miyamae-ku, Kawasaki, 213, Japan

ABSTRACT

A monolithic high voltage operational amplifier with a novel high voltage offset-gate SOS/MOS transistor is proposed and shown to operate at $\pm 100V$ (200V peak to peak). A high voltage offset-gate SOS/CMOS IC (1,2) is very suitable for high voltage analog circuits by its inherent complete dielectric isolation and latch up free property, which make high voltage circuit design as easy as designing a low voltage circuit.

The novel high voltage offset-gate SOS/MOS transistor proposed in this paper has an additional middle electrode at its offset-gate region, which works as a voltage level shifter.

When the novel high voltage offset-gate SOS/MOS transistor is used as a load transistor for a differential amplifier, the output of the middle electrode can be directly supplied to a gate input for a next high voltage SOS/CMOS inverter amplifier, therefore compact chip size and high gain are realized. The monolithic high voltage SOS/CMOS operational amplifier has 1.6mm X 1.6mm chip size and works with $\pm 100V$ power supply. Its open loop gain is 110dB ($f < 1kHz$), and $\pm 100V$ output is obtained for $f < 20kHz$, and $\pm 20V$ output for $f < 100kHz$.

INTRODUCTION

A monolithic high voltage operational amplifier is a component for miniaturizing high voltage analog circuits, such as SLIC (Subscriber Line Interface Circuits) in a telephone system and piezoelectric actuator driver circuits.

To realize a high voltage circuit in a monolithic form, it is necessary, in addition to high voltage property, that transistors are electrically isolated from each other. Several dielectric isolation technologies for high voltage circuits have been proposed, for example, silicon island embedded in SiO_2 and poly-silicon (3), or silicon island on insulating substrate (4). The former technology is suitable to bipolar transistor circuits and gives a small ON resistance. Its fabrication process is, however, rather complicated, because precise thickness control is necessary to get a silicon layer with uniform thickness. On the other hand, the latter technology is used for MOS transistor circuits and has an advantage of easy fabrication process and small size integration.

An offset-gate structure SOS/MOS transistor (1,2), which belongs to the latter technology, is very suitable to integrate a high voltage analog circuit monolithically from these advantages; complete dielectric isolation, latch up free CMOS, low power dissipation, circuit design flexibility, high packing density, simple fabrication process and low parasitic capacitance.

A monolithic high voltage operational amplifier is proposed which uses offset-gate SOS/MOS transistors and novel offset-gate SOS/MOS transistors. The novel offset-gate SOS/MOS transistor realizes a level shifter in a simple manner and gives a high gain. Its function was confirmed by measuring a potential distribution in the offset-gate region. The measurement also revealed the high voltage mechanism for the offset-gate SOS/MOS transistor and the relationship between the breakdown voltage and impurity amounts in the offset-gate region.

The experimental result shows the proposed circuit is suitable to high voltage analog ICs.

PROPOSED CIRCUIT AND TRANSISTOR

In a high voltage analog circuit, it is also desirable that a gate insulator for a high voltage MOS transistor be as thin as in a low voltage circuit, because a thin gate insulator can give a large g_m (mutual conductance) value, which contributes to a high gain amplifier circuit. When high voltage MOS transistors with thin gate insulator are used, a level shift circuit becomes necessary, because the thin gate insulator is broken when a high voltage input is supplied to the transistor gate.

The voltage level shift circuit has been realized by using series connected resistors or a combination of two transistors. These voltage level shift circuits, however, make the circuit complicated and increase the device area.

To remove the above adverse points, a novel high voltage offset-gate SOS/MOS transistor is proposed. The structure is shown in Fig. 1 and Fig. 2 (a),(b). It has an additional middle electrode (M) at the offset-gate region. Middle electrode M works as a voltage level shifter. It is formed only by extending a part of the offset-gate region silicon island over a sapphire substrate and does not reduce drain breakdown voltage BV_D.

When drain voltage V_D is less than offset-gate region pinch off voltage V_P, middle electrode voltage V_M follows V_D. When V_D exceeds V_P, the offset-gate region is depleted and V_M saturates, being maintained under a gate breakdown voltage ($\sim 40V$), as shown in Fig. 3. The level shift mechanism was confirmed by measuring potential distribution in the offset-gate region, which will be described in the next section.

When the high voltage offset-gate SOS/MOS transistor with the middle electrode is used as a load transistor for a differential amplifier, output voltage V_M can be readily supplied to a gate input for a next high voltage SOS/CMOS inverter amplifier and high gain is obtained. Adopting the novel high voltage offset-gate SOS/MOS transistor makes high voltage circuit design as easy as designing low voltage circuits and realizes monolithic high voltage analog ICs in a very small area by its inherent complete dielectric isolation.

EXPERIMENTAL RESULTS

To verify the high voltage mechanism of the offset-gate SOS/MOS transistor and middle electrode's function, the potential distribution in the offset-gate region was

Reprinted from *IEEE 29th Int. Electron Devices Meeting*, pp. 432-435, 1983.

measured by using several electrodes which are made in the offset-gate region and have a similar structure to the middle electrode.

Figure 4a shows the relationship between pinched resistor ion implantation dose N_I and drain breakdown voltage BV_D. Figure 4b shows the surface potential distributions in the offset-gate region. Two kinds of p-channel SOS/MOS transistors, which are fabricated on the same wafer with the same ion implantation dose, are used for the measurement ; one has a 30 μm offset-gate region and the other has a 100 μm offset-gate region.

From Fig. 4a and Fig. 4b, it is shown that, when the impurity amount in the offset-gate pinched resistor Q_I is equal to that in the offset-gate region substrate Q_S ($N_I=2.5 \times 10^{12}$/cm^2), the potential in the offset-gate region increases linearly from gate to drain and electric field is uniform (Fig. 4b center), giving maximum drain breakdown voltage BV_D. When Q_I is less than Q_S, the potential in the offset-gate region changes steeply near the drain and the electric field is locally strong at the drain (Fig. 4b left), decreasing BV_D. When Q_I is larger than Q_S, the potential in the offset-gate is almost the same as the drain voltage and the electric field is locally strong at gate (Fig. 4b right), also decreasing BV_D.

Fig. 4b shows that the offset-gate pinched resistor is depleted above pinch off voltage V_p, when Q_I is smaller than or equal to Q_S. Middle electrode voltage V_M is maintained near the pinch off voltage under these conditions.

The high voltage offset-gate SOS/MOS transistors used in the proposed operational amplifier have 30 μm long offset-gate region and the breakdown voltage is more than 300V. The novel high voltage offset-gate SOS/MOS transistors, which are used as load transistors for a differential amplifier, have a 50 μm long offset-gate region. Middle electrode M is positioned 14 μm distant from the gate poly-silicon. The source field plate has a 6 μm extension from the gate. The drain field plate has 8 μm extension from the drain. Enhancement channel length L_E and depletion channel length L_D are 4 μm and 2 μm, respectively.

Figure 5 shows a monolithic high voltage SOS/CMOS operational amplifier top view. Chip size is 1.6mm X 1.6mm and most of the device area is occupied by output transistors and bonding electrodes. Output transistors N_5 and P_7 have about 100 Ω ON resistance.

Figure 6 shows the proposed high voltage SOS/CMOS operatioanl amplifier circuit, which is composed of current mirror, differential amplifier, inverter amplifier and output. Adopting the novel high voltage offset-gate SOS/MOS transitors as load transistors for the differential amplifier, output voltage V_M can be directly supplied to a gate input for a next high voltage SOS/MOS inverter amplifier, and high gain is obtained. Resistor R and capacitor C are outside the IC. A quiescent current is less than 2mA at R=10MΩ .

Figure 7 shows an open loop gain and phase shift for high voltage SOS/CMOS operational amplifier without phase compensation (C=O). The circuit works with ± 100V power supply. A 110dB high gain is obtained under 1kHz. The high gain is attributed to the use of the novel high voltage offset-gate SOS/MOS transistor and CMOS configuration. Figure 8 shows input and output waveforms for the high voltage operational amplifier with 60dB feedback loop at 10kHz. A sine wave output is obtained with little distortion. ± 100V output is obtained for f<20kHz, and ±20V output for f<100kHz.

CONCLUSION

The conclusions reached in this paper are :
(1)   A monolithic high voltage operational amplifier is realized by using high voltage offset-gate SOS/MOS transistors. It operates at 100V (200V peak to peak) and 110dB open loop gain is obtained for f 1kHz.
(2)   A novel high voltage offset-gate SOS/MOS transistor proposed in this paper has an additioanl middle electrode which works as a voltage level shifer. It contributes to obtaining a simple circuit and a compact device.
(3)   The middle electrode function was verified by measuring a potential distribution in the offset-gate region. The measurement explains the high voltage mechanism of the high voltage offset-gate SOS/MOS transistor.
(4)   The proposed circuit can be widely used in various high voltage analog ICs.

ACKNOWLEDGEMENT

The authors wish to thank Dr. K. Ayaki, Dr. H. Shiraki and Dr. H. Kato for their support and encouragement in this work.

REFERENCES

(1)   H. Sakuma, T. Kuriyama and T. Suzuki, "A High Voltage Offset-Gate SOS/MOS Transistor", IEDM'79 Technical digest, pp. 594-597.
(2)   T. Suzuki, T. Kuriyama and H. Sakuma, "A High Voltage-High Frequency SOS/CMOS Pulse Generator", IEDM'80 Technical Digest, PP. 264-267.
(3)   P.J. Meza, D.P. Laude, R.C. Strawbrich, R.M. Sirisi, "A Two-Chip Subscriber Line Interface circuit with Ringing", ISSCC'83 Digest of technical paper, pp. 16-17.
(4)   R.S. Ronen, M.R. Splinter and R.E. Treamain; IEEE J. Solid-state Circuits, vol. SC-11, p.431 (1976).

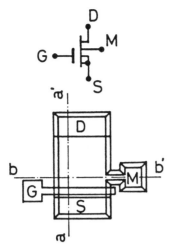

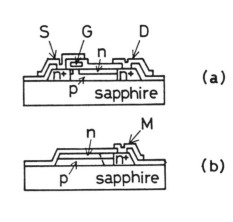

Fig. 1 Novel HV offset-gate SOS/MOS transistor structure. Middle electrode (M) extends from the offset-gate region and works as a voltage level shifter. A symbol is also shown. S:Source, G:Gate, D:Drain.

Fig. 2 Cross sectional views of novel HV offset-gate SOS/MOS transistor. Upper view is at a-a', lower view is at b-b' in Fig. 1.

Fig. 3 Relation between middle electrode V_M voltage and drain V_D voltage. After the offset-gate region pinches off, V_M saturates and is maintained under a gate breakdown voltage.

Fig. 4a Relationship between pinched resistor ion implantation dose N_I and drain breakdown voltage BV_D.

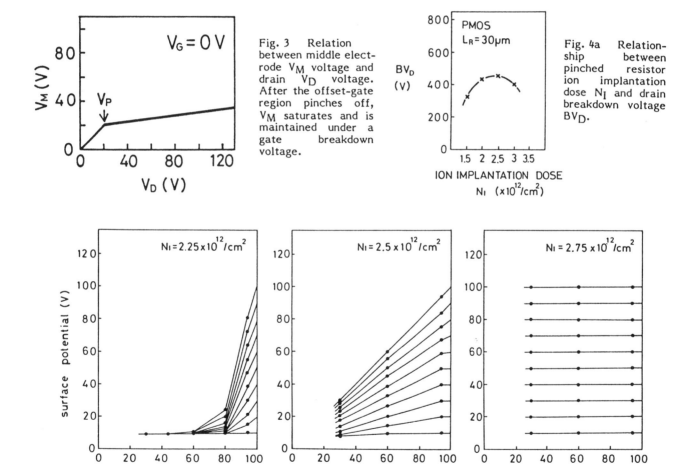

Fig. 4b Relationship between pinched resistor ion implantation dose N_I and surface potential distrubution in the offset-gate region.

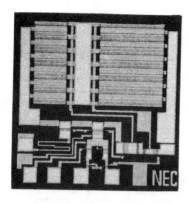

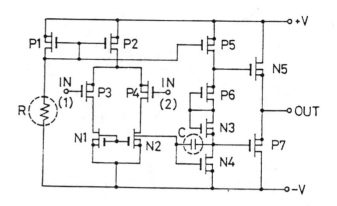

Fig. 5 Monolithic HV SOS/CMOS operational amplifier top view. Chip size is 1.6mm X 1.6mm. Most of the device area is occupied by output transistors and bonding electrodes.

Fig. 6 Proposed HV SOS/CMOS operational amplifier circuit. N shows an n-channel transistor and P shows a p-channel transistor. N_1 and N_2 are novel HV offset-gate SOS/MOS transistors. $P_2 \sim P_5$, P_7, N_4 and N_5 are HV offset-gate SOS/MOS transistors. P_1, P_6 and N_3 are conventional low voltage transistors. Output voltage for N_2 is maintained under N_4 gate breakdown voltage. R and C are outside the IC.

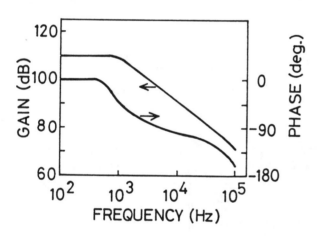

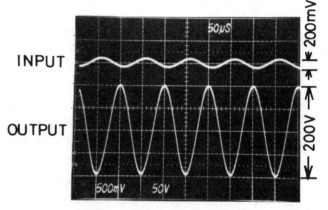

Fig. 7 Open loop gain and phase shift for HV SOS/CMOS operational amplifier (without phase compensation). 110dB gain is obtained under 1 kHz.

Fig. 8 Input and output voltage wave-forms for HV SOS/CMOS operational amplifier (with feedback 60dB at 10 kHz).

Part VII

High Voltage Telecommunication Chips

THE development of integrated circuits for telecommunication applications has received considerable attention due to the large volume of chips required to satisfy the needs of complex networks. Due to the relatively large voltages present in the ringing circuits, many of the applications need the availability of integrated circuits that contain multiple high voltage devices. A typical example in this category is a cross-point switching matrix that requires arrays of high voltage devices that exhibit low forward voltage drops in the on-state. The most commonly used device that satisfies these requirements is the silicon controlled rectifier (SCR). Arrays of this device have been integrated initially using junction isolation technology, and more recently using dielectric isolation technology.

This part of the book contains six papers that describe high voltage integrated circuits developed for telecommunication applications. One of these papers deals with junction isolated technology. Using this approach a relatively low voltage (30 volts) blocking capability was achieved. The rest of the papers describe chips developed by using dielectric isolation techniques. In these, chips arrays of devices can be formed with a voltage blocking capability of over 500 volts.

The first paper, by Hartman et al. published in the digest of the 1976 International Electron Devices meeting describes the fabrication of an array of 32 junction isolated SCRs. A vertical pnpn structure is formed by starting with a P-substrate, diffusing an N-plus buried layer, and growing a P-epitaxial layer. The N-plus buried layer is utilized with the N-plus isolation (sinker) diffusion to create a wrap-around cathode region for the SCR in order to obtain device isolation. Undesirable substrate current flow is reduced by performing gold doping to attenuate the gain of the parasitic transistor formed at the reverse biased substrate junction.

Monolithic cross-point switching circuits have more recently been made by using dielectrical isolation technology. The next two papers discuss the fabrication of chips using the conventional V-groove dielectrically isolated silicon tub formation process. Thyristors (SCRs) with breakover voltages in excess of 250 volts have been formed using this approach. The paper by Beasom reviews the design considerations for achieving good device performance in this dielectrically isolated tub technology. The following paper, by Mori et al., published in the IEEE JOURNAL OF SOLID STATE CIRCUITS discusses a cross-point array in which optical coupling is used. A photocoupling structure that allows the triggering of four pnpn elements with only one LED is described. Breakover voltages of up to 450 volts have been achieved with a dv/dt of 200 V/0.1 microseconds.

As mentioned earlier one of the important needs in the telecommunication circuits is a high voltage device that can be operated at large forward conduction current densities with a low voltage drop. Although the SCR was used in previous papers, a unique device called the gated diode switch has also been developed for this application. The design and fabrication of devices that can be operated at over 600 volts is discussed in the paper by Weston et al. Problems experienced with high electric fields at the corners of the dielectrically isolated tubs, where the metal cross-over occurs, are pointed out.

The last two papers deal with high voltage integrated circuits developed for telecommunication applications by using an advanced dielectric isolation technology referred to as SIMOX. The formation of dielectrically isolated devices by the SIMOX process is described in a paper in Part VIII of this book. The paper by Nakashima and Maeda published in ELECTRONICS LETTERS describes a chip developed for a subscriber line interface circuit. The chip contains high voltage p-MOS and n-MOS lateral transistors integrated with low voltage CMOS logic. The last paper, by Ohno et al., published in the IEEE JOURNAL OF SOLID STATE CIRCUITS also describes a subscriber line interface circuit. This circuit performs the functions of battery feed, over-voltage protection, ringing, and testing. The chip, formed by using SIMOX technology, contains high voltage NPN, PNP transistors, and PNPN thyristor devices which are used in the 400 volt section of the chip to implement the ringing, over-voltage protection, and test functions. It also contains 100 volt NPN and PNP transistors which are used in the 60 volt section to perform some of the other functions, such as battery feed and supervision.

REPRINT PAPERS

[1] A. R. Hartman, P. W. Shackle, and P. L. Pritchett, "A Junction Isolation Technology for Integrating Silicon Controlled Rectifiers in Cross-Point Switching Circuits," IEEE Int. Electron Devices Meeting Digest, Abst. 3.6, pp. 55–57, 1976.

[2] J. D. Beasom, "High Voltage Dielectric Isolation SCR Integrated Circuit Process," IEEE Int. Electron Devices Meeting Digest, Abst. 9.4, pp. 178–180, 1977.

[3] H. Mori, T. Ishida, K. Hagimura, K. Kato, and S. Ohkoshi, "An Optically-Coupled High-Voltage p-n-p-n Crosspoint Array," IEEE J. Solid State Circuits, vol. SC-14, pp. 998–1003, 1979.

[4] H. T. Weston, H. W. Becke, J. E. Berthold, J. C. Gammel, A. R. Hartman, J. E. Kohl, M. A. Shibib, R. K. Smith, and Y. H. Wong, "Monolithic High Voltage Gated Diode Crosspoint Array IC," IEEE Int. Electron Devices Meeting Digest, Abst. 4.5, pp. 85–88, 1982.

[5] S. Nakashima and Y. Maeda, "Subscriber Line Interface Circuit LSI Fabricated Using High-Voltage CMOS/SIMOX Technology," Electronics Letters, vol. 19, pp. 1095–1097, 1983.

[6] T. Ohno, T. Sakurai, Y. Inabe and T. Koinuma, "A Single Chip High-Voltage Shallow Junction BORSHT-LSI," IEEE J. Solid State Circuits, vol. SC-19, pp. 899–905, 1984.

A JUNCTION ISOLATION TECHNOLOGY FOR INTEGRATING SILICON CONTROLLED RECTIFIERS IN CROSSPOINT SWITCHING CIRCUITS

A. R. Hartman and P. W. Shackle
Bell Laboratories
Murray Hill, New Jersey 07974

and

R. L. Pritchett
Bell Laboratories
Allentown, Pennsylvania 18103

ABSTRACT

An integrated circuit technology has been developed to fabricate a matrix array of 32 junction isolated Silicon Controlled Rectifiers (SCR) for telephone switching systems. Other integrated SCR arrays have employed the more complicated dielectric or air isolation technologies to eliminate parasitic substrate leakages. This leakage in junction isolated structures results from the collection of minority carriers by the substrate. Our technology employs a vertical pnpn structure similar to collector diffusion isolation (1) with a p-substrate, n^+ buried layer, p-epitaxy, wrap around n^+ isolation diffusion, implanted n-gate and diffused p^+ anode regions. Through the use of gold recombination centers for carrier lifetime reduction, the structure achieves substrate leakages of less than one part in 10^5. The SCRs also have adequately low leakages of typically 10 nA at 30V forward or reverse.

INTRODUCTION

Because of the silicon controlled rectifier's large impedance ratio between its blocking and conducting states and its low off capacitance, the silicon controlled rectifier (SCR) has long been recognized as a viable alternative in the evolution of a semiconductor based switching system for telephone communications (2). Integrated arrays of SCRs composed of vertical npn and lateral pnp transistors have been developed (3). However, the integration of the SCRs on a junction isolated chip has posed serious technical obstacles due to parasitic transistor action involving the reverse biased substrate junction. This junction collects a fraction of the injected minority carriers associated with the signal current. The substrate current thus generated subtracts directly from the signal current and produces an attenuation in each SCR.

The transmission requirements for a central office make it desirable that no more than one part in ten thousand of the SCR current is lost to the substrate. Previous solutions to the substrate leakage problem have involved air isolation (4) or dielectric isolation (5) to eliminate the collecting substrate junction.

In this talk we describe a junction isolation technology employing gold doping to reduce the substrate current. This approach provides a less complicated process technology than dielectric or air isolation. A crosspoint switching matrix of 32 SCRs has been fabricated with on-chip gate diodes and shunt resistors on a 1982 micron square chip. The chip meets all of the transmission requirements for an electronic switching system.

DESIGN

The cross section of any one SCR in the array is shown on the left in Fig. 1. It is a vertical structure that has many similarities with collector diffusion isolation. The device employs p-type substrates and p-type epitaxy. It is isolated with a wrap around n+ isolation diffusion which is contiguous with an n+ buried layer. Within the p-type isolated tub are small n-gate and p+ anode and guard ring regions. In the blocking state the n-gate to p-epitaxy junction is reverse biased providing low capacitance (1 pF), high impedance (10^9 ohms) and blocking to voltages as great as 50V. The SCR switches regeneratively to its conducting state in response to forward anode-gate current and establishes a vertical electron-hole plasma directly under the anode.

SUBSTRATE AND JUNCTION LEAKAGES

The parasitic substrate leakage in this technology is the hole current that is collected by the p-substrate when a current (10 mA) flows from anode to cathode. Because the current densities are high ($10^3 A/cm^2$), the injected electron and hole population increases substantially in the p-epitaxial region causing a substantial fraction of the p-epitaxy to n+ buried layer current to be carried by hole injection into the buried layer. For standard buried collector profiles (width 8 microns) and minority carrier

Reprinted from *IEEE 1976 Int. Electron Devices Meeting*, pp. 55–57, 1976.

lifetimes that are typical of IC technology (0.1 - 1.0 microseconds) the substrate current would be up to 10% of the SCR current. By introducing gold recombination centers and providing a wider buried layer, it has been possible to reduce the substrate leakage to nominal values of less than one part in 10^5. The reduction in substrate current results from two beneficial consequences of minority carrier lifetime reduction with gold doping. First, the density of minority carriers in the P-epi region plasma is reduced, so that less of the current across the buried layer to p-epitaxial junction is carried by holes. Second, the hole recombination in the wide buried layer greatly attenuates the flux of holes across the buried layer-substrate junction.

The substrate leakages obtained with two gold doping conditions are shown in Figs. 2 and 3. These measurements were done on a test structure having one junction isolated SCR. The device of Fig. 2 is gold doped, however the concentration of recombination centers was reduced by omitting the high temperature thermal cycle following the silicon nitride deposition. The process sequence is discussed in the following section entitled fabrication. The substrate leakage, which is on the order of $40\,\mu A$, depends strongly on the anode to cathode current of the SCR. The leakage is also nearly independent of reverse bias. In effect the measurement describes a parasitic PNP transistor with the substrate as the collector. The transistor's common base current gain is 0.005 for ac operation between 5 and 15 mA of emitter current. Devices which are not doped with gold show a common base current gain of 0.1 or substrate leakages of approximately 1 mA. In Fig. 3 the substrate leakage is shown for an SCR having gold recombination centers activated through a high temperature spike. The leakage is reduced by three orders of magnitude over the previous example. The device now shows only a small parasitic transistor effect as a function of SCR current, exhibiting a common base current gain of 4×10^{-7}. It instead exhibits voltage dependent leakage due to depletion layer generation in the buried layer-substrate junction. In the integrated array the SCRs operate at higher current densities than the test structure and exhibit typical substrate leakages of 30 nA ac for 10 mA ac of SCR current - an effective common base current gain of 3×10^{-6}.

The gold doping increases the depletion layer carrier generation for all of the junctions in the circuit. For example, Figs. 4 and 5 show the leakages obtained for the SCRs in forward and reverse biases. The devices are from the same wafers as the examples of the previous two figures. Note, however, the measurements of Fig. 4 were done on a test structure, while those of Fig. 5 were done on an SCR in the array

which has smaller junction areas. The higher active gold concentration of the sample in Fig. 5 causes an approximately two orders of magnitude increase in the leakage current density. The leakage of a wafer with no gold doping would also be substantially smaller than both of these devices. However, the increased leakage is well within the requirements for an electronic switching office. The forward and reverse leakage dc of an SCR in the integrated array is typically 10 nA at 30V bias.

FABRICATION

The fabrication sequence begins with a p-type substrate. An ion-implantation of arsenic is done in the buried layer regions through a silicon dioxide mask, and the arsenic is driven to the desired depth. A p-type epitaxial layer doped with boron is grown in commercial reactors. Care must be taken to avoid n-skins in the first two microns of epitaxial growth. The n-skins are the result of arsenic autodoping from the buried layers. When present, they defeat the isolation by connecting the buried layers together with buried n-channel JFETs. A deep phosphorus n+-isolation diffusion is done through the epitaxial layer to the buried layer. This wrap around diffusion and the buried layer isolate a p-epitaxial tub. The n-base is formed in the tub from phosphorus which is ion-implanted and driven. An n+ contact diffusion is then done in the contact window to the n-base regions. Gold is deposited on the back surface of the wafer and diffused through the wafer to the circuit side during the p+ emitter diffusion. Guard ring regions are also formed during this diffusion around all p-epitaxial regions to cut off surface inversion layers. Silicon nitride is deposited to passivate the structure. The wafer is then given a high temperature thermal cycle with a fast cool to place the gold in active recombination centers. The devices are metallized with PtSi,Ti,Pt,Au and beam leaded for bonding on a metallized ceramic. The 4×8 SCR matrix is coated with RTV and packaged in an 18 pin DIP.

CIRCUIT PROPERTIES

The circuit schematic is shown in Fig. 6. In addition to the SCR each crosspoint has a 1.3 kilohm resistor shunting the anode and gate. As shown on the right in Fig. 1, the resistor is an elongated n-region within an isolated p-epitaxial well. Its resistance in combination with the effects of the gold doping set the gate current at approximately 0.6 mA and the hold current at approximately 1.1 mA. A series diode to each gate is formed between the gate access line and the p-epi region containing the shunt resistors. This diode provides full 30V reverse blocking capability on the gate access line. The matrix is arranged in rows of n+ buried layer regions with four n+ common cathode lines alternating with four gate access lines. The columns of the matrix are formed with 8 metal bus bars, each one connecting the corresponding four p+ anode regions in the cathode line. This arrangement allows a one level metal layout, but adds approximately 1.5 ohms of series resistance at the semiconductor cross-unders below the p-lines.

Typical operating characteristics for the 4×8 matrix array of junction isolated SCRs is given in Table 1. In addition to the leakage characteristics discussed above, the matrix offers an on-resistance of 9 ohms at 10 mA of SCR current, a gate trigger voltage of 1.35V at an anode to cathode bias of 20V, and a forward voltage of 0.9V for 10 mA in the SCR. The DC cathode-substrate leakage measures the leakage with one anode line, cathode line and gate line grounded. Because many devices are contacted by the p-line, this current is the sum of the leakages from the cathode line and four gate lines plus a small contribution from crosspoint devices in the other cathode lines.

With the development of this junction isolation technology, employing gold doping, there is now a means of fabricating with conventional integrated circuit manufacturing techniques a matrix array of silicon controlled rectifiers. Furthermore, a circuit designed in this technology is suitable as a space division switching matrix for electronic switching systems.

ACKNOWLEDGMENTS

The assistance of R. S. D'Angelo is the process development and the work of R. G. McMahon (Western Electric, Allentown, Pennsylvania) in the epitaxial material development were greatly appreciated. The assistances of P. B. Smalley in the reliability certification and C. Bures in the test program development are also acknowledged. Many discussions with J. M. Adrian J. D. Smith, D. C. Smith, W. R. Costello, G. R. Weber, T. J. Riley and R. A. Moline were also very helpful.

REFERENCES

(1) B. T. Murphy and V. J. Glinski, IEEE Journal of Solid State Circuits, 1, pp. 261-267; Sept. 1968.

(2) J. L. Moll, M. Tanenbaum, J. M. Goldey and N. Holonyak, Proc. IRE, 44, 1174; 1956.

(3) L. L. Rosier, C. Turrel and W. K. Liebman, Semiconductor Crosspoints IBMJ Res. Dev., pp. 439-446; July 1969.

(4) A. A. Ahmed, S. C. Ahrens and M. A. Polinsky, ISSCC 74, Philadelphia, Pennsylvania, 120; 1974.

(5) A. G. Bryan and L. L. Wisseman, Motorola Application Note MCBH7601.

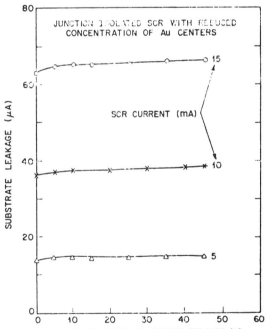

Fig. 2. Substrate leakage versus cathode to substrate reverse bias. The wafer has a reduced density of gold recombination centers because the gold activation thermal cycle was omitted in the process. Junction area = $3.0 \times 10^{-3} cm^2$.

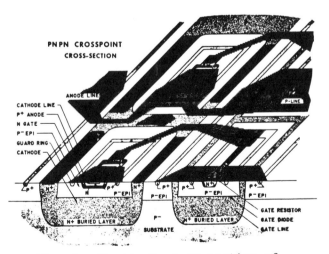

Fig. 1. Vertical cross section of a junction-isolated SCR.

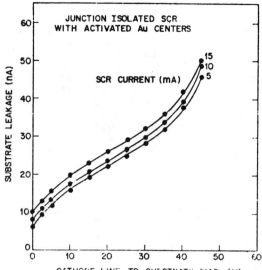

Fig. 3. Substrate leakage versus cathode to substrate reverse bias. The wafer has a typical gold recombination center concentration. Junction area = 3.0×10^{-3} cm^2.

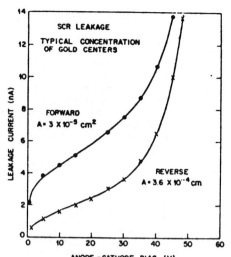

Fig. 5. Forward and reverse leakage for the SCR as a function of anode-to-cathode bias at room temperature. The wafer has a typical density of gold recombination centers.

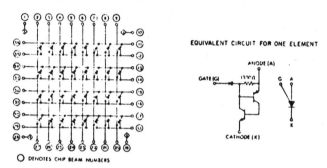

○ DENOTES CHIP BEAM NUMBERS

◈ SUBSTRATE

Fig. 6. Circuit schematic of 4×8 silicon controlled rectifier cross-point switching matrix. Each of the 32 crosspoints has an SCR, gate diode and anode-gate shunt resistor.

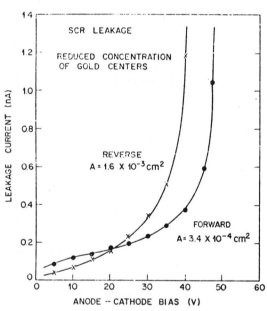

Fig. 4. Forward and reverse leakage for the SCR as a function of anode-to-cathode bias at room temperature. The wafer has a reduced density of gold recombination centers.

TABLE 1

CHARACTERISTICS & CONDITIONS	TYPICAL (T=25°C)	UNITS
DC CATHODE-SUBSTRATE LEAKAGE CURRENT ($I_{AK} = 0$, $V_{KS} = 35V$)	0.6	μA dc
AC CATHODE-SUBSTRATE LEAKAGE CURRENT ($I_{AK} = 10$ mA dc, $i_{AK} = 10$ mA pp, $V_{AS} = 20V$ dc)	0.03	μA pp
FORWARD LEAKAGE ($V_{AK} = 30V$ dc, $V_{KS} = 0$)	0.01	μA dc
REVERSE LEAKAGE ($V_{AK} = -30V$ dc, $V_{KS} = 0$)	0.01	μA dc
GATE-ANODE LEAKAGE CURRENT ($V_{AG} = -30V$ dc, $V_{AS} = 0$)	0.01	μA dc
ON RESISTANCE ($I_{AK} = 10$ mA)	9.0	Ω
FORWARD VOLTAGE ($I_{AK} = 10$ mA)	0.9	V dc
HOLDING CURRENT	1.1	mA dc
dc GATE TRIGGER VOLTAGE ($V_{AK} = 20V$ dc)	1.35	V dc
dc GATE TRIGGER CURRENT ($V_{AK} = 20V$ dc)	0.6	mA dc
ANODE LINE TO CATHODE LINE CAPACITANCE	1.0	pF

TABLE 1

HIGH VOLTAGE DIELECTRIC ISOLATION SCR INTEGRATED CIRCUIT PROCESS

J. D. Beasom

Harris Semiconductor
Melbourne, FL 32901

ABSTRACT

High voltage integrated circuit SCR's are required for applications such as cross point switching in telephone networks. This paper describes a process which produces these components in integrated form using dielectric isolation to eliminate substrate current, isolation leakage and latch-up and to achieve improved packing density.

Significant characteristics of the devices produced are: breakover voltage > 250V; $V_F <$ 1.6v at anode current density = 100ma/mil^2; anode current >1mA per mil^2 of chip area; $r_{on} <$ 10 ohms; gate turn off by cathode gate.

Analysis and experimental results of two effects unique to dielectric isolation will be presented. One is confinement of minority carriers in a limited volume by the impenetrable oxide isolation. The other is the effect on breakdown voltage of spreading a depletion layer through a lightly doped region and against oxide isolation and the variation of this voltage with bias on the poly silicon substrate.

INTRODUCTION

Several papers (1,2) have described SCR IC processes in the last year. They used junction isolation to achieve SCR's with moderate (<100v) breakover capability. Much of the effort in these papers was focused on achieving an acceptable trade off between off leakage and substrate collection of a fraction of the anode current in the on state. This paper presents a process which utilizes dielectric isolation to eliminate substrate current and to make higher voltage feasible.

The geometry used for the SCR design is the conventional vertical NPN, lateral PNP structure formed in an isolated N type island. It provides top contact to all four layers of the device: anode, anode gate, cathode and cathode gate.

The breakover voltage depends primarily on the substrate doping and to a lesser extent on the gradient of the P base which together with the substrate forms the blocking junction.

A substrate doping of about 2×10^{14} is chosen to achieve breakover voltage >250v. Anode diffusion to P base diffusion spacing is chosen to be 2 mils so that reach through between them will not limit the blocking voltage. A P base region with surface concentration less than 1×10^{19} is chosen to provide a graded blocking junction for high breakdown voltage and to allow easy fabrication of NPN HFE >50.

High NPN HFE is required so that the product of the non saturated NPN and PNP HFE's is greater than one (which is a necessary condition for the SCR to turn on) even for a lateral PNP HFE as low as 0.1 as can occur in the wide base width high voltage structure.

Consider now the SCR in the on condition in more detail. The on SCR is composed of three forward biased junctions of alternating polarity in series connected by bulk regions and with a bulk region at either end to which the metallization connects.

In normal operation the structure is heavily saturated and all junctions are in high level injection. To a first approximation the forward voltages of two of the diodes cancel one another leaving the forward voltage of the SCR equal to the anode current times the sum of the bulk resistance plus one diode forward voltage.

In order to minimize the V_F, the bulk resistances must be minimized. Consider each of the bulk resistive terms in turn starting with the anode. For simplicity assume that the anode junction depth is small compared to its horizontal dimensions so that the anode current can be considered to flow vertically from the metallization through the anode diffusion. Then the bulk resistance of the anode can be obtained from:

$$R_A = \frac{1}{A_A} \int_0^{X_1} \rho(x)dx$$

where A_A = anode area; $\rho(x)$=anode diffusion resistivity at distance X from the surface of the wafer X_1 = a pont within a diffusion length of the anode junction where majority carrier drift is no longer the dominant conduction mechanism.

Applying this expression to an anode of Gaussian profile typical of the usual vertical-lateral transistor structure in which the same

Reprinted from *IEEE 1977 Int. Electron Devices Meeting*, p. 178–180, 1977.

diffusion is used both for P base and anode with surface concentration = 1×10^{19}, junction depth = 3μ, junction area = 0.54 mil^2 and assuming X_1 = 2μ we obtain R_A = 2.9 ohms.

This may seem a very small resistance, however one desires to hold the total series resistance to less than 10 ohms of which 2.9 ohms would be a significant part. It could be reduced by increasing the surface concentration. However, such an increase would increase the NPN base charge and hence reduce its HFE. To avoid this dilemma a P+ diffusion is added to the process to form the anode. It's surface concentration is made greater than 1×10^{20} resulting in an R_A less than 0.7 ohm.

Now consider the N base. The N base is the lightly doped region which supports the reverse voltage in the off state. The anode current must flow through it for a distance greater than 2 mils to reach the cathode. With proper processing, the lifetime can be made high enough hat the hole diffusion length is greater then 3 mils. In that case the holes injected into the N base by the anode and by the P base conductivity modulate it reducing its resistivity by several orders of magnitude from its off state value.

The minority carrier concentration and hence the degree of conductivity modulation is maximum at the edge of the anode and P base junctions. Clearly the concentration there cannot exceed the maximum impurity concentration on the P side of the junction. The use of a very heavily doped anode diffusion makes possible a higher degree of conductivity modulation and resulting lower resistance for this reason.

The resistance of the P base region is reduced by conductivity modulation just as is that of the N base. Since the P base is a relatively narrow region (the NPN base width) this is more easily achieved than in the N base).

Finally, the bulk cathode resistance is minimized by utilizing a heavily doped abrupt diffusion just as for the anode. The high doping also insures good emitter efficiency to enhance the NPN HFE and to achieve the high level of minority carrier injection necessary for maximum conductivity modulation of the base layers.

Effects of Dielectric Isolation

The design of the dielectrically isolated island which contains the SCR can have a significant effect on its performance. For maximum packing density one would place the edge of the island close to or in contact with the device diffusions. In a high voltage structure where depletion layer widths may exceed 2 mils this will result in the blocking junction depletion layer abuting the edge of the island and will distort the field and hence the breakdown compared to that which would be obtained in an island large enough that the depletion layer did not reach it.

It also introduces the poly silicon substrate as a fifth terminal of the device whose bias affects the device operation.

To visualize how and why the breakdown voltage can be affected, consider the P base be grounded and assume voltage on the N base which is low enough that the depletion layer does not reach the isolation oxide. There are two field patterns terminating in the N base: one from P base and the other across the isolation oxide from the poly silicon substrate. A neutral region at the N base potential separates them. If the island potential is increased, the P base depletion layer will reach the isolation oxide. At this point a continuous field will extend from P base through depleted N base, across isolation oxide and into the poly where it terminates. Further increase in the N base region voltage will have little effect on the fully depleted region except near its boundary with the undepleted N base where a transverse field component will develop. There are now two relatively uncoupled field patterns either one of which can reach the critical field necessary to induce avalanche. If the bias on the poly substrate is such that critical field is attained by the field from substrate to P base then avalanche will occur at the N base voltage which forces the depletion layer agianst the substrate forming this field from the separate N base - P base and N base substrate fields. If the substrate to base field is less than that required for avalanche, the N base voltage can be increased further until the critical field is obtained in that portion of the depletion layer which does not reach the isolation oxide.

If both anode and P base depletion layers touch isolation oxide, breakdown will be limited by substrate bias in a different way. When the substrate is made sufficiently by negative with respect to the N base it will develop a P type inversion layer on the island surface which will join the two P regions forming a parasitic PMOS device.

Even when only one P region depletion layer contacts a substrate bias induced inversion layer several device parameters are affected. The inversion layer acts as an extension of the junction. The extra area that results leads to higher junction leakage and capacitance.

A potentially beneficial effect of terminating the depletion layer on the isolation is that it reduces the depletion volume in which leakage current is generated. The gain may be negated by a high hole-electron generation rate at the isolation-island interface if substrate bias and or surface quality are unfavorable.

The island surfaces influence device performance even when depletion layers don't reach them if they are within a diffusion length of a source of minority carriers. They provide a boundary which carriers cannot cross but at which they have a surface recombination velocity.

The presence of this boundary can significantly modify the distribution of minority carriers in the isolated region from what it would be in an unbounded region. Of particular importance for the SCR is the fact that, at least if surface recombination velocity is sufficiently low, lateral PNP HFE may be enhanced by constraining holes injected by the emitter from diffusion in directions away from its collector where they would otherwise recombine before they could be collected.

RESULTS

Table 1 presents some characteristics for an SCR built with this process. Island thickness is 24μ, P base depth is 15μ, P+ anode depth is 3μ and N base doping is $2X10^{14}$. The sides of the islands are approximately 5 mils from the outer most device diffusions so that interaction between device and substrate is primarily limited to the bottom of the island. Substrate is connected to cathode for all measurements.

Table 2 presents data illustrating the effect of the substrate on component operation. Included are parameters as a function of substrate bias and parameter comparisons between components in DI and non isolated substrates of the same starting crystal which were built together in the same wafer fabrication lot.

The I_{CBO}'s of the NPN portion of the SCR show the effect of extension of a depletion layer by a substrate bias induced inversion layer. The NPN BV_{CBO}'s illustrate effect of substrate bias on breakdown voltage. Also, the comparison to the non isolated wafer shows no change in breakdown for optimum substrate bias DI. The lateral PNP HFE's for DI and non isolated wafers illustrate the effect of the isolation as a boundary condition for minority carriers.

TABLE 1

$T = 25^{\circ}C$

Breakover voltage @ $10\mu a$	350 v
r_{on} @ $I_F = 30$ ma	10 Ω
Maximum J_A for gate turn off	$0.5ma/mil^2$

TABLE 2

$25^{\circ}C$

NPN I_{CBO} @ 200v with substrate tied to base $125^{\circ}C$	350na
NPN I_{CBO} @ 200v with substrate tied to collector $125^{\circ}C$	40na
NPN BV_{CBO} @ $10\mu a$ with substrate tied to base	350v
NPN BV_{CBO} @ 10v, $100\mu a$ with substrate tied to collector	270v
NPN BV_{CBO} @ $10\mu a$ non isolated wafer	350v
PNP HFE DI wafer @ 10v, $100\mu a$	1.4
PNP HFE @ 10v, $100\mu a$ non isolated wafer	0.85

REFERENCES

1) A.R. Hartman & P.W. Shackle, "A Junction Isolation Technology for Integrating Silicon Controlled Rectifiers in Crosspoint Switching Circuits", IEDM 1976, pp. 55-57.

2) W.L. England & Heinz Lehning, "Junction Isolated Thyristors for PBX Switching", ISCC 1977, pp. 38-39.

An Optically-Coupled High-Voltage p-n-p-n Crosspoint Array

HARUO MORI, TOSHIMASA ISHIDA, KAZUO HAGIMURA, KOTARO KATO, AND SEIEI OHKOSHI

Abstract—A solid-state crosspoint array compatible with electromechanical switches has been developed in order to realize high-performance telephone exchange networks.

The optically-coupled high breakover voltage crosspoint array discussed in this paper has achieved complete isolation of the speech path from the triggering circuit while it can be triggered directly by a transistor–transistor logic (TTL) level signal from the control circuit.

The crosspoint array has a unique photo-coupling structure which allows four p-n-p-n elements to be triggered effectively by only one LED, maintaining up to 200 V/0.1 μs dv/dt characteristics. It provides breakover voltage of up to 450 V, gate trigger LED current less than 20 mA, ON-state resistance within 4.5 Ω, and OFF-state capacitance less than 7 pF. The matrix arrangement is a 1 $\times$ 4 configuration; it is composed of a two wire bidirectional circuit and packaged in a 16-pin ceramic DIP.

These device characteristics make possible the realization of solid-state crosspoint array practically compatible with the conventional electromechanical switch, particularly meeting requirements of miniaturization, low-power dissipation, and inexpensive construction. Accordingly, direct interface with conventional telephone sets is possible.

I. INTRODUCTION

RECENTLY, the rapid development of high-quality solid-state crosspoints has permitted their application to high-performance telephone exchange networks. A variety of approaches are being made to accomplish the system, switching by using bipolar transistors [1], DMOS transistors [2], and either low-breakover voltage [3] or high-breakover voltage [4] current triggering of p-n-p-n's. Although excellent results have been obtained in these approaches respectively, it has been difficult to meet the demands for adequate tolerance of over voltage, for example, required by lightning surges, overall transmission capability of high voltage signals, such as ringing or howler signals, and capability of isolating the speech path from the triggering circuit.

The crosspoint array discussed in this paper features not only high-breakover voltage characteristics, but also complete isolation of the speech path from the triggering circuit by using optically-coupled structure. These characteristics make its function practically compatible with the conventional electromechanical switches, thereby permitting direct interfacing with the conventional telephone set. In addition, the crosspoint is also easily controllable by transistor–transistor logic (TTL).

Manuscript received May 4, 1979; revised July 9, 1979.

H. Mori, T. Ishida, and K. Hagimura are with the Electron Devices Division, OKI Electric Industry Company, Ltd., Tokyo, Japan.

K. Kato is with Musashino Electrical Communication Laboratory, Nippon Telegraph and Telephone Public Corporation, Tokyo, Japan.

S. Ohkoshi is with the Engineering Bureau, Nippon Telegraph and Telephone Public Corporation, Tokyo, Japan.

The major considerations in the development of this crosspoint array were to attain: 1) high breakover characteristics, 2) high dv/dt firing voltage characteristics, 3) controllability by TTL, and 4) low fabrication cost. The approach adopted in the design reported here uses high-breakover voltage planar photo-p-n-p-n devices and high-radiance GaAs LED's. The unique photocoupling structure by the detectors–emitters combination also constitutes at the basis of this crosspoint array. Generally, the use of low gate to cathode resistance can improve the dv/dt firing voltage characteristics, but this result reduces the gate sensitivity, eventually raising the gate trigger LED current up to a very high level. To eliminate these disadvantages, in this device, the basewidth of the lateral parasitic p-n-p transistor which is a part of the p-n-p-n device has been chosen so as to maximize the dv/dt firing voltage and the gate trigger characteristics.

The process selected for this device are a high-voltage dielectric isolation, a nitride film passivation for p-n-p-n's, and selective liquid phase epitaxy for LED's.

II. DESCRIPTION OF THE DESIGN

A. Arrangement of the Crosspoint

The basic design concept of this new optically-coupled crosspoint array is a matrix arrangement of a 1 $\times$ 4 configuration based on two wire bidirectional circuit composition. Fig. 1 shows the circuitry of the crosspoint array. In operation, for example, both A-$A1$, and B-$B1$ paths, which are to be connected to wire A and wire B of two telephone lines, may be switched by irradiation from a LED between LA and $LC1$. Either of A-$A1$, B-$B1$ through A-$A4$, B-$B4$ pairs of lines also can operate in the same way. The bottleneck in the development of this crosspoint array has been the lack of high performance characteristics such as high breakover voltage, low triggering current, and high-dv/dt firing voltage, coupled with the realization of a low fabrication cost. From this point of view, the new type of crosspoint has been designed.

The 1 $\times$ 4 two wire bidirectional circuit has been made up of four single crosspoint cell chips to avoid the crosstalk between one crosspoint with the adjacent one on one or both sides. To facilitate the integration of the circuits, the planar junction formation technology has been applied. In the single crosspoint, the four p-n-p-n elements are arranged to form two groups of bidirectional connection. Fig. 2 shows the photomicrograph of the p-n-p-n cell chip. The anode and cathode are each connected with a diffused gate to cathode resistance layer. Separation between each group of elements thus connected bidirectionally, which are to be connected to two tele-

Reprinted from *IEEE J. Solid-State Circuits*, vol. SC-14, no. 6, pp. 998–1003, Dec. 1979.

288

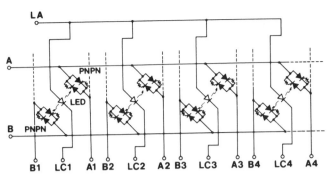

Fig. 1. Schematic of the 1 × 4 crosspoint array configuration.

(a)

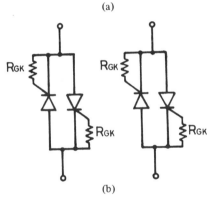

(b)

Fig. 2. Single crosspoint cell. (a) Photomicrograph of the p-n-p-n cell chip. (b) Schematic circuitry.

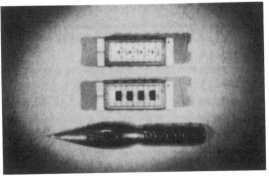

Fig. 3. Photograph of the crosspoint array in 16 pin dual-in-line ceramic package.

phone lines, has been achieved by dielectric isolation. p-n-p-n single crosspoint chip size is 1.6 mm × 2.5 mm. Particularly to satisfy low cost fabrication demands, in the single crosspoint structure, four p-n-p-n elements are triggered by one LED. All elements were housed in a 16-pin dual-in-line ceramic package as shown in Fig. 3.

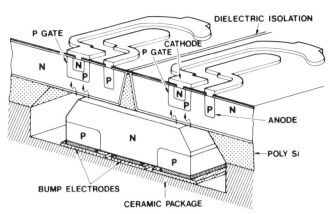

Fig. 4. Cross-sectional view of the photocoupling structure.

B. Photocoupling and p-n-p-n Design

The design of this crosspoint switch is based on unique photocoupling structure [5]. To satisfy low-cost fabrication demands, triggering of the four p-n-p-n elements by one LED was essential. The major problem in this respect was that existing p-n-p-n elements with high dv/dt firing voltage generally require a high triggering current. In this connection, the new type of p-n-p-n element was devised to have a low p-type gate junction capacitance, specifically to have a small photosensitive area, while attaining a high photocoupling efficiency.

In combining the p-n-p-n elements, more difficulty than originally expected was found in triggering these four p-n-p-n elements with the photocurrent initiated by only one LED in an ordinally photocoupling structure. The photocoupling structure of the crosspoint is illustrated in Fig. 4. The LED is mounted on the metallized parts on the bottom of ceramic package by using Au–Sn bump electrodes. The photo-p-n-p-n chip is fixed on the top with thermoconductive resin, locating the n-p-n parts of the p-n-p-n elements just over the p-type light emitimg areas of LED, within the accuracy of 50 μm both in horizontal and vertical directions. Then the transparent resin for index matching is filled in the space between them. Irradiation from the LED is detected on the backside of the p-n-p-n elements. Not to prevent the irradiation, the poly Si layer at the back side of the p-n-p-n elements has been removed selectively by KOH etchant. The SiO_2 layer which is for dielectric isolation has another role to stop the etching. To maximize the photosensitivity, the thickness of n-type substrate has been determined with due consideration given to the relationship between diffusion length of the generated carriers and the absorption coefficient of the substrate.

In the case of n-type side irradiation, photosensitivity of the p-n junction, S is given as below [6]:

$$S = S_1 + S_2 \tag{1}$$

$$S_1 = \alpha \cdot \exp(-\alpha \cdot W_n) \cdot L_h/(\alpha^2 \cdot L_h^2 - 1)$$
$$\cdot [\alpha \cdot L_h \cdot \exp(\alpha \cdot W_n)$$
$$\cdot \operatorname{sech}(W_n/L_h) - \alpha \cdot L_h - \tanh(W_n/L_h)] \tag{2}$$

$$S_2 = \alpha \cdot \exp(-\alpha \cdot W_n) \cdot L_e/(\alpha_2 \cdot L_h^2 - 1)$$
$$\cdot [\alpha \cdot L_e \cdot \exp(\alpha \cdot W_p) \cdot \operatorname{sech}(W_p/L_e)$$
$$- \tanh(W_p/L_e)] \tag{3}$$

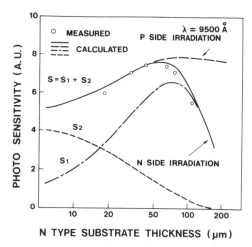

Fig. 5. Photosensitivity characteristics as a function of n-type substrate thickness.

Fig. 6. Infrared photomicrograph of the LED irradiation through the p-n-p-n cell chip. One LED radiates almost equally on all four p-n-p-n elements.

where

α absorption coefficient
W_n thickness of n-type substrate
W_p thickness of p-type layer
L_h hole diffusion length
L_e electron diffusion length.

The component S_1 of the sensitivity S is associated with carriers generated in the irradiated n-type region of the junction, and the component S_2 is related to carriers generated in the p-region of the junction. Both measured and calculated values of photosensitivity at a wavelength at 9500 Å are shown in Fig. 5. From these results, the maximum photosensitivity has been attained with the thickness of the n type substrate at 60 μm.

Power reflected from the package wall is also utilized in an effective manner. As a result, the photocoupling efficiency was improved by 30 percent.

Fig. 6 shows an infrared photomicrograph of the LED irradiation through the p-n-p-n element chip. One LED radiates almost equally on all four p-n-p-n elements.

C. LED Design

The LED used to trigger the p-n-p-n elements is a highly efficient GaAs amphoteric Si LED which was newly designed. It has an external efficiency reaching about 8 percent with a radi-

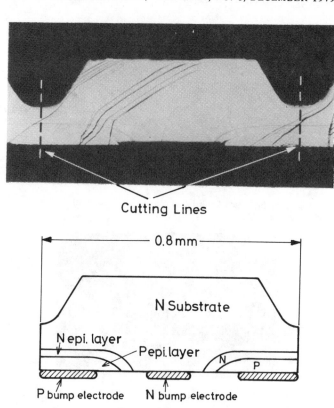

Fig. 7. High-efficiency GaAs (Si–Si) LED used in this design. Photomicrograph of the LED cross section and schematic cross section.

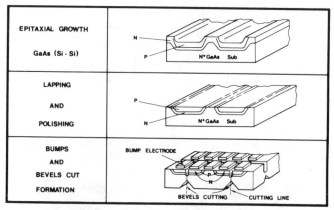

Fig. 8. Fabrication process of the LED.

ative power peak at 9500 Å. Fig. 7 shows a cross section of the LED. The LED used with this design has been developed through the application of selective liquid phase epitaxy and polishing technology. Both p and n bump electrodes are formed on one side of the LED chip.

The step-by-step LED fabrication process is shown in Fig. 8. Initially, a GaAs n-type substrate has been etched selectively in the proper region. Next, the n- and p-type epitaxial layers were grown in sequence evenly across the surface of the n type substrate. Finally, the top surface of the layers were polished to a precise flat since the surface of the layers were found to be quite uneven after the epitaxial process. Bevels cut at the corners of the LED result in an increase in the photocoupling efficiency of more than 50 percent. In Fig. 7, the dotted line shows cutting lines. Both the bevel shaping and chip cutting were made by a dicing blade.

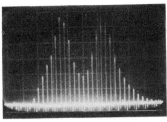

Fig. 9. Scope photograph of the LED irradiation pattern. Vertical sensitivity indicates intensity of the irradiation; horizontal axis indicates the distance at 200 μm/div (60 μm pitch). 512 bit photodiode array has been used for the measurement.

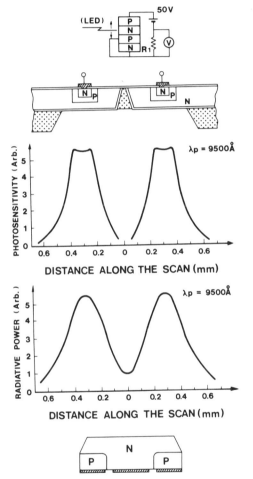

Fig. 10. Radiative power of the LED and photosensitivity of the p-n-p-n elements as a function of distance along the scan.

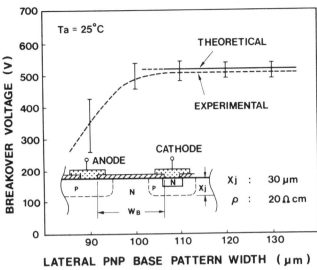

Fig. 11. High breakover voltage characteristics.

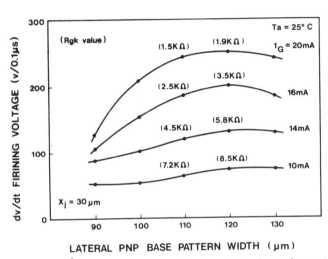

Fig. 12. The *dv/dt* firing voltage as a function of lateral p-n-p base pattern width with the gate trigger LED current I_G as parameter. A R_{GK} value of each condition is indicated in the parentheses.

Fig. 9 shows the radiative power distribution of the LED, measured by a 512 bit photodiode array. The distribution of the LED closely follows that of the photosensitivity of the p-n-p-n elements, as shown in Fig. 10. The resultant increase in photocoupling efficiency gives an obvious economic advantage by permitting a reduction in the gate trigger LED current to less than about 20 mA.

D. Characteristics of Breakover Voltage and dv/dt

To meet requirements of high breakover voltage and high *dv/dt* firing voltage characteristics, as previously mentioned, stress was placed on the following three points: selection of substrate, the processing, and pattern design. The character- istics of the high breakover voltage of the p-n-p-n element have been attained by setting the depth of the junction at 30 μm, the substrate resistivity at 20 $\Omega \cdot$ cm, and the lateral parasitic p-n-p base pattern width at least 90 μm. Fig. 11 shows the high- breakover voltage characteristics of the p-n-p-n element. Below 90 μm, a punchthrough phenomenon occurs and, thus, the breakover voltage has been decreased. Also, a passivation was applied to the p-n-p-n substrate surface with a Si_3N_4 film to improve the reliability of the element.

The *dv/dt* as well as gate trigger characteristics have been im- proved through optimization of the parasitic lateral p-n-p base pattern width. Fig. 12 shows representative *dv/dt* firing volt- age and gate trigger characteristics as a function of the parasitic lateral p-n-p base pattern width. This figure is based on two relationships: one between the *dv/dt* firing voltage and the R_{GK} value and the other between the gate trigger LED current and the R_{GK} value. The R_{GK} values of various points are given within parentheses.

In order to simplify the circuit, the associated circuitry, which has been commonly used with other p-n-p-n crosspoint switches

TABLE I
BASIC FEATURES OF THE CROSSPOINT ARRAY

	$T_a = 25°C$
CHIP SIZE (1 CROSSPOINT) LED	0.4mm x 0.8mm
PNPN	1.6mm x 2.5mm
BREAKOVER VOLTAGE	> 450V ($I_{BO} = 10\mu A$)
FORWARD VOLTAGE, ON-STATE	1.1V ($I_F = 50mA$)
RESISTANCE, ON-STATE	4.5Ω ($I_F = 50mA$)
RESISTANCE, OFF-STATE	> 100MΩ ($V_{AC} = 50V$)
HOLDING CURRENT	0.7mA
CAPACITANCE	< 7pF (f = 1kHz)
dv/dt FIRING	200V/0.1μs ($V_{AC} = 200V$)
AVERAGE FORWARD CURRENT	200mA
INPUT CURRENT TO TRIGGER	< 20mA (Pulse width 15μs)
INPUT TO OUTPUT CAPACITANCE	< 5pF (f = 1MHz)
ISOLATION VOLTAGE	> 1000V

to improve the dv/dt firing [7], has been eliminated. Instead, a compromise gate resistance R_{GK} has been chosen so as to maximize the dv/dt firing within the allowed range of gate trigger LED current. This is because there is a trade off relationship between the two. Thus, in the design, it has been necessary to produce a minimum gate trigger current and a maximum dv/dt firing with the specified p-type gate area and R_{GK} limits. It is found that a R_{GK} value of 3.0 kΩ and base pattern width of 120 μm are optimum.

III. DEVICE CHARACTERISTICS

Table I shows the basic features of the crosspoint array. Breakover voltage of up to 450 V at leakage of 10 μA, gate trigger current less than 20 mA, ON-state resistance less than 4.5 Ω, and OFF-state capacitance less than 7 pF were attained. These device characteristics, for example, sufficiently fulfilled the demand for the application to line concentrators [8].

IV. CONCLUSIONS

An optically-coupled breakover voltage of 450 V, 1 X 4 (two wire/bidirectional) crosspoint array for the telephone speech path has been described above. This crosspoint has been perfectly isolated electrically between speech paths and triggering circuits by using a photocoupling construction. This approach uses high breakover voltage p-n-p-n devices with the dielectric isolation technique, high radiance GaAs LED's with the selective liquid phase epitaxy, and the unique photocoupling structure. The crosspoint array achieves the performance as shown in Table I, including meeting the difficult requirment of low triggering current controllable by a TTL level signal and high dv/dt firing voltage 200 V/0.1 μs. These device characteristics have made it possible to permit the direct interface with a conventional telephone set.

This crosspoint array will find a wide range of other applications including line concentrators, private branch exchanges (PBX), and other electronic exhange networks.

ACKNOWLEDGMENT

The authors wish to thank Dr. H. Mukai of Musashino Electrical Communication Laboratory, Nippon Telegraph and Telephone Public Corporation, and Dr. T. Imai and Y. Hirose of OKI Electric Industrial Company, Ltd., both for their support and for considerable technical advice.

The authors also wish to acknowledge the members of this project for their constant support.

REFERENCES

[1] W. M. C. Sansen and J. M. R. Danneels, "An active bipolar 4 X 4 crosspoint for balanced telephone networks," in *ISSCC Dig. Tech. Papers*, Feb. 1976, pp. 30–31.
[2] C. H. Moss and T. P. Gauge, "Integrated circuit D-MOS telephone crosspoint array," in *ISSCC Dig. Tech. Papers*, Feb. 1976, pp. 32–33.
[3] P. W. Shackle, A. R. Hartman, J. M. Adrian, and R. L. Pritchett, "A low substrate leakage junction isolated p-n-p-n crosspoint array," *IEEE J. Solid-State Circuits*, vol. SC-13, pp. 210–218, Apr. 1978.
[4] M. Tokunaga, T. Kamei, I. Ishii, and M. Kawanami, "Development of integrated semiconductor crosspoint switches and a fully electronic switching system," in *Proc. ISS 76 Int. Switching Symp.*, 1976, pp. 221–224.
[5] H. Mori, T. Ishida, K. Hagimura, K. Kato, and S. Ohkoshi, "An optically-coupled high-voltage p-n-p-n crosspoint array," in *ISSCC Dig. Tech. Papers*, Feb. 1979, pp. 32–33.
[6] A. Ambroziak, *Semiconductor Photoelectric Devices*. New York: Gordon and Breach, 1969.
[7] Y. Sugawara, T. Kamei, A. Mimura, "Integrated photocoupled semiconductor crosspoint switches," in *Proc. 10th Conf. Solid-State Devices*, Tokyo, 1978, pp. 405–410.
[8] S. Usuda, Y. Suzuki, H. Yamada, and M. Suzuki, "The BORSHT in digital local switching system," in *Proc. ISS 79 Int. Switching Symp.*, 1979, pp. 913–920.

MONOLITHIC HIGH VOLTAGE GATED DIODE CROSSPOINT ARRAY IC

H. T. Weston, H. W. Becke, J. E. Berthold, J. C. Gammel,
A. R. Hartman, J. E. Kohl, M. A. Shibib, R. K. Smith, Y. H. Wong

Bell Laboratories
Murray Hill, New Jersey 07974
Reading, Pennsylvania 19604

ABSTRACT

A new gated diode crosspoint integrated circuit has been developed for telephone switching system applications. Central to the design of this high voltage device has been the extensive use of numerical modeling techniques. Two-dimensional simulation of the individual dielectrically isolated components that comprise the switch array has led to an improvement in their electrical parameters together with size reduction for each of their geometries. Additional calculations dealing with the routing of interconnect metalization about the perimeter of components has indicated how such runners may encroach upon these elements without degrading their performance so that higher density circuitry could be assembled onto a chip. The resulting IC therefore realizes substantial advances over its predecessors, including: increased scale of integration (9 vs. 4 crosspoint pairs), more compact design (2.1 vs. 3.6mm^2 per crosspoint pair), higher OFF state minimum blocking voltage (600 vs. 530 volts), and reduced ON state incremental resistance (10 vs. 18 ohms).

INTRODUCTION

High voltage integrated circuits are generally composed of rather large components with wide separations between them to insure adequate electrical isolation. Consequently, an important design goal is to make efficient use of chip area by shrinking as much as possible both the intra-device dimensions and inter-device spacings.

Concerning the reduction of the separation between components, dielectric isolation has proven to be quite useful. It is an effective means for minimizing parasitic cross coupling between circuit elements, and the presence of oxide to share some of the potential difference between high voltage components allows for their separation to be considerably less than that which can be achieved in silicon alone with conventional junction isolation.

Further reduction of chip size requires optimization of device geometries so that each high voltage component occupies as little area as possible. To this end, a computational technique has been employed which has proven very useful for gaining insight into the compact design of high voltage devices and their subsequent assembly into integrated circuits. In this paper, we illustrate the numerical modeling scheme with the design of a 1000 volt gated diode switch, followed by a discussion of how foreign metal runners may be routed over the edge of such device structures to achieve tightly packed circuit layouts. We then focus on the specific application of these methods to the realization of a new 600 volt gated diode crosspoint (GDX) array for use in the subscriber line unit of the Bell System's digital electronic switching system, No. 5 ESS.

NUMERICAL MODELING OF DEVICES

Computer simulation of the OFF state of high voltage structures may be exploited as a design tool for both optimizing the performance and minimizing the size of such components. An algorithm particularly suitable for this purpose has evolved which entails a finite element approach with adaptive grid refinement for obtaining the two dimensional solution of Poisson's equation in the depletion region. Input to the associated program, for a dielectrically isolated device, includes: dimensions of the silicon island, oxide thickness, surface state charge density, diffusion profiles, field plate overlap and spacing, and the potentials of the electrodes and substrate. Beginning with a coarse triangular grid, the program solves for the potential at every vertex and estimates the error over each three sided grid element. The network is appropriately subdivided in those local regions where the error is large and the solution is interpolated on the new grid to give a better approximation to the actual potential distribution. These steps are then repeated to yield successively finer grids until convergence to some predetermined accuracy is attained.

Consideration of the design of a gated diode switch is helpful for illustrating the mechanics of the calculations. This device functions basically as an asymmetric PIN diode which can be switched off when an appropriate positive signal is applied to its n-type gate centered in the lightly doped π bulk material between the anode and cathode. With full depletion of the π silicon, punch through between the gate and cathode is prevented by a p-type shield surrounding the cathode. The specific application of the modeling scheme to a 1000 volt gated diode switch is depicted in Figure 1. Whereas in actual operation, the voltages of the anode and cathode are generally not equal, the simulation is performed with the same potential on both main terminals in order to optimize their positions simultaneously. Shown in Figure 1(a) is a typical

Reprinted from *IEEE 28th Int. Electron Devices Meeting*, pp. 85–88, 1982.

293

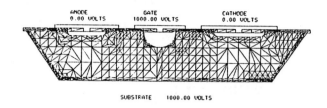

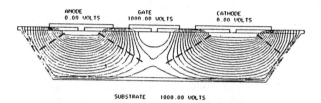

Fig. 1(a)   Representative Grid and
    1(b)   Equipotential Distribution for a
           1000 Volt Gated Diode Switch

grid obtained after several iterations of refinement. It exhibits greater detail near the edges
of the field plates and junctions, where the potential is a strong function of position, than in
those regions where the potential varies more
slowly. The corresponding equipotential distribution is plotted in Figure 1(b) with a 50 volt potential difference between adjacent contours.

    The procedure followed to arrive at the final
device configuration involves several considerations. First, the anode, gate, cathode, and walls
of the silicon island are positioned relative to
one another such that the magnitude of the electric fields at the inner and outer edges of the
anode and cathode are approximately equal. However, it is the ionization integrals rather than
the electric field itself which are best suited
for determining the onset of avalanche breakdown.
Therefore, the ionization coefficients are integrated along paths through the radii of the p-
diffusions as indicated by the four broken lines
in Figure 1(b), and dimensions are further adjusted such that the ionization integrals are nowhere
larger than unity. Next, the field plate overlap
is varied to give the most uniform field profile
along the upper Si-SiO$_2$ interface. The ionization
integrals along this interface are made 10 to 20%
smaller than in the bulk, thereby assuring that
avalanche is not initiated near the top surface.
In this way, hot electron injection into the oxide
is avoided and device reliability should be improved. Lastly, the depth of the silicon island
is fixed so that the electric field under the
cathode/emitter of the open base npn transistor,
which is inherent to the gated diode structure, is
such that the sustaining voltage is adequate for
the maximum current gain expected.

CORNER BREAKDOWN AND INTERCONNECT METALIZATION

    One of the input parameters to the device
simulations which influences the details of the
resulting geometries is the thickness of the oxide

walls which enclose each of the structures. Primarily, there needs to be sufficient oxide to provide full voltage isolation for any component from
both the supporting polycrystalline silicon substrate and the overlying interconnect metalization.
However, a more stringent requirement of the oxide
is that it be thick enough to prevent avalanche
multiplication in the strong electric field present near the perimeter of a silicon island when a
metal runner of hostile potential is in the
vicinity.

    To understand this corner breakdown phenom-
enon and how the required oxide thickness is derived, it is helpful to again consider a particular example. Figure 2 illustrates the worse case
situation which may occur at the edge of the island
for a 1000 volt device. Here, metal at ground potential sandwiches a thin wedge of silicon between

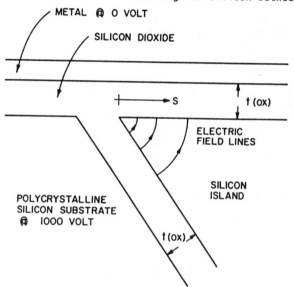

Fig. 2 Corner Breakdown Geometry

itself and the high potential substrate below and
this silicon is assumed to be already fully depleted by some remote reverse biased junction elsewhere in the island. The mathematical technique
discussed above may then be used to determine the
potential distribution in the corner region. It
is found that the electric field in the silicon is
highest just at the apex of the corner where the
metal conductor is closest to the substrate and
monotonically diminishes with the distance S from
this location.

    Then, the spatial variation of the multipli-
cation rate is calculated by integrating the
ionization coefficients along a number of field
lines in the silicon which terminate at different
positions S on the upper oxide interface. The
results are shown in Figure 3 where both the
ionization integral for electrons and the ionization integral for holes are plotted as a function
of S. Although they are distinct, because the
ionization coefficients for electrons and holes
each have a different quantitative dependence on
electric field strength, both these curves exhibit

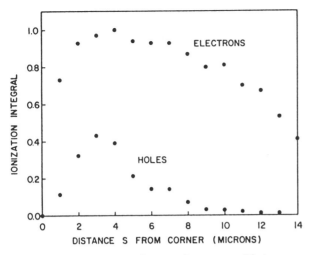

Fig. 3 Ionization Integrals versus Distance
from Corner of Silicon Island

the same general shape. That is, they both reach
a maximum at a distance of a few microns inside
the edge of the island.

Finally, in order to avoid a divergence of
the multiplication rates to infinity near the edge
of silicon islands, the oxide thickness t(ox) is
adjusted so that the ionization integrals are
everywhere less than unity. For 1000 volt devices
with geometries as shown in Figure 2, the result
is that t(ox) = 5 microns is just enough to fix
the peak value of the electron ionization integral
close to one. It is for this specific oxide
thickness then that the numerical data are presented in Figure 3.

With the appropriate amount of oxide determined in this fashion, metal runners may be routed
across the edge of a silicon island to provide
interconnection for the circuit element therein
without upsetting its operation via avalanche injection of carriers. Furthermore, even metalization paths which do not directly connect to a
device may encroach upon its perimeter unrestrict-
ed by corner breakdown considerations. This
allows for tight packing of islands so that a high
density of components can be assembled onto a chip.

SIX HUNDRED VOLT INTEGRATED CIRCUIT

The above computational methods are
sufficiently flexible that they may be utilized
for generating designs at any voltage level. They
were, therefore, employed in the design of a new
gated diode crosspoint (GDX) integrated circuit
which is intended for use in the subscriber line
unit of the Bell System's digital electronic
switching system, No. 5 ESS. For this application,
the avalanche breakdown voltage of each active component was targeted for 750 volts along with a
minimum sustaining voltage of 650 volts to provide
adequate margin above the 590 volt circuit requirement. The resulting device designs were
successfully implemented in a switch array chip
that has, in fact, demonstrated satisfactory voltage capability. Figure 4 is a photograph of the

chip wire bonded into a 32 I/O chip carrier package.

Fig. 4 Chip-Package Photograph

Further verification of the numerical simulations has been provided by several experimental
structures in the test patterns which accompany
the IC's on the fabricated wafers. Figure 5 illustrates how the avalanche BV(CES) and sustaining
BV(CEO) breakdown voltages depend on the separation between the gate/collector and p-shield/base
of the npn transistor inherent to the gated diode
device. It is seen that the gate to p-shield
separation suggested by the model (and incorporated as the design choice) is very close to optimum
in that it gives rise to a sustaining voltage
slightly higher than the 650 volt goal. Separations larger than the design choice are area inefficient, whereas smaller separations are likely
to yield inadequate breakdown voltages.

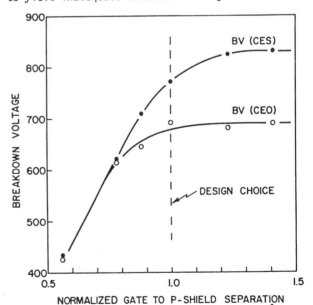

Fig. 5 Breakdown Voltages versus Gate to
P-Shield Separation

The area optimizations that resulted from the numerical device simulations, together with an improved circuit concept requiring 20% fewer elements in each crosspoint control cell, have enabled us to advance to nine bidirectional tip and ring switch pairs on a single chip. This represents a scale of integration beyond that of previously reported high voltage solid state switch arrays (1, 2, 3).

The capabilities of the present chip are best illustrated by way of comparison with the most recently reported gated diode switch IC (3). More than twice the number of crosspoint pairs (9 vs. 4) are now contained on a chip of area 19.1mm², which is only one third larger than the 14.3mm² of the previous GDX design. A more quantitative measure of compactness is given by the ratio of chip area to the number of its crosspoint pairs, and this has been reduced 42% from 3.6mm² previously to 2.1mm² presently. Furthermore, this higher density is accompanied by improvements in circuit performance. For example, with avalanche and sustaining voltages now at least 650 volts, the OFF state blocking voltage of the switching devices (which is equal to the breakdown voltage less the applied gate signal) has been raised to 600 volts which is 70 volts greater than the minimum required. Also, the ON state incremental resistance at the 30mA current level has been reduced from 18 ohms to 10 ohms. This is a consequence of an almost twofold decrease in the gated diode switch aspect ratio of anode-cathode spacing to cathode width. Although this required an increased width for the switch element, its overall size is actually slightly smaller than that of its predecessor due to the shorter length of this component which resulted in part from the numerical simulations.

SUMMARY

A new gated diode crosspoint integrated circuit has been developed for application in the subscriber line unit of the Bell System's No. 5 Electronic Switching System. This high voltage device exhibits improved electrical characteristics and increased functional capability per unit area. As such, it possesses significant performance and cost advantages over earlier devices.

ACKNOWLEDGEMENTS

We wish to thank T. J. Riley and J. Godfrey for their guidance in carrying out this work. Also, we are indebted to the following individuals for their technical contributions: J. Anidjar, J. P. Ballantyne, G. K. Chang, R. B. Comizzoli, A. M. Gottlieb, R. T. Kraetsch, R. Lieberman, M. A. Menendez, M. Robinson, R. S. Scott, D. F. Swayne, and R. F. Yock.

REFERENCES

(1) T. Kamei, "High Voltage Integrated Circuits for Telecommunications", IEDM Tech. Digest, p. 254, Dec. 1981.

(2) K. Kawarada, T. Hayashi, Y. Inabe, H. Imagawa, "High Voltage Subscriber Line Interface LSIs", ISSCC Digest of Technical Papers, pp. 202-203, Feb. 1982.

(3) J. E. Kohl, W. F. MacPherson, J. A. Davis, T. J. Riley, A. R. Hartman, J. E. Berthold, H. T. Weston, H. E. Mussman, "An Integrated Control Circuit for 530V Gated Diode Crosspoint Arrays", Proc. Custom IC Conf., pp. 238-241, May 1982.

SUBSCRIBER LINE INTERFACE CIRCUIT LSI FABRICATED USING HIGH-VOLTAGE CMOS/SIMOX TECHNOLOGY

Indexing terms: Integrated circuits, CMOS devices

High-voltage buried-channel CMOS/SIMOX technology which is characterised with the existence of an electric-field-shielding layer formed by oxygen implanatation was applied to fabricate a BSH-LSI for a subscriber line interface circuit, providing three functions of battery feed, supervision and hybrid. In this CMOS BSH-LSI, a high breakdown voltage of higher than 60 V and a low breakdown voltage of 15 V were fabricated by the same process. This BSH-LSI showed a high level of performance during operation. The chip size and dissipation power of the BSH-LSI were reduced to approximately one-third and one-half, respectively, compared with a conventional BSH-LSI fabricated with bipolar technology.

SIMOX (separation by implanted oxygen) technology, originally proposed by Izumi *et al.*,[1] makes it possible to realise an SOI (silicon on insulator) structure using ion implantation. Nakashima *et al.*[2] reported that an EFS (electric field shielding) layer, which was formed between a buried oxide and an upper Si layer, made it possible to fabricate a high-voltage buried-channel CMOS on a SIMOX substrate. This is called high-voltage buried-channel CMOS/SIMOX technology.

High-voltage LSIs have been developed for the subscriber line interface circuit (SLIC) in a digital local switching system by using dielectrically isolated bipolar technology,[3] while low-voltage LSIs of the SLIC have been fabricated separately on another chip using a low-voltage conventional CMOS/bulk technology for ease of integration and fabrication. A one-chip SLIC LSI has been desired, however, for purposes of miniaturisation and economy, but CMOS latch-up at high voltage has prevented the realisation of the one-chip SLIC LSI. On this, the authors applied the latch-up-free CMOS/SIMOX technology to fabricate a BSH-LSI, one of the high-voltage SLIC LSIs, for the first step to this end. The BSH is an acronym of battery feed, supervision and hybrid (2 wire/4 wire conversion).[3]

The high-voltage buried-channel CMOS/SIMOX technology applied in the fabrication of this BSH-LSI has the following advantages: (i) the devices are free from CMOS latch-up due to the dielectric isolation; (ii) the operation of CMOS/SIMOX is not affected by the substrate bias because of the existence of the EFS layer;[2] (iii) in the fabrication of CMOS/SIMOX, it is not necessary to add any special process except oxygen implantation to the existing conventional MOS process line.

Fig. 1 shows the steps involved in the fabrication of a BSH-LSI using high-voltage buried-channel CMOS/SIMOX technology. In step (*a*) the buried SiO_2 and the EFS layer are simultaneously formed by controlling the beam current during implantation.[2] For the normally-off operation, phosphorus- and boron-doped polycrystalline-silicon gates were employed in *p*MOS and *n*MOS, respectively. Offset-gate structures were employed to achieve a high-voltage CMOS. To reduce the offset resistance, ion implantation was carried out with a dose of 3.5×10^{12} cm^{-2} B^+ at 80 keV for *p*MOS and a dose of 1.2×10^{12} cm^{-2} P^+ at 120 keV for *n*MOS. Silicon island height and gate oxide thickness were 390 nm and 70 nm, respectively. In this process, a low-voltage CMOS has the same structure as the high-voltage one except that the former

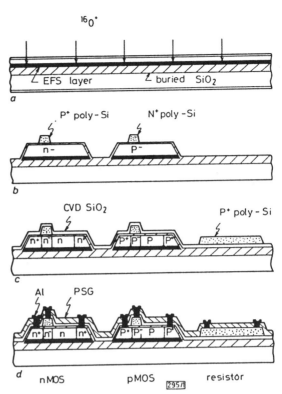

Fig. 1 *Fabrication steps of a BSH-LSI using high-voltage buried-channel CMOS/SIMOX technology*

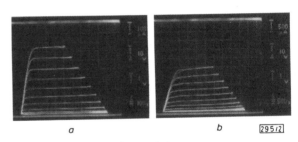

Fig. 2 *Current/voltage characteristics*

a High-voltage *p*MOS/SIMOX with $L_{off} = 20$ μm (L_{off}: offset-gate length)
b High-voltage *n*MOS/SIMOX with $L_{off} = 20$ μm
$W/L = 50/20$ (*W* is gate width, μm; *L* is gate length, μm)

has no offset-gate region. In step (*c*) resistors are formed using boron-doped polycrystalline silicon.

Fig. 2 shows current/voltage characteristics for both a typical high-voltage buried-channel *p*MOS/SIMOX and an *n*MOS/SIMOX with $L_{off} = 20$ μm (L_{off}: offset-gate length). Source-to-drain breakdown voltages were higher than 60 V for both cases. The threshold voltages for the *p*MOS and the *n*MOS were -1.1 and 0.8 V. The peak value of the field-effect mobility was 240 cm²/Vs for *p*MOS and 750 cm²/Vs for *n*MOS. The sheet resistance of the boron-doped polycrystalline silicon was 157 Ω/□. Dummy resistor patterns were placed on both sides of the resistor array to achieve high relative accuracy. The obtained relative accuracy of the resistors was better than $\pm 0.3\%$.

Fig. 3 shows a block diagram of the fabricated BSH-LSI. It consists mainly of operational amplifiers and current mirrors.[4] The measured performance of the BSH-LSI is shown in Table

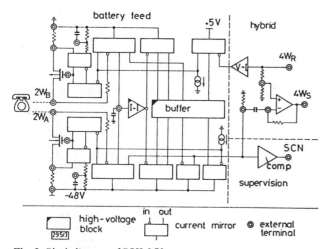

Fig. 3 *Block diagram of BSH-LSI*

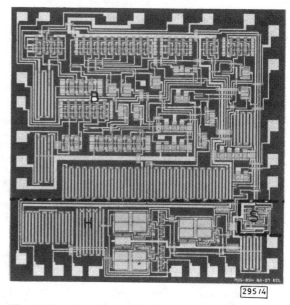

Fig. 4 *Chip microphotograph of fabricated BSH-LSI*

Table 1 MEASURED PERFORMANCE OF BSH-LSI

	Results
Breakdown voltage	>60 V
Insertion loss (2 W/4 W)	±0·07 dB
Longitudinal balance (2 W) (at 0·3–3·4 kHz)	40 dB
Trans-hybrid loss (at 0·3–3·4 kHz)	27 dB
Return loss (600 Ω)	26 dB
Idle channel noise (2 W)	−41 dBm Op
Dissipation power (on-hook state)	50 mW

1. The battery feed circuit has been designed to be compatible with standards for existing subscriber loops, which are characterised at 440 Ω for DC internal resistance. The hybrid circuit, which performs the transmission of audio signals between 2 and 4 W, gives trans-hybrid loss of 27 dB from 4 W_R to 4 W_S. Only the idle channel noise gave unsatisfactory performance because of a lack of careful attention in this first fabrication. The idle channel noise, however, may be reduced by lowering the operation current level and extending the gate area of some MOS transistors. Power dissipation in the on-hook state is 50 mW. A microphotograph of the 2·55 × 2·58 mm chip is shown in Fig. 4. The fabricated BSH-LSI was composed of about 200 elements, including six high-voltage *p*MOS transistors and four high-voltage *n*MOS ones. By using CMOS/SIMOX current mirror circuits, a high level of accuracy[4] and circuit integration has been realised in this LSI. The chip size and dissipation power of the BSH-LSI were reduced to approximately one-third and one-half, respectively, compared with conventional BSH-LSIs fabricated with bipolar technology.[3]

In conclusion, a BSH-LSI for SLIC was successfully developed by using high-voltage buried-channel CMOS/SIMOX technology, and it showed a high level of performance in operation.

Acknowledgments: The authors would like to acknowledge the encouragement and advice of H. Ikawa, N. Ohwada, K. Kato, T. Kimura, K. Izumi, M. Akiya and T. Hayashi.

S. NAKASHIMA   *12th October 1983*
Y. MAEDA

Atsugi Electrical Communication Laboratory
Nippon Telegraph & Telephone Public Corporation
Atsugi-shi, Kanagawa 243-01, Japan

References

1 IZUMI, K., DOKEN, M., and ARIYOSHI, H.: 'CMOS devices fabricated on buried SiO$_2$ layers formed by oxygen implantation into silicon', *Electron. Lett.*, 1978, **14**, pp. 593–594
2 NAKASHIMA, S., AKIYA, M., and KATO, K.: 'Electric-field-shielding layers formed by oxygen implantation into silicon', *ibid.*, 1983, **19**, pp. 568–570
3 KAWARADA, K., HAYASHI, T., INABE, Y., and IMAGAWA, H.: 'High voltage subscriber line interface LSIs'. ISSCC Tech. Digest, Washington DC, 1982, pp. 202–204
4 AKIYA, M., NAKASHIMA, S., and KATO, K.: 'Compatible high and low voltage CMOS devices using SIMOX technology'. Proceedings 14th International Conference on solid state devices, Tokyo, 1982, pp. 57–58

SESSION XVI: TELECOMMUNICATION SYSTEM ICs

THPM 16.1: A Single-Chip High-Voltage Shallow-Junction BORSHT-LSI

Terukazu Ohno, Tetsuma Sakurai, Yasunobu Inabe

NTT Atsugi Electrical Communication Laboratory

Kanagawa, Japan

Takeo Koinuma

NTT Musashino Electrical Communication Laboratory

Tokyo, Japan

A SINGLE CHIP BORSHT-LSI, developed for the basic segment of Subscriber Line Interface Circuits (SLIC), will be described. The chip has been fabricated by use of 350 V PNPN devices and a CEPIC technique[1] which can implement complementary high- and low-voltage transistors with the same junction depth on a dielectrically-isolated IC. The LSI performs six fundamental functions: (1) battery feed (B), (2) overvoltage protection (O), (3) ringing signal sending (R), (4) supervision (S), (5) 2W/4W conversion (hybrid/H), and (6) network testing (T). Moreover, it has been designed to have additional functions: (7) high-voltage ring-trip interface, (8) normal/reverse switching of line current and (9) insertion of a 5dB analog pad in a 4WR-circuit.

A cross section of the PNPN device is schematically shown in Figure 1. The most important aspect of this design is its employment of shallow junctions with a depth of $2\mu m$. A semi-insulating film lying between the interconnection and the N+ buried layer and a field plate having non-uniform oxide thickness achieve high breakdown characteristics in spite of the shallow junctions used. The former serves to shield electrically the N-island surface under it from the interconnection and reduce the electric field intensity at the N^+ buried layer. The latter is used to avoid the electric field concentration at the junction curvature. The field plate structure was optimized through computer aided calculations.

The main features of the PNPN chip, including high- and low-voltage transistors, are shown in Table 1, in comparison with those for conventional devices. In conventional practice[2], NPN transistors were formed in a vertical structure, while PNP transistors employed a lateral structure for ease of fabrication. Thus, high- and low-voltage transistors were formed in N-type islands with different impurity concentrations to satisfy varying requirements such as breakdown voltage and h_{FE}, and also had different junction depths. Consequently, high- and low-voltage LSI components were fabricated on separate chips (RT-chip and BSH-chip). In this study, on the other hand, PNP as well as NPN transistors have a vertical structure and the same junction depth as that of the PNPN device. Therefore, it has become possible to fabricate all of the devices simultaneously by the same process in a single chip, and to obtain complementry characteristics between NPN and PNP transistors.

Figure 2 shows the block diagram of the BORSHT-LSI. The RT portion of the LSI consists of current controlled PNPN switches and on/off control circuit elements. All switches have a dV/dt protection circuit. Gate-turn-off (GTO) circuits are added for switches S3-S6 which require a compulsory cutoff function. A 16Hz-79V_{rms} ringing signal is transmitted through switches S1, S2 and S6, and a silent pause is sent through S5 and S6 by battery feed. Switches S5 and S6 are also used to supply reverse direct current to the subscriber loop. Thus, the number of switches has been reduced by 5 in comparison with a previous report[2]. The 16Hz-79V_{rms} ringing wave is attenuated through the high-voltage interface circuit (IF), and the off-hook signal is detected by an external low-voltage ring-trip circuit connected at the terminal TRP. The BSH part of the LSI consists mainly of current mirrors to reduce circuit components. Battery-feed power transistors and their emitter resistors in current mirrors A1 and A2 are made from external components to reduce power dissipation in the chip. The 2-wire input impedance has been designed to be compatible with the standards for existing subscriber loops, which are characterized as 440Ω for dc and 600Ω + 1μF for ac. The 2-wire ac input impedance can be determined by the values of the external components connected to the terminals Ro and Zx. Because these components need only 10V blocking voltage, the component size can be much smaller than conventional ones with a 250V blocking voltage connected to the terminals TIP and RING.

A photomicrograph of the LSI is shwon in Figure 3. The LSI is composed of about 500 elements including PNPN devices. The chip size is 4.25mm x 6.21mm, 33% smaller compared with the sum of BSH-LSI and RT-LSI sizes previously reported[2]. This miniaturization of the LSI was achieved by adopting shallow junctions, vertical structures for both NPN and PNP transistors and the newly designed circuit. The LSI is mounted onto a 40 pin package.

Table 2 summarizes the measured characteristics of a single chip BORSHT-LSI.

Acknowledgments

The authors would like to thank T. Sakai, N. Ohwada, T. Egawa, K. Kato, T. Kimura, K. Izumi and T. Hayashi for their support and encouragement.

[Right]
FIGURE 3—Photomicrograph of single chip BORSHT-LSI.
Chip size is 6.21mm x 4.25mm.

[1] Sakurai, T., et. al., "A Dielectrically Isolated Complementary Bipolar Technique for Analog/Digital Compatible LSI's", *IEEE Trans. Electron Devices*, ED-30, Vol. 10; Oct., 1983.

[2] Kawarada, K., et. al., "High Voltage Subscriber Line Interface LSIs", ISSCC DIGEST OF TECHNICAL PAPERS, p. 202-203; Feb., 1982.

Reprinted from *IEEE 31st Int. Solid-State Circuits Conf.*, vol. SC-19, pp. 230–231, 1984.

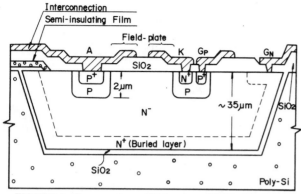

FIGURE 1—Cross section of high-voltage PNPN with shallow junctions.

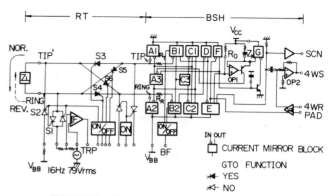

FIGURE 2—Block diagram of BORSHT-LSI.

Devices	Features		This work	Conventional work
			Value	
High-Voltage PNPN Device	Junction Depth		2 μm	~15 μm
	Imp. Concent. of Island		~3 x 10^{14} cm^{-3}	~3 x 10^{14} cm^{-3}
	On-Resistance		5 Ω	5 Ω
	Blocking Voltage		350 V	400 V
High-Voltage Tr	Junction Depth		2 μm	~15 μm
	Imp. Concent. of Island		~3 x 10^{14} cm^{-3}	~3 x 10^{14} cm^{-3}
	NPN	BV$_{CBO}$	350 V	400 V
		h$_{FE}$	75	20
	PNP	BV$_{CBO}$	350 V	400 V
		h$_{FE}$	60	< 5
Low-Voltage Tr	Junction Depth		2 μm	~3 μm
	Imp. Concent. of Island		~3 x 10^{14} cm^{-3}	~1 x 10^{15} cm^{-3}
	NPN	BV$_{CBO}$	100 V	100 V
		h$_{FE}$	60	50
	PNP	BV$_{CBO}$	100 V	100 V
		h$_{FE}$	60	50

TABLE 1—Characteristics of PNPN device, transistors and conventional devices.

Characteristics	Value
Blocking Voltage	350 V
On-Resistance	5 Ω
dv/dt Capability	>3000 v/μs
DC Current Capability	250 mA
2W DC Input Resistance	440 Ω
Idle Channel Noise (2W, I$_L$=50mA)	− 82 dB$_{mop}$
Longitudinal Balance (I$_L$=50mA, f=1kHz)	49 dB
Return Loss	29 dB
Transhybrid Loss	28 dB
Level Linearity (−50dBm to +3dBm)	± 0.1 dB
Frequency Response (300Hz to 3.4 kHz)	± 0.05 dB
On-Hook Power Dissipation	110 mW

TABLE 2—Measured characteristics of BORSHT-LSI.

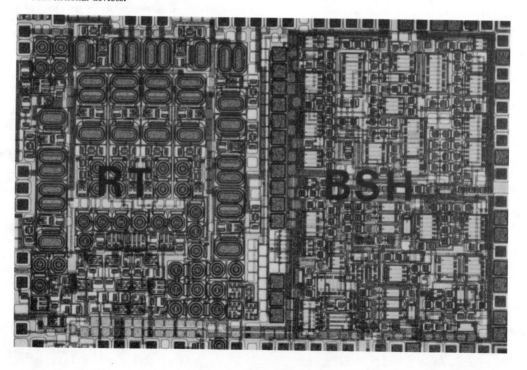

Part VIII
High Voltage Dielectric Isolation Technology

MOST of the high voltage integrated circuits today are made using junction isolation. Some of the problems that are encountered with this approach are the inability to integrate lateral bipolar devices without parasitic substrate current flow, latch-up in CMOS circuits under the high dv/dt conditions that are commonly prevalent during high voltage switching, and relatively high leakage currents at high ambient temperatures. The use of dielectric isolation offers a solution to all of these issues.

The first dielectric isolation technology to become commercially available utilized the formation of a V-groove in (100) oriented wafers, growth of an oxide on this contoured surface, deposition of a thick polysilicon supporting layer on the wafer, and the lapping of the original single crystal substrate down to the surface of the V-grooves. This technique has been successfully utilized to form thick silicon tubs that are completely surrounded by an oxide isolation layer. High voltage vertical channel transistors can be conveniently built in this technology by using well understood design rules evolved during the development of discrete power devices. This process for fabrication of dielectrically isolated devices is described briefly in the first paper of this part published by Gammel at Electro 1986. The formation of several high voltage devices such as the thyristor and gated diode switch are described. A linear solid state switch has been developed with optical coupling.

The following two papers by Sugawara and his co-workers discuss the application of the above technology to fabricate 350 volt circuits. In the first of these papers, published at the 1983 International Electron Devices meeting, design rules for the high voltage devices are provided. A combination of a field plate with field reduction diffusion at the edges of the dielectric tubs is found to result in more compact device structures. In the second of these papers, a 350 volt analog-digital power integrated circuit process is described. A new self-aligned double diffused lateral (SADDL) transistor structure and an optimized high voltage lateral thyristor structure are discussed. In addition, the impact of stresses in the dielectrically isolated tubs upon device leakage current is related to the polysilicon thickness and deposition conditions.

The above dielectric isolation technology is the only one that is commercially available at this time. Unfortunately, the cost of wafer fabrication with this technology exceeds that for junction isolation by a factor ranging from 1.5 to 3. This cost differential cannot offset the benefits of the reduced die size and flexibility of circuit design that dielectric isolation offers. Consequently, dielectrical isolation is not used often at present.

It would be highly desirable to create a new dielectric isolation technique that can be used to fabricate the wafers at a lower cost. For this reason several alternate methods for achieving dielectric isolation are currently under investigation. The next four papers in this part deal with these novel approaches.

The paper by Sakuma et al. describes the formation of a high voltage transistor structure using silicon-on-sapphire for achieving dielectric isolation. One thousand volt lateral transistors have been fabricated using an offset gate structure. This technology has the merits of utilizing a well characterized CMOS technology, especially if radiation hardness is a requirement. The high cost of the SOS starting material precludes the application of this approach to commercial circuits.

In the previous paper, the silicon layer is grown on a single crystal insulating substrate. A novel method for achieving dielectric isolation described in the next paper, by Ihara et al., inverts the process. In this approach, a low cost single crystal silicon substrate is used and a single crystal insulating layer is grown on it, followed by the growth of a single crystal active layer of silicon to create the desired dielectrically isolated wafer. The single crystal insulating layer chosen by the authors was spinel. A simple circuit with 250 volt driver transistors has been demonstrated.

Another novel approach to obtaining dielectrically isolated structures is the bonding together of wafers of oxide-coated single crystal silicon. To achieve the bonding, mirror polished silicon wafers are washed to form hydrophilic surfaces, placed in intimate contact, and subjected to thermal treatment. This method has the advantage of being a simple process that could be scaled to large volume production to obtain high quality dielectrically isolated silicon layers. Voltage isolation of up to 100 volts has been reported.

The last paper in this part, by Nakashima, was published in the IEEE TRANSACTIONS ON ELECTRON DEVICES. In this case, the dielectric isolation is achieved by using high energy, high dose oxygen ion implantation to form a subsurface layer of oxide while retaining a thin single crystal silicon layer on the top surface. A 0.3 micron thick silicon layer has been achieved with an underlying oxide film of 0.35 microns in thickness. High and low voltage lateral n-MOS transistors have been fabricated in the top silicon layer. Drain-source breakdown voltages as high as 180 volts were observed. A BHS circuit for telecommunications has been built using this technology. Due to the significantly increased funding being directed at the development of this technology for application to integrated circuits, this approach promises to become the lowest cost option in the future.

REPRINT PAPERS

[1] J. C. Gammel, "High Voltage Solid State Relays for Telecommunications," *IEEE Electro,* Session 24, Paper 1, pp. 1–4, 1986.

[2] Y. Sugawara, T. Kamei, Y. Hosokawa, and M. Okamura, "Practical

Size Limits of High Voltage IC's," *IEEE Int. Electron Devices Meeting Digest,* Abst. 16.2, pp. 412–415, 1983.

[3] Y. Sugawara, K. Miyata, and M. Okamura, "350V Analog Digital Compatible Power ICs Using Dielectrically Isolated Substrates," *IEEE Trans. Electron Devices,* vol. ED-33, pp. 2002–2007, 1986.

[4] H. Sakuma, T. Kuriyama, and T. Suzuki, "A High Voltage Offset-Gate SOS/MOS Transistor," *IEEE Int. Electron Devices Meeting Digest,* Abst. 25.5, pp. 594–597, 1979.

[5] M. Ihara, Y. Arimoto, M. Jifuku, T. Yamaoka, and K. Kurokawa, "Spinel-Isolated High-Voltage IC's," *IEEE Int. Solid State Circuits Conference Digest,* Abst. FAM 15.2, pp. 210–211, 1981.

[6] H. Ohashi, J. Ohura, T. Tsukakoshi, and M. Simbo, "Improved Dielectrically Isolated Device Integration by Silicon-wafer Direct Bonding (SDB) Technique," *IEEE Int. Electron Devices Meeting Digest,* Abstr. 9.1, pp. 210–213, 1986.

[7] S. Nakashima, Y. Maeda, and M. Akiya, "High-Voltage CMOS SIMOX Technology and Its Application to a BSH-LSI," *IEEE Trans. Electron Devices,* vol. ED-33, pp. 126–132, 1986.

High Voltage Solid State Relays
for Telecommunications
J. C. Gammel
AT&T Bell Laboratories
Reading, PA   19604

INTRODUCTION

Newcomers to conventional telecommunications signalling (e.g., residential telephone service) are often surprised by the high voltages encountered on subscriber loops connecting a central office to a telephone. The two main sources of high voltage in telecommunications applications are battery feed and ringing. The battery feed is typically 48V but may be considerably higher in certain situations. The maximum ringing signal is about 90V RMS. The peak voltages encountered during transient conditions (e.g., lightning) conditions can range from ±250V to about ±1000V depending on the protection scheme being used.

Recent developments in High Voltage Integrated Circuit (HVIC) technology have made it possible to integrate solid state relays capable of handling these high voltages along with associated control circuitry. The remainder of this paper will describe selected HVIC telecommunications relays in greater detail. This paper deals only with solid state relays based on HVICs and does not attempt to cover the broad topic of hybrid solid state relays.

TECHNOLOGY

Fundamentally, all of the techniques for designing discrete high voltage devices (such as the use of deep, graded junctions or surface field plates) can be applied to high voltage integrated circuits. At above 100V to 200V the area required for isolating individual transistors from each other by a reverse biased junction (junction isolation) becomes prohibitive. For the voltage requirements of telecommunications relays, the use of Dielectric Isolation (DI) becomes economical.

Using the DI technique[1] (see Figure 1), each device in a HVIC can be fabricated in its own "tub" of single crystalline silicon. Since all devices are isolated from each other by a thick layer of SiO_2, arbitrarily diverse device types may be fabricated and interconnected. Some of these devices will be illustrated in the following section on applications.

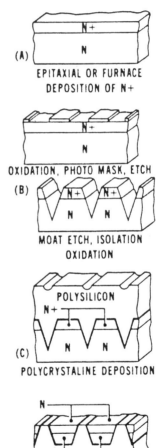

(A) EPITAXIAL OR FURNACE DEPOSITION OF N+

(B) OXIDATION, PHOTO MASK, ETCH

MOAT ETCH, ISOLATION OXIDATION

(C) POLYSILICON POLYCRYSTALINE DEPOSITION

(D) POLYSILICON GRIND, LAP & POLISH ORIGINAL SUBSTRATE

Figure 1

Typical fabrication sequence for the Dielectric Isolation Process.

Reprinted from *Electro, Session 24*, pp. 1-4, 1986.

All of the HVICs described in this paper were fabricated using D.I. wafers. Due to the high voltages required for telecommunications, there are very few examples[5] of alternative approaches. The subsequent processing steps vary from bipolar to MOS based with many uses of mixed device types. No attempt will be made to describe the processing in detail, but this does confirm the flexibility of the D.I. approach.

APPLICATIONS

Information has been published on the application of HVICs to central telephone office switching functions, such as concentration[2,3,4,5] of subscriber loops onto a single interface circuit and access[6,7] onto these loops for ringing, testing or battery feed. After reviewing selected applications, this paper will introduce a new HVIC developed at AT&T Bell Laboratories for electronic switchhook applications.

The first applications for HVICs as telecommunications relays were in the concentration of subscriber loops onto interface circuits in central office switching systems such as the 5ESS[TM] (see Figure 2). Representative switching element cross sections are shown in Figures 3 and 4. The Hitachi[2] approach (Figure 4) uses an SCR whereas the AT&T Bell Laboratories approach[3,4] (Figure 3) uses a novel gated diode switch. Both switch elements block for positive and negative signals when off, but conduct in only one direction when on. Each switch connection (or crosspoint) therefore requires an anti-parallel connection of devices (as in Figure 3) for bi-directional blocking and conduction. The switches must be biased with a small DC current (a few miliamperes) to achieve low incremental on resistance for AC signals. The highest reported level of integration[4] is 9 crosspoint pairs (or 18 600V switches) on one chip.

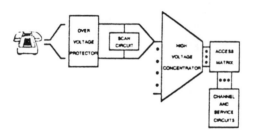

Figure 2

Concentrator concept used in the 5ESS[TM]. The concentrator is basically a relay matrix implemented with HVICs. In this application, the scan and access connections are also implemented with HVIC relays.

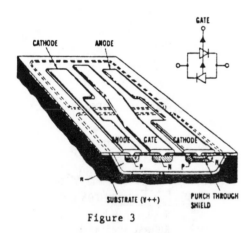

Figure 3

Gated Diode Switch structure used by AT&T Bell Laboratories for a relay matrix HVIC. An antiparallel pair is shown along with its device symbol.

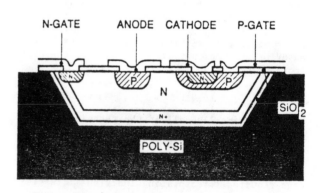

Figure 4

SCR structure used by Hitachi for a relay matrix HVIC.

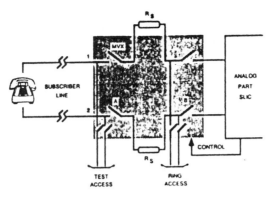

Figure 5

Ring and test access provided by Bell Telephone Research (Belgium) HVIC.

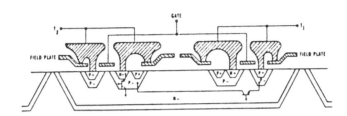

Figure 6

"Trimos" structure used for switches on Bell Telephone Research (Belgium) HVIC. A built-in lateral n-channel DMOS triggers the device on and a built-in PMOS will turn the device off.

Closely related to the concentrator application is the ring and test access connection for subscriber loops. As an example, Bell Telephone Research (Belgium) has reported[6] the development of a HVIC specialized for applications where each subscriber loop is serviced by its own interface circuit (see Figure 5). This development is significant in that the switch elements are MOS controlled (see Figure 6). A unique capacitive coupling of the control signal was achieved on-chip. This requires a significant mixture of smaller low breakdown voltage transistors with the high voltage switches on a single HVIC.

THE HV700A LINEAR SOLID STATE SWITCH

In applications such as cordless telephone, the switch hook must be electronically controlled. For many applications, good electrical isolation is required between the switch and the control. The HV700A has been developed at AT&T Bell Laboratories to fill this need using a single HVIC.

A simplified circuit diagram for this device is shown in Figure 7. The device is controlled by two series-connected LEDs to meet the requirement for isolation of the control.

The HVIC contains all of the circuitry in Figure 7 including the photodiode array (PDA). This was made possible by the use of D.I. technology. In this circuit, the DMOS transistors provide linear through the origin conduction and the SCRs provide surge protection. Although it is not shown, dV/dt protection circuitry is also included. While several versions of this switch have been built, representative specifications for the DPST configuration are 150V per pole, 20Ω on-resistance per pole, and 10 amp surge capability for a 1msec pulse.

The LEDs are packaged along with the HVIC as shown in Figure 8. Control currents as low as 2mA with 2500V input/output isolation have been achieved.

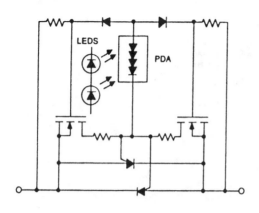

Figure 7

Simplified circuit diagram for the AT&T Bell
Laboratories HV700A linear solid state switch.
Each HVIC contains two identical circuits for
a DPST connection.

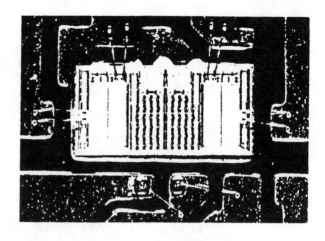

Figure 8

HV700A prior to encapsulation. An optical
bubble is used to couple light from the LEDs
to the HVIC.

CONCLUSION

This paper has reviewed a number of applications for High Voltage Integrated Circuits for
telecommunications relay replacement. A new
High Voltage Integrated Circuit, the HV700A
linear solid state switch, has been described.

As telecommunication signal switching
inherently requires high voltage relays, many
more HVICs for these applications are expected
to be developed. As illustrated by the examples
in this paper, the trend is expected to be
towards MOS-controlled switches with sophisticated control circuitry and perhaps related
circuit blocks integrated on the same chip.

References

1. P. W. Shackle, "High Voltage ICs are Here,"
    Integrated Circuits, pp. 19-26, March
    April, 1984.

2. Y. Sugawara, T. Kamei, Y. Hosokawa and M.
    Okamura, "Practical Size Limits of High
    Voltage ICs," IEDM Technical Digest,
    Washington, D.C., pp. 250-253, Dec. 8,
    1981.

3. J. E. Kohl, W. F. MacPherson, J. A. Davis,
    T. J. Riley, A. R. Hartman, J. E. Berthold,
    H. T. Weston, H. E. Mussman, "An Integrated
    Control Circuit for 530V Gated Diode
    Crosspoint Arrays," Proc. Custom I.C.
    Conference, pp. 238-241, May, 1982.

4. H. T. Weston, H. W. Becke, J. E. Berthold,
    J. C. Gammel, A. R. Hartman, J. E. Kohl, M.
    A. Shibib, R. K. Smith, Y. H. Wong,
    "Monolithic High Voltage Gated Diode
    Crosspoint Array I.C.," IEDM Technical
    Digest, Washington, D.C., pp. 85-88, 1982.

5. J. Ueda, H. Tsukada, H. Mori, K. Kato,
    T. Matsumoto, "An Optically Coupled Cross-
    point Array with High dV/dt Capability and
    High Gate Sensitivity," IEEE J. Solid State
    Circuits, Vol. SC-16, pp. 286-292, 1981.

6. G. Remmerie and L. V. Bossche, "10Ω 370V
    High Voltage Switches for Line Circuit
    Application," IEEE J. Solid State Circuits,
    Vol. SC-19, pp. 406-413, 1984.

7. K. Kawarada, T. Hayashi, Y. Inabe, H.
    Imagawa, "High Voltage Subscriber Line
    Interface LSIs," ISSCC Digest of Technical
    Papers, San Francisco, CA, pp. 202-203,
    Feb. 11, 1982.

PRACTICAL SIZE LIMITS OF HIGH VOLTAGE IC's

Y. Sugawara, T. Kamei, Y. Hosokawa and M. Okamura

Hitachi Research Laboratory, Hitachi, Ltd.,
Hitachi, Ibaraki, 319-12, Japan

ABSTRACT

To develop high voltage IC's of small chip sizes, relationships between geomtrical parameters and electrical properties of dielectrically isolated high voltage devices were investigated, and practical size limits of the lateral devices were determined. Device techniques for electric field reduction and efficient carrier transfer were introduced.

Using these techniques, each of the thyristor and an ac switch was fabricated in the area of 0.07 mm² and 2.03mm² per one crosspoint pairs. Their main specifications were 350 V blocking voltage, 250 mA dc current and 7 Ω on-resistance.

INTRODUCTION

Recently, high voltage IC's for telecommunications, office automation and consumer uses have been developed(1). We have also developed high voltage switching IC's using thyristors as main switches (2,3). In these IC's, a dielectric isolation technology, such as the EPIC (Epitaxial Passivated Integrated Circuit) process, is used because it is superior to a pn junction isolation technology in terms of smaller isolation areas, no latch-up actions and lower parasitic capacitances (2-7).

But high voltage IC's by EPIC process have an disadvantage to be solved for widespread practical uses. This is their high cost which results from the complicated manufacturing process and large device areas. The large area is needed mainly for realization of high voltages. Namely, a deeper junction and a deeper dielectically isolated island are adopted for reduction of the electric field at the junction corner. The former causes a larger lateral expansion of the junction. The latter causes the larger area of a minimum dielectrically isolated island because the shape of the isoland is that of a pyramid having a constant vertical angle. Furthermore, a broader field region is adopted to reduce the electric fields at the n+ channel stopper, which prevents breakdown voltage of an element in the dielectrically isolated island from being affected by the potencial of the polysilicon substrate (3, 8).

This paper will describe new device structures, geometry optimization and their application to development of high voltage IC's with smaller chip sizes.

FIELD REDUCTION LAYERS

Figure 1 shows a cross-sectional view of high voltage IC which was fabricated by the EPIC process. A field plate was used to reduce the surface electric field near the junction and a channel stopper also used to prevent the breakdown phenomena affected by the potential of the polysilicon substrate (3).

The depth of the junction was about $5.0\,\mu$m. To realize a high breakdown voltage of this junction, the structure of the field plate was optimized, namely the oxide thickness under the field plate was reduced from $2.0'\,\mu$m to $1.0\,\mu$m. Furthermore, fixed charge density in the oxide was reduced also (3). Thus, the depletion layer near the junction became wider by this field plate and electric field at the corner of the junction was reduced. On the other hand, because the depletion layer spread along the Si surface easily and was stopped at the n+ channel stopper, the electric field at the n+ channel stopper became higher, especially under the interconnections. Thus, breakdown voltage decreased.

To reduce the electric field at the channel stopper, it is necessary to use a wider field region W_F. This results in the larger device areas. Therefore, new field reduction layers, as shown in Figure 1, were introduced to reduce the width of the field regions. This layer must be designed so that it has a higher impurity concentration than the n⁻ layer and is deplated completely when a high voltage was applied to the device. Therefore, the field reduction layers could take charge of more part of an applied voltage and reduce the electric field at the n+ channel stopper. When the electric field at the channel stopper was kept at a constant value, the width of the field regions could be reduced. To

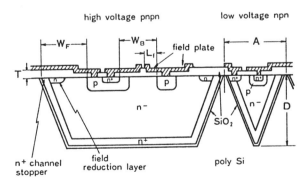

Fig.1 Cross-sectional view of the high voltage IC

Reprinted from *IEEE 29th Int. Electron Devices Meeting*, pp. 412–415, 1983.

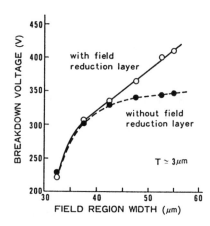

Fig.2 Effect of the field reduction layer.
The new structure with a field reduction layer can achieve equally high BVs as the conventional type in spite of a narrower W_F.

increase the voltage in field reduction layer without causing voltage breakdown, two dimensional numerical calculations were utilized, and both the impurity and the depth of the layer were optimized.

Figure 2 shows the relationships between breakdown voltage and the field region width W_F when the oxide thickness T was $3\,\mu m$ and junction depth was $5\,\mu m$. The least W_F, which was necessary to achieve high breakdown voltage more than 350 V, was reduced by the field reduction layer.

PRACTICAL SIZE LIMITS OF DEVICES

Shrinkage of devices must be performed without deterioration of electrical characteristics. Because the lateral devices occupy such a large area of the high voltage IC compared with other devices, the structure dependences of their characteristics were investigated in this section to reduce their sizes.

Lateral thyristor

Influences of device parameters, such as lateral dimention of thyristor and island depth, on the electrical characteristics were investigated.

Figure 3 shows the relationships between the base width and major electrical characteristics of lateral thyristors. Since on-resistance Ron (at I=30mA) depended on not only the surface length between p emitter and p base, but also the length between n^+ emitter and n^- base, the basewidth in Figure 3 is defined as the length between n^+ emitter and p emitter W_B. However, since breakdown voltage BV and interruption current I_{off} depended on the length between p emitter and p base only, the surface length between n^+ emitter and n^- base was fixed at a constant value for the measured samples. R_{on} decreased with decreasing base width, and it was much smaller than $10\,\Omega$ which was the practical limit in wide use (4). Therefore, practical size limits of W_B were determined by the breakdown voltage. The length of the p emitter was $150\,\mu m$, but R_{on} was so

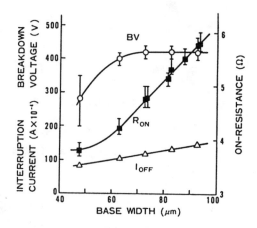

Fig.3 Relationships between device characteristics and base width.

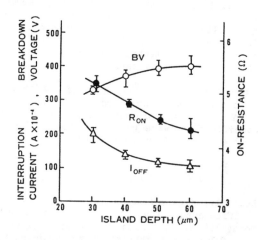

Fig.4 Relationships between device characteristics and island depth.
With decreasing island depth, I_{off} increases, but R_{on} increases and BV decreases.

small that the length could be shortened.

Figure 4 shows the relationships between the characteristics and island depth D. With decreasing island depth, I_{off} increased but R_{on} also increased and BV decreased. According to this data, island depth should be determined by BV too.

The thyristor in on-state behaves as a pin diode having i layer corresponding to n^- base, R_{on} increased with increasing W_B and decreasing D because the resistance of the n^- base increased(9).

By decreasing thyristor length, BV did not change and I_{off} increased, but R_{on} also increased. Therefore, the thyristor length was determined by R_{on}.

- Lateral pnp transistor

It was found that current gain h_{FE} of a lateral pnp transistor became larger when its island became smaller or its emitter approached more closely the side wall of the island. As to the cause of the effects, it seemed to be the decrease of holes that

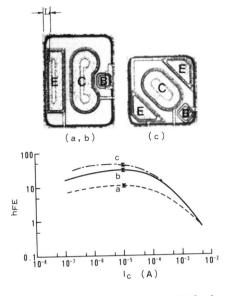

Fig.5 Comparison of pnp transistor's h_{FE}
(a) Conventional type L=80 μ m
(b) Improved type L=22.5 μ m
(c) New disposed type.

Table 1. Comparison of device sizes.

		(A) prior mm²	(B) new mm²	B/A (%)
high voltage device	pnpn	0.224	0.070	31
	pnp	0.180	0.036	20
low voltage device	pn	0.058	0.010	17

recombined at the surface and in the bulk of the islands. And, not only the n⁺ buried layer along the bottom of the island, but also the n⁺ buried layer along the inclined side wall of the island acted effectively (3). These new findings were utilized to develop high voltage lateral transistors with high h_{FE} values as shown in Figure 5.

Transistor (a) was a previous type and its length from the side wall oxide to the diffusion pattern of p emitter L was 80 μ m. The transistor (b) was an improved type which had a shortened L of 22.5 μ m. The transistor (c) was the new diagonally disposed type with two p emitters. Since the emitters of the transistor (c) were surrounded by n⁺ buried layer, except in the direction toward the collector and L was 22.5 μ m, the effect of the n⁺ buried layers was larger. Therefore, transistors (c) had the smallest island area, the largest h_{FE} and the same BV about 380V as compared with the transistor (a) and (b).

HIGH VOLTAGE IC's

The above mentioned device techniques and the improved circuit technologies were applied to the high voltage IC's. Table 1 compares typical device sizes. Each device was reduced in area to 17-31% of prior devices (2, 3).

Figure 6 shows comparison of two high voltage switching IC's, which have almost the same functions. The chip area of the new IC was 3.2 × 3.2 mm². It was 29% the size of the previous IC(3). The new IC was composed of 11-lateral thyristors as main switches and 240-other devices. Table 2 lists some electrical properties of this IC. An ac switch, which integrated 4 crosspoint pairs and had as same electrical properties as those of a previous one

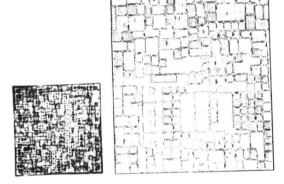

Fig.6 Comparison of high voltage IC's.

(a) A new IC. (b) A previous IC.

Table 2. Electrical properties of the compact high voltage switching IC.

Blocking voltage	> ± 350	V
DC current	> 250	mA
Interruption current	> 10	mA
On resistance	< 7	Ω
Dv/dt capability	> 500	V/μs
Triggering gate current	~ 0.5	mA

(2), was also fabricated with new devices and the area per one crosspoint pairs was 2.03mm².

SUMMARY

To develop high voltage IC's of small chip sizes, relationships between geometrical parameters and electrical properties of dielectrically isolated high voltage devices have been investigated, and practical size limits of the lateral devices were determined. Electric field reduction layers were introduced to reduce the field region width. A n^+ channel stopper along the inclined side wall of the island was utilized to decrease an area of a lateral pnp transistor without decreasing its hFE.

Using these techniques, each of the thyristor and an ac switch was fabricated in the area of 0.07 mm^2 and 2.03mm^2 per one crosspoint pairs. Their main specifications were 350 V blocking voltage, 250 mA dc current and 7 Ω on-resistance.

ACKNOWLEDGEMENTS

The authors wish to thank Drs. T. Takasuna, T. Kariya and Messers. K. Miyata, N. Kawakami, Y. Arai, M. Kawanami and M. Tokunaga for their continuous encouragement and guidances. Appreciation is also expressed to members of the IC fabrication and circuit design group for their constant support.

REFERENCES

1) J. Tihanyi: IEDM Technical Digest, p.6, Dec, 1982.
2) T. Kamei: IEDM Technical Digest, p.254, Dec. 1981.
3) Y. Sugawara, T. Kamei and Y. Hosokawa: Proc. 14th Conf. (4th International) Solid State Devices, Tokyo, Aug. 1982; Japan J. Appl. Phys., 22, Suppl. 22-1, p.77 (1983).
4) W.H.A. Mattheus: ISSCC Digest of Technical Papers, p.238, Feb. 1981.
5) A.R. Hartman, J.E. Berthold, T.J. Riley, J.E. Kohl, Y. Wong, H.T. Weston and R.S. Scott: IEDM Technical Digest, p.250, Dec. 1981.
6) K. Kawarada, T. Hayashi, Y. Inabe and H. Imagawa: ISSCC Digest of Technical Papers, p.202, Feb. 1982.
7) T. Sakurai, K. Kato, Y. Inabe and T. Hayashi: IEDM Technical Digest, p.793, Dec. 1982.
8) J.D. Beasom:IEDM Technical Digest, p.175, Dec. 1977.
9) T. Nakagawa: J. IEE Japan, vol 83, p.1765, 1963.

350-V Analog–Digital Compatible Power IC's Using Dielectrically Isolated Substrates

YOSHITAKA SUGAWARA, KENJI MIYATA, AND MASAHIRO OKAMURA, MEMBER, IEEE

Abstract—Using a dielectric isolation process, 350-V analog-digital compatible power IC technologies were developed. Good complemental electrical characteristics were achieved by vertical n-p-n and new lateral p-n-p transistors, and the transistor noise was reduced by removing crystal defects specific to dielectrically isolated wafers. Furthermore, high accuracy of resistance was achieved by a symmetrical layout. The technologies were applied to the development of a high-voltage power IC for telecommunication uses.

I. INTRODUCTION

RECENTLY, HIGH-VOLTAGE analog–digital compatible power IC's for telecommunications [1]–[3], office automation [4], and industrial uses [5], [6] have been developed. In these IC's, in order to achieve a high operating voltage, a complete isolation technique between the devices is required in addition to the conventional analog–digital compatible IC technique. A combination of bipolar device technology and dielectric isolation technology is desirable, if the scale of the control logics is not large, for the reasons that bipolar transistors offer higher drivability and lower noise than MOS transistors, while dielectric isolation offers completeness in the isolation and a reduced device area.

However, there are problems in realizing the high-voltage analog–digital compatible IC by combining bipolar device technology and dielectric isolation technology. One problem is the difficulty of realizing complemental n-p-n and p-n-p transistors through a simple fabrication process. While excellent performance has been achieved in some IC's by using vertical n-p-n and vertical p-n-p transistors [2], [3], thick lightly doped single-silicon islands of both n- and p-types must be fabricated in a dielectrically isolated substrate [7], [8]. A second problem is that the electrical characteristics of the bipolar devices depend on the depth of the dielectrically isolated Si islands. A third problem is the large stress that exists in dielectrically isolated Si islands [9]. The stress results in lower resistor accuracy and more crystal defects, which cause large transistor noise.

This paper reports on the solutions of these problems and the realization of high-voltage dielectrically isolated IC's by a simple process. The realization of complemental electric characteristics by using a vertical n-p-n tran-

sistor and a new lateral p-n-p transistor, which is named self-aligned double diffused lateral (SADDL) transistor [10], is described in Section II. The optimization of the dielectrically isolated island depth for the realization of a practical lateral thyristor, which is a main device for the digital circuits, is reported in Section III. Next, the relationship between transistor noise and crystal defects and the layout method for the resistors are described in Sections IV and V, respectively. Finally, the development of a 350-V analog–digital compatible power IC is described in Section VI.

II. COMPLEMENTAL TRANSISTORS

Fig. 1 shows a cross-sectional view of a part of the investigated IC that is fabricated by the epitaxial passivated integrated circuit (EPIC) process. The lateral p-n-p-n thyristor is a switching device for digital circuits. The n-p-n and SADDL p-n-p transistors are devices for both analog and digital circuits.

The p-emitter and the n-base of the SADDL transistor are fabricated by a self-aligned technique [10]. Therefore, its lateral n-base (n_B) is narrow and the drift electric field is formed by an impurity distribution, as in a vertical transistor. This results in high h_{FE} and high f_T. To achieve high BV_{ceo}, a lightly doped p-layer (p_C^-) is fabricated. Its impurity concentration is chosen to be lower than n_B, but higher than the n^- island. When a high voltage is applied to the SADDL transistor, the depletion layer extends mainly into p_C^-, and only slightly into n_B. This results in a high Early voltage and the high BV_{ceo} since punch through of n_B is avoided, in spite of its narrow width. The p_C^- must act as the collector in the range of the operating voltage. When the impurity concentration of p_C^- is low, the collector resistance R_c becomes high and the current capacity becomes low because of the base spreading effect [10].

To decrease R_c and increase the current capacity without deterioration of BV_{ceo}, the p_C^- layer is designed with a high impurity concentration and the electric field at the p_C^-–n_B junction is reduced by the field effect of the p_E electrode. Fig. 2 shows the relationships between BV_{ceo} and the length of the p_E electrode L. BV_{ceo} is about 270 V at a p_C^- dose of 3×10^{12} cm^{-2}, but decreases to about 130 V at a p_C^- dose of 6×10^{12} cm^{-2}. When the length of the p_E electrode L extends over the p_C^-–n_B junction, BV_{ceo} is constant for the dose of 3×10^{12} cm^{-2} because the p_C^-

Manuscript received May 14, 1986; revised July 18, 1986.

The authors are with the Hitachi Research Laboratory, Hitachi Ltd., Hitachi, Ibaraki, 319-12, Japan.

IEEE Log Number 8610706.

Reprinted from *IEEE Trans. Electron Devices*, vol. ED-33, pp. 2002–2007, Dec. 1986.

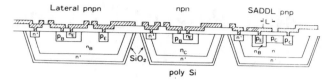

Fig. 1. Cross-sectional view of the high-voltage IC.

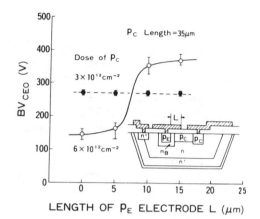

Fig. 2. Effect of p_E electrode.

layer is depleted fully and BV_{ceo} is limited by the electric-field concentration at the p_C collector contact layer; how-ever, BV_{ceo} increases abruptly for the dose of 6×10^{12} cm^{-2} because depletion occurs in proportion to length L. Thus, R_c can be reduced and the current capacity can be increased without deterioration of BV_{ceo}.

Fig. 3 shows the output characteristics of both vertical n-p-n and lateral p-n-p transistors of the 100-V class. These n-p-n and p-n-p transistors have almost the same cell sizes, which are 0.013 and 0.027 mm^2, respectively. The collector current of the conventional lateral p-n-p transistor depends on the applied voltage, but that of the SADDL transistor has hardly any dependence on the ap-plied voltage. Namely, the Early voltage of the SADDL transistor is larger than that of the conventional one, being roughly 1400 V for the former and 300 V for the latter. The h_{FE} of the SADDL transistor is high, about 100, and depends only slightly on the collector current, but the h_{FE} of the conventional one is low and becomes lower with increased collector current.

Therefore, the current capacity of the SADDL transis-tor is larger than that of the conventional one. The output characteristic of the SADDL p-n-p transistor comple-ments that of the n-p-n transistor.

Fig. 4 shows the output characteristics of both vertical n-p-n and SADDL p-n-p power transistors with high BV_{ceo} (350 V). The BV_{ceo} of the latter is higher than that of the former, although both have the same h_{FE}. The Early volt-age of the SADDL transistor is also higher (>1000 V) than that of the vertical n-p-n one (850 V).

Fig. 5 shows the dependence of f_T on I_c of both high- and low-voltage transistors. The f_T's of the SADDL p-n-p transistors are enhanced by over 50 times those of the conventional low- and high-voltage lateral p-n-p tran-sistors, the f_T's of which are 1.5 and 0.1 MHz, respec-

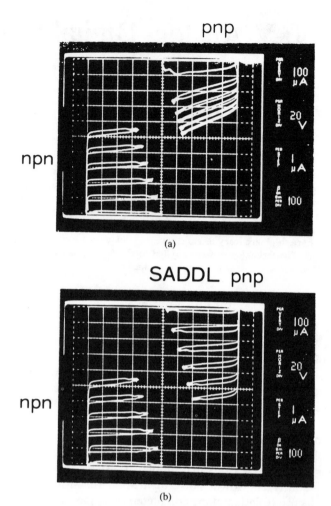

Fig. 3. Output characteristics of both vertical n-p-n and p-n-p transistors of 100-V class.

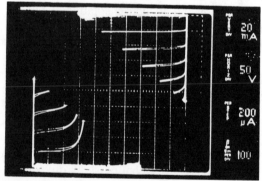

Fig. 4. Output characteristics of both vertical n-p-n and p-n-p power tran-sistors of 350-V class. (a) Conventional. (b) SADDL.

tively. It is clear from Figs. 3–5 that good complementary electrical characteristics are achieved by the vertical n-p-n transistor and SADDL p-n-p transistors. Since these transistors can be fabricated in a dielectrically isolated wafer with single silicon islands of only an n-type, the fabricating process is simplified.

III. LATERAL THYRISTOR FOR DIGITAL CIRCUITS

Fig. 6 shows the relationships between the electrical characteristics of the lateral p-n-p-n thyristor. Interruption

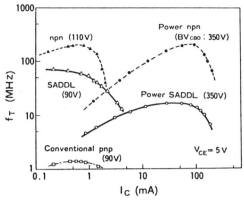

Fig. 5. Dependence of f_T on I_c.

Fig. 7. An etched lateral p-n-p transistor.

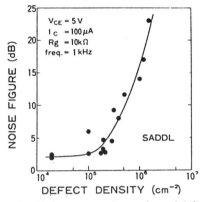

Fig. 8. Relationship between transistor noise and defect density.

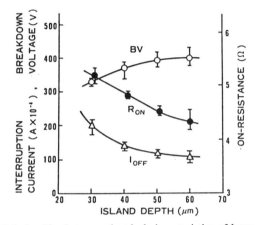

Fig. 6. Relationships between electrical characteristics of lateral p-n-p-n thyristors and island depth.

current I_{OFF} is the maximum current that is interrupted by shorting between p_B and n_E of the thyristor. On resistance R_{ON} is the differential resistance at anode current of 30 mA when the thyristor is conducting. With decreasing island depth, I_{OFF} and R_{ON} increase and breakdown voltage decreases.

In the lateral thyristor with low on-state current density as the same level as the holding current, the lateral p-n-p transistor part of the thyristor is in the condition of low carrier injection. Therefore, holes injected from the p_E emitter into n_B^- base are scattered by the built-in potential at the n^+–n_B^- junction and diffuse toward the p_B base [11]. With decreasing island depth, the injected holes are scattered more effectively at the junction and the holes that reach the p_B base without recombination in the n_B^- base increase. Therefore, the thyristor becomes hard to interrupt and I_{OFF} increases with decreasing island depth.

The thyristor with the high on-state current density behaves as a lateral p-i-n diode having an i-layer corresponding to the n_B^- base. The resistance of the diode's i-layer increases with decreasing the thickness of the n_B^- base, namely the island depth [12]. Therefore, R_{ON} of the lateral thyristor increases.

Breakdown voltage decreases because the electric field at the corner of the p_B–n_B^- junctions becomes higher since the n^+ buried layer approaches the junction as the island depth decreases. According to these facts, the island depth

can be optimized by selecting the required characteristics of the thyristor.

IV. TRANSISTOR NOISE

The noise of the transistor fabricated in the EPIC wafer is larger and more scattered than that of a transistor fabricated in a single-crystal Si wafer. It is typically $1/f$ noise, which has been attributed by many authors to the dislocation near the bulk and surface junction (see, for example, [13]). Accordingly, the correlation between transistor noise and crystal defects is investigated.

After measuring the noise of the transistors fabricated in the EPIC wafer, the passivation films and electrodes are removed from the transistors. The transistors are then etched in Wright etchant for 5 min to expose the crystal defects. Fig. 7 shows a photomicrograph of an etched transistor. Etch-pits, i.e., crystal defects, are observed in the base area.

Fig. 8 shows the relationships between the noise figure of the transistors and the density of the crystal defects, which are observed as etch-pits. The etch-pits that exist in the active area are counted. The conditions for the measurement of the noise figure are shown in Fig. 8. R_g is the source resistance and is connected with the base of the transistor in series. The noise figure decreases with reduction of the defect density and saturates at 2–3 dB at a density of less than 10^5 cm^{-2}. Four transistors of the investigated 82 transistors have abnormally large noise figures that deviate from the curve in Fig. 8, but the existence of stacking faults across the emitter junction is found in all of them. From the results described above, the main cause of the large noise figure of the transistors fabricated in the EPIC wafer seems to be the crystal defects, which are observed as etch-pits.

The same kind of etch-pits are already present in EPIC wafers before the transistor fabrication process, but they are not observed in the single-crystal Si wafer. These crystal defects have been observed to generate directly after polysilicon deposition in the EPIC process, along with bowing of the wafer. Additionally, it has been seen that the density of the crystal defect and bowing of the wafer increased with larger polysilicon thickness and decreased with higher deposition temperature. From these results, the crystal defects seem to be caused by the stress generated through contraction of the growing polysilicon layer at high temperature [9].

Since these crystal defects specific to the EPIC wafer can be removed by reduction of the polysilicon thickness and polysilicon deposition temperature, transister noise can be reduced.

V. ACCURACY OF RESISTORS

The dependencies of the accuracy of resistance on resistor positions in the chip and the isolated single silicon island are studied too. The resistance is shown to be independent of the resistor positions in the chip, but does depend on the positions in the island.

Fig. 9 shows the dependence of resistance on the distance of the resistor from the isolation SiO_2 film. The resistance increases with decreasing distance, and a resistor 20 μm from the SiO_2 film has a resistance about 0.5 percent higher than that 140 μm from the SiO_2 film. This increase becomes a problem in the realization of resistor pairs with high accuracy (≤ 1.0 percent).

In the isolated n-well that is fabricated by the EPIC method, compression stress exists, which is generated through contraction of the growing polysilicon layer [9]. In the case shown in Fig. 9, the compression stress in the X direction makes the resistance increase, but the compression stress in the Y direction makes it decrease [14]. The compression stress in the X direction increases with shorter distance between the resistor and the SiO_2 isolation film. This explains the dependence of resistance on distance. Therefore, pairs of resistors, which must have high accuracy (± 1 percent), should be fabricated at symmetrical positions in the dielectrically isolated Si islands.

VI. HIGH-VOLTAGE POWER IC

The described techniques are applied to the development of a 350-V analog–digital compatible power IC for telecommunication uses.

A. High-Voltage Power Operational Amplifier

Fig. 10 shows the circuit of the operational amplifier part in the power IC. It is composed of 31 devices. Transistors $Q1$ and $Q2$ compose an input differential amplifier. A bias current for the amplifier is supplied by devices $Q6$, $Q7$, $Q8$, $Q12$, $R3$, $R4$, and $R6$. Transistors $Q10$ and $Q11$ compose a high-gain amplifier and C is a capacitor for a phase compensation. Devices $Q17$, $Q18$, $R9$, and $R10$ are

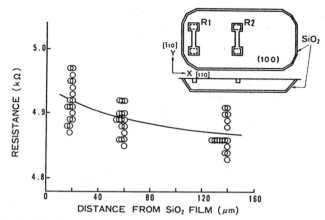

Fig. 9. Relationship between resistance and distance of resistors from SiO_2 isolation film.

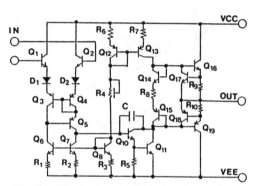

Fig. 10. Circuit of an operational power amplifier.

for current limitation of the output driver transistors $Q16$ and $Q19$, and transistors $Q14$ and $Q15$ are for elimination of crossover distortion.

All the p-n-p transistors are the SADDL type. Transistors $Q5$, $Q12$, $Q13$, and $Q19$ are high-voltage SADDL transistors with BV_{ceo} of the 350-V class and transistors $Q3$, $Q4$, $Q15$, and $Q18$ are intermediate-voltage SADDL transistors with BV_{ceo} of the 70-V class. Both types of transistors are fabricated with the same diffusion process for realization of a simple IC process, and the lengths of the p_C^- layer and field region of the intermediate-voltage SADDL transistors are designed to be shorter than those of the high-voltage ones for a reduction in IC chip area. Therefore, both types of the transistors have the same h_{FE} ($= 100$) and same f_T ($= 20$–25 MHz) values.

To realize a high-voltage power operational amplifier, some modifications are added to the conventional low-voltage operational amplifier besides the ones mentioned above. To protect the emitter junctions of transistors $Q1$–$Q4$ from damage due to input high-voltage surges, high-voltage diodes $D1$ and $D2$ are connected to the circuit. To reduce an increase in bias current with increasing supply voltage, a high-voltage resistor $R4$, which has the function of current-limiting action when high voltage is applied, is utilized.

Fig. 11 shows the open-loop voltage gain versus frequency of the operational amplifier part. The gain in low frequency is more than 100 dB at the output voltage of

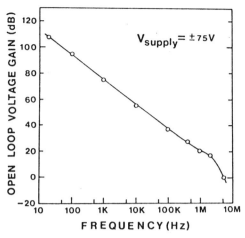

Fig. 11. Open-loop voltage gain versus frequency of the operational power amplifier.

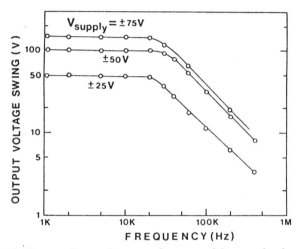

Fig. 12. Output voltage swing versus frequency of the operational power amplifier.

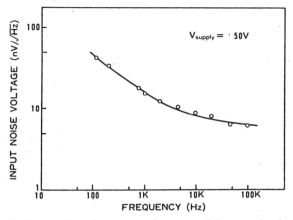

Fig. 13. Input noise voltage versus frequency of the operational power amplifier.

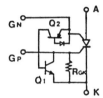

Fig. 14. Circuit of a p-n-p-n switch.

Input offset voltage is 2–5 mV. Input and output impedances are about 1 MΩ and 100 Ω, respectively. The slew rate is about 5 V/μs and output current is 60 mA.

B. High-Voltage Digital Switching Circuits

Fig. 14 shows a circuit for the typical digital switch of the 350-V 250-mA class. The switch is composed of a p-n-p-n thyristor and dV/dt protection circuits. When the switch is in the forward bias condition, it can be driven under any potential; namely, it is driven by the current that flows out from the terminal G_N when the potential of the cathode is higher than that of G_N, and it is driven by the current that flows in from the terminal G_P when the potential of the anode is lower than that of the G_P.

The switch can achieve conflicting requirements, high allowable dV/dt capability, and low gate drive current. When the anode voltage rises rapidly, the transistor $Q1$ is driven into its saturation state by a displacement current of the collector junction of the transistor $Q2$. Therefore, the triggering sensitivity of the thyristor by dV/dt is limited to a small value by the saturation resistance of the transistor $Q1$, i.e., less than 100 Ω [15]. On the other hand, its triggering gate sensitivity for the gate drive current is high, since the resistor R_{GK} can be designed accurately and independently of dV/dt.

C. High-Voltage Power IC

Fig. 15 shows the high-voltage power IC for telecommunication uses, which is composed of 392 devices and 2 power Darlington transistors. Its chip area is 5.7 × 6.3 mm². The analog control circuit and both power n-p-n and SADDL p-n-p transistors of the 350-V 100-mA class compose the complementary large current amplifier with high gain. The digital control circuit integrates 11 lateral

150 V and gain-bandwidth is about 5 MHz. It seems that the rapid drop in gain at frequencies above 2 MHz is not caused by the SADDL transistor but rather by the n-p-n transistor $Q11$ because its emitter is grounded and the $f\beta$ of $Q11$, which is about 2 MHz, limits the frequency characteristics of the high-gain amplifier part composed of $Q10$ and $Q11$. Therefore, the gain-bandwidth is increased above 10 MHz by modification of the high-gain amplifier's circuit.

Fig. 12 shows the relationship between output voltage swing and frequency. Output voltage swing is the maximum voltage that can be obtained without distortion when the voltage of input signal with sine wave form is increased. The peak-to-peak voltage swing is about 150 V at a supply voltage of ±75 V.

Fig. 13 shows the dependence of input noise voltage on frequency. Input noise voltage is the equivalent differential input noise voltage that reproduces the noise at the output if all amplifier noise sources are set to zero when the source resistances are zero. The input noise voltage is about 15 nV/√Hz at 1 kHz and at a voltage swing of ±50 V. This low-noise voltage is achieved by removing the crystal defects specific to the EPIC wafer.

Other electrical characteristics obtained are as follows.

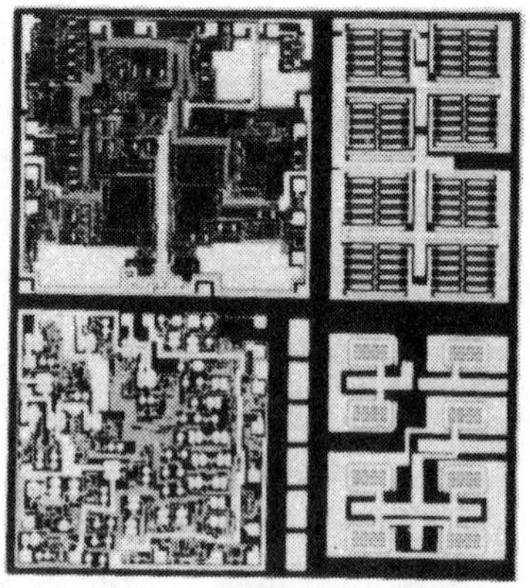

Fig. 15. Photomicrograph of a high-voltage power IC for telecommunication uses.

TABLE I
ELECTRICAL CHARACTERISTICS OF THE HIGH-VOLTAGE SWITCHING IC

Blocking Voltage	> ±350 V
DC Current	> 250 mA
Interruptable Current	> 10 mA
On-Resistance	< 7 Ω
dV/dt Capability	> 500 V/µs
Triggering Gate Current	~ 0.5 mA

p-n-p-n switches (shown in Fig. 14) and the gate driver circuits for p-n-p-n switches. The digital control circuit has the switching function of the large current, which is pushed or pulled by the complementary large current amplifier, and it has the same electrical properties, listed in Table I, as an earlier IC [16]. The power IC shows good characteristics for practical telecommunication uses at an IC power dissipation of 2.5 W.

VII. SUMMARY

To realize low-cost high-voltage analog–digital compatible power IC's, simple IC technologies, based on a dielectric isolation process, were investigated. Good complementary electrical characteristics were achieved by vertical n-p-n and SADDL p-n-p transistors, which were fabricated in a dielectrically isolated wafer with single sil-icon islands of only n-type. The depth of the islands was optimized to meet the desired electrical characteristics of the lateral p-n-p-n thyristor. Transistor noise was reduced by removing crystal defects, which are specific to wafers fabricated by the EPIC process. A high accuracy of resistors was achieved by a symmetrical layout of a pair of resistors in the dielectrically isolated single silicon island. Using these techniques, a 350-V analog–digital compatible power IC was fabricated for telecommunication uses.

ACKNOWLEDGMENT

The authors wish to thank Dr. T. Takasuna, Dr. Y. Kawamoto, T. Kamei, T. Yatsuo, T. Kariya, and N. Kawanami for their continuous encouragement and guidance. Appreciation also is expressed to the members of the IC Fabrication and Circuit Design Group, especially T. Shirasawa, S. Kawamata, and J. Kitano, for their constant support.

REFERENCES

[1] Y. Sugawara, T. Kamei, and Y. Hosokawa, presented at the 14th Int. Conf. Solid-State Devices, Tokyo, 1982; also in *Japan J. Appl. Phys.*, vol. 22, suppl. 22-1, p. 77, 1983.
[2] P. J. Meza, D. P. Laude, R. C. Strawbrich, and R. M. Sirisi, in *ISSCC Dig. Tech. Papers*, p. 16, Feb. 1983.
[3] T. Ohno, T. Sakurai, Y. Inabe, and T. Koinuma, in *ISSCC Dig. Tech. Papers*, p. 230, Feb. 1984.
[4] T. Okabe, M. Kimura, I. Shimizu, Y. Nagai, and K. Hoya, in *ISSCC Dig. Tech. Papers*, p. 100, Feb. 1986.
[5] B. G. Bynum and D. L. Cve, in *ISSCC Dig. Tech. Papers*, p. 290, Feb. 1984.
[6] E. J. Wildi, J. P. Walden, and M. S. Adler, in *ISSCC Dig. Tech. Papers*, p. 266, Feb. 1985.
[7] J. D. Beason, in *IEDM Tech. Dig.*, p. 89, Dec. 1982.
[8] T. Sakurai, T. Ohno, K. Kato, Y. Inabe, and T. Hayashi, *IEEE Trans. Electron Devices*, vol. ED-30, p. 1278, 1983.
[9] T. Suzuki, A. Mimura, T. Kamei, and T. Ogawa, *J. Electro. Chem.*, vol. 127, p. 1537, 1980.
[10] Y. Sugawara and T. Kamei, *IEEE Trans. Electron Devices*, vol. ED-33, p. 23, 1986.
[11] W. K. Tang and K. M. Busen, in *IEDM Tech. Dig.*, 1965.
[12] T. Nakagawa, *J. IEE Japan.*, vol. 83, p. 1765, 1963.
[13] S. R. Morrison, *Phys. Rev.*, vol. 99, p. 1904, 1955.
[14] C. S. Smith, *Phys. Rev.*, vol. 94, p. 42, 1954.
[15] M. Tokunaga, T. Kamei, I. Ishi, and M. Kawanami, in *Int. Switching Symp. Tech. Dig.*, pp. 221–224, 1976.
[16] Y. Sugawara, T. Kamei, Y. Hosokawa, and M. Okamura, in *IEDM Tech. Dig.*, p. 412, 1983.

A HIGH VOLTAGE OFFSET-GATE SOS/MOS TRANSISTOR

H. Sakuma, T. Kuriyama and T. Suzuki

Central Research Laboratories, Nippon Electric Co., Ltd.

Kawasaki, 213, Japan

ABSTRACT

A high voltage SOS/MOS transistor with a new offset-gate structure is proposed and verified experimentally to realize completely dielectrically isolated high voltage CMOS ICs.

Since its offset-gate region, consisting of a pinched resistor and an underlying substrate layer, is designed to deplete vertically throughout the silicon epi-layer at above the drain voltage equal to the offset-gate pinched-off voltage, the proposed transistor shows a high drain breakdown voltage characteristic that is not limited by the substrate doping level, but depends only on the offset-gate length.

The offset-gate PMOS and NMOS transistors were successfully fabricated on the same intrinsic SOS wafer by ion implantation substrate doping and resulted in drain breakdown voltages of up to 950V and 1100V, respectively, at 100 μm offset-gate length.

INTRODUCTION

CMOS configuration is most suitable for high voltage MOS ICs (e.g., driver ICs for gas discharge displays ($BV_{DS} > 125V$), electroluminescent displays ($BV_{DS} \sim 250V$) etc.) because of low power dissipation, circuit design flexibility etc. However it is rather difficult to realize high voltage CMOS ICs on conventional bulk silicon chips because of the difficulties involved in device isolation and wiring.

On the other hand, SOS (Silicon On Sapphire) structure can demonstrate its inherent advantages for high voltage applications (1), such as complete device isolation, no metal interconnection problems, high packing density, simple fabrication process, low parasitic capacitance, realization of on-chip high voltage CMOS devices etc., if a basic high voltage device with high performance and high reliability can be obtained on an SOS wafer.

This paper proposes a new offset-gate MOS structure for high voltage SOS/CMOS devices, which will have the advantages of both SOS and CMOS configurations.

Preliminary experimental results proved that the offset-gate SOS/MOS transistor is not a mere substitute with dielectric isolation for similar bulk silicon MOS devices, but is superior in many points to them, especially in drain breakdown voltage and on-resistance characteristics.

PROPOSED TRANSISTOR CHARACTERISTICS

It is well known that breakdown voltages for conventional bulk silicon high voltage transistors, including offset-gate MOS transistor (2), are finally limited by voltages for drain-"substrate" PN junctions, that is, by "substrate" doping concentrations. Therefore, low impurity concentration substrates or wafers are required in high voltage devices. This fact usually brings about severe trade-off requirements between drain breakdown voltage BV_{DS} and on-resistance Ron of the transistor. A high voltage "extended drain" SOS/MOS transistor (1), which resembles a "DMOS" on SOS, is not an exception. The gate electrode, which entirely covers the highly resistive "extended drain" region through a thick gate oxide, greatly improves Ron, but at the same time, limits BV_{DS} to a low value ($\sim 70V$).

The high voltage SOS/MOS structure described here has a newly designed offset-gate region, which consists of an ion-implanted pinched resistor and an underlying substrate layer, as shown in Fig. 1. Since these two layers are fabricated to have the same amount of opposite impurity Q_I per unit area, the offset-gate region is depleted vertically throughout the silicon epi-layer at above a relatively low drain voltage (e.g., 10-40V) equal to the offset-gate pinched-off voltage. This brings about a high lateral drain-source breakdown voltage characteristic (3).

1)   Thus, one of the important transistor features is that drain breakdown voltage BV_{DS} is not limited by the substrate doping Nsub, but depends only on offset-gate length L_R. That means the longer L_R is, the higher BV_{DS} is.

2)   On-resistance Ron, another key factor for high voltage transistors, is determined by effective impurity amount Q_I for the offset-gate pinched resistor. Since Q_I is equal to (Nsub) x (substrate layer thickness t_{Si}) according to the design principle, Ron can be reduced by increasing Nsub and/or t_{Si}, independently of BV_{DS} requirements. Lowest Ron will be determined by the vertical electric field strength limitation in the offset-gate region. When Q_I is fixed, that is, Nsub and t_{Si} are constant, Ron is a linear function of L_R. As a result, the trade-off between BV_{DS} and Ron, inevitable in high voltage transistors, is greatly improved. That is, $BV_{DS}/$Ron ratio, a figure of merit for high voltage devices, is expected to be constant in this kind of transistor.

Reprinted from *IEEE 25th Int. Electron Devices Meeting*, pp. 594–597, 1979.

3) In addition, the fact that Nsub can be chosen independently of BV_{DS} enables adopting higher Nsub and shorter MOS gate length than those in conventional bulk devices without any fear of punch-through effect.

Of course, previously mentioned characteristics, originated from SOS dielectric isolation structure, should be added to these points.

EXPERIMENTAL RESULTS

To verify the proposed design concept experimentally, SOS/MOS transistors with impurity amount-controlled offset-gate regions were fabricated on SOS wafers with different substrate doping and epi-layer thickness values. Fabrication process was rather simple, compared with processes for high voltage bulk devices, which usually require deep diffusion processes or thick epi-layers, because only an ion implantation step for a pinched resistor was required to be added to conventional low voltage SOS/MOS IC process.

Ion implantation substrate doping was adopted in the following experiments to get a precise substrate doping control and to realize on-chip high voltage CMOS configuration.

Figure 2 shows typical BV_{DS} vs. L_R relationships in the offset-gate SOS/PMOS and NMOS transistors with optimally-doped pinched resistors. These transistors were fabricated on the same 2 μm thick intrinsic SOS wafer and designed to have average substrate dopings of 5-6 x 10^{15}/cm^3 in PMOS and 8-9 x 10^{15}/cm^3 in NMOS for their threshold voltage control. In spite of such high substrate dopings, BV_{DS} values for both PMOS and NMOS transistors increase almost linearly with L_R increase. Maximum BV_{DS} values of 950V and 1100V are obtained at L_R =100 μm, respectively.

Figure 3 shows the relationships between BV_{DS} at L_R = 100 μm and ion-implantation dose Nds for a pinched resistor. The maximum BV_{DS} values were obtained at Nds=2.5 x 10^{12}/cm^2 in PMOS and 3.0 x 10^{12}/cm^2 in NMOS, respectively. Effective Q_I values for pinched resistors at the optimum doping conditions were estimated to be about 0.9 x 10^{12}/cm^2 in PMOS and 1.35 x 10^{12}/cm^2 in NMOS from both ion-implantation impurity profiles and offset-gate pinched-off voltages. These values are closely equal to Nsub x t_{Si} values. Transistors having different L_R also showed their maximum BV_{DS} values at the same Nds values. BV_{DS} lowered when Nds deviated from the optimum doping condition.

Linear relationships between Ron and L_R in the transistors with optimally-doped pinched resistors are shown in Fig. 4. Then, nearly constant BV_{DS}/Ron ratios are obtained (∿0.4A/mm in PMOS and ∿1.27A/mm in NMOS) from the BV_{DS}-L_R and the Ron-L_R relationships shown in Fig. 2 and Fig. 4.

Figure 5 shows BV_{DS} vs. Nds relationships in 30 μm-long offset-gate SOS/MOS transistors formed on 1 μm thick and 2 μm thick silicon epi-layers. Since ion implantation doses for substrate doping were equal (1 x 10^{12}/cm^2) in both cases, maximum BV_{DS} values were

obained at the same Nds (=2.5 x 10^{12}/cm^2).

Typical I_D-V_D characteristics for ring-shape SOS/PMOS and NMOS transistors at L_R =100 μm are shown in Fig. 6. Those for 1.5cm-wide and 30 μm-long offset-gate SOS/PMOS and NMOS transistors are also shown in Fig. 7.

The MOS channel structure and dimensions used in the experimental devices are not optimum ones for the proposed transistor. For instance, shorter MOS gate length should be used in an improved device.

SUMMARY

A high voltage SOS/MOS transistor with a new offset-gate structure is proposed for realization of completely dielectrically isolated high voltage CMOS ICs.

The features of the proposed transistor are: (1) BV_{DS} is not limited by Nsub. (2) BV_{DS}/Ron ratio is constant over a wide BV_{DS} range. (3) Ron can be lowered using a thicker silicon epi-layer and/or higher Nsub. (4) Short channel MOS gate can be used without punch-through effect, also using high Nsub.

Offset-gate PMOS and NMOS transistors were successfully fabricated on the same intrinsic SOS wafer by ion implantation substrate doping and resulted in BV_{DS} values up to 950V and 1100V at L_R =100 μm and BV_{DS}/Ron ratios of over 0.4A/mm and 1.27A/mm, respectively. Since these transistors are process-compatible with low voltage SOS/CMOS ICs, they can be used as circuit elements for high voltage SOS/CMOS ICs.

ACKNOWLEDGMENT

The authors wish to thank Dr. M. Matsumura for his invaluable suggestions and discussions about the offset-gate design concept, and Drs. K. Ayaki and H. Shiraki for their support and encouragement of this work. They also wish to thank K. Hirata and M. Matsuhashi for device fabrication.

REFERENCES

(1) R. S. Ronen, M. R. Splinter and R. E. Treamain; IEEE J. Solid-State Circuits, vol. SC-11, p.431 (1976)
(2) I. Yoshida, T. Masuhara, M. Kubo and T. Tokuyama:Proc. 6th Conf. on Solid State Devices, p.249 (Tokyo 1974)
(3) H. Sakuma, T. Suzuki and H. Matsumura: IECE of Japan Nat. Conv. Rec., No.153 (Aug. 1977)

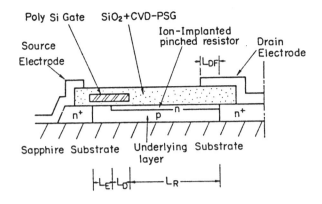

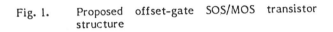

L_E: MOS-enhancement channel length

L_D: MOS-depletion channel length

L_R: Offset-gate length

L_{DF}: Drain field plate length

Fig. 1.   Proposed offset-gate SOS/MOS transistor structure

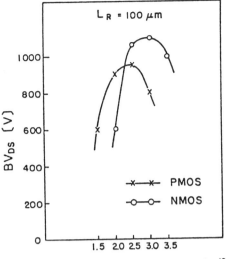

Fig. 3.   Drain breakdown voltage as a function of pinched resistor-ion implantation dose. (P^+ and B^+ ions were implanted through 1300Å thick gate oxide at 150keV and 40keV, respectively.)

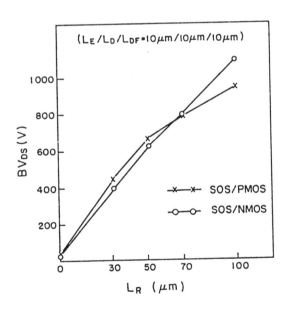

Fig. 2.   Drain breakdown voltage as a function of offset-gate length in SOS/PMOS and NMOS transistors

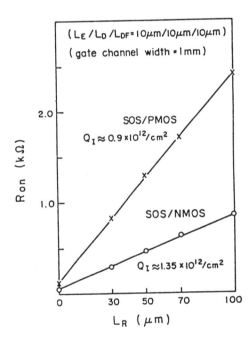

Fig. 4.   On-resistance as a function of offset-gate length.

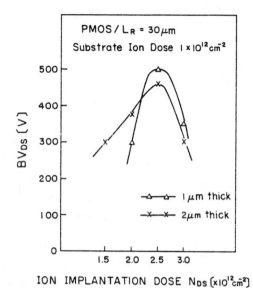

Fig. 5. Drain breakdown voltage as a function of pinched resistor-ion implantation dose in 1 μm thick and 2 μm thick SOS wafers. (Ion implantation conditions are the same as in Fig. 3.)

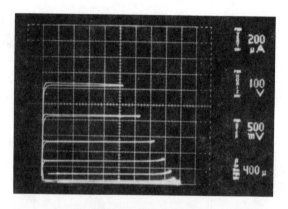

(a) SOS/PMOS transistor

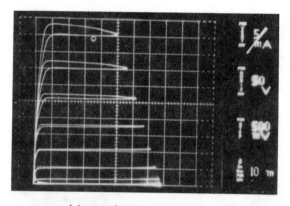

(a) SOS/PMOS transistor

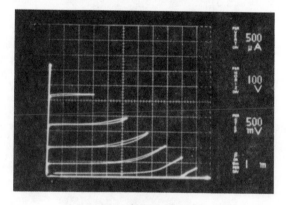

(b) SOS/NMOS transistor

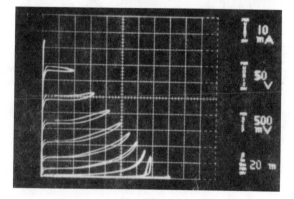

(b) SOS/NMOS transistor

Fig. 6. Offset-gate SOS/PMOS and NMOS transistor I_D-V_D characteristics. Offset-gate length is 100μm. (ring shape/offset-gate region width ∿ 750 μm.)

Fig. 7. I_D-V_D characteristics for 15mm wide and 30 μm-long offset-gate SOS/PMOS and NMOS transistors.

SESSION XV: ADVANCED PROCESS TECHNOLOGY

FAM 15.2: Spinel-Isolated High-Voltage ICs

Masaru Ihara, Yoshihiro Arimoto, Masayuki Jifuku, Toyoshi Yamaoka and Kaneyuki Kurokawa

Fujitsu Laboratories, Ltd.

Kawasaki, Japan

HIGH-VOLTAGE DRIVER CIRCUITS are being used to drive deflection coils in TV sets, plasma display panels, electrostatic printers and other peripheral devices. For integrating these high-voltage circuits, it is often desirable to integrate both low-voltage and high-voltage circuits onto a single chip. Epitaxially grown spinel offers suitable isolation for such high-voltage integrated circuits. Since devices are separated by an insulator which produces no stress-induced defects in silicon, spinel isolation will in the future facilitate the integration of cross-point switches[1] for line interface circuits in subscriber loops.

For spinel isolation, shallow wells are initially etched into the silicon substrate. Then, the entire surface is covered by a thin layer of spinel ($MgO \cdot Al_2O_3$) grown by open-tube vapor transport epitaxy. Finally, silicon is epitaxially grown on top of spinel to fill the wells. After grinding excess silicon away and polishing the surface, the result is as illustrated in Figure 1, where two wells filled with silicon are separated by spinel. MOS transistors, high-voltage bipolar transistors or any other associated circuits can be fabricated in these wells using standard processes. The breakdown voltage between two adjacent wells was 450V when the thickness of each spinel layer was $1\mu m$. The electron mobility of epitaxially grown silicon on spinel was $\bar{\mu}_n = 1,400 cm^2/Vs$ when the silicon thickness was $8\mu m$ and the doping concentration was $n = 2 \times 10^{14}/cm^3$. The etch pit density was $1 \times 10^4/cm^2$. These results show that the quality of silicon on spinel epitaxially grown on silicon is superior to that of silicon-on-sapphire (SOS). The leak current through a spinel layer was less than $2 \times 10^{-12}A/cm^2$ at 5V.

A 13-stage ring oscillator was built using enhancement type N-channel MOS transistors. The transistors were fabricated in $3\mu m$ thick silicon on spinel epitaxially grown on silicon. When the gate length was $2\mu m$, the switching speed was 240ps per stage and the power consumption 1.7mW per stage. These values are identical to these obtained with a ring oscillator built on an ordinary silicon wafer using the same masks.

A cross section of a high-voltage bipolar transistor with spinel isolation is shown in Figure 2. The well is $42\mu m$ deep, of which $7\mu m$ is heavily doped silicon of $N = 5 \times 10^{18}/cm^3$. This serves as the collector electrode. The I-V characteristics of the transistor are shown in Figure 3. The collector-emitter breakdown voltage was 250V. The current gain was $h_{FE} = 25$ when the base width was $1.0\mu m$. Note that high-voltage bipolar transistors are difficult to make using the silicon on sapphire technology.

To demonstrate the feasibility of integration, a simple driver circuit was fabricated. The circuit diagram and a micrograph of the circuit are shown in Figures 4 and 5, respectively. Four low-voltage NPN transistors and one P-N diode are followed by a high-voltage NPN transistor. Each device was built in a separate well. Figure 6 shows the input and output waveforms. The output swing of 260V at 25mA was obtained and the risetime was 400ns when the input swing was 3V. The output is sufficient to drive a plasma display panel.

Acknowledgments

The authors wish to thank T. Kimura, S. Kodama and H. Yamawaki for their experimental support and T. Oshida, T. Misugi, O. Ryuzan, K. Dazai and H. Ishikawa for their continued encouragement.

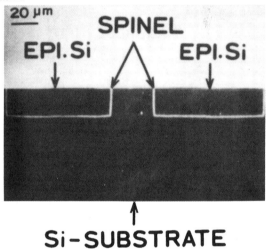

FIGURE 1—SEM photograph of the well structure with epitaxially grown spinel isolation.

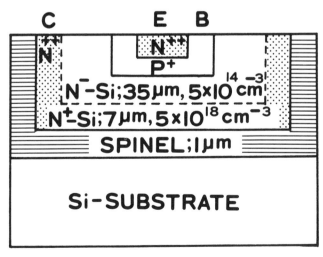

FIGURE 2—Cross section of the spinel isolated high-voltage NPN transistor.

[1] Shackle, P. W., Hartman, A. R., Riley, T. J., North, J. C., Berthold, J. E. and Davis, J. A., *ISSCC DIGEST OF TECHNICAL PAPERS*, p. 170-171; Feb., 1980.

Reprinted from *IEEE 28th Int. Solid-State Circuits*, pp. 210–211, 1981.

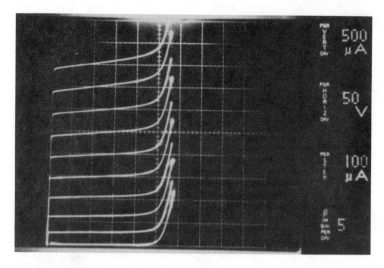

FIGURE 3—I-V characteristics of the high-voltage NPN transistor.

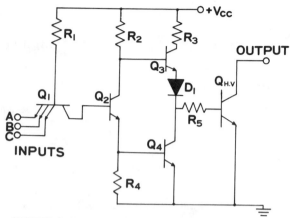

FIGURE 4—Circuit diagram of the high-voltage driver.

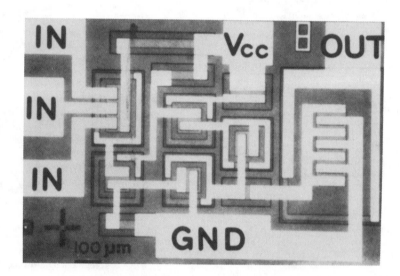

FIGURE 5—Micrograph of the high-voltage driver circuit.

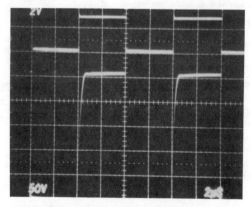

FIGURE 6—Input and output waveforms of the high-voltage driver circuit.

Improved Dielectrically Isolated Device Integration by Silicon-wafer Direct Bonding(SDB) Technique

Hiromichi Ohashi, Junichi Ohura, Tsuneo Tsukakoshi and Masaru Simbo

Toshiba Resarch and Development Center
1, Komukai Toshiba-cho, Saiwai-ku Kawasaki 210

Abstract

An improved Dielectric Isolation (DI) technique, involving a novel Silicon-wafer Direct Bonding(SDB) method was investigated, including the SDB key processes and thermographic SDB wafer evaluation technique. In order to study the novel DI technique application feasibility, a series connected 23 photo-diode array was fabricated. All of the results showed attractive features for use in overcoming conventional DI technique limitations for high voltage,high current device integration.

Introduction

In comparison with widely used junction isolation technology, Dielectric Isolation (DI) technology has peculiar advantages, such as a non-latch up feature due to less leakage current even at higher operation temperature, lower parastic capacitance, and a smaller isolation area for higher voltage devices integration. Conventional DI structures, in which dielectrically isolated single crystal wells are embedded in polysilicon substrate, have been widely investigated. However, the drawbacks for this conventional DI technique is it's thick polysilicon substrate, set up to furnish mechanical strength, which causes lower thermal conductivity than that for single crystalline silicon. The thick polysilicon layer also necessitates complicated processes to prevent substrate bending during high temperature processes in device fabrications. Thus,the conventional DI technique is limited in applications to lower on-chip power dissipation and special applications which need superior isolation properties such as the requirements for high voltage telecommunication ICs.

A new technology for use in producing a Silicon On Insulator (SOI) wafer, a Silicxon Direct Bonding (SDB) technique has been recently proposed and examined, showing successful results. This novel SDB technique has make it possible to improve or overcome the above mentioned DI [1] [2] [3] technique drawbacks. To investigate SDB application feasibility for dielectric isolation, a series connected 23 photodiode array has been fabricated. This paper describes an improved DI integration, achieved using the SDB technique.

SDB technique features

The SDB technique is based on a newly discovered phenomenon wherein strong adhesion takes place when mirror polished silicon wafers are washed to form hydrophilic surfaces, then contacted face to face at room temperature. Subsequent heat treatment completes the bonding. No weight or pressure is necessary throughout the bonding process. This method is very simple and has many advantages such as 1) the heating temperature being below that in which lattice defects are formed, 2)both

Reprinted from *IEEE 1986 Int. Electron Devices Meeting*, pp. 210–213, 1986.

excellent electrical contact and insulation are obtained, 3)voidless bonding is formed with high bonding strength,and 4) adhered wafers are stable in thermal and chemical treatments. Since a defect-free single crystalline layer is easily obtained on an insulator by bonding oxidized wafers, all of these features are preferable for conventional DI technique improvement.

In addition to SOI wafer formations, replacing long time deep impurity diffusion and high resistivity epitaxial growth is another preferable SDB technique 4) 5) application, as well as machining in silicon bodies by bonding grooved or holed surfaces. These additional advantages are useful for power and senser devices.

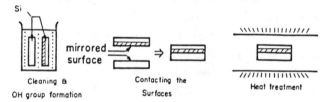

Fig.1 A new SOI wafer formation process outline.

New SOI-wafer formation

A new SOI wafer formation processes outline is shown in Fig.1. A wafer was first chemically polished and then thermally oxidized in wet oxygen. As is shown in the figure, the oxidized wafer and another chemically polished bare silicon wafer were cleaned by treating with $H_2O_2-H_2SO_4$ mixture.Then an O-H group was formed on the wafer surfaces by treating in acid solution. After the wafers were dried, they were closely contacted face to face at room temperature in clean air. As this contact was self-adhesive ,no weight or pressure was applied to the contact. The self-adhering wafer pairs were bonded by heat treatment in a nitrogen atomsphere,forming the SOI structure.

It is important to investigate factors which dominate a reduction in an uncontacted area or voids at the interface between the bonded wafers. These factors were investigated, using thermographic technique. Typical thermographic images of the SOI wafer are shown in Fig.2. In Fig.2-(A), dark contrasted parts indicate detected void images. A thermographic image of a voidless wafer is shown in Fig.2-(B). Using this method, voidless wafer formation processes were realized with high production yields.

Fracture strength for the bonded SOI wafer was also measured. The bonding strength, after contact at room temperature was sufficiently large for wafer treatment, implying the existence of an attractive force between the surfaces, in addition to atmospheric pressure force. The bonded strength increased with an increase in temperature, fianally reaching the fracture strength of single crystalline for a silicon body ($100-200kg/cm^2$) at above $1000°C$.

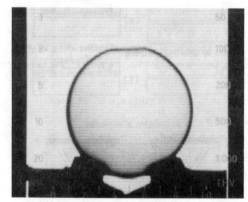

(A):Detected voids image

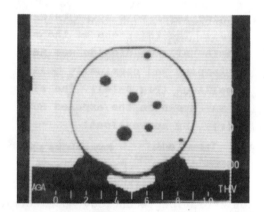

(B):Void-less wafer

Fig. 2 Thermografic image

Photodiode array fabricaton

A dielectrically isolated photodiode array has been monolithically fabricated, applying the SDB technique. A typical device fabrication sequence is illstrated in Fig.3. An n-type 9-12 ohm·cm silicon wafer was first thermally oxidized by a normal method. The wafer and another bare silicon wafer were closely contacted at room temperature after the previously mentioned wafer treatment, and were bonded by heat treatment, at 1100°C applied for 4 hours.(Figs.3-(a) and (b))

As is shown in Fig.3-(c),the upper part of the silicon wafer was lapped and was chemically poloished until the SOI wafer residual thickness became 70μm. V-grooves were formed by a newly developed anisotropic etching method and silicon dioxide was regrown to cover the entire surface area. Polysilicon was grown on top of the oxide layer to a 100μm thickness (Fig.3-(d)). The thickness of the silicon layer on the silicon dioxide was made to be 50μm by lapping and chemically polishing the polysilicon (Fig.3-(e)). The silicon dioxide was grown on the exposed surface (Fig.3-(f)). By conventional

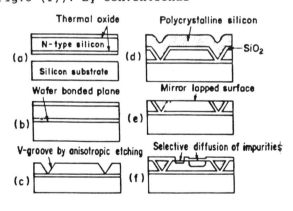

Fig.3   Isolation process by SDB technique.

photolithography and ipmurity diffusion techniques, dielectrically isolated planar pn-junction photodiode arrays were fabricated (Fig.3-(g)). Figure 4 shows a top view of a series conected 23 photodiode array, whose chip size is 5x5 mm. The photodiode array showed suffcent photo current characteristics for driving MOS gate power device, such as MOSFET relays.

Fig.4 Top-view of dielectrically isolated silicon photodiode array

Discussions

As previously described, the major drawbacks in the conventional DI technique is the requirement for a thick polysilicon substrate.A thermal expansion coefficent difference, between the polysilicon substrate and single crystalline wells embedded in the substrate, causes of wafer bending. The wafer bending amount for the conventional SOI wafer was experimentally compared with that for the new SOI wafer.

Figure 5 shows the relationships between substrate thickness and SOI wafer bending amout. In comparison with the conventional SOI wafer, the bending amount for the new SOI wafer, made using the SDB method, is suffcently small to allow device fabrication without any means for wafer bending prevention. The new SDB technique promises less expensive SOI wafer fabrication.

One of the DI technique advantage is it's smaller isolation area for high voltage device integration. Voltage isolation capability between devices (photodiodes) in different silicon dioxide bathtubs was also measured. Typical measured results are shown in Fig.6. As is apparent in the figure, more than 750-1000V isolation voltage capability was confirmed. This value is suffcently high for high voltage device integration.

In addition to the above mentioned merits, there are also several advantages owing to the use of a single crystal substrate, such as easy vertical power device integration and higher substrate thermal conductivity. These advantages are an attractive feature for use in overcoming limitations in the conventional DI [6] technique for high voltage ,high power device integrations.

The V-groove device seperation method, used in this work for neighboring elements, is not profitable from the effective isolation area utilization viewpoint. However, high speed, narrow and deep trench etching technogy, developed for VLSIs, such as HiRRIY,[7] will fairly improve packing density .

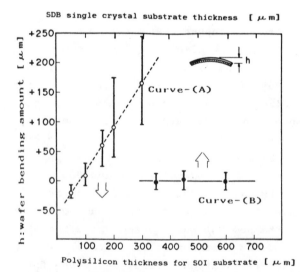

Fig.5   Relationship between substrate thickness and wafer bending amount. Curve-(A):Conventional SOI wafer(450μm single crystal layer). Curve-(B) : A new SOI wafer(same thick single crystal wafer were directly bonded).

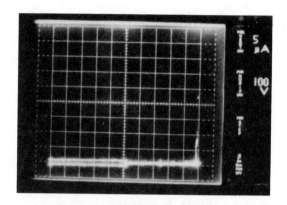

Fig.6 Voltage isolation capability

Conclusion

A new SOI technique by the SDB method was developed to improve the convertioanal dielectric device isolation technique. The new SOI wafer formation was realized with high production yield, as a result of invetigation by a thermographic void detecting method. A series connected 23 photodiode array was fabricated by the SDB method to investigate improved dielectric device isolation technique application feasibility. Results confirmed that the new method allows device fabrication without any requirement for wafer bending prevention. The photodiode array showed sufficiently high photocurrent characteristics for driving MOS-gate power devices, as well as more than 750-1000V voltage isolation capability between photodiodes. All of these results are very attractive for high voltage, high current power device integration.

Acknoledgment

The authors would like to thank K. Fukuda and K. Tanzawa for thier SDB wafer preperation.

Reference
1): J.B.Lasky,et.al.,1985 IEDM Technical Digest,pp.684
2): M.Simbo,et.al.,ECS Extended abstract,vol.89,Abstract 232(1986),pp.337
3): M.Simbo,et.al.,J.A.P.(1,Oct.1986)
4):A.Nakagawa,et.al.,Extended abstract of Conference on SSDM,Tokyo(1986)pp.89-92
5):K.Furukawa,et.al,ibib,pp.533-536
6):F.H.Lee,IEEE Trans.on ED., ED-15 (1968) pp.337
7):T.Aricado,et.al.,Proc.of 7th Symposium onDry Process,Tokyo 1985,pp.114-119

High-Voltage CMOS SIMOX Technology and Its Application to a BSH-LSI

SADAO NAKASHIMA, YOUICHI MAEDA, MEMBER, IEEE, AND MASAHIRO AKIYA

Abstract—This paper describes high-voltage CMOS separation by implanted oxygen (SIMOX) technology and its application to a BSH-LSI that provides the basic functions of battery feed, supervision, and hybrid for subscriber line interface cuircuits. This technology is characterized by the existence of an electric-field-shielding (EFS) layer formed between the buried SiO_2 and the surface Si layer by oxygen implantation. The density of localized states at the Fermi level of the EFS layer has been estimated to be about 1×10^{19} cm$^{-3} \cdot$ eV^{-1} using the Cohen–Fritzsche–Ovshinsky model. The EFS layer reduces substrate voltage dependence of the threshold voltage and increases the drain-to-source breakdown voltage for MOSFET's. Specifically, the drain-to-source breakdown voltage has been raised to 180 V. The BSH-LSI, which is composed of high-voltage CMOS of more than 60 V and low-voltage CMOS of 15 V, has been successfully fabricated containing resistors and capacitors. Compared with a conventional bipolar BSH-LSI, the chip size and the dissipation power of the LSI have been reduced to approximately one-third and one-half, respectively.

I. INTRODUCTION

THE CMOS SOI does not latch up and is convenient for attaining a high level of circuit integration. Separation by implanted oxygen (SIMOX) technology, one of the SOI technologies, has been proposed by Izumi *et al.* [1]. This technology has the following advantages:

1) CMOS SIMOX can be fabricated with the existing conventional CMOS process line because there is no contamination by metals such as Al, which is a serious problem with silicon-on-saphire (SOS) technology.
2) The field-effect mobility of a MOSFET SIMOX is comparable to that of a MOSFET bulk [2]–[4].

SIMOX technology, however, has the disadvantage that high dose implantation of oxygen ions ($\sim 1 \times 10^{18}$ cm^{-2}) is required [1], [2].

The authors have studied buried-channel CMOS using SIMOX technology for high-voltage use, called high-voltage CMOS SIMOX technology [5], and it is applied to a BSH-LSI [6]. It provides the basic functions, battery feed (*B*), supervision (*S*), and 2*W*/4*W* conversion (hybrid; *H*) of subscriber line interface circuits. The oxygen atom depth profile changes from Gaussian to rectangular [7] when the implanted oxygen dose is increased and the buried SiO_2 is made thicker in order to attain high breakdown

Manuscript received September 25, 1984; revised August 22, 1985.

The authors are with the Atsugi Electrical Communication Laboratory, Nippon Telegraph and Telephone Corporation, 1839, Ono, Atsugi-shi, Kanagawa 243-01, Japan.

IEEE Log Number 8405975.

voltage for the buried-oxide layer. The interface between the buried SiO_2 and the surface Si layer becomes abrupt. The electrical characteristics of this abrupt interface are similar to those of thermal oxide [8]. However, the authors found that such an abrupt interface causes serious problems when applied to high-voltage MOSFET's or CMOS devices, as will be described in the following section. To eliminate these problems, a new SIMOX substrate which has an electric-field-shielding (EFS) layer between the buried SiO_2 and the surface single-crystalline Si layer, is made available.

In this paper, a new SIMOX substrate having an EFS layer (EFS substrate) is proposed for high-voltage use. High-voltage CMOS SIMOX as well as low-voltage ones have been successfully fabricated using the new substrate. This technology is applied to a BSH-LSI. Furthermore, an electronic structure of the EFS layer is considered.

II. HIGH-VOLTAGE CMOS SIMOX TECHNOLOGY

A. A New Substrate for High-Voltage Use

Fig. 1 shows the results of Auger electron spectroscopy (AES) analysis of implanted oxygen atoms in the SIMOX substrate which the authors propose for high-voltage use. This is called an EFS substrate. $^{16}O^+$ was implanted on a 2 cm $\times$ 2 cm area of a p-type (100) 3-in Si wafer with 1000 $\Omega \cdot$ cm, using an EXTRION 200-20A implanter. The wafer holders used are standard for the implanter. The EFS substrate was prepared with an ion dose of 1.8×10^{18} cm^{-2} at 150 keV. The beam current was kept at 70 μA. Then, the wafers were annealed for 2 h in N_2 at 1150°C before the AES measurements. The EFS substrate shown in Fig. 1 is characterized with an EFS layer between the buried SiO_2 and the surface Si layer. The EFS layer containing a narrow peak is composed of a mixture of silicon and silicon oxide, while the surface Si is in single [7]. The oxygen atom concentration of this layer ranges from around 20 percent (at the hollow point) to around 60 percent (at the peak point). The narrow peak distinguishes the EFS layer from the surface Si layer. The layer thickness is about 80 nm. Hayashi *et al.* [7] postulated that precipitation of excess oxygen atoms in the surface single Si to the interface between the surface Si and poly-Si layers by annealing results in formation of this peak.

Fig. 2 shows the distribution dependence of implanted oxygen atoms on beam current. The implant conditions of accelerating energy and oxygen dose, and the annealing

Reprinted from *IEEE Trans. Electron Devices*, vol. ED-33, pp. 126–132, Jan. 1986.

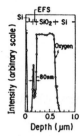

Fig. 1. The results of AES analysis of oxygen atoms for an EFS substrate. Oxygen implantation condition: a dose of 1.8×10^{18} cm^{-2} and a beam current of 70 μA at 150 keV.

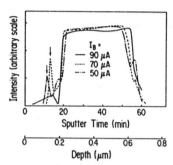

Fig. 2. The beam current dependence of the distribution of implanted oxygen atoms. A dose of 1.8×10^{18} cm^{-2} is implanted at 150 keV.

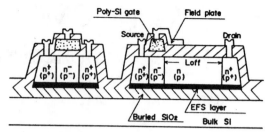

Fig. 3. A cross-sectional view of a high- and low-voltage buried-channel MOSFET SIMOX fabricated in an EFS substrate.

TABLE I
DEVICE PARAMETERS

	nMOS	pMOS
Buried SiO₂ thickness	0.37μm	
EFS layer thickness	80nm	
Island height	0.29, 0.39μm	
Gate oxide thickness	70nm	
Channel length	5,10,20,30,50μm	
Offset-gate length	10,20,80μm	
Impurity concentration of channel region	1.5×10¹⁵cm⁻³	
Impurity concentration of offset-gate region	3×10¹⁶cm⁻³	1×10¹⁷cm⁻³

treatment were the same as in Fig. 1. The formation of EFS layers strongly depends on beam current. SIMOX substrates formed in a beam current of 90 μA have no EFS layer between the buried SiO$_2$ and the surface Si layers. No EFS layers were found at beam currents higher than 80 μA. At 70 and 50 μA, fabricated SIMOX substrates have narrow peaks. The peak position is nearer the surface as the beam current decreases. Next, the surface Si layer completely turned to poly-Si at current values lower than 30 μA. The wafer temperature during implantation raises to about 400°C at a beam current of 80 μA [9]. This indicates that the beam current, which is related to the wafer temperature during ion implantation, influences the distribution profile of implanted oxygen atoms. This relates to the formation of an EFS layer between the buried SiO$_2$ and the surface Si layers. Hayashi *et al.* [7] observed a similar result, that of narrow-peak shift depending on beam current, for substrates formed with a dose of 1.2×10^{18} cm^{-2} at 150 keV. In addition, Tuppen *et al.* [13] pointed out that poly-Si layers, which are considered to correspond to EFS layers, are formed by annealing from amorphous regions produced during ion implantation.

Next, the authors will try to explain why EFS layers containing narrow peaks are formed for beam currents ranging from 50 to 70 μA. In an oxygen ion implant of 150 keV, the deposit damage energy is about 5 eV/A/ion at the surface [11], [12]. It increases monotonically with depth to 0.3 μm [11], [12]. The maximum value is about 15 eV/A/ion [11], [12]. Accordingly, single Si begins to change into amorphous silicon at a 0.3-μm depth from the surface as the oxygen dose increases and the deposited damage energy becomes higher. The surface, however, remains single because the energy at the surface is lower

than in that region. When the oxygen dose significantly increases, the single Si layer completely changes to be amorphous. Under the present implantation condition (150 keV, 1.8×10^{18} cm^{-2}), the deposited damage energy is sufficient to completely amorphize the surface Si layer at room temperature [13]. However, the critical deposited damage energy during the implant increases for production of an amorphous layer in silicon since defect annealing becomes predominant [13] when wafer temperature is raised, which corresponds to an increase in beam current in these experiments. As a result, it is considered that the silicon layer near the surface remains single at a beam current of 50 μA in spite of a high dose of 1.8×10^{18} cm^{-2}. As beam current increases, the surface single Si layer becomes thicker since the critical energy increases for production of an amorphous layer. In other words, a narrow peak shifts to a deeper position; that is, the thickness of an EFS layer decreases as the beam current increases. It is considered that at beam currents higher than 80 μA, the position where the critical energy is deposited is inside the buried SiO$_2$ or the implant dose is less than the critical dose.

B. Device Structure and Device Characteristics

Fig. 3 shows a cross-sectional view of high- and low-voltage buried-channel SIMOX MOSFET's formed in an EFS substrate. The MOSFET's are electrically isolated from the Si substrate by the buried SiO$_2$ formed by oxygen ion implantation. The high-voltage MOSFET has an offset-gate structure with an extended gate field plate. For normally-off operation, a boron-doped poly-Si gate is employed in the nMOSFET and a phosphorous-doped poly-Si gate is employed in the pMOSFET. The low-voltage MOSFET has the same structure as the high-voltage one, except that the former has no offset-gate region. The EFS

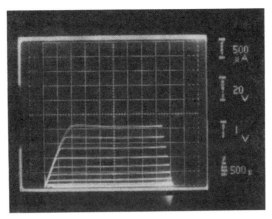

Fig. 4. The current–voltage characteristics for an nMOSFET SIMOX fabricated in an EFS substrate with L_{off} = 80 μm. W/L = 50/20 (W is the gate width and L is the gate length; both are in micrometers).

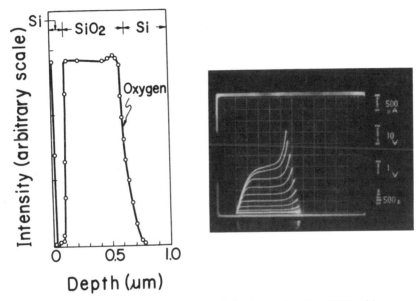

Fig. 5. The current–voltage characteristics for an nMOSFET SIMOX fabricated in a substrate with no EFS layer and an oxygen depth profile for its substrate. L_{off} = 20 μm, W/L = 50/20. Oxygen implantation condition: a dose of 2.4×10^{18} cm^{-2} and a beam current of 90 μA at 150 keV.

layer shown in Fig. 1 is located between the buried SiO_2 and the surface Si layer. The device parameters of these MOSFET's are listed in Table I. The island height is the sum of the active Si layer thickness and the EFS layer.

Fig. 4 shows current–voltage characteristics for an nMOSFET SIMOX with L_{off} = 80 μm (L_{off} is the offset-gate length). The drain-to-source breakdown voltage at a 0-V gate voltage is more than 180 V with a drain leakage current of less than 10 μA. A breakdown voltage of more than 90 V was obtained for nMOSFET's and pMOSFET's with L_{off} = 20 μm. Fig. 5 shows current–voltage characteristics for an nMOSFET fabricated in a SIMOX substrate with no EFS layer, and the oxygen depth profile for its substrate, which was annealed at 1150°C for 2 h after oxygen implantation. The authors call this substrate ABT because an ABrupT interface is formed between the buried SiO_2 and the surface Si layer. The ABT substrate was prepared with a $^{16}O^+$ ion dose of 2.4×10^{18} cm^{-2} at 150

keV. The beam current was kept at 90 μA. MOSFET's fabricated in ABT substrates had drain-to-source breakdown voltages of between 56 and 58 V at a 0-V gate voltage. The breakdown characteristics were similar to avalanche one. The breakdown voltage was independent of L_{off}. The difference in current–voltage characteristics between MOSFET's fabricated in EFS and those fabricated in ABT substrates indicate that the EFS layer improves drain-to-source breakdown voltage. Fig. 6 shows the substrate voltage (V_{sub}) dependence of the threshold voltage (V_{th}). For MOSFET's formed in EFS substrates, V_{th} are almost independent of V_{sub}. However, V_{th} for MOSFET's fabricated in ABT substrates are greatly affected by V_{sub}. For nMOSFET's, normally-off operation changes into normally-on with a V_{sub} increase. For pMOSFET's, the same change occurs with a V_{sub} decrease. The above-described dependence of V_{th} on V_{sub} indicates that ABT substrates are not suitable for high-voltage and also low-volt-

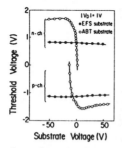

Fig. 6. The substrate voltage dependence of threshold voltage at a drain (V_D) of ± 1 V with $W/L = 50/20$.

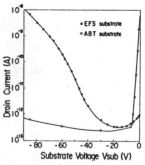

Fig. 7. The drain currents for SIMOX nMOSFET's fabricated in EFS and ABT substrates with $W/L = 50/20$. The gate and drain voltages are 0 and 0.1 V, respectively.

age CMOS devices. The drain-to-source leakage current for MOSFET's in EFS substrates was less than or approximately 1×10^{-13} A/μm channel width at a 5-V drain voltage for nMOSFET's, and at a -5 V for pMOSFET's.

For MOSFET's fabricated in an ABT substrate, the drain-to-source breakdown voltage is reduced and the V_{th} are strongly affected by V_{sub} because the buried SiO_2 functions as a gate oxide and the Si substrate as a gate electrode, that is, because of back-gate effect. The EFS layer eliminates the back-gate effect by screening the surface Si layer from the substrate electric field, i.e., the electric field caused by the potential difference between the Si substrate and the surface Si layer.

An abrupt interface is obtained between the buried SiO_2 and the surface Si layer at oxygen doses higher than 1.8×10^{18} cm^{-2} and beam currents higher than 80 μA (corresponding to higher wafer temperature) at 150 keV. Such an abrupt interface causes serious problems for fabricated MOS devices. If the current is lower than 30 μA, the surface Si layer is completely amorphized during implantation, as previously mentioned. Therefore, for fabrication of high-voltage SIMOX MOSFET's, it is important to implant oxygen ions into a wafer at beam currents ranging from 50 to 70 μA (within a certain wafer temperature range).

III. MECHANISM OF THE EFS EFFECT

The existence of the EFS layer improves MOSFET SIMOX characteristics, as described in the previous section. In this section, the electronic structure of the EFS layer and its effect are discussed. First, the electronic structure is investigated in terms of field-effect conductance change measurements. Neudeck and Malhotra [14] estimated the density of localized states of amorphous silicon and Hamasaki *et al.* [15] calculated those of semi-insulating polycrystalline silicon (SIPOS) using the field-effect conductance change due to a transverse electric field. The field-effect experiment measures interface traps as well as localized bulk states [16]. It is assumed here that the localized bulk states are much larger than the interface traps due to the following:

1) The interface traps within the bandgap are low (4×10^{11} cm$^{-2} \cdot$ eV^{-1}) in samples formed with a beam current of 90 μA and a dose of 1.8×10^{18} cm^{-2} at 150 keV [8]. In addition, the oxygen ion implanation condition

is the same as that for the substrate with a beam current of 90 μA as shown in Fig. 2.

2) The buried SiO_2 layer is the EFS substrate formed with a beam current of 70 μA has almost the same oxygen depth profile as that of the substrate with a beam current of 90 μA except for only the EFS layer, as shown in Fig. 2.

When an EFS layer has a high density of localized states given by the Cohen–Fritzsche–Ovshinsky model [17], the conductance change in the EFS layer ΔG induced by substrate voltage is [16]

$$\Delta G \simeq q(\mu_p n_b L \int_0^{y_s} (e^{-y} - 1)/y \, dy$$

$$+ \mu_n n_b L \int_0^{y_s} (e^y - 1)/y \, dy \quad (1)$$

$$L = \{(q^2/\epsilon_E \epsilon_0) \cdot N_t\}^{-1/2}$$

Here, q is an elementary charge; μ_p and μ_n are the hole and electron mobilities in the extended states, respectively; n_b is the intrinsic bulk density of mobile electrons; and y_s is the amount of band bending in units of kT due to an external electric field at the interface between the buried SiO_2 and the EFS layer. Furthermore, L is the screening length, ϵ_E is the relative dielectric constant of the EFS layer, ϵ_0 is the permitivity in vacuum, and N_t is the density of localized bulk states at the Fermi level. It is assumed that the Fermi level is somewhere within the mobility gap, and that the density of localized states near the Fermi level is constant. The amount of band-bending is

$$y_s = C_b(V_{\text{sub}} - V_{fb}) \bigg/ \left(\frac{\epsilon_E \epsilon_0 kT}{qL} \right) \quad (2)$$

where C_b is the capacitance of the buried SiO_2, V_{sub} is the applied voltage, V_{fb} is the flat-band voltage, k is Boltzmann's constant, and T is the absolute temperature. In $y_s < -1$, (1) is

$$\Delta G \simeq q\mu_p n_b L \frac{e^{-y_s}}{(-y_s)} \sim \frac{e^{|y_s|}}{|y_s|}. \quad (3)$$

Fig. 7 shows drain current dependence on substrate voltage for nMOSFET's fabricated in EFS and ABT sub-

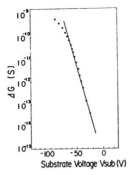

Fig. 8. The substrate voltage dependence of the conductance-modulation for an nMOSFET SIMOX fabricated in an EFS substrate when $W/L =$ 50/20. The gate and drain voltages are 0 and 0.1 V, respectively.

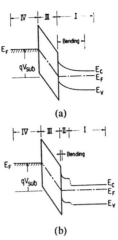

Fig. 9. The energy band diagrams of (a) Si–SiO$_2$–metal and (b) Si-EFS-SiO$_2$-metal.

strates at a gate voltage of 0 V. Since these MOSFET's function in the normally-off operation condition, the active layers are kept completly depleted or inverted in V_{sub} < 0 V. Then, the drain current difference between the two types of MOSFET's fabricated in EFS and ABT substrates is considered to be mainly derived from the current flow through the EFS layer. Fig. 8 shows the ΔG-V_{sub} characteristics of the EFS substrate. A gate voltage of 0 V was applied, so that these are due to a conductance change in the EFS layer. From the slope, N_t and L are calculated to be 1.7 × 10^{19} cm^{-3} · eV^{-1} and 5.8 nm, respectively. The values of the three measured samples ranged from 1 × 10^{19} cm^{-3} · eV^{-1} to 3 × 10^{19} cm^{-3} · eV^{-1} and from 5 to 6 nm for N_t and L, respectively. To estimate these values, ϵ_E (= 10) was assumed by interpolation between the values for Si and SiO$_2$ respective to the oxygen concentration (20 percent) of the EFS layer at the interface between the buried SiO$_2$ and the EFS layer (see Fig. 1), and 3.8 was used as the value for the relative dielectric constant of the buried SiO$_2$.

The density of localized states is constant to 0.27 eV below the Fermi level since the slope shown in Fig. 8 is constant up to $V_{sub} = -65$ V, where a value of $V_{fb} = -5 V$ is assumed [8]. The tendency of ΔG saturation at a substrate voltage less than −65 V might be due to an increase in the density of localized states below 0.27 eV beneath the Fermi level, as Nuedeck and Malhotra [14] pointed out. The screening length L is less than $\frac{1}{10}$ of the EFS layer thickness. The values of N_t and L are the same order of magnitude as those of a SIPOS film containing 23 atomic percent of oxygen [15].

Next, the mechanism of the EFS effect is explained based on the above result. Fig. 9 shows energy-band diagrams of Si–SiO$_2$–Metal in (a) and Si-EFS-SiO$_2$-Metal structures in (b) at an applied voltage. Regions I, II, III, and IV correspond to the active layer of the SIMOX nMOSFET's, the EFS layer, the buried SiO$_2$ and the Si substrate, respectively (the Si substrate is regarded as metal to simplify the following explanation). For Fig. 9(a), the active layer is stronly affected by the substrate electric field. The band is bent and then an inversion layer (V_{sub} < 0) or an accumulation layer (V_{sub} > 0) is easily formed. As a result, characteristics such as drain current and V_{th}

of a MOSFET fabricated in a substrate shown in Fig. 9(a), which corresponds to an ABT substrate, depend on the substrate electric field, as shown in the previous section. For Fig. 9(b), the substrate electric field does not bend the band of the active layer since the EFS layer exists. The EFS layer has such a high density of localized states (~ 1 × 10^{19} cm^{-3} · eV^{-1} at the Fermi level) that small band bending of the EFS layer enables the substrate electric field to be terminated.

Now, the amount of band bending for external substrate voltage is estimated from the above obtained results of N_t and L. When a substrate voltage of −10 V is applied, the interface of the active layer of the nMOSFET for ABT substrates is inverted ($V_{fb} = -5$ V [8]). The amount of bending is 0.6 eV for an impurity density of 1.5 × 10^{15} cm^{-3}. On the contrary, the amount of band bending of the EFS layer is only 0.02 eV from (2). Even at a substrate voltage of −50 V, the band bends by 0.2 eV. The amount of this bending exponentially decays and decreases to l/e at a 6 nm depth from the interface.

IV. APPLICATION TO A BSH-LSI

A BSH-LSI circuit block diagram is shown in Fig. 10. The LSI must handle a maximum operating voltage of about 60 V ($V_{DD} = 5$ V, $V_{BB} = 48$ V) and realize precise dc and ac performance without any resistor trimming. This LSI, which employs a high-voltage CMOS of more than 60 V, a low-voltage CMOS of 15 V, and poly-Si resistors, is mainly composed of "current mirrors" (current-controlled current source) and operational amplifiers.

Fig. 11 shows the major steps in the fabrication of a BSH-LSI. In step (a), $^{16}O^+$ is implanted into a Si wafer through a thermal oxide 25 nm in thickness at the same conditions that were described for high-voltage use in the previous section. The buried SiO$_2$ and the EFS layer are simultaneously formed by controlling the beam current during implantation. After implanted wafers are oxidized for 4 min and annealed for 116 min at 1150°C, a 0.26-μm undoped epitaxial layer is grown on the remaining surface single Si layer. Into the islands where nMOSFET's and

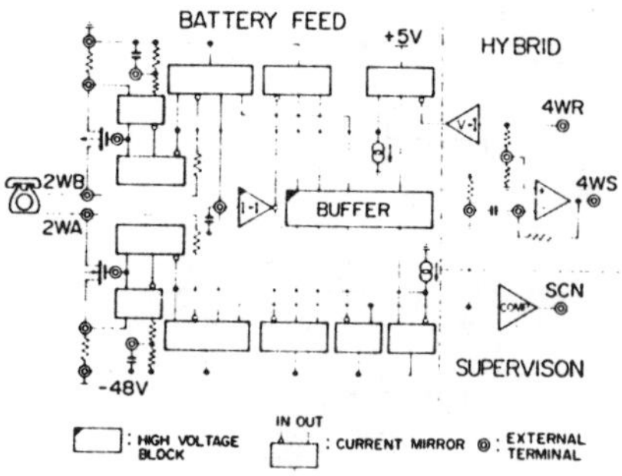

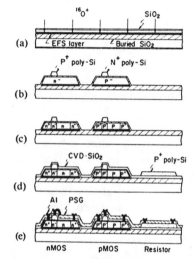

Fig. 10. The BSH-LSI circuit block diagram.

Fig. 11. Major steps in the fabrication of the BSH-LSI using high-voltage CMOS SIMOX technology.

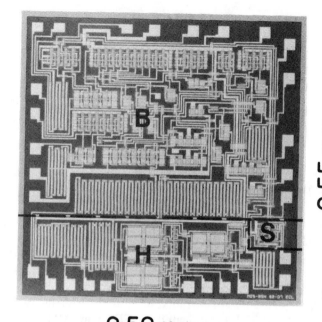

Fig. 12. The BSH-LSI chip microphotograph.

pMOSFET's will be formed, phosphorus and boron ions, respectively, are implanted. Then, an oxidation 70 nm in thickness is carried out, followed by boron- and phosphorus-implanted poly-Si gate fabrication as shown in step (b). In step (c), phosphorus ion implantaion is performed for the offset-gate region of nMOSFET's and boron ion implantation is performed for pMOSFET's, to reduce the offset resistance. In step (d), boron-implanted poly-Si resistors 0.4 μm in thickness are formed on a CVD SiO$_2$ film which is 150 nm thick. The implantation condition is an accelerating energy of 25 keV and a dose of 2.65×10^{15} cm^{-2}. Capacitors are simultaneously formed with boron-implanted poly-Si prepared as electrodes in step (b) and (d). In step (e), Al electrode patterning is carried out after the contact windows have been opened. Five-micrometer process technology is adopted in this process.

The main characteristics of the fabricated devices are shown in Table II. The sheet resistance of boron-doped poly-Si formed in step (d) is 157 $\Omega/\square$. Dummy resistor patterns were placed on both sides of the resistor array to achieve a high level of relative accuracy. The obtained relative accuracy of the resistors is less than 0.3 percent.

Measured BSH-LSI performance is summarized in Table III. A dc internal resistance of 423 Ω is obtained for the design value of 440 Ω by compensating for the threshold voltage. Longitudinal balance of above 40 dB is ob-

TABLE II
CHARACTERISTICS OF DEVICES

Drain-to-source breakdown voltage	>60 V
Threshold voltage	0.8 V for nMOS −1.1 V for pMOS
Peak value of field-effect mobility	750 cm²/Vs for nMOS 240 cm²/Vs for pMOS
Sheet resistance	157 Ω/□ p-type
Relative accuracy of resistors	<0.3 %
Capacitance	2 pF / 100μm x 100μm
Breakdown voltage of buried SiO₂	240 ~ 270 V

TABLE III
MEASURED PERFORMANCE OF BSH-LSI AT 25°C

	Results
Breakdown voltage	>60 V
DC internal resistance	423 Ω
Insertion loss (2W/4W)	±0.07 dB
Longitudinal balance (2W)	40 dB
Trans−hybrid loss	27 dB
Return loss (600 Ω)	26 dB
Idle channel noise (2W)	−41 dBmOp
Dissipation power (on hook state)	50 mW

tained without any resistor trimming. Power dissipation in the on-hook state is 50 mW. A microphotograph of a 2.55 mm × 2.58 mm chip is shown in Fig. 12. The fabricated BSH-LSI with 5-μm process technology is composed of about 200 elements. The LSI chip size and dissipation power have been reduced to approximately one-third and one-fourth, respectively, compared with those of the BSH-

LSI fabricated using the conventional bipolar technology [2].

V. Conclusion

High-voltage CMOS SIMOX technology has been proposed. This technology is characterized by the existence of an EFS layer between the buried SiO_2 and the surface Si layer. The density of localized states at the Fermi level of the EFS layer was estimated to be about 1×10^{19} $cm^{-3} \cdot eV^{-1}$, which plays an important role in screening the surface Si layer from the substrate electric field. By forming the layer, high-voltage CMOS SIMOX as well as low-voltage ones were able to be successfully realized at the same time. The drain-to-source breakdown voltage was raised to 180 V. The threshold voltages were almost independent of the substrate voltage. The chip size and the dissipation power of the BSH-LSI fabricated in an EFS substrate were reduced to approximately one-third and one-half, respectively, compared with a conventional bipolar BSH-LSI.

Acknowledgment

The authors wish to thank H. Ikawa, and N. Ohwada for supporting their work, and T. Sakai, Dr. K. Kajiyama, K. Kato, T. Kimura, K. Izumi, K. Ohwada, and T. Hayashi for their encouragement and profitable discussion.

References

[1] K. Izumi, M. Doken, and H. Ariyoshi, "C.M.O.S. devices fabricated on buried SiO_2 layers formed by oxygen implantation into silicon," *Electron. Lett.*, vol. 14, pp. 593–594, 1978.

[2] ——, "High speed IC using buried SiO_2 layers formed by ion implantation," *Japan J. Appl. Phys. Suppl.*, vol. 19-1, pp. 151–154, 1980.

[3] K. Ohwada, Y. Omura, and E. Sano, "A high speed buried channel MOSFET isolated by an implanted silicon dioxide layers," in *IEDM Tech. Dig.*, pp. 756–759, 1980.

[4] K. Nishiuchi, H. Oka, T. Nakamura, H. Ishikawa, and M. Shinoda, "A normally-off type buried channel MOSFET for VLSI circuits," in *IEDM Tech. Dig.*, pp. 26–29, 1978.

[5] S. Nakashima, M. Akiya, and K. Kato, "Electric-field-shielding layers formed by oxygen implantation into silicon," *Electron. Lett.*, vol. 19, pp. 568–570, 1983.

[6] S. Nakashima and Y. Maeda, "Subscriber line interface circuit LSI fabricated using high-voltage CMOS/SIMOX technology," *Electron. Lett.*, vol. 19, pp. 1095–1097, 1983.

[7] T. Hayashi, H. Okamoto, and Y. Homma, "Defects in Si on buried SiO_2 layer formed by very high dose oxygen implantation," *Inst. Phys. Conf.*, no. 59, ch. 11, pp. 533–538, 1981.

[8] S. Nakashima and K. Ohwada, "Electrical characteristics of an upper interface on a buried SiO_2 layer formed by oxygen implantation," *Japan J. Appl. Phys.*, vol. 12, pp. 1119–1124, 1983.

[9] K. Kajiyama, private communication.

[10] C. G. Tuppen, M. R. Taylor, P. L. Hemment, and R. P. Arrowsmith, "Effects of implantation temperature on the purpose of buried oxide layers in silicon formed by oxygen ion implantation," *Appl. Phys. Lett.*, vol. 45, pp. 57–59, 1984.

[11] D. K. Brice, *Ion Implantation range and Energy Deposition Distribution.* New York: Plenum, vol. 1.

[12] T. Tsurushima and H. Tanoue, "Spatial distribution of energy deposited by energetic heavy ions in semiconductors," *J. Phys. Soc. Japan*, vol. 31, no. 6, pp. 1695–1711, 1971.

[13] F. L. Vook, *Radiation Damage During Implantation.* London: Institute of Phys., 1973, pp. 60–71.

[14] G. W. Neudeck and A. K. Malhotra, "Theory and interpretation of the field-effect conductance experiment in amorphous silicon," *J. Appl. Phys.*, vol. 46, pp. 2662–2669, 1975.

[15] M. Hamasaki, T. Adachi, S. Wakayama, and M. Kikuchi, "Electronic properties of semi-insulating polycrystalline-silicon (SIPOS) doped with oxygen atoms," *Solid State Commun.*, vol. 21, pp. 591–593, 1977.

[16] D. F. Barbe, "Theory of the field effect in amorphous covalent semiconductor films," *J. Vac. Sci. Technol.*, vol. 8, pp. 102–107, 1971.

[17] M. H. Cohen, H. Fritzeche, and S. R. Ovshinsky, "Simple band model for amorphous semiconducting alloys," *Phys. Rev. Lett.*, vol. 22, pp. 1065–1068, 1969.

Bibliography

[1] G. Bergman, "Linear compatible I²L technology with high voltage transistors," *IEEE J. Solid State Circuits,* vol. SC-12, pp. 566–572, 1977.

[2] K. Awane *et al,* "High voltage DSA-MOS transistor for electroluminescent display," in *IEEE Int. Solid State Circuits Conf.,* Abstr. FAM 16.7, pp. 224–225, 1978.

[3] R. A. Blauschild, "High voltage analog performance from low voltage digital devices," in *IEEE Int. Solid State Circuits Conf.,* Abstr. FAM 17.3, pp. 232–233, 1978.

[4] M. Pomper *et al,* "On-chip power supply for 110 V-line input," in *IEEE Int. Solid State Circuits Conf.,* Abstr. FAM 17.7, pp. 240–241, 1978.

[5] O. Ozawa, S. Kameyama, and Y. Sasaki, "A high speed I²L compatible with high voltage analog devices," in *IEEE Int. Electron Devices Mtg.,* Abstr. 8.3, pp. 188–191, 1979.

[6] W. A. Lane and C. A. T. Salama, "Compatible VMOS and NMOS technology for power MOS IC's," in *IEEE Int. Electron Devices Mtg.,* Abstr. 25.6, pp. 598–600, 1979.

[7] M. Pomper *et al,* "High voltage DIMOS driver circuit," *IEEE J. Solid State Circuits,* vol. SC-15, pp. 328–330, 1980.

[8] G. R. David, J. C. Vallee, and J. Lebailly, "A new VMOS/bipolar Darlington transistor for power applications," in *IEEE Int. Electron Devices Mtg.,* Abstr. 4.4, pp. 83–86, 1980.

[9] H. M. J. Vaes and J. A. Appels, "High voltage, high current lateral devices," in *IEEE Int. Electron Devices Mtg.,* Abstr. 4.5, pp. 87–90, 1980.

[10] T. Suzuki, T. Kuriyama, and H. Sakuma, "A high voltage-high frequency SOS/CMOS pulse generator," in *IEEE Int. Electron Devices Mtg.,* Abstr. 10.6, pp. 264–267, 1980.

[11] B. DesCamps and J. C. Rufray, "Integrated high voltage video amplifier for color TV," in *IEEE Int. Solid State Circuits Conf.,* Abstr. WAM 2.3, pp. 28–29, 1981.

[12] J. Ueda, H. Tsukukada, and H. Mori, "An optically coupled crosspoint array," in *IEEE Int. Solid State Circuits Conf.,* Abstr. FAM 17.1, pp. 236–237, 1981.

[13] W. H. A. Mattheus, "400 V switches for subscriber line interface," in *IEEE Int. Solid State Circuits Conf.,* Abstr. FAM 17.2, pp. 238–239, 1981.

[14] D. Waull *et al,* "A 60 V IC for a transformerless trunk and subscriber line interface," in *IEEE Solid State Circuits Conf.,* Abstr. FAM 17.6, pp. 246–247, 1981.

[15] W. S. Gontowski, "High voltage, semi-custom component arrays," in *Proc. IEEE Custom IC Conf.,* pp. 16–19, 1981.

[16] K. Fujii *et al,* "400 V MOS IC for EL display," in *IEEE Solid State Circuits Conf.,* Abstr. WAM 3.6, pp. 46–47, 1981.

[17] S. A. Buhler *et al,* "Integrated high voltage/low voltage MOS devices," in *IEEE Int. Electron Devices Mtg.,* Abstr. 11.4, pp. 259–262, 1981.

[18] N. Zommer, "The monolithic HV BIPMOS," in *IEEE Int. Electron Devices Mtg.,* Abstr. 11.5, pp. 263–266, 1981.

[19] K. Nakagawa *et al,* "A 1000 V high voltage P-channel DSAMOS-IC," in *IEEE Int. Electron Devices Mtg.,* Abstr. 4.1, pp. 72–75, 1982.

[20] R. S. Wrathall and S. P. Robb, "A solid state current sense for high current Epi base power transistors," in *IEEE Int. Electron Devices Mtg.,* Abstr. 4.7, pp. 92–95, 1982.

[21] H. Sakuma, Tsuzuki, and M. Saito, "Parasitic free, high voltage MOS IC's with shielded source structure," *IEEE Int. Electron Devices Mtg.,* Abstr. 10.3, pp. 254–257, 1982.

[22] L. Leipold and C. Fellinger, "600 V/5 A FET triggered lateral opto-triac," in *IEEE Int. Electron Devices Mtg.,* Abstr. 10.5, pp. 261–263, 1982.

[23] E. J. Wildi *et al,* "Modeling and process implementation of implanted RESURF type devices," in *IEEE Int. Electron Devices Mtg.,* Abstr. 10.7, pp. 268–271, 1982.

[24] J. E. Kohl *et al,* "A regional analytic model for current interruption in high voltage center gated bipolar switches," in *IEEE Int. Electron Devices Mtg.,* Abstr. 18.2, pp. 484–487, 1982.

[25] R. K. Smith *et al,* "An analytical model for the forward characteristics of gated P-I-N switches applied to lateral structures," in *IEEE Int. Electron Devices Mtg.,* Abstr. 18.3, pp. 488–491, 1982.

[26] A. R. Alvarez *et al,* "Lateral DMOS transistor optimized for high voltage BIMOS applications," in *IEEE Int. Electron Devices Mtg.,* Abstr. 16.4, pp. 420–423, 1983.

[27] L. Leipold and J. Tihanyi, "Experimental study of a high voltage power MOSFET with integrated input amplifier," in *IEEE Int. Electron Devices Mtg.,* Abstr. 16.6, pp. 428–431, 1983.

[28] R. Roop, "Trends in high voltage integrated circuit technology," *Solid State Technology,* pp. 147–151, May 1984.

[29] E. J. Wildi *et al,* "New high voltage IC technology," in *IEEE Int. Electron Devices Mtg.,* Abstr. 10.2, pp. 262–265, 1984.

[30] P. W. Shackle, "Custom high voltage integrated for industry," in *Electro,* Abstr. 24.3, 1985.

[31] R. A. Martin and S. A. Buhler, "Considerations for

product reliability of high voltage integrated circuits,'' in *Electro,* Abstr. 24.4, 1985.

[32] E. J. Wildi *et al,* "500 V BIMOS technology and its applications,'' in *IEEE Power Electronics Specialists Conf.,* pp. 37–41, 1985.

[33] M. G. Meyer *et al,* "Integrable high voltage CMOS: devices, process, applications,'' in *IEEE Int. Electron Devices Mtg.,* Abstr. 30.3, pp. 732–735, 1985.

[34] Y. Sugawara, K. Miyata, and M. Okamura, "350 V analog-digital compatible power IC technologies,'' in *IEEE Int. Electron Devices Mtg.,* Abstr. 30.2, pp. 728–731, 1985.

[35] H. W. Becke, "Approaches to isolation in high voltage integrated circuits,'' in *IEEE Int. Electron Devices Mtg.,* Abstr. 30.1, pp. 724–727, 1985.

[36] L. Wofford, "New pulse width modulator IC controls 1 MHz switchers,'' *Power Circuits Int. Mag.,* pp. 12–16, Dec. 1985.

[37] J. Einzinger *et al,* "Monolithic IC power switch for automotive applications,'' *IEEE Solid State Circuits Conf.,* Abstr. WAM 1.6, pp. 22–23, 1986.

[38] W. Schultz, "Lossless current sensing with SENSE-FETs,'' *Power Control Int. Mag.,* pp. 30–34, Apr. 1986.

[39] J. L. Sutor *et al,* "A novel isolation structure for smart power ICs,'' in *IEEE Int. Electron Devices Mtg.,* Abstr. 9.2, pp. 214–217, 1986.

[40] P. A. Gough, M. R. Simpson, and V. Rumennik, "Fast switching lateral insulated gate transistor,'' in *IEEE Int. Electron Devices Mtg.,* Abstr. 9.3, pp. 218–221, 1986.

[41] J. K. O. Sin, C. A. T. Salama, and L. Z. Hou, "Analysis and characterization of the hybrid Schottky injection FET,'' in *IEEE Int. Electron Devices Mtg.,* Abstr. 9.4, pp. 222–225, 1986.

[42] A. L. Robinson *et al,* "Lateral insulated gate transistors with improved latching characteristics,'' *IEEE Electron Device Letters,* vol. EDL-7, pp. 61–63, 1986.

[43] B. A. MacIver and K. C. Jain, "j-MOS transistors fabricated in oxygen implanted silicon-on insulator,'' *IEEE Trans. Electron Devices,* vol. ED-33, pp. 1953–1955, 1986.

Author Index

Subject Index

339

Editor's Biography

B. Jayant Baliga (S'71–M'74–SM'79–F'83) was born in Madras, India, in 1948. He received the B.Tech. degree in electrical engineering from the Indian Institute of Technology, Madras, in 1969, and the M.S. and Ph.D. degrees from Rensselaer Polytechnic Institute, Troy, NY, in 1971 and 1974, respectively. His thesis work involved experimental studies of diffusion and epitaxial growth technology for III-V compound semiconductors.

In 1974 he joined the General Electric Corporate Research and Development Center, Schenectady, NY, and has been working on the physics and technology of silicon and gallium arsenide power devices. His activities have included studies of lifetime and processing upon power device characteristics, and the development of high-power field-controlled devices. He is currently continuing his pioneering studies of MOS-bipolar functional integration for the development of superior power switching devices. In December 1979, he was appointed the technical coordinator of the gallium arsenide power device development program. In May 1981, he was appointed the Acting Manager of the Device Physics Unit. This was followed by his appointment as Manager of the High Voltage Device and Integrated Circuits Unit in April 1982. Since 1974, he has served as an Adjunct Faculty Member at Rensselaer Polytechnic Institute where he has assisted in research on transparent semiconducting films and their application to solar cells. He has written and presented over 200 papers on diffusion and epitaxy for III-V compounds, chemical vapor deposition, lifetime control in power devices, field-controlled devices, and solar cells. He has contributed to several books including an extensive review chapter titled *Silicon Power Field Controlled Devices and Integrated Circuits* published in the Applied Solid State Science Series by Academic Press. In April 1982, he taught an IEEE short course based upon this review. He is the author of the books *Epitaxial Silicon Technology* (Academic, 1986) and *Modern Power Devices* (Wiley, 1987) and co-editor (with D. Y. Chen) of *Power Transistors: Device Design and Applications* (IEEE PRESS, 1985). He is the holder of 25 U.S. patents with many others pending.

Dr. Baliga was awarded the Indian Institute of Technology Special Merit Prize and the Philips Indian Award in 1969, the IBM Fellowship in 1972, and the Allen B. Dumont Prize in 1974. In addition, he has been awarded several publication and patent awards at GE. He has served as an officer of the IEEE student branch in 1971, and the IEEE Schenectady Section Electron Devices Chapter in 1975 and 1976. In 1982, he received the IEEE Region I award for his work on power field-controlled devices. In 1983 he was the recipient of an IR100 Award, and the General Electric Dushman and Coolidge Fellowship Awards. He is a member of Sigma Xi, the Electrochemical Society of AIME Electronic Materials Committee, and the IEEE International Electron Devices Subcommittee on Solid-State Devices. He is listed in Who's Who in Engineering, Who's Who in Technology, Who's Who in America, International Who's Who in Engineering, American Men and Women of Science, and Outstanding Young Men of America. In 1984, he was selected by *Science Digest* as one of the 100 Brightest Young Scientists in America.